LAS ANIMAS HIGH SCHOOL
T 3285

D0396437

THE MODERN LIBRARY

of the World's Best Books

THE SELECTED WORK OF
TOM PAINE

&

CITIZEN TOM PAINE

THE SELECTED WORK OF
TOM PAINE
&
CITIZEN TOM PAINE

BY

HOWARD FAST

THE MODERN LIBRARY
NEW YORK

Distributed in Canada by Random House of Canada Limited, Toronto

---

THE MODERN LIBRARY
is published by RANDOM HOUSE, INC.
BENNETT CERF • DONALD S. KLOPFER

Manufactured in the United States of America by H. Wolff

Contents

For Carl Van Doren

Introduction

HARDLY was the American Revolution finished, when the seeds were sown for the Federalist Plot, which ultimately shook the young nation to its very foundations—and almost destroyed it. More will be said of this conspiracy later; now I would like to recall one incident. It concerns a letter which John Adams, one of the Federalist leaders, sent to the traitor, Timothy Pickering. In it, Adams said contemptuously:

"There is not an idea in it (the Declaration of Independence) but what had been hackneyed in Congress for two years before . . ."

Jefferson, the well-loved and trusted leader of the democratic forces in America, had been for some time the foremost target of the Federalists. He knew how to take mud-slinging; quietly, he answered:

"I did not consider it as any part of my charge to invent new ideas altogether and to offer no sentiment which had never been expressed before. Not to find out new principles, or new arguments, never before thought of, not merely to say things which had never been said before; but to place before mankind the *common sense* of the subject. Neither aiming at originality of principles or sentiments, it was intended to be an *expression of the American mind.*"

The italics are mine; but it is no accident that, so many years after, Jefferson refers to the ideas incorporated in the Declaration of Independence as *common sense*—the title of Paine's first and far-reaching major work. And the phrase "expression of the American mind" is one of the most important clues, not only to the writings of Paine and Jefferson, but to the whole democratic system that sprang from their times.

The difference, however, between the writings of Paine and Jefferson, is the difference between an almost uneducated working man and the foremost philosopher of the culture of democracy that the eighteenth century produced. The question most often asked about Paine, is how he did it, a question no one asks concerning Jefferson; so much of a fetish has the idea of formal education become. Paine never hid his lack of education; he had read very few books, never studied in the formal sense; yet this very fact is looked upon suspiciously—a sort of ridiculous hindsight that accuses Paine of ostentatiously wearing the clothes of the common man, clothes he did not own. It is the sort of thinking that proclaims to the world, year in, year out, tediously, that Shakespeare could not have written Shakespeare, since the thoughts, needs, and emotions of people cannot be gathered from the people themselves but only from the printed page.

Both Paine and Jefferson knew otherwise; both were immensely sensitive to the people. A new time was coming into the world, the time of the common man, a new sound, a new hope, a new way of life.

Thomas Paine was born in Thetford on January 29, 1737. Thetford is a little village in Norfolk, England; and it is important, for any real understanding of Paine, to note and remember that he was born an Englishman—and an Englishman he remained, an Englishman because he loved the tight little isle that fathered him, the strange complex of liberty and bondage, hope and despair; and a citizen of the world because he loved all mankind. That was Paine, and that was one of the things that branded him apart from other American and French patriots.

We don't know too much of Paine's early life. An intense and clean objectivity was so much a quality of Paine's writing, that he himself as an individual comes to light only in the briefest snatches. And when, many years later, serious biographers undertook an investigation of the boy who had fathered the incredible man, they found almost nothing on which to base any conclusions. Those who had known him personally were dead; hearsay was colored out of any resemblance to the truth by the years of calumny and praise that were heaped on the man.

So all that Conway * and others say of his early life must be

* Moncure D. Conway, *The Life of Thomas Paine,* Two Volumes, New York, 1892.

taken with many grains of salt. Much we can surmise. He came of the lowest landless class when class divisions were knife-sharp. As a child, he saw too much, and most of it hurt; if there was any real happiness in his childhood, he would have recalled more of it than he did, not shunned it as a bad dream. He had some schooling at the charity school at Thetford; how much we don't know. Early, he learned his father's trade of corset making; and that he hated it is proven by the fact that so much of his early life was an attempt to escape it.

What surrounded him at Thetford, what made him? The squire who lorded the place, the Quaker influence of his father, the dull mother who forgot him a decade after he left home, the bucolic drift of country life, the servile trade he learned—all that should not have marked him apart. There was more, much more that we don't know and can only guess at—but whatever it was it forged a rebel, a stiff-necked, defiant prophet who from his teens pleaded the cause of justice and right.

Twice, young Tom Paine attempted to run away to sea, to ship aboard a privateer. Well, that was one of the few ways out; but it was like leaving Nazi Germany by way of a concentration camp, and the boy must have been desperate indeed. The second time, he succeeded in escaping Thetford, and he did not return for many years. He was sixteen when he made his escape, but he stuck to the privateer only for the coastwise trip down to London; there, somehow, he managed to desert the ship.

There was a period of London wandering—which ended in Paine's apprenticing himself to a staymaker. Many such periods appear in Paine's pre-American life; they must have been times of futile desperation, attempts to escape the rat cage that always closed him in at the end. But they were periods of education too. London of the latter eighteenth century was, for at least half its population, as close an approximation of hell as is possible to create on this earth. The enclosure laws of the previous two centuries had created a huge landless population that gravitated toward the urban centers, mostly toward London, to form a half-human mob, not peasants, not craftsmen—the first tragic beginnings of a real working class. But the primitive capitalism of the time could not absorb even a fraction of the mob. Starvation, thievery, murder, and drunkenness were the order of the day. The section where these people lived was known as the Gin Mill; gin was their only escape. No doubt, when Paine went into the Gin Mill, when he sought to escape staymaking through that valley of hopelessness, gin was his surcease too. He went as low as the people, suffered with them, attempted their avenues of escape, and thereby came to understand them. Admirers of Paine attempt to make him a teetotaler; his enemies make him out a drunkard. He was neither; he lived in an age of heavy drinking, and in that age, Paine was an exceptionally moderate drinker. His drunkenness was periodic, an attempt to escape; it was the only way of escape he had, for he could not go into himself and leave the world alone.

That was Paine's pre-American life, up and down, hope and despair. Staymaking, revolt, wandering—desperate ventures at other trades. At the age of twenty-two, Paine married a servant girl; less than a year later she died: another chapter that Paine was loath to recall. What was she like—what was their relationship like? That, we don't know.

At the age of twenty-five, Paine escaped staymaking—into one of the most unenviable trades in Britain, that of an exciseman. Tax collecting in a country that existed only by virtue of wholesale smuggling and tax evasion was not a happy business. He stood it for a while, and then, as before, went back, hopelessly, to staymaking. He tried other trades, cobbling, some cabinet-making; but the degree of hopelessness was the same. Always back to staymaking. Again desperation, and again a return to tax collecting.

This was the time of Paine's second marriage. He was a boarder with a tobacconist in Lewes, and when the shopkeeper died, Paine married his daughter, Elizabeth Ollive. Whether he was motivated by love or pity, we don't know, but he took on the responsibilities of the girl, the widowed mother, and a shop that was fast going into bankruptcy. Stretch the ends as he would, they could not be made to meet; and from this came Paine's first groping effort toward organization and his first written work *The Case of the Officers of the Excise.*

Wages of tax officers had been fixed more than a century before, and the rising spiral of prices had made these men long and silent sufferers, forced finally to choose between dishonesty or starvation. Paine organized them, organized their case, and pled it in a petition to Parliament. The plea was refused.

Again the old pattern in Paine's life, the shop in debt, bankruptcy, Paine fleeing to escape the debtor's prison, Paine going down and down and down, the shadow-land bottom layer of society, the gin mill. Paine left his wife; or perhaps she left him. That part of his life remained closed, and he never opened it. Paine disappeared into the maw of beggar's London. Paine re-emerged, passage money to America in his pocket, to confront Benjamin Franklin, demanding help from the great man, and a letter of introduction to an American. What drew Franklin to Paine, to the unprepossessing, poverty-stricken corset-maker and tax collector? Franklin never wrote the details of that first meeting; Paine's objectivity did not later permit a discussion of what Franklin thought, of what he, Paine, thought. Again, only surmise can fill the gap. But Franklin gave Paine a letter of introduction to a man in America, advised him to go to the new world—and so began the political history of the first great international champion of mankind.

Even with these few sketchy facts, we can begin to understand what made the man, Thomas Paine, and what forces gave birth to the flaming documents he wrote—documents that moved more men to more earth-shaking results, politically, than any up to that time and even since that time, if we except the writings of Marx, Engels, and Lenin.

The single, most important clue to Paine's writings is that they are *dynamic*. Let us see what is meant by that and whether we cannot relate the meaning to both the man and his experiences. Before Paine ever wrote a word, there were political philosophers in plenty: Voltaire, Locke, Milton, Cromwell, Rousseau, to name only a few. In America, long before Paine's time, such popular leaders as William Penn and Roger Williams had put the most advanced social and political theory of the age into practice, and what's more had, within limits of time and space, made those theories operate successfully. But there was a most important difference between the writing of these men and Paine's writing—indeed, between Paine's writing and the writing of so many political philosophers who came after him. And the difference may be summed up in this fashion:

They wrote abstractly of the pattern of change; Paine wrote realistically of the method of change. They were philosophers who created political philosophy; Paine was a revolutionist who created a method for revolution. They moved men to thought; Paine moved men to thought and action. They dealt with theory and ideals; Paine dealt with the dynamics of one force playing against another.

Note how these factors in Paine's writing are forecast by the events during the first thirty-seven years of his life. Thoughtless persons will say that the picture presented is simply that of a rebel, an unconscious rebel who protested against anything and everything. I call them thoughtless because rebellion is a term for action, not belief; Paine's belief was in change; this was his faith, that all is dynamic and subject to change, that nothing is immutable. That is the pattern of both his life and his writing, subjectively and objectively: an unconquerable desire to substitute good for bad, hope for despair. He believed in change, and so fervent was his belief that never, regardless of how bloody his head, would he accept the status quo.

Paine was never content with his lot, nor was he ever content with the lot of his fellow man. He believed it could be better. Follow the pattern: he believed there were better things to occupy a man than corset-making or cobbling. He believed that the lot of tax collectors could be bettered, if they worked actively toward that betterment. He saw poverty, the deepest kind of poverty, and he felt that a thing so evil should be wiped from the face of the earth. He never accepted anything but change.

And in November of 1774, he came to America, where change was the order of the day. He came to an America that was rumbling and quivering like a volcano about to erupt, and he put his ear to the ground and listened.

Let us glance, very briefly, at the America Paine came to. It was not a single, unified nation, but thirteen separate colonial areas—areas, however, with many things in common: they were being exploited by the same overseas empire; they spoke—the majority of them—the same language; they all suffered from the colonial status to which they were relegated; and they each of them possessed democratic movements in one stage or another of development: far advanced, for example, in Pennsylvania, much less advanced in New York.

In contrast with England, Paine found here in America comparatively little class differentiation. Land was so abundant that there was no real landless class, only a flux that went onto the land, away from the land, and back to it. There was a merchant class fast being ruined by British trade restrictions; a planter class that was also being ruined by the colonial policy of the British. Thus, under outside pressure, these two united firmly with the free farmers and artisans, presenting an almost solid front. *Almost* because more than ten percent of the three million Americans were Tories, bound to the British by blood and class, exploiting the Americans as colonials, thinking of themselves always as British, sending their children to Britain to be educated, wearing titles, depending upon the force of the redcoat army to secure them their property.

The America Paine came to was an armed and embattled people, who flared into guerrilla warfare only five months after he set foot on our soil. It was a land where almost every male adult possessed a gun of some sort, and where a century of border warfare had given them assurance with their arms.

Much of what America was and what it promised to be, Paine put into *Common Sense*. And he wrote it down there with the terrible sense of urgency which a man feels who has come on sudden and splendid good fortune—such good fortune that every waking moment plants the fear that all this wonder may slip from his grasp.

That was what drove Paine. He stepped off a boat and into the ripest and most gorgeous revolutionary opportunity that had existed. He looked around him, and the more he looked, the more he realized. The prophet of the common man stepped into the land and era of the common man. The fine gears of history, so often haphazard, now purposefully meshed.

The Selected Work of

TOM PAINE

ONE

Common Sense

LET us see how the writing of *Common Sense* came about. It was in November of 1774 that Paine landed in Philadelphia, a sick and almost beaten man. Five months later, at Lexington, the first real encounter of the American Revolution occurred; that and the Battle of Concord Bridge and the retreat of the British to Boston set into motion a popular people's uprising; two months later, an army of angry New England farmers was hanging onto the flanks of Boston like a pack of wolves, and within Boston the British army of occupation was worriedly on the defensive. And seven months later, there appeared all over the land a slim booklet, entitled *Common Sense*. And by April of 1776, almost every adult in the thirteen colonies had read or had read to him some part of the booklet. In December of 1775, only wild-eyed radicals called for independence; six months later only the most conservative elements—and few they were—of the American popular front stood out against independence. In that six-month period, the country united itself, tightened itself, and set its face solidly against the enemy, the loose alliance of thirteen far-flung colonies becoming a solid coalition.

And by testimony of many, not a little of this was due to the slim book Tom Paine wrote.

His arrival in America was not auspicious. He came to shore sick, unshaven, almost penniless. When he recovered his health, he worked at many things but not staymaking: odds and ends of jobs, teaching, free lance writing, letter writing. But he looked at the country. He cocked an ear, and he listened. The speech was English, but the dialect was different. The turn of a phrase was bold and sure, and the tall people walked with their heads high. Very tall people; they ate quantities of fresh meat, fresh vegetables. No one pulled a forelock. The speech was English, but the tone was different. What talk—what endless talk! Liberty, freedom, inalienable rights! You may be sure that he listened. Perhaps he read Locke and Voltaire; perhaps he didn't have to read them, since their ideas, in homely phrases, were on every tongue.

Then he found himself a good job. Robert Aitken, a Philadelphia printer, had the idea of a publication to be called *The Pennsylvania Magazine,* and Paine, the Englishman, talked himself into the job of editor.

True, he had no experience at that sort of thing; he must have convinced Aitken in some way, perhaps by showing him the things he had written, perhaps by talking to him. At any rate, under Paine's editorship, the magazine gained a position of some influence, not only in Pennsylvania but in many outlying colonies. Paine himself wrote for the magazine, some things under his own name, some under other names.

During this time, life, for Tom Paine, moved at a tremendously accelerated pace. Keep in mind that his whole personality revolved around the conception of change; for thirty-seven years of his life, change had resisted him and the people about him. And now, here in America, was a situation that changed so rapidly the average person had trouble keeping pace with it. As an editor, Paine met and spoke with people he could not have otherwise known. Washington, Jefferson, Rush, Franklin, Randolph, Sam Adams—how many long hours were spent arguing, discussing, understanding! Paine was an Englishman; that made him a sort of sounding board, for most of the patriots were American born and bred, and they had none too clear a conception of what the old country was like. To them, the American situation was matter of fact; it had come to a head as slowly as a cist; to them, America was their habitat; to Paine, the lower-class Englishman, it was utopia arriving. They didn't realize what a treasure chest they possessed until Paine, like a miser, added and added every asset that was America. The rich man can't conceive poverty. Their America, their boundless, rich and wonderful land had always been; it always would be. Paine cried: "No! No! You'll lose it—and if you lose it here, all the world loses!"

The idea became an obsession with him. He found it inconceivable that while a few hundred miles to the north, in the colony of Massachusetts, bitter war raged, men here in Pennsylvania could calmly debate the whys and wherefors of union, independence, and resistance. For him, again, it was a matter of dynamics; forces were at work; new forces must be added. A blow must be struck. Nothing "happened"; men took advantage of a situation and consciously made history.

He was an Englishman. These Americans were fools; they were fools to think that the spark they had lit concerned only them; it concerned the whole world; it concerned men of good will in every land. Even then Paine foresaw the international character which the American struggle would assume. They, the patriots, said independence was impossible. Did the impossible exist until it was attempted? They said union was impossible. But if it was impossible, then so was hope—and that Paine would never admit.

He left the *Pennsylvania Magazine,* and, a few shillings in his jeans, he set out to write the case of *America against tyranny and for mankind.* And because to him it was so obvious, so natural a progression of history, of all man's struggles, he knew before he began that it would be called *Common Sense.*

He wrote simply, yet with a shrewd turn for the practical that Yankees would love. When he reasoned, he was calm and cold; when he exhorted, by God, he exhorted. He called names, because those he was against, he hated. No grays for him; black was black, white was white, and a Tory, a reactionary, was a cursed enemy of mankind. He was no sentimentalist, no idealist; a realist, he wrote for the most realistic people he knew, and he wrote in a language they would understand. He was not interested in originating a philosophy; he intended only to turn what democratic philosophy existed into a program of action for men with guns.

And he succeeded. When he had finished the manuscript, he set about finding a printer. His old friend and former employer, Aitken, turned him down. This was fire—incitement to rebellion. Benjamin Rush and others read the manuscript and realized that here, perhaps, was some of the heat that would fuse the colonies into a united whole. Yet in their wildest dreams, they could not have foreseen the results of the small book.

Through Rush, Robert Bell, a small printer, was persuaded to print the booklet. And early in January, 1776, without fuss or fanfare, there appeared the work entitled COMMON SENSE *written by an Englishman.*

Common Sense

ON THE ORIGIN AND DESIGN OF GOVERNMENT IN GENERAL, WITH CONCISE REMARKS ON THE ENGLISH CONSTITUTION

SOME writers have so confounded society with government, as to leave little or no distinction between them; whereas they are not only different, but have different origins. Society is produced by our wants, and government by our wickedness; the former promotes our happiness *positively* by uniting our affections, the latter *negatively* by restraining our vices. The one encourages intercourse, the other creates distinctions. The first is a patron, the last a punisher.

Society in every state is a blessing, but Government, even in its best state, is but a necessary evil; in its worst state an intolerable one: for when we suffer, or are exposed to the same miseries *by a Government,* which we might expect in a country *without Government,* our calamity is heightened by reflecting that we furnish the means by which we suffer. Government, like dress, is the badge of lost innocence; the palaces of kings are built upon the ruins of the bowers of paradise. For were the impulses of conscience clear, uniform and irresistibly obeyed, man would need no other lawgiver; but that not being the case, he finds it necessary to surrender up a part of his property to furnish means for the protection of the rest; and this he is induced to do by the same prudence which in every other case advises him, out of two evils to choose the least. Wherefore, security being the true design and end of government, it unanswerably follows that whatever form thereof appears most likely to ensure it to us, with the least expense and greatest benefit, is preferable to all others.

In order to gain a clear and just idea of the design and end of government, let us suppose a small number of persons settled in some sequestered part of the earth, unconnected with the rest; they will then represent the first peopling of any country, or of the world. In this state of natural liberty, society will be their first thought. A thousand motives will excite them thereto; the strength of one man is so unequal to his wants, and his mind so unfitted for perpetual solitude, that he is soon obliged to seek assistance and relief of another, who in his turn requires the same. Four or five united would be able to raise a tolerable dwelling in the midst of a wilderness, but one man might labour out the common period of life without accomplishing any thing; when he had felled his timber he could not remove it, nor erect it after it was removed; hunger in the mean time would urge him to quit his work, and every different want would call him a different way. Disease, nay even misfortune, would be death; for, though neither might be mortal, yet either would disable him from living, and reduce him to a state in which he might rather be said to perish than to die.

Thus necessity, like a gravitating power, would soon form our newly arrived emigrants into society, the reciprocal blessings of which would supercede, and render the obligations of law and government unnecessary while they remained perfectly just to each other; but as nothing but Heaven is impregnable to vice, it will unavoidably happen that in proportion as they surmount the first difficulties of emigration, which bound them together in a common cause, they will begin to relax in their duty and attachment to each other: and this remissness will point out the necessity of establishing some form of government to supply the defect of moral virtue.

Some convenient tree will afford them a State House, under the branches of which the whole Colony may assemble to deliberate on public matters. It is more than probable that their first laws will have the title only of Regulations and be enforced by no other penalty than public disesteem. In this first parliament every man by natural right will have a seat.

But as the Colony encreases, the public concerns will encrease likewise, and the distance at which the members may be separated, will render it too inconvenient for all of them to meet on every occasion as at first, when their number was small, their habitations near, and the public concerns few and trifling. This will point out the convenience of their consenting to leave the legislative part to be managed by a select number chosen from the whole body, who are supposed to have the same concerns at stake which those have who appointed them, and who will act in the same manner as the whole body would act were they present. If the colony continue encreasing, it will become necessary to augment the number of representatives, and that the interest of every part of the colony may be attended to, it will be found best to divide the whole into convenient parts, each part sending its proper number: and that the *elected* might never form to themselves an interest separate from the *electors,* prudence will point out the propriety of having elections often: because as the *elected* might by that means return and mix again with the general body of the *electors* in a few months, their fidelity to the public will be secured by the prudent reflection of not making a rod for themselves. And as this frequent interchange will establish a common interest with every part of the community, they will mutually and naturally support each other, and on this, (not on the unmeaning name of king,) depends the *strength of government, and the happiness of the governed.*

Here then is the origin and rise of government; namely, a mode rendered necessary by the inability of moral virtue to govern the world; here too is the design and end of government, viz. Freedom and security. And however our eyes may be dazzled with show, or our ears deceived by sound; however prejudice may warp our wills, or interest darken our understanding, the simple voice of nature and reason will say, 'tis right.

I draw my idea of the form of government from a principle in nature which no art can overturn, viz. that the more simple any thing is, the less liable it is to be disordered, and the easier repaired when disordered; and with this maxim in view I offer a few remarks on the so much boasted constitution of England. That it was noble for the dark and slavish times in which it was erected, is granted. When the world was overrun with tyranny the least remove therefrom was a glorious rescue. But that it is imperfect, subject to convulsions, and incapable of producing what it seems to promise, is easily demonstrated.

Absolute governments, (tho' the disgrace of human nature) have this advantage with them, they are simple; if the people suffer, they know the head from which their suffering springs; know likewise the remedy; and are not bewildered by a variety of causes and cures. But the constitution of England is so exceedingly complex, that the nation may suffer for years together without being able to discover in which part the fault lies; some will say in one and some in another, and every political physician will advise a different medicine.

I know it is difficult to get over local or long standing prejudices, yet if we will suffer ourselves to examine the component parts of the English constitution, we shall find them to be the base remains of two ancient tyrannies, compounded with some new Republican materials.

First.—The remains of Monarchical tyranny in the person of the King.

Secondly.—The remains of Aristocratical tyranny in the persons of the Peers.

Thirdly.—The new Republican materials, in the persons of the Commons, on whose virtue depends the freedom of England.

The two first, by being hereditary, are independent of the People; wherefore in a *constitutional sense* they contribute nothing towards the freedom of the State.

To say that the constitution of England is an *union* of three powers, reciprocally *checking* each other, is farcical; either the words have no meaning, or they are flat contradictions.

To say that the Commons is a check upon the King, presupposes two things.

First.—That the King it not to be trusted without being looked after; or in other words, that a thirst for absolute power is the natural disease of monarchy.

Secondly.—That the Commons, by being appointed for that purpose, are either wiser or more worthy of confidence than the Crown.

But as the same constitution which gives the Commons a power to check the King by withholding the supplies, gives afterwards the King a power to check the Commons, by empowering him to reject their other bills; it again supposes that the King is wiser than those whom it has already supposed to be wiser than him. A mere absurdity!

There is something exceedingly ridiculous in the composition of Monarchy; it first excludes a man from the means of information, yet empowers him to act in cases where the highest judgment is required. The state of a king shuts him from the World, yet the business of a king requires him to know it thoroughly; wherefore the different parts, by unnaturally opposing and destroying each other, prove the whole character to be absurd and useless.

Some writers have explained the English constitution thus: the King, say they, is one, the people another; the Peers are a house in behalf of the King, the commons in behalf of the people; but this hath all the distinctions of a house divided against itself; and though the expressions be pleasantly arranged, yet when examined they appear idle and ambiguous; and it will always happen, that the nicest construction that words are capable of, when applied to the description of something which either cannot exist, or is too incomprehensible to be within the compass of description, will be words of sound only, and though they may amuse the ear, they cannot inform the mind: for this explanation includes a previous question, viz. *how came the king by a power which the people are afraid to trust, and always obliged to check?* Such a power could not be the gift of a wise people, neither can any power, *which needs checking,* be from God; yet the provision which the constitution makes supposes such a power to exist.

But the provision is unequal to the task; the means either cannot or will not accomplish the end, and the whole affair is a *Felo de se:* for as the greater weight will always carry up the less, and as all the wheels of a machine are put in motion by one, it only remains to know which power in the constitution has the most weight, for that will govern: and tho' the others, or a part of them, may clog, or, as the phrase is, check the rapidity of its motion, yet so long as they cannot stop it, their endeavours will be ineffectual: The first moving power will at last have its way, and what it wants in speed is supplied by time.

That the crown is this overbearing part in the English constitution needs not be mentioned, and that it derives its whole consequence merely from being the giver of places and pensions is self-evident; wherefore, though we have been wise enough to shut and lock a door against absolute Monarchy, we at the same time have been foolish enough to put the Crown in possession of the key.

The prejudice of Englishmen, in favour of their own government, by King, Lords and Commons, arises as much or more from national pride than reason. Individuals are undoubtedly safer in England than in some other countries: but the will of the king is as much the law of the land in Britain as in France, with this difference, that instead of proceeding directly from his mouth, it is handed to the people under the formidable shape of an act of parliament. For the fate of Charles the First hath only made kings more subtle—not more just.

Wherefore, laying aside all national pride and prejudice in favour of modes and forms, the plain truth is that *it is wholly owing to the constitution of the people, and not to the constitution of the government* that the crown is not as oppressive in England as in Turkey.

An inquiry into the *constitutional errors* in the English form of government, is at this time highly necessary; for as we are never in a proper condition of doing justice to others, while we continue under the influence of some leading partiality, so neither are we capable of doing it to ourselves while we remain fettered by any obstinate prejudice. And as a man who is attached to a prostitute is unfitted to choose or judge of a wife, so any prepossession in favour of a rotten constitution of government will disable us from discerning a good one.

OF MONARCHY AND HEREDITARY SUCCESSION

MANKIND being originally equals in the order of creation, the equality could only be destroyed by some subsequent circumstance: the distinctions of rich and poor may in a great measure be accounted for, and that without having recourse to the harsh ill-sounding names of oppression and avarice. Oppression is often the *consequence,* but seldom or never the *means* of riches; and tho' avarice will preserve a man from being necessitously poor, it generally makes him too timorous to be wealthy.

But there is another and great distinction for which no truly natural or religious reason can be assigned, and that is the distinction of men into KINGS and SUBJECTS. Male and female are the distinctions of nature, good and bad the distinctions of Heaven; but how a race of men came into the world so exalted above the rest, and distinguished like some new species, is worth inquiring into, and whether they are the means of happiness or of misery to mankind.

In the early ages of the world, according to the scripture chronology there were no kings; the consequence of which was, there were no wars; it is the pride of kings which throws mankind into confusion. Holland, without a king hath enjoyed more peace for this last century than any of the monarchical governments in Europe. Antiquity favours the same remark; for the quiet and rural lives of the first Patriarchs have a snappy something in them, which vanishes when we come to the history of Jewish royalty.

Government by kings was first introduced into the world by the Heathens, from whom the children of Israel copied the custom. It was the most prosperous invention the Devil ever set on foot for the promotion of idolatry. The Heathens paid divine honours to their deceased kings, and the Christian World hath improved on the plan by doing the same to their living ones. How impious is the title of sacred Majesty applied to a worm, who in the midst of his splendor is crumbling into dust!

As the exalting one man so greatly above the rest cannot be justified on the equal rights of nature, so neither can it be defended on the authority of scripture; for the will of the Almighty as declared by Gideon, and the prophet Samuel, expressly disapproves of government by Kings

All anti-monarchical parts of scripture, have been very smoothly glossed over in monarchical governments, but they undoubtedly merit the attention of countries which have their governments yet to form. *Render unto Cesar the things which are Cesar's* is the scripture doctrine of courts, yet it is no support of monarchical government, for the Jews at that time were without a king, and in a state of vassalage to the Romans.

Near three thousand years passed away, from the Mosaic account of the creation, till the Jews under a national delusion requested a king. Till then their form of government (except in extraordinary cases where the Almighty interposed) was a kind of Republic, administered by a judge and the elders of the tribes. Kings they had none, and it was held sinful to acknowledge any being under that title but the Lord of Hosts. And when a man seriously reflects on the idolatrous homage which is paid to the persons of kings, he need not wonder that the Almighty, ever jealous of his honour, should disapprove a form of government which so impiously invades the prerogative of Heaven.

Monarchy is ranked in scripture as one of the sins of the Jews, for which a curse in reserve is denounced against them. The history of that transaction is worth attending to.

The children of Israel being oppressed by the Midianites, Gideon marched against them with a small army, and victory thro' the divine interposition decided in his favour. The Jews, elate with success, and attributing it to the generalship of Gideon, proposed making him a king, saying, *Rule thou over us, thou and thy son, and thy son's son.* Here was temptation in its fullest extent; not a kingdom only, but an hereditary one; but Gideon in the piety of his soul replied, *I will not rule over you, neither shall my son rule over you.* THE LORD SHALL RULE OVER YOU. Words need not be more explicit: Gideon doth not decline the honour, but denieth their right to give it; neither doth he compliment them with invented declarations of his thanks, but in the positive style of a prophet charges them with disaffection to their proper Sovereign, the King of Heaven.

About one hundred and thirty years after this, they fell again into the same error. The hankering which the Jews had for the idolatrous customs of the Heathens, is something exceedingly unaccountable; but so it was, that laying hold of the misconduct of Samuel's two sons, who were intrusted with some secular concerns, they came in an abrupt and clamorous manner to Samuel, saying, *Behold thou art old, and they sons walk not in thy ways, now make us a king to judge us like all the other nations.* And here we cannot observe but that their motives were bad, viz. that they might be *like* unto other nations, i. e. the Heathens, whereas their true glory lay in being as much *unlike* them as possible. *But the thing displeased Samuel when they said, give us a King to judge us; and Samuel prayed unto the Lord, and the Lord said unto Samuel, hearken unto the voice of the people in all that they say unto thee, for they have not rejected thee, but they have rejected me,* THAT I SHOULD NOT REIGN OVER THEM. *According to all the works which they have done since the day that I brought them up out of Egypt even unto this day, wherewith they have forsaken me, and served other Gods: so do they also unto thee. Now therefore hearken unto their voice, howbeit, protest solemnly unto them and show them the manner of the King that shall reign over them,* i. e. not of any particular King, but the general manner of the Kings of the earth whom Israel was so eagerly copying after. And notwithstanding the great distance of time and difference of manners, the character is still in fashion. *And Samuel told all the words of the Lord unto the people, that asked of him a King. And he said, This shall be the manner of the King that shall reign over you. He will take your sons and appoint them for himself for his chariots and to be his horsemen, and some shall run before his chariots* (this description agrees with the present mode of impressing men) *and he will appoint him captains over thousands and captains over fifties, will set them to ear his ground and to reap his harvest, and to make his instruments of war, and instruments of his chariots, And he will take your daughters to be confectionaries, and to be cooks, and to be bakers* (this describes the expense and luxury as well as the oppression of Kings) *and he will take your fields and your vineyards, and your olive yards, even the best of them, and give them to his servants. And he will take the tenth of your seed, and of your vineyards, and give them to his officers and to his servants* (by which we see that bribery, corruption, and favouritism, are the standing vices of Kings) *and he will take the tenth of your men servants, and your maid servants, and your goodliest young men, and your asses, and put them to his work: and he will take the tenth of your sheep, and ye shall be his servants, and ye shall cry out in that day because of your king which ye shall have chosen,* AND THE LORD WILL NOT HEAR YOU IN THAT DAY. This accounts for the continuation of Monarchy; neither do the characters of the few good kings which have lived since, either sanctify the title, or blot out the sinfulness of the origin; the high encomium of David takes no notice of him *officially as a King,* but only as a *man* after God's own heart. *Nevertheless the people refused to obey the voice of Samuel, and they said, Nay, but we will have a king over us, that we may be like all the nations, and that our king may judge us, and go out before us and fight our battles.* Samuel continued to reason with them but to no purpose; he set before them their ingratitude, but all would not avail; and seeing them fully bent on their folly, he cried out, *I will call unto the Lord, and he shall send thunder and rain* (which was then a punishment, being in the time of wheat harvest) *that ye may perceive and see that your wickedness is great which ye have done in the sight of the Lord,* IN ASKING YOU A KING. *So Samuel called unto the Lord, and the Lord sent thunder and rain that day, and all the people greatly feared the Lord and Samuel. And all the people said unto Samuel, Pray for thy servants unto the Lord thy God that we die not, for* WE HAVE ADDED UNTO OUR SINS THIS EVIL, TO ASK A KING. These portions of scripture are direct and positive. They admit of no equivocal construction. That the Almighty hath here entered his protest against monarchical government is true, or the scripture is false. And a man hath good reason to believe that there is as much of kingcraft as priestcraft in withholding the scripture from the public in popish countries. For monarchy in every instance is the popery of government.

To the evil of monarchy we have added that of hereditary succession; and as the first is a degradation and lessening of ourselves, so the second, claimed as a matter of right, is an insult and imposition on posterity. For all men being originally equals, no one by birth could have a right to set up his own family in perpetual preference to all others for ever, and tho' himself might deserve some decent degree of honours of his contemporaries, yet his descendants might be far too unworthy to inherit them. One of the strongest natural proofs of the folly of hereditary right in Kings, is that nature disapproves it, otherwise she would not so frequently turn it into ridicule, by giving mankind an *Ass for a Lion.*

Secondly, as no man at first could possess any other public honors than were bestowed upon him, so the givers of those honors could have no power to give away the right of posterity, and though they might say "We choose you for our head," they could not without manifest injustice to their children say "that your children and your children's children shall reign over ours forever." Because such an unwise, unjust, unnatural compact might (perhaps) in the next succession put them under the government of a rogue or a fool. Most wise men in their private sentiments have ever treated hereditary right with contempt; yet it is one of those evils which when once established is not easily removed: many submit from fear, others from superstition, and the more powerful part shares with the king the plunder of the rest.

This is supposing the present race of kings in the world to have had an honorable origin: whereas it is more than probable, that, could we take off the dark covering of antiquity and trace them to their first rise, we should find the first of them nothing better than the principal ruffian of some restless gang, whose savage manners of pre-eminence in subtilty obtained him the title of chief among plunderers; and who by increasing in power and extending his depredations, overawed the quiet and defenseless to purchase their safety by frequent contributions. Yet his electors could have no idea of giving hereditary right to his descendants, because such a perpetual exclusion of themselves was incompatible with the free and restrained principles they professed to live by. Wherefore, hereditary succession in the early ages of monarchy could not take place as a matter of claim, but as something casual or complemental; but as few or no records were extant in those days, the traditionary history stuff'd with fables, it was very easy, after the lapse of a few generations, to trump up some superstitious tale conveniently timed, Mahomet-like, to cram hereditary right down the throats of the vulgar. Perhaps the disorders which threatened, or seemed to threaten, on the decease of a leader and the choice of a new one (for elections among ruffians could not be very orderly) induced many at first to favour hereditary pretensions; by which means it happened, as it hath happened since, that what at first was submitted to as a convenience was afterwards claimed as a right.

England since the conquest hath known some few good monarchs, but groaned beneath a much larger number of bad ones: yet no man in his senses can say that their claim under William the Conqueror is a very honourable one. A French bastard landing with an armed Banditti and establishing himself king of England against the consent of the natives, is in plain terms a very paltry rascally original. It certainly hath no divinity in it. However it is needless to spend much time in exposing the folly of hereditary right; if there are any so weak as to believe it, let them promiscuously worship the Ass and the Lion, and welcome. I shall neither copy their humility, nor disturb their devotion.

Yet I should be glad to ask how they suppose kings came at first? The question admits but of three answers, viz. either by lot, by election, or by usurpation. If the first king was taken by lot, it establishes a precedent for the next, which excludes hereditary succession. Saul was by lot, yet the succession was not hereditary, neither does it appear from that transaction that there was any intention it ever should. If the first king of any country was by election, that likewise establishes a precedent for the next; for to say, that the right of all future generations is taken away, by the act of the first electors, in their choice not only of a king but of a family of kings for ever, hath no parallel in or out of scripture but the doctrine of original sin, which supposes the free will of all men lost in Adam; and from such comparison, and it will admit of no other, hereditary succession can derive no glory. For as in Adam all sinned, and as in the first electors all men obeyed; as in the one all mankind were subjected to Satan, and in the other to sovereignty; as our innocence was lost in the first, and our authority in the last; and as both disable us from re-assuming some former state and privilege, it unanswerably follows that original sin and hereditary succession are parallels. Dishonourable rank! inglorious connection! yet the most subtle sophist cannot produce a juster simile.

As to usurpation, no man will be so hardy as to defend it; and that William the Conqueror was an usurper is a fact not to be contradicted. The plain truth is, that the antiquity of English monarchy will not bear looking into.

But it is not so much the absurdity as the evil of hereditary succession which concerns mankind. Did it ensure a race of good and wise men it would have the seal of divine authority, but as it opens a door to the *foolish*, the *wicked*, and the *improper*, it hath in it the nature of oppression. Men who look upon themselves born to reign, and others to obey, soon grow insolent. Selected from the rest of mankind, their minds are early poisoned by importance; and the world they act in differs so materially from the world at large, that they have but little opportunity of knowing its true interests, and when they succeed in the government are frequently the most ignorant and unfit of any throughout the dominions.

Another evil which attends hereditary succession is, that the throne is subject to be possessed by a minor at any age; all which time the regency acting under the cover of a king have every opportunity and inducement to betray their trust. The same national misfortune happens when a king worn out with age and infirmity enters the last stage of human weakness. In both these cases the public becomes a prey to every miscreant who can tamper successfully with the follies either of age or infancy.

The most plausible plea which hath ever been offered in favor of hereditary succession is, that it preserves a nation from civil wars; and were this true, it would be weighty; whereas it is the most bare-faced falsity ever imposed upon mankind. The whole history of England disowns the fact. Thirty kings and two minors have reigned in that distracted kingdom since the conquest, in which time there has been (including the revolution) no less than eight civil wars and nineteen Rebellions. Wherefore instead of making for peace, it makes against it, and destroys the very foundation it seems to stand upon.

The contest for monarchy and succession, between the houses of York and Lancaster, laid England in a scene of blood for many years. Twelve pitched battles besides skirmishes and sieges were fought between Henry and Edward. Twice was Henry prisoner to Edward, who in his turn was prisoner to Henry. And so uncertain is the fate of war and the temper of a nation, when nothing but personal matters are the ground of a quarrel, that Henry was taken in triumph from a prison to a palace, and Edward obliged to fly from a palace to a foreign land; yet, as sudden transitions of temper are seldom lasting, Henry in his turn was driven from the throne, and Edward re-called to succeed him. The parliament always following the strongest side.

This contest began in the reign of Henry the Sixth, and was not entirely extinguished till Henry the Seventh, in whom the families were united. Including a period of 67 years, viz. from 1422 to 1489.

In short, monarchy and succession have laid (not this or that kingdom only) but the world in blood and ashes. 'Tis a form of government which the word of God bears testimony against, and blood will attend it.

If we enquire into the business of a King, we shall find that in some countries they may have none; and after sauntering away their lives without pleasure to themselves or advantage to the nation, withdraw from the scene, and leave their successors to tread the same idle round. In absolute monarchies the whole weight of business civil and military lies on the King; the children of Israel in their request for a king urged this plea, "that he may judge us, and go out before us and fight our battles." But in countries where he is neither a Judge nor a General, as in England, a man would be puzzled to know what *is* his business.

The nearer any government approaches to a Republic, the less business there is for a King. It is somewhat difficult to find a proper name for the government of England. Sir William Meredith calls it a Republic; but in its present state it is unworthy of the name, because the corrupt influence of the Crown, by having all the places in its disposal, hath so effectually swallowed up the power, and eaten out the virtue of the House of Commons (the Republican part in the constitution) that the government of England is nearly as monarchical as that of France or Spain. Men fall out with names without understanding them. For 'tis the Republican and not the Monarchical part of the Constitution of England which Englishmen glory in, viz. the liberty of choosing an House of Commons from out of their own body—and it is easy to see that when Republican virtues fail, slavery ensues. Why is the constitution of England sickly, but because monarchy hath poisoned the Republic; the Crown hath engrossed the Commons.

In England a King hath little more to do than to make war and give away places; which, in plain terms, is to empoverish the nation and set it together by the ears. A pretty business indeed for a man to be allowed eight hundred thousand sterling a year for, and worshipped into the bargain! Of more worth is one honest man to society, and in the sight of God, than all the crowned ruffians that ever lived.

THOUGHTS ON THE PRESENT STATE OF AMERICAN AFFAIRS

In the following pages I offer nothing more than simple facts, plain arguments, and common sense: and have no other preliminaries to settle with the reader, than that he will divest himself of prejudice and prepossession, and suffer his reason and his feelings to determine for themselves: that he will put on, or rather that he will not put off, the true character of a man, and generously enlarge his views beyond the present day.

Volumes have been written on the subject of the struggle between England and America. Men of all ranks have embarked in the controversy, from different motives, and with various designs; but all have been ineffectual, and the period of debate is closed. Arms as the last resource decide the contest; the appeal was the choice of the King, and the Continent has accepted the challenge.

It hath been reported of the late Mr. Pelham (who tho' an able minister was not without his faults) that on his being attacked in the House of Commons on the score that his measures were only of a temporary kind, replied, *"they will last my time."* Should a thought so fatal and unmanly possess the Colonies in the present contest, the name of ancestors will be remembered by future generations with detestation.

The Sun never shined on a cause of greater worth. 'Tis not the affair of a City, a County, a Province, or a Kingdom; but of a Continent—of at least one-eighth part of the habitable Globe. 'Tis not the concern of a day, a year, or an age; posterity are virtually involved in the contest, and will be more or less affected even to the end of time, by the proceedings now. Now is the seed-time of Continental union, faith and honour. The least fracture now will be like a name engraved with the point of a pin on the tender rind of a young oak; the wound would enlarge with the tree, and posterity read in it full grown characters.

By referring the matter from argument to arms, a new era for politics is struck—a new method of thinking hath arisen. All plans, proposals, &c. prior to the nineteenth of April, *i. e.* to the commencement of hostilities, are like the almanacks of the last year; which tho' proper then, are superceded and useless now. Whatever was advanced by the advocates on either side of the question then, terminated in one and the same point, viz. a union with Great Britain; the only difference between the parties was the method of effecting it; the one proposing force, the other friendship; but it hath so far happened that the first hath failed, and the second hath withdrawn her influence.

As much hath been said of the advantages of reconciliation, which, like an agreeable dream, hath passed away and left us as we were, it is but right that we should examine the contrary side of the argument, and enquire into some of the many material injuries which these Colonies sustain, and always will sustain, by being connected with and dependant on Great Britain. To examine that connection and dependance, on the principles of nature and common sense, to see what we have to trust to, if separated, and wnat we are to expect, if dependant.

I have heard it asserted by some, that as America has flourished under her former connection with Great Britain, the same connection is necessary towards her future happiness, and will always have the same effect. Nothing can be more fallacious than this kind of argument. We may as well assert that because a child has thrived upon milk, that it is never to have meat, or that the first twenty years of our lives is to become a precedent for the next twenty. But even this is admitting more than is true; for I answer roundly that America would have flourished as much and probably much more, had no European power taken any notice of her. The commerce by which she hath enriched herself are the necessaries of life, and will always have a market while eating is the custom of Europe.

But she has protected us, say some. That she hath engrossed us is true, and defended the Continent at our expense as well as her own, is admitted; and she would have defended Turkey from the same motive, *viz.* for the sake of trade and dominion.

Alas! we have been long led away by ancient prejudices and made large sacrifices to superstition. We have boasted the protection of Great Britain, without considering, that her motive was *interest* not *attach-*

ment; and that she did not protect us from *our enemies* on *our account:* but from *her enemies* on *her own account,* from those who had no quarrel with us on any *other account,* and who will always be our enemies on the *same account.* Let Britain waive her pretensions to the Continent, or the Continent throw off the dependance, and we should be at peace with France and Spain, were they at war with Britain. The miseries of Hanover last war ought to warn us against connections.

It hath lately been asserted in parliament, that the Colonies have no relation to each other but through the Parent Country, *i. e.* that Pennsylvania and the Jerseys and so on for the rest, are sister Colonies by the way of England; this is certainly a very roundabout way of proving relationship, but it is the nearest and only true way of proving enmity (or enemyship, if I may so call it.) France and Spain never were, nor perhaps ever will be, our enemies as *Americans,* but as our being the *subjects of Great Britain.*

But Britain is the parent country, say some. Then the more shame upon her conduct. Even brutes do not devour their young, nor savages make war upon their families. Wherefore, the assertion, if true, turns to her reproach; but it happens not to be true, or only partly so, and the phrase *parent or mother country* hath been jesuitically adopted by the King and his parasites, with a low papistical design of gaining an unfair bias on the credulous weakness of our minds. Europe, and not England, is the parent country of America. This new World hath been the asylum for the persecuted lovers of civil and religious liberty from *every part* of Europe. Hither have they fled, not from the tender embraces of the mother, but from the cruelty of the monster; and it is so far true of England, that the same tyranny which drove the first emigrants from home, pursues their descendants still.

In this extensive quarter of the globe, we forget the narrow limits of three hundred and sixty miles (the extent of England) and carry our friendship on a larger scale; we claim brotherhood with every European Christian, and triumph in the generosity of the sentiment.

It is pleasant to observe by what regular gradations we surmount the force of local prejudices, as we enlarge our acquaintance with the World. A man born in any town in England divided into parishes, will naturally associate most with his fellow parishioners (because their interests in many cases will be common) and distinguish him by the name of *neighbour;* if he meet him but a few miles from home, he drops the narrow idea of a street, and salutes him by the name of *townsman;* if he travel out of the county and meet him in any other, he forgets the minor divisions of street and town, and calls him *countryman, i. e. countyman;* but if in their foreign excursions they should associate in France, or any other part of *Europe,* their local remembrance would be enlarged into that of *Englishmen.* And by a just parity of reasoning, all Europeans meeting in America, or any other quarter of the globe, are *countrymen;* for England, Holland, Germany, or Sweden, when compared with the whole, stand in the same places on the larger scale, which the divisions of street, town, and county do on the smaller ones; Distinctions too limited for Continental minds. Not one third of the inhabitants, even of this province, [Pennsylvania], are of English descent. Wherefore, I reprobate the phrase of Parent or Mother Country applied to England only, as being false, selfish, narrow and ungenerous.

But, admitting that we were all of English descent, what does it amount to? Nothing. Britain, being now an open enemy, extinguishes every other name and title: and to say that reconciliation is our duty, is truly farcical. The first king of England, of the present line (William the Conqueror) was a Frenchman, and half the peers of England are descendants from the same country; wherefore, by the same method of reasoning, England ought to be governed by France.

Much hath been said of the united strength of Britain and the Colonies, that in conjunction they might bid defiance to the world. But this is mere presumption; the fate of war is uncertain, neither do the expressions mean anything; for this continent would never suffer itself to be drained of inhabitants, to support the British arms in either Asia, Africa, or Europe.

Besides, what have we to do with setting the world at defiance? Our plan is commerce, and that, well attended to, will secure us the peace and friendship of all Europe; because it is the interest of all Europe to have America a free port. Her trade will always be a protection, and her barrenness of gold and silver secure her from invaders.

I challenge the warmest advocate for reconciliation to show a single advantage that this continent can reap by being connected with Great Britain. I repeat the challenge; not a single advantage is derived. Our corn will fetch its price in any market in Europe, and our imported goods must be paid for buy them where we will.

But the injuries and disadvantages which we sustain by that connection, are without number; and our duty to mankind at large, as well as to ourselves, instruct us to renounce the alliance: because, any submission to, or dependance on, Great Britain, tends directly to involve this Continent in European wars and quarrels, and set us at variance with nations who would otherwise seek our friendship, and against whom we have neither anger nor complaint. As Europe is our market for trade, we ought to form no partial connection with any part of it. It is the true interest of America to steer clear of European contentions, which she never can do, while, by her dependance on Britain, she is made the make-weight in the scale of British politics.

Europe is too thickly planted with Kingdoms to be long at peace, and whenever a war breaks out between England and any foreign power, the trade of America goes to ruin, *because of her connection with Britain.* The next war may not turn out like the last, and should it not, the advocates for reconciliation now will be wishing for separation then, because neutrality in that case would be a safer convoy than a man of war. Every thing that is right or reasonable pleads for separation. The blood of the slain, the weeping voice of nature cries, 'TIS TIME TO PART. Even the distance at which the Almighty hath placed England and America is a strong and natural proof that the authority of the one over the other, was never the design of Heaven. The time likewise at which the Continent was discovered, adds weight to the argument, and the manner in which it was peopled, encreases the force of it. The Reformation was preceded by the discovery of America: As if the Almighty graciously meant to open a sanctuary to the persecuted in future years, when home should afford neither friendship nor safety.

The authority of Great Britain over this continent, is a form of government, which sooner or later must have an end: And a serious mind can draw no true pleasure by looking forward, under the painful and positive conviction that what he calls "the present constitution" is merely temporary. As parents, we can have no joy, knowing that this government is not sufficiently lasting to ensure any thing which we may bequeath to posterity: And by a plain method of argument, as we are running the next generation into debt, we ought to do the work of it, otherwise we use them meanly and pitifully. In order to discover the line of our duty rightly, we should take our children in our hand, and fix our station a few years farther into life; that eminence will present a prospect which a few present fears and prejudices conceal from our sight.

Though I would carefully avoid giving unnecessary offence, yet I am inclined to believe, that all those who espouse the doctrine of reconciliation, may be included within the following descriptions.

Interested men, who are not to be trusted, weak men who *cannot* see, prejudiced men who will not see, and a certain set of moderate men who think better of the European world than it deserves; and this last class, by an ill-judged deliberation, will be the cause of more calamities to this Continent than all the other three.

It is the good fortune of many to live distant from the scene of present sorrow; the evil is not sufficiently brought to their doors to make them feel the precariousness with which all American property is possessed. But let our imaginations transport us a few moments to Boston; that seat of wretchedness will teach us wisdom, and instruct us for ever to renounce a power in whom we can have no trust. The inhabitants of that unfortunate city who but a few months ago were in ease and affluence, have now no other alternative than to stay and starve, or turn out to beg. Endangered by the fire of their friends if they continue within the city and plundered by the soldiery if they leave it, in their present situation they are prisoners without the hope of redemption, and in a general attack for their relief they would be exposed to the fury of both armies.

Men of passive tempers look somewhat lightly over the offences of Great Britain, and, still hoping for the best, are apt to call out, *Come, come, we shall be friends again for all this*. But examine the passions and feelings of mankind: bring the doctrine of reconciliation to the touchstone of nature, and then tell me whether you can hereafter love, honour, and faithfully serve the power that hath carried fire and sword into your land? If you cannot do all these, then are you only deceiving yourselves, and by your delay bringing ruin upon posterity. Your future connection with Britain, whom you can neither love nor honour, will be forced and unnatural, and being formed only on the plan of present convenience, will in a little time fall into a relapse more wretched than the first. But if you say, you can still pass the violations over, then I ask, hath your house been burnt? Hath your property been destroyed before your face? Are your wife and children destitute of a bed to lie on, or bread to live on? Have you lost a parent or a child by their hands, and yourself the ruined and wretched survivor? If you have not, then are you not a judge of those who have. But if you have, and can still shake hands with the murderers, then are you unworthy the name of husband, father, friend or lover, and whatever may be your rank or title in life, you have the heart of a coward, and the spirit of a sycophant.

This is not inflaming or exaggerating matters, but trying them by those feelings and affections which nature justifies, and without which we should be incapable of discharging the social duties of life, or enjoying the felicities of it. I mean not to exhibit horror for the purpose of provoking revenge, but to awaken us from fatal and unmanly slumbers, that we may pursue determinately some fixed object. 'Tis not in the power of Britain or of Europe to conquer America, if she doth not conquer herself by delay and timidity. The present winter is worth an age if rightly employed, but if lost or neglected the whole Continent will partake of the misfortune; and there is no punishment which that man doth not deserve, be he who, or what, or where he will, that may be the means of sacrificing a season so precious and useful.

'Tis repugnant to reason, to the universal order of things, to all examples from former ages, to suppose that this Continent can long remain subject to any external power. The most sanguine in Britain doth not think so. The utmost stretch of human wisdom cannot, at this time, compass a plan, short of separation, which can promise the continent even a year's security. Reconciliation is *now* a fallacious dream. Nature hath deserted the connection, and art cannot supply her place. For, as Milton wisely expresses, "never can true reconcilement grow where wounds of deadly hate have pierced so deep."

Every quiet method for peace hath been ineffectual. Our prayers have been rejected with disdain; and hath tended to convince us that nothing flatters vanity or confirms obstinacy in Kings more than repeated petitioning—and nothing hath contributed more than that very measure to make the Kings of Europe absolute. Witness Denmark and Sweden. Wherefore, since nothing but blows will do, for God's sake let us come to a final separation, and not leave the next generation to be cutting throats under the violated unmeaning names of parent and child.

To say they will never attempt it again is idle and visionary; we thought so at the repeal of the stamp act, yet a year or two undeceived us; as well may we suppose that nations which have been once defeated will never renew the quarrel.

As to government matters, 'tis not in the power of Britain to do this continent justice: the business of it will soon be too weighty and intricate to be managed with any tolerable degree of convenience, by a power so distant from us, and so very ignorant of us; for if they cannot conquer us, they cannot govern us. To be always running three or four thousand miles with a tale or petition, waiting for four or five months for an answer, which, when obtained, requires five or six more to explain it in, will in a few years be looked upon as folly and childishness. There was a time when it was proper, and there is a proper time for it to cease.

Small islands not capable of protecting themselves are the proper objects for government to take under their care; but there is something absurd, in supposing a Continent to be perpetually governed by an island. In no instance hath nature made the satellite larger than its primary planet; and as England and America, with respect to each other, reverse the common order of nature, it is evident that they belong to different systems. England to Europe: America to itself.

I am not induced by motives of pride, party, or resentment to espouse the doctrine of separation and independence; I am clearly, positively, and conscientiously persuaded that it is the true interest of this Continent to be so; that every thing short of *that* is mere patchwork, that it can afford no lasting felicity,—that it is leaving the sword to our children, and shrinking back at a time when a little more, a little further, would have rendered this Continent the glory of the earth.

As Britain hath not manifested the least inclination towards a compromise, we may be assured that no terms can be obtained worthy the acceptance of the Continent, or any ways equal to the expense of blood and treasure we have been already put to.

The object contended for, ought always to bear some just proportion to the expense. The removal of North, or the whole detestable junto, is a matter unworthy the millions we have expended. A temporary stoppage of trade was an inconvenience, which would have sufficiently balanced the repeal of all the acts complained of, had such repeals been obtained; but if the whole Continent must take up arms, if every man must be a soldier, 'tis scarcely worth our while to fight against a contemptible ministry only. Dearly, dearly do we pay for the repeal of the acts, if that is all we fight for; for, in a just estimation 'tis as great a folly to pay a Bunker-hill price for law as for land. As I have always considered the independancy of this Continent, as an event which sooner or later must arrive, so from the late rapid progress of the Continent to maturity, the event cannot be far off. Wherefore, on the breaking out of hostilities, it was not worth the while to have disputed a matter which time would have finally redressed, unless we meant to be in earnest: otherwise it is like wasting an estate on a suit at law, to regulate the tresspasses of a tenant whose lease is just expiring. No man was a warmer wisher for a reconciliation than myself, before the fatal nineteenth of April, 1775, but the moment the event of that day was made known, I rejected the hardened, sullen-tempered Pharaoh of England for ever; and disdain the wretch, that with the pretended title of FATHER OF HIS PEOPLE can unfeelingly hear of their slaughter, and composedly sleep with their blood upon his soul.

But admitting that matters were now made up, what would be the event? I answer, the ruin of the Continent. And that for several reasons.

First. The powers of governing still remaining in the hands of the King, he will have a negative over the whole legislation of this Continent. And as he hath shown himself such an inveterate enemy to liberty, and discovered such a thirst for arbitrary powers, is he, or is he not, a proper person to say to these colonies, *You shall make no laws but what I please!?* And is there any inhabitant of America so ignorant as not to know, that according to what is called the *present constitution,* this Continent can make no laws but what the king gives leave to; and is there any man so unwise as not to see, that (considering what has happened) he will suffer no law to be made here but such as suits *his* purpose? We may be as effectually enslaved by the want of laws in America, as by submitting to laws made for us in England. After matters are made up (as it is called) can there be any doubt, but the whole power of the crown will be exerted to keep this continent as low and humble as possible? Instead of going forward we shall go backward, or be perpetually quarrelling, or ridiculously petitioning. We are already greater than the King wishes us to be, and will he not hereafter endeavor to make us less? To bring the matter to one point, Is the power who is jealous of our prosperity, a proper power to govern us? Whoever says *No,* to this question, is an Independant for independency means no more than this, whether we shall make our own laws, or, whether the King, the greatest enemy this continent hath, or can have, shall tell us *there shall be no laws but such as I like.*

But the King, you will say, has a negative in England; the people there can make no laws without his consent. In point of right and good order, it is something very ridiculous that a youth of twenty-one (which hath often happened) shall say to several millions of people older and wiser than himself, "I forbid this or that act of yours to be law." But in this place I decline this sort of reply, though I will never cease to expose the absurdity of it, and only answer that England being the King's residence, and America not so, makes quite another case. The King's negative here is ten times more dangerous and fatal than it can be in England; for there he will scarcely refuse his consent to a bill for putting England into as strong a state of defense as possible, and in America he would never suffer such a bill to be passed.

America is only a secondary object in the system of British politics. England consults the good of this country no further than it answers her own purpose. Wherefore, her own interest leads her to suppress the growth of ours in every case which doth not promote her advantage, or in the least interferes with it. A pretty state we should soon be in under such a second hand government, considering what has happened. Men do not change from enemies to friends by the alteration of a name: And in order to show that reconciliation now is a dangerous doctrine, I affirm, *that it would be policy in the King at this time to repeal the acts, for the sake of reinstating himself in the government of the provinces;* In order that HE MAY ACCOMPLISH BY CRAFT AND SUBTLETY, IN THE LONG RUN, WHAT HE CANNOT DO BY FORCE AND VIOLENCE IN THE SHORT RUN. Reconciliation and ruin are nearly related.

Secondly. That as even the best terms which we can expect to obtain can amount to no more than a temporary expedient, or a kind of government by guardianship, which can last no longer than till the Colonies come of age, so the general face and state of things in the interim will be unsettled and unpromising. Emigrants of property will not choose to come to a country whose form of government hangs but by a thread, and who is every day tottering on the brink of commotion and disturbance; and numbers of the present inhabitants would lay hold of the interval to dispose of their effects, and quit the Continent.

But the most powerful of all arguments is, that nothing but independence, *i. e.* a Continental form of government, can keep the peace of the Continent and preserve it inviolate from civil wars. I dread the event of a reconciliation with Britain now, as it is more than probable that it will be followed by a revolt some where or other, the consequences of which may be far more fatal than all the malice of Britain.

Thousands are already ruined by British barbarity; (thousands more will probably suffer the same fate.) Those men have other feelings than us who have nothing suffered. All they now possess is liberty; what they before enjoyed is sacrificed to its service, and having nothing more to lose they disdain submission. Besides, the general temper of the Colonies, towards a British government will be like that of a youth who is nearly out of his time; they will care very little about her: And a government which cannot preserve the peace is no government at all, and in that case we pay our money for nothing; and pray what is it that Britain can do, whose power will be wholly on paper, should a civil tumult break out the very day after reconciliation? I have heard men say, many of whom I believe spoke without thinking, that they dreaded an independance, fearing that it would produce civil wars: It is but seldom that our first thoughts are truly correct, and that is the case here; for there is ten times more to dread from a patched up connection than from independance. I make the sufferer's case my own, and I protest, that were I driven from house and home, my property destroyed, and my circumstances ruined, that as a man, sensible of injuries, I could never relish the doctrine of reconciliation, or consider myself bound thereby.

The Colonies have manifested such a spirit of good order and obedience to Continental government, as is sufficient to make every reasonable person easy and happy on that head. No man can assign the least pretence for his fears, on any other grounds, than such as are truly childish and ridiculous, viz., that one colony will be striving for superiority over another.

Where there are no distinctions there can be no superiority; perfect equality affords no temptation. The Republics of Europe are all (and we may say always) in peace. Holland and Switzerland are without wars, foreign or domestic: Monarchial governments, it is true are never long at rest: the crown itself is a temptation to enterprising ruffians at home; and that degree of pride and insolence ever attendant on regal authority, swells into a rupture with foreign powers in instances where a republican government, by being formed on more natural principles, would negotiate the mistake.

If there is any true cause of fear respecting independance, it is because no plan is yet laid down. Men do not see their way out. Wherefore, as an opening into that business I offer the following hints; at the same time modestly affirming, that I have no other opinion of them myself, than that they may be the means of giving rise to something better. Could the straggling thoughts of individuals be collected, they would frequently form materials for wise and able men to improve into useful matter.

Let the assemblies be annual, with a president only. The representation more equal, their business wholly domestic, and subject to the authority of a Continental Congress.

Let each Colony be divided into six, eight, or ten, convenient districts, each district to send a proper number of Delegates to Congress, so that each Colony send at least thirty. The whole number in Congress will be at least 390. Each congress to sit and to choose a President by the following method. When the Delegates are met, let a Colony be taken from the whole thirteen Colonies by lot, after which let the Congress choose (by ballot) a president from out of the Delegates of that Province. In the next Congress, let a Colony be taken by lot from twelve only, omitting that Colony from which the president was taken in the former Congress, and so proceeding on till the whole thirteen shall have had their proper rotation. And in order that nothing may pass into a law but what is satisfactorily just, not less than three fifths of the Congress to be called a majority. He that will promote discord, under a government so equally formed as this, would have joined Lucifer in his revolt.

But as there is a peculiar delicacy from whom, or in what manner, this business must first arise, and as it seems most agreeable and consistent that it should come from some intermediate body between the governed and the governors, that is, between the Congress and the People, let a Continental Conference be held in the following manner, and for the following purpose,

A Committee of twenty-six members of congress, *viz.* Two for each Colony. Two Members from each House of Assembly, or Provincial Convention; and five Representatives of the people at large, to be chosen in the capital city or town of each Province, for, in behalf of the whole Province, by as many qualified voters as shall think proper to attend from all parts of the Province for that purpose; or, if more convenient, the Representatives may be chosen in two or three of the most populous parts thereof. In this conference, thus assembled, will be united the two grand principles of business, *knowledge* and *power*. The Members of Congress, Assemblies, or Conventions, by having had experience in national concerns, will be able and useful counsellors, and the whole, being impowered by the people, will have a truly legal authority.

The conferring members being met, let their business be to frame a Continental Charter, or Charter of the United Colonies; (answering what is called the Magna Charta of England) fixing the number and manner of choosing Members of Congress, Members of Assembly, with their date of sitting; and drawing the line of business and jurisdiction between them: Always remembering, that our strength is Continental, not provincial. Securing freedom and property to all men, and above all things, the free exercise of religion, according to the dictates of conscience; with such other matter as it is necessary for a charter to contain. Immediately after which, the said conference to dissolve, and the bodies which shall be chosen conformable to the said charter, to be the Legislators and Governors of this Continent for the time being: Whose peace and happiness, may God preserve. Amen.

Should any body of men be hereafter delegated for this or some similar purpose, I offer them the following extracts from that wise observer on Governments, Dragonetti. "The science," says he, "of the Politician consists in fixing the true point of happiness and freedom. Those men would deserve the gratitude of ages, who should discover a mode of government that contained the greatest sum of individual happiness, with the least national expense." (Dragonetti on "Virtues and Reward.")

But where, say some, is the King of America? I'll tell you, friend, he reigns above, and doth not make havoc of mankind like the Royal Brute of Great Britain. Yet that we may not appear to be defective even in earthly honours, let a day be solemnly set apart for proclaiming the Charter; let it be brought forth placed on the Divine Law, the Word of God; let a crown be placed thereon, by which the world may know, that so far as we approve of monarchy, that in America the law is king. For as in absolute governments the King is law, so in free countries the law ought to be king; and there ought to be no other. But lest any ill use should afterwards arise, let the Crown at the conclusion of the ceremony be demolished, and scattered among the people whose right it is.

A government of our own is our natural right: and when a man seriously reflects on the precariousness of human affairs, he will become convinced, that it is infinitely wiser and safer, to form a constitution of our own in a cool deliberate manner, while we have it in our power, than to trust such an interesting event to time and chance. If we omit it now, some Massanello may hereafter arise, who, laying hold of popular disquietudes, may collect together the desperate and the discontented, and by assuming to themselves the powers of government, finally sweep away the liberties of the Continent like a deluge. Should the government of America return again into the hands of Britain, the tottering situation of things will be a temptation for some desperate adventurer to try his fortune; and in such a case, what relief can Britain give? Ere she could hear the news, the fatal business might be done; and ourselves suffering like the wretched Britons under the oppression of the Conqueror. Ye that oppose independance now, ye know not what ye do: ye are opening a door to eternal tyranny, by keeping vacant the seat of government. There are thousands and tens of thousands, who would think it glorious to expel from the Continent, that barbarous and hellish power, which hath stirred up the Indians and the Negroes to destroy us; the cruelty hath a double guilt, it is dealing brutally by us, and treacherously by them.

To talk of friendship with those in whom our reason forbids us to have faith, and our affections wounded thro' a thousand pores instruct us to detest, is madness and folly. Every day wears out the little remains of kindred between us and them; and can there be any reason to hope, that as the relationship expires, the affection will encrease, or that we shall agree better when we have ten times more and greater concerns to quarrel over than ever?

Ye that tell us of harmony and reconciliation, can ye restore to us the time that is past? Can ye give to prostitution its former innocence?

neither can ye reconcile Britain and America. The last cord now is broken, the people of England are presenting addresses against us. There are injuries which nature cannot forgive; she would cease to be nature if she did. As well can the lover forgive the ravisher of his mistress, as the Continent forgive the murders of Britain. The Almighty hath implanted in us these unextinguishable feelings for good and wise purposes. They are the Guardians of his Image in our hearts. They distinguish us from the herd of common animals. The social compact would dissolve, and justice be extirpated from the earth, or have only a casual existence were we callous to the touches of affection. The robber and the murderer would often escape unpunished, did not the injuries which our tempers sustain, provoke us into justice.

O! ye that love mankind! Ye that dare oppose not only the tyranny but the tyrant, stand forth! Every spot of the old world is overrun with oppression. Freedom hath been hunted round the Globe. Asia and Africa have long expelled her. Europe regards her like a stranger, and England hath given her warning to depart. O! receive the fugitive, and prepare in time an asylum for mankind.

OF THE PRESENT ABILITY OF AMERICA: WITH SOME MISCELLANEOUS REFLECTIONS

I HAVE never met with a man, either in England or America, who hath not confessed his opinion, that a separation between the countries would take place one time or other: And there is no instance in which we have shown less judgment, than in endeavoring to describe, what we call, the ripeness or fitness of the continent for independence.

As all men allow the measure, and vary only in their opinion of the time, let us, in order to remove mistakes, take a general survey of things, and endeavor if possible to find out the *very* time. But I need not go far, the inquiry ceases at once, for the *time hath found us*. The general concurrence, the glorious union of all things, proves the fact.

'Tis not in numbers but in unity that our great strength lies: yet our present numbers are sufficient to repel the force of all the world. The Continent hath at this time the largest body of armed and disciplined men of any power under Heaven: and is just arrived at that pitch of strength, in which no single colony is able to support itself, and the whole, when united, is able to do any thing. Our land force is more than sufficient, and as to Naval affairs, we cannot be insensible that Britain would never suffer an American man of war to be built, while the Continent remained in her hands. Wherefore, we should be no forwarder an hundred years hence in that branch than we are now; but the truth is, we should be less so, because the timber of the Country is every day diminishing, and that which will remain at last, will be far off or difficult to procure.

Were the Continent crowded with inhabitants, her sufferings under the present circumstances would be intolerable. The more seaport-towns we had, the more should we have both to defend and to lose. Our present numbers are so happily proportioned to our wants, that no man need be idle. The diminution of trade affords an army, and the necessities of an army create a new trade.

Debts we have none: and whatever we may contract on this account will serve as a glorious memento of our virtue. Can we but leave posterity with a settled form of government, an independent constitution of its own, the purchase at any price will be cheap. But to expend millions for the sake of getting a few vile acts repealed, and routing the present ministry only, is unworthy the charge, and is using posterity with the utmost cruelty; because it is leaving them the great work to do, and a debt upon their backs from which they derive no advantage. Such a thought's unworthy a man of honour, and is the true characteristic of a narrow heart and a piddling politician.

The debt we may contract doth not deserve our regard if the work be but accomplished. No nation ought to be without a debt. A national debt is a national bond; and when it bears no interest, is in no case a grievance. Britain is oppressed with a debt of upwards of one hundred and forty millions sterling, for which she pays upwards of four millions interest. And as a compensation for her debt, she has a large navy; America is without a debt, and without a navy; yet for the twentieth part of the English national debt, could have a navy as large again. The navy of England is not worth at this time more than three millions and a half sterling.

The first and second editions of this pamphlet were published without the following calculations, which are now given as a proof that the above estimation of the navy is a just one. See Entic's "Naval History," Intro., p. 56.

The charge of building a ship of each rate, and furnishing her with masts, yards, sails, and rigging, together with a proportion of eight months boatswain's and carpenter's sea-stores, as calculated by Mr. Burchett, Secretary to the navy.

For a ship of 100 guns,	....	35,553 £
90 "	....	29,886
80 "	....	23,638
70 "	....	17,785
60 "	....	14,197
50 "	....	10,606
40 "	....	7,558
30 "	....	5,846
20 "	....	3,710

And hence it is easy to sum up the value, or cost, rather, of the whole British navy, which, in the year 1757, when it was at its greatest glory, consisted of the following ships and guns.

Ships	*Guns*	*Cost of One*	*Cost of All*
6	100	55,553 £	213,318 £
12	90	29,886	358,632
12	80	23,638	283,656
43	70	17,785	764,755
35	60	14,197	496,895
40	50	10,605	424,240
45	40	7,558	340,110
58	20	3,710	215,180
85	sloops, bombs, and fireships, one with another at	2,000	170,000
		Cost,	3,266,786 £
		Remains for guns,	233,214
		Total,	3,500,000 £

No country on the globe is so happily situated, or so internally capable of raising a fleet as America. Tar, timber, iron, and cordage are her natural produce. We need go abroad for nothing. Whereas the Dutch, who make large profits by hiring out their ships of war to the Spaniards and Portuguese, are obliged to import most of the materials they use. We ought to view the building a fleet as an article of commerce, it being the natural manufactory of this country. 'Tis the best money we can lay out. A navy when finished is worth more than it cost: And is that nice point in national policy, in which commerce and protection are united. Let us build; if we want them not, we can sell; and by that means replace our paper currency with ready gold and silver.

In point of manning a fleet, people in general run into great errors; it is not necessary that one-fourth part should be sailors. The Terrible privateer, captain Death, stood the hottest engagement of any ship last war, yet had not twenty sailors on board, though her complement of men was upwards of two hundred. A few able and social sailors will soon instruct a sufficient number of active landsmen in the common work of a ship. Wherefore we never can be more capable of beginning on maritime matters than now, while our timber is standing, our fisheries blocked up, and our sailors and shipwrights out of employ. Men of war, of seventy and eighty guns, were built forty years ago in New England, and why not the same now? Ship building is America's greatest pride, and in which she will, in time, excel the whole world. The great empires of the east are mainly inland, and consequently excluded from the possibility of rivalling her. Africa is in a state of barbarism; and no power in Europe hath either such an extent of coast, or such an internal supply of materials. Where nature hath given the one, she hath withheld the other; to America only hath she been liberal to both. The vast empire of Russia is almost shut out from the sea; wherefore her boundless forests, her tar, iron and cordage are only articles of commerce.

In point of safety, ought we to be without a fleet? We are not the little people now which we were sixty years ago; at that time we might have trusted our property in the streets, or fields rather, and slept securely without locks or bolts to our doors and windows. The case is now altered, and our methods of defence ought to improve with our increase of property. A common pirate, twelve months ago, might have come up the Delaware, and laid the city of Philadelphia under contribution for what sum he pleased; and the same might have happened to other places. Nay, any daring fellow, in a brig of fourteen or sixteen guns, might have robbed the whole Continent, and carried off half a million of money. These are circumstances which demand our attention, and point out the necessity of naval protection.

Some perhaps will say, that after we have made it up with Britain, she will protect us. Can they be so unwise as to mean that she will keep a navy in our harbors for that purpose? Common sense will tell us that the power which hath endeavoured to subdue us, is of all others the most improper to defend us. Conquest may be effected under the pretence of friendship; and ourselves, after a long and brave resistance, be at last cheated into slavery. And if her ships are not to be admitted into our harbours, I would ask, how is she going to protect us? A navy three or four thousand miles off can be of little use, and on sudden emergencies, none at all. Wherefore if we must hereafter protect ourselves, why not do it for ourselves? Why do it for another?

The English list of ships of war is long and formidable, but not a tenth part of them are at any time fit for service, numbers of them are not in being; yet their names are pompously continued in the list; if only a plank be left of the ship; and not a fifth part of such as are fit for service can be spared on any one station at one time. The East and West Indies, Mediterranean, Africa, and other parts, over which Britain extends her claim, make large demands upon her navy. From a mixture of prejudice and inattention we have contracted a false notion respecting the navy of England, and have talked as if we should have the whole of it to encounter at once, and for that reason supposed that we must have one as large; which not being instantly practicable, has been made use of by a set of disguised Tories to discourage our beginning thereon. Nothing can be further from truth than this; for if America had only a twentieth part of the naval force of Britain, she would be by far an over-match for her; because, as we neither have, nor claim any foreign dominion, our whole force would be employed on our own coast, where we should, in the long run, have two to one the advantage of those who had three or four thousand miles to sail over before they could attack us, and the same distance to return in order to refit and recruit. And although Britain, by her fleet, hath a check over our trade to Europe, we have as large a one over her trade to the West Indies, which, by laying in the neighborhood of the Continent, lies entirely at its mercy.

Some method might be fallen on to keep up a naval force in time of peace, if we should judge it necessary to support a constant navy. If premiums were to be given to merchants to build and employ in their service ships mounted with twenty, thirty, forty, or fifty guns (the premiums to be in proportion to the loss of bulk to the merchant), fifty or sixty of those ships, with a few guardships on constant duty, would keep up a sufficient navy, and that without burdening ourselves with the evil so loudly complained of in England, of suffering their fleet in time of peace to lie rotting in the docks. To unite the sinews of commerce and defence is sound policy; for when our strength and our riches play into each other's hand, we need fear no external enemy.

In almost every article of defence we abound. Hemp flourishes even to rankness, so that we need not want cordage. Our iron is superior to that of other countries. Our small arms equal to any in the world. Cannon we can cast at pleasure. Saltpetre and gunpowder we are every day producing. Our knowledge is hourly improving. Resolution is our inherent character, and courage hath never yet forsaken us. Wherefore, what is it that we want? Why is it that we hesitate? From Britain we can expect nothing but ruin. If she is once admitted to the government of America again, this Continent will not be worth living in. Jealousies will be always arising; insurrections will be constantly happening; and who will go forth to quell them? Who will venture his life to reduce his own countrymen to a foreign obedience? The difference between Pennsylvania and Connecticut, respecting some unlocated lands, shows the insignificance of a British government, and fully proves that nothing but Continental authority can regulate Continental matters.

Another reason why the present time is preferable to all others is, that the fewer our numbers are, the more land there is yet unoccupied, which, instead of being lavished by the king on his worthless dependents, may be hereafter applied, not only to the discharge of the present debt, but to the constant support of government. No nation under Heaven hath such an advantage as this.

The infant state of the Colonies, as it is called, so far from being against, is an argument in favour of independence. We are sufficiently numerous, and were we more so we might be less united. 'Tis a matter worthy of observation that the more a country is peopled, the smaller their armies are. In military numbers, the ancients far exceeded the moderns; and the reason is evident, for trade being the consequence of population, men became too much absorbed thereby to attend to anything else. Commerce diminishes the spirit both of patriotism and military defence. And history sufficiently informs us that the bravest achievements were always accomplished in the non-age of a nation. With the increase of commerce England hath lost its spirit. The city of London, notwithstanding its numbers, submits to continued insults with the patience of a coward. The more men have to lose, the less willing are they to venture. The rich are in general slaves to fear, and submit to courtly power with the trembling duplicity of a spaniel.

Youth is the seed-time of good habits as well in nations as in individuals. It might be difficult, if not impossible, to form the Continent into one government half a century hence. The vast variety of interests, occasioned by an increase of trade and population, would create confusion. Colony would be against colony. Each being able would scorn each other's assistance; and while the proud and foolish gloried in their little distinctions the wise would lament that the union had not been formed before. Wherefore the present time is the true time for establishing it. The intimacy which is contracted in infancy, and the friendship which is formed in misfortune, are of all others the most lasting and unalterable. Our present union is marked with both these characters; we are young, and we have been distressed; but our concord hath withstood our troubles, and fixes a memorable era for posterity to glory in.

The present time, likewise, is that peculiar time which never happens to a nation but once, viz., the time of forming itself into a government. Most nations have let slip the opportunity, and by that means have been compelled to receive laws from their conquerors, instead of making laws for themselves. First, they had a king, and then a form of government; whereas the articles or charter of government should be formed first, and men delegated to execute them afterwards; but from the errors of other nations let us learn wisdom, and lay hold of the present opportunity—*to begin government at the right end.*

When William the Conqueror subdued England, he gave them law at the point of the sword; and, until we consent that the seat of government in America be legally and authoritatively occupied, we shall be in danger of having it filled by some fortunate ruffian, who may treat us in the same manner, and then, where will be our freedom? where our property?

As to religion, I hold it to be the indispensable duty of government to protect all conscientious professors thereof, and I know of no other business which government hath to do therewith. Let a man throw aside that narrowness of soul, that selfishness of principle, which the niggards of all professions are so unwilling to part with, and he will be at once delivered of his fears on that head. Suspicion is the companion of mean souls, and the bane of all good society. For myself, I fully and conscientiously believe that it is the will of the Almighty that there should be a diversity of religious opinions among us. It affords a larger field for our Christian kindness; were we all of one way of thinking, our religious dispositions would want matter for probation; and on this liberal principle I look on the various denominations among us to be like children of the same family, differing only in what is called their Christian names.

In page [97] I threw out a few thoughts on the propriety of a Continental Charter (for I only presume to offer hints, not plans) and in this place I take the liberty of re-mentioning the subject, by observing that a charter is to be understood as a bond of solemn obligation, which the whole enters into, to support the right of every separate part, whether of religion, professional freedom, or property. A firm bargain and a right reckoning make long friends.

I have heretofore likewise mentioned the necessity of a large and equal representation; and there is no political matter which more deserves our attention. A small number of electors, or a small number of representatives, are equally dangerous. But if the number of the representatives be not only small, but unequal, the danger is increased. As an instance of this, I mention the following: when the petition of the associators was before the House of Assembly of Pennsylvania, twenty-eight members only were present; all the Bucks county members, being eight, voted against it, and had seven of the Chester members done the same, this whole province had been governed by two counties only; and this danger it is always exposed to. The unwarrantable stretch likewise, which that house made in their last sitting, to gain an undue authority over the delegates of that province, ought to warn the people at large how they trust power out of their own hands. A set of instructions for their delegates were put together, which in point of sense and business would have dishonoured a school-boy, and after being approved by a few, a very few, without doors, were carried into the house, and there passed *in behalf of the whole colony;* whereas, did the whole colony know with what ill will that house had entered on some necessary public measures, they would not hesitate a moment to think them unworthy of such a trust.

Immediate necessity makes many things convenient, which if continued would grow into oppressions. Expedience and right are different things. When the calamities of America required a consultation, there was no method so ready, or at that time so proper, as to appoint persons from the several houses of assembly for that purpose; and the wisdom with which they have proceeded hath preserved this Continent from ruin. But as it is more than probable that we shall never be without a CONGRESS, every well wisher to good order must own that the mode for choosing members of that body deserves consideration. And I put it as a question to those who make a study of mankind, whether representation and election is not too great a power for one and the same body of men to possess? When we are planning for posterity, we ought to remember that virtue is not hereditary.

It is from our enemies that we often gain excellent maxims, and are frequently surprised into reason by their mistakes. Mr. Cornwall (one of the Lords of the Treasury) treated the petition of the New York Assembly with contempt, because *that* house, he said, consisted but of twenty-six members, which trifling number, he argued, could not with decency be put for the whole. We thank him for his involuntary honesty.

TO CONCLUDE, however strange it may appear to some, or however unwilling they may be to think so, matters not, but many strong and striking reasons may be given to show that nothing can settle our affairs so expeditiously as an open and determined declaration for independence. Some of which are,

First—It is the custom of Nations, when any two are at war, for some other powers, not engaged in the quarrel, to step in as mediators, and bring about the preliminaries of a peace; But while America calls herself the subject of Great Britain, no power, however well disposed she may be, can offer her mediation. Wherefore, in our present state we may quarrel on for ever.

Secondly—It is unreasonable to suppose that France or Spain will give us any kind of assistance, if we mean only to make use of that assistance for the purpose of repairing the breach, and strengthening the connection between Britain and America; because, those powers would be sufferers by the consequences.

Thirdly—While we profess ourselves the subjects of Britain, we must, in the eyes of foreign nations, be considered as Rebels. The precedent is somewhat dangerous to their peace, for men to be in arms under the name of subjects; we, on the spot, can solve the paradox; but to unite resistance and subjection requires an idea much too refined for common understanding.

Fourthly—Were a manifesto to be published, and despatched to foreign Courts, setting forth the miseries we have endured, and the peaceful methods which we have ineffectually used for redress; declaring at the same time that not being able longer to live happily or safely under the cruel disposition of the British Court, we had been driven to the necessity of breaking off all connections with her; at the same time, assuring all such Courts of our peaceable disposition towards them, and of our desire of entering into trade with them; such a memorial would produce more good effects to this Continent than if a ship were freighted with petitions to Britain.

Under our present denomination of British subjects, we can neither be received nor heard abroad; the custom of all Courts is against us, and will be so, until by an independence we take rank with other nations.

These proceedings may at first seem strange and difficult, but like all other steps which we have already passed over, will in a little time become familiar and agreeable; and until an independence is declared, the Continent will feel itself like a man who continues putting off some unpleasant business from day to day, yet knows it must be done, hates to set about it, wishes it over, and is continually haunted with the thoughts of its necessity.

☆ ☆ ☆

There is no way now, so many years later, to determine accurately the number of copies of *Common Sense* that were printed, sold, and read. Estimates range from 175,000 to 350,000, and it is not unlikely that the real total was close to or over 300,000. That would be ten percent of the entire population of America, or, translated into terms of a book published today, a sale of thirteen million copies. That would mean, proportionately, that *Common Sense* was the most extraordinary best seller in American history.

In those days there were no copyright laws. The first shipments of books Bell printed were immediately pirated, and printers all over the country set their own editions. Bell himself lost count of the number of copies he turned out on his creaking press, but the total was well over a hundred thousand. Editions were gotten out in Boston, Baltimore, Charleston; in Vermont, Connecticut, in Virginia and the Carolinas during the next ten months. Its influence was tremendous. More than any other single factor of the time, it united the colonies and swung the balance toward Independence.

In what did its appeal lie? Primarily, as I pointed out before, it was a call to action, and much of America's population thought in the realistic terms of action. Paine's headlong and melodramatic attack on monarchy found instant acceptance from a people whose every instinct was to fear and hate a hereditary aristocracy.

His arguments were couched in homely terms. In a time when colloquial writing was almost unknown, he found a language to which the average American was immediately responsive; not the speech of the man in the street but the vivid, fiery roar of the early Methodist and Baptist preachers. In literary terms it was as great a departure as the colloquial would have been, and it has since earned Paine the scorn of generations of critics. But Paine knew his problem, and he approached it soundly. He had an ear for speech, and all the many hours he had spent in England listening to the denunciations of Methodist preachers bore fruit. Note how carefully and cleverly he quotes scripture, mostly from the Old Testament, so dear to the Congregationalists and the Methodists. Note the rhythm of his arguments, the balanced repetition, so like the fierce and beautiful old Hebrew poetry.

Paine was amazingly sensitive to the Yankee; something in him gave him kinship and understanding; the American, boastful, emotional, proud, defiant, yet so amazingly sentimental, was a creature Paine knew from head to heels;—afterwards he suffered from the fact that he did not understand the French or the English half so well. Paine understood the Yankee's pride in his own common sense; that gave him his title and greatest selling point. "All was obvious," he wheedled; and he put things down in dollars and cents. On the surface, he was writing a practical book for practical people; actually he wrote a flaming call to arms, based on the eighteenth century philosophy of natural rights, and we may thank God that the people who read it were not exclusively practical.

Today, there seems to be nothing amazingly revolutionary in *Common Sense;* but when you read Paine, try to read him with the viewpoint of his day. Remember that he called for action in specific and not in abstract terms; he invited men to fight for freedom, whereas others invited men to think of it.

TWO

The Crisis Papers

THERE is no doubt that Paine was utterly dumfounded at the success of *Common Sense*. Catapulted overnight from his place as an anonymous Englishman to a position as foremost protagonist of the rebel cause, he was faced with a curious problem: should he go ahead with this strange, unprecedented trade of propagandist against tyranny? And if so, how should he go about it, and what was his position in this country hurtling toward war? The circumstances made the choice for him; the success of his pamphlet threw him into the forefront of the struggle, and only by the most craven resistance to his own belief in change could he have withdrawn. He did not withdraw, but at the same time, he did not become an American and identify himself completely with the cause of the patriots. He remained an Englishman, and in doing so broadened the whole base of the struggle and at least gropingly found a means whereby nationalism, in its true sense, could become a beginning for international peace and co-operation.

It is not my purpose here to go into the many adventures and experiences of Thomas Paine during the American Revolution. That tale is better told elsewhere; here we are concerned with the series of unique manifestoes which followed *Common Sense*, and which are known to history as *The Crisis Papers* or *The American Crisis*. These exhortations, some of them so magnificently potent that even today they take our breath away, have no precise duplication in history. Modern political leaders have written brilliant interpretations of changing situations; Winston Churchill has spoken, time and again, words that rallied his whole country behind him; so has Franklin Roosevelt, so has Joseph Stalin. But, none of these is a counterpart to *The Crisis Papers*. Paine was not a political leader; he was not an enlisted soldier; he was an international volunteer who, at times of the deepest despair, spoke up clearly, confidently, and through some magic of his own, rallied the nation behind him. And this self-appointed task, he performed again and again.

Most dramatic, of course, partaking the quality of a legend, is the origin of the first *Crisis*. Paine had gone up into Jersey after the signing of the Declaration of Independence, a document which he considered the fruition of his plea, in *Common Sense,* for complete independence—and which, to a great extent, it was. He went with a group of Philadelphia volunteers, not as a soldier, but as a sort of civilian secretary to their commander. He needed a position of some kind, for he had refused all royalties from *Common Sense*.

At Amboy, the volunteers fell to pieces, as did so many volunteer regiments in the early days of the war. The men deserted and went home; Paine made his way to Fort Lee, where Washington's defeated army was taking a breathing spell. Paine stayed with that army on its heartbreaking retreat to the Delaware River. He lived with the men, marched with them, spoke with them, pleaded with them. His anomalous position, neither a soldier nor an officer, gave him entree to both groups.

If we accept the thesis, and there is much evidence for it, that out of a revolutionary situation will spring certain constant forms, then we may say that Paine became the political instructor to the ragged remnants of George Washington's army. At that time, and remember, it was in 1776, the American Revolution had not yet formulated itself; not in military structure, not in a dynamic ideology for those who fought. An army of twenty thousand had withered away to a few hundred beaten and hopeless men, and this in a period of months. Defeats and desertions robbed the American cause of thousands, and December of 1776 seemed close to the end.

And at that point, Paine wrote his first *American Crisis*.

How he came to write it is, as I said, already beclouded with legend. We do know that he accompanied Washington's army on the retreat through Jersey, and we know that as the ranks thinned he became more and more of a focal point for whatever ideological strength could be gathered. And that strength became more and more important, as other revolutionists have discovered since. There is no doubt that, at a very low point, Washington asked the author of *Common Sense* whether he could not write something which would do, for this crucial situation, what his book had done for the cause of independence. Whether or not he wrote the *Crisis* on a drumhead, the cold and tattered Continentals gathered around him, is beside the point; time has given it that setting, just as time has robed so many American events with drama we love so much; and I, for one, would not disturb the legend.

We do know that Washington read this essay—we know that he was tremendously moved and ordered it to be read aloud to the assembled brigades. We can picture the scene, the few war-weary and tattered volunteers who had stayed by the cause, the dispirited officers, the lonely commander in chief who had yet to win a battle, and the sergeants-at-arms reading aloud for the first time those immortal words:

"These are the times that try men's souls . . ."

At that point, I believe, Paine had written only a part of what was later published in Philadelphia; only the ringing, impassioned beginning and end. Yet what he added came up to that, and altogether the document is a work of genius, for me the most unique and constant part of all Paine's writing. It is for no period, no time, but for the cause of free men always—and more than a century and a half later, the transmitters of the OWI, at a time when there were no victories for us to tell, sent the *Crisis* to all of Europe, where underground newspapers published once more the words with which Paine had rallied America in her darkest hour.

Printed in Philadelphia, the *Crisis* had, if anything, more of a success than *Common Sense*. That is understandable; it was short enough to be set in one block and printed with a single twist of the old up-and-down presses on a single sheet of paper. It was folded and sold as a pamphlet; it was posted everywhere as a bill. It was memorized by thousands, and the phrases "Summer soldier" and "Sunshine patriot," were on every tongue. It became the battlecry of the day, and the splendid moral tale of the Tory at Amboy drew a complete and hearty response from the deeply religious American population.

I think that the highest point in Paine's political understanding was reached during the years he wrote his series of *Crisis Papers,* the years between 1776 and 1783. In these seven years, moulded by history, reacting to history, and—and this is most important—understanding history, Paine produced a vital and lasting interpretation of a revolutionary movement. Neither in England nor in France, years later, did he succeed; now he let himself freely be shaped as an instrument of American freedom; in England and France, he tried to impose that same pattern, and thereby he failed. But that in its place.

With the *Crisis,* Paine began to complete his definition of the issues at stake in America. More than any other, he took these issues away from a locality and presented them, and the responsibility for them, to all mankind. He called upon mankind to strike for freedom. He defined men objectively, just as we are forced to today. He became the sparkplug for the fierce and necessary hatred that was growing between patriots and Tories, completing the process he began in *Common Sense.*

Reading the *Crisis Papers* you are presented with a curiously different slant on the American Revolution than what you might have had before. They take that struggle out of the histories and make it come alive. They give you only one small part of the picture, however, for Paine never admitted how bad things were; his propaganda was conscious, and he developed the method into an art. He told what it suited him to tell, and his telling was a weapon.

As to the effect of the *Crisis Papers,* that is hard to measure accurately. We know that in many instances he rallied the country with astonishing effect; on the other hand, some of the later *Crisis Papers* had much less influence. It is more important to see the Revolution as a whole, not the work of one man or another, but the work of many, many men, all operating within a frame of forces, and directing those forces through the conscious application of their will, determination, and courage. And of those men, Paine was by no means the least.

It should be noted that Paine saw a great deal of the war; he saw it from the battlefield and the encampment, and he saw it from the home front, there, I think, more clearly than anyone of his time.

The Crisis

NUMBER I

THESE are the times that try men's souls. The summer soldier and the sunshine patriot will in this crisis, shrink from the service of his country; but he that stands it NOW, deserves the love and thanks of man and woman. Tyranny, like hell, is not easily conquered; yet we have this consolation with us, that the harder the conflict, the more glorious the triumph. What we obtain too cheap, we esteem too lightly; 'tis dearness only that gives everything its value. Heaven knows how to put a proper price upon its goods; and it would be strange indeed, if so celestial an article as FREEDOM should not be highly rated. Britain, with an army to enforce her tyranny, has declared that she has a right (*not only to* TAX) but "to BIND *us in* ALL CASES WHATSOEVER," and if being *bound in that manner*, is not slavery, then is there not such a thing as slavery upon earth. Even the expression is impious, for so unlimited a power can belong only to God.

Whether the independence of the continent was declared too soon, or delayed too long, I will not now enter into as an argument; my own simple opinion is, that had it been eight months earlier, it would have been much better. We did not make a proper use of last winter, neither could we, while we were in a dependent state. However, the fault, if it were one, was all our own; we have none to blame but ourselves. But no great deal is lost yet; all that Howe has been doing for this month past, is rather a ravage than a conquest, which the spirit of the Jerseys a year ago would have quickly repulsed, and which time and a little resolution will soon recover.

I have as little superstition in me as any man living, but my secret opinion has ever been, and still is, that God Almighty will not give up a people to military destruction, or leave them unsupportedly to perish, who have so earnestly and so repeatedly sought to avoid the calamities of war, by every decent method which wisdom could invent. Neither have I so much of the infidel in me, as to suppose that he has relinquished the government of the world, and given us up to the care of devils; and as I do not, I cannot see on what grounds the king of Britain can look up to heaven for help against us: a common murderer, a highwayman, or a house-breaker, has as good a pretence as he.

'Tis surprising to see how rapidly a panic will sometimes run through a country. All nations and ages have been subject to them: Britain has trembled like an ague at the report of a French fleet of flat-bottomed boats; and in the fourteenth century the whole English army, after ravaging the kingdom of France, was driven back like men petrified with fear; and this brave exploit was performed by a few broken forces collected and headed by a woman, Joan of Arc. Would that heaven might inspire some Jersey maid to spirit up her countrymen, and save her fair fellow sufferers from ravage and ravishment! Yet panics, in some cases, have their uses; they produce as much good as hurt. Their duration is always short; the mind soon grows through them, and acquires a firmer habit than before. But their peculiar advantage is, that they are the touchstones of sincerity and hypocrisy, and bring things and men to light, which might otherwise have lain forever undiscovered. In fact, they have the same effect on secret traitors which an imaginary apparition would have upon a private murderer. They sift out the hidden thoughts of man, and hold them up in public to the world. Many a disguised tory has lately shown his head, that shall penitentially solemnize with curses the day on which Howe arrived upon the Delaware.

As I was with the troops at Fort Lee, and marched with them to the edge of Pennsylvania, I am well acquainted with many circumstances, which those who live at a distance, know but little or nothing of. Our situation there, was exceedingly cramped, the place being a narrow neck of land between the North River and the Hackensack. Our force was inconsiderable, being not one-fourth so great as Howe could bring against us. We had no army at hand to have relieved the garrison, had we shut ourselves up and stood on our defence. Our ammunition, light artillery, and the best part of our stores, had been removed, on the apprehension that Howe would endeavor to penetrate the Jerseys, in which case Fort Lee could be of no use to us; for it must occur to every thinking man, whether in the army or not, that these kind of field forts are only for temporary purposes, and last in use no longer than the enemy directs his force against the particular object, which such forts are raised to defend. Such was our situation and condition at fort Lee on the morning of the 20th of November, when an officer arrived with information that the enemy with 200 boats had landed about seven miles above: Major General Green, who commanded the garrison, immediately ordered them under arms, and sent express to General Washington at the town of Hackensack, distant by the way of the ferry, six miles. Our first object was to secure the bridge over the Hackensack, which laid up the river between the enemy and us, about six miles from us, and three from them. General Washington arrived in about three quarters of an hour, and marched at the head of the troops towards the bridge, which place I expected we should have a brush for; however, they did not choose to dispute it with us, and the greatest part of our troops went over the bridge, the rest over the ferry except some which passed at a mill on a small creek, between the bridge and the ferry, and made their way through some marshy grounds up to the town of Hackensack, and there passed the river. We brought off as much baggage as the wagons could contain, the rest was lost. The simple object was to bring off the garrison, and march them on till they could be strengthened by the Jersey or Pennsylvania militia, so as to be enabled to make a stand. We stayed four days at Newark, collected our out-posts with some of the Jersey militia, and marched out twice to meet the enemy, on being informed that they were advancing, though our numbers were greatly inferior to theirs. Howe, in my little opinion, committed a great error in generalship in not throwing a body of forces off from Staten Island through Amboy, by which means he might have seized all our stores at Brunswick, and intercepted our march into Pennsylvania: but if we believe the power of hell to be limited, we must likewise believe that their agents are under some providential control.

I shall not now attempt to give all the particulars of our retreat to the Delaware; suffice for the present to say, that both officers and men, though greatly harassed and fatigued, without rest, covering, or provision, the inevitable consequences of a long retreat, bore it with a manly and martial spirit. All their wishes centred in one, which was, that the country would turn out and help them to drive the enemy back. Voltaire has remarked that King William never appeared to full advantage but in difficulties and in action; the same remark may be made on General Washington, for the character fits him. There is a natural firmness in some minds which cannot be unlocked by trifles, but which, when unlocked, discovers a cabinet of fortitude; and I reckon it among those kind of public blessings, which we do not immediately see, that God hath blest him with uninterrupted health, and given him a mind that can even flourish upon care.

I shall conclude this paper with some miscellaneous remarks on the state of our affairs; and shall begin with asking the following question: Why is it that the enemy have left the New-England provinces, and made these middle ones the seat of war? The answer is easy: New-England is not infested with tories, and we are. I have been tender in raising the cry against these men, and I used numberless arguments to show them their danger, but it will not do to sacrifice a world either to their folly or their baseness. The period is now arrived, in which either they or we must change our sentiments, or one or both must fall. And what is a tory? Good God! what is he? I should not be afraid to go with a hundred whigs against a thousand tories, were they to attempt to get into arms. Every tory is a coward; for servile, slavish, self-interested fear is the foundation of toryism; and a man under such influence, though he may be cruel, never can be brave.

But, before the line of irrecoverable separation be drawn between us, let us reason the matter together: your conduct is an invitation to the enemy, yet not one in a thousand of you has heart enough to join him. Howe is as much deceived by you as the American cause is injured by you. He expects you will all take up arms, and flock to his standard, with muskets on your shoulders. Your opinions are of no use to him, unless you support him personally, for 'tis soldiers, and not tories that he wants.

I once felt all that kind of anger, which a man ought to feel, against the mean principles that are held by the tories: a noted one, who kept a tavern at Amboy, was standing at his door, with as pretty a child in his hand, about eight or nine years old, as I ever saw, and after speaking his mind as freely as he thought was prudent, finished with this unfatherly expression, *"Well! give me peace in my day."* Not a man lives on the continent but fully believes that a separation must some time or other finally take place, and a generous parent should have said, *"If there must be trouble let it be in my day, that my child may have peace;"* and this single reflection, well applied, is sufficient to awaken every man to duty. Not a place upon earth might be so happy as America. Her situation is remote from all the wrangling world, and she has nothing to do but to trade with them. A man can distinguish himself between temper and principle, and I am as confident, as I am that God governs the world, that America will never be happy till she gets clear of foreign dominion. Wars, without ceasing, will break out till that period arrives, and the continent must in the end be conqueror; for though the flame of liberty may sometimes cease to shine, the coal can never expire.

America did not, nor does not want force; but she wanted a proper application of that force. Wisdom is not the purchase of a day, and it is no wonder that we should err at the first setting off. From an excess of tenderness, we were unwilling to raise an army, and trusted our cause to the temporary defence of a well-meaning militia. A summer's experience has now taught us better; yet with those troops, while they were collected, we were able to set bounds to the progress of the enemy, and, thank God! they are again assembling. I always consider militia as the best troops in the world for a sudden exertion, but they will not do for a long campaign. Howe, it is probable, will make an attempt on this city; should he fail on this side the Delaware, he is ruined: if he succeeds, our cause is not ruined. He stakes all on his side against a part on ours; admitting he succeeds, the consequence will be, that armies from both ends of the continent will march to assist their suffering friends in the middle states; for he cannot go everywhere; it is impossible. I consider Howe the greatest enemy the tories have; he is bringing a war into their country, which, had it not been for him and partly for themselves, they had been clear of. Should he now be expelled, I wish with all the devotion of a *Christian,* that the names of whig and tory may never more be mentioned; but should the tories give him encouragement to come, or assistance if he come, I as sincerely wish that our next year's arms may expel them from the continent, and that congress appropriate their possessions to the relief of those who have suffered in well doing. A single successful battle next year will settle the whole. America could carry on a two years' war by the confiscation of the property of disaffected persons; and be made happy by their expulsion. Say not that this is revenge, call it rather the soft resentment of a suffering people, who, having no object in view but the *good* of *all,* have staked their *own all* upon a seemingly doubtful event. Yet it is folly to argue against determined hardness; eloquence may strike the ear, and the language of sorrow draw forth the tear of compassion, but nothing can reach the heart that is steeled with prejudice.

Quitting this class of men, I turn with the warm ardor of a friend to those who have nobly stood, and are yet determined to stand the matter out: I call not upon a few, but upon all; not on *this* state or *that* state, but on *every* state; up and help us; lay your shoulders to the wheel; better have too much force than too little, when so great an object is at stake. Let it be told to the future world, that in the depth of winter, when nothing but hope and virtue could survive, that the city and the country, alarmed at one common danger, came forth to meet and to repulse it. Say not that thousands are gone, turn out your tens of thousands; throw not the burden of the day upon Providence, but *"show your faith by your works,"* that God may bless you. It matters not where you live, or what rank of life you hold, the evil or the blessing will reach you all. The far and the near, the home counties and the back, the rich and the poor, will suffer or rejoice alike. The heart that feels not now, is dead: the blood of his children will curse his cowardice, who shrinks back at a time when a little might have saved the whole, and made *them* happy. (I love the man that can smile at trouble; that can gather strength from distress, and grow brave by reflection.) 'Tis the business of little minds to shrink; but he whose heart is firm, and whose conscience approves his conduct, will pursue his principles unto death. My own line of reasoning is to myself as straight and clear as a ray of light. Not all the treasures of the world, so far as I believe, could have induced me to support an offensive war, for I think it murder; but if a thief breaks into my house, burns and destroys my property, and kills or threatens to kill me, or those that are in it, and to *"bind me in all cases whatsoever,"* to his absolute will, am I to suffer it? What signifies it to me, whether he who does it is a king or a common man; my countryman, or not my countryman; whether it be done by an individual villain or an army of them? If we reason to the root of things we shall find no difference; neither can any just cause be assigned why we should punish in the one case and pardon in the other. Let them call me rebel, and welcome, I feel no concern from it; but I should suffer the misery of devils, werc I to make a whore of my soul by swearing allegiance to one whose character is that of a sottish, stupid, stubborn, worthless, brutish man. I conceive likewise a horrid idea in receiving mercy from a being, who at the last day shall be shrieking to the rocks and mountains to cover him, and fleeing with terror from the orphan, the widow, and the slain of America.

There are cases which cannot be overdone by language, and this is one. There are persons too who see not the full extent of the evil which threatens them; they solace themselves with hopes that the enemy, if he succeed, will be merciful. Is this the madness of folly, to expect mercy from those who have refused to do justice; and even mercy, where conquest is the object, is only a trick of war; the cunning of the fox is as murderous as the violence of the wolf; and we ought to guard equally against both. Howe's first object is partly by threats and partly by promises, to terrify or seduce the people to deliver up their arms and to receive mercy. The ministry recommended the same plan to Gage, and this is what the tories call making their peace, *"a peace which passeth all understanding," indeed!* A peace which would be the immediate forerunner of a worse ruin than any we have yet thought of. Ye men of Pennsylvania, do reason upon these things! Were the back counties to give up their arms, they would fall an easy prey to the Indians, who are all armed; this perhaps is what some tories would not be sorry for. Were the home counties to deliver up their arms, they would be exposed to the resentment of the back counties, who would then have it in their power to chastise their defection at pleasure. And were any one state to give up its arms, *that* state must be garrisoned by Howe's army of Britains and Hessians to preserve it from the anger of the rest. Mutual fear is the principal link in the chain of mutual love, and woe be to that state that breaks the compact. Howe is mercifully inviting you to barbarous destruction, and men must be either rogues or fools that will not see it. I dwell not upon the powers of imagination; I bring reason to your ears; and in language as plain as A, B, C, hold up truth to your eyes.

I thank God that I fear not. I see no real cause for fear. I know our situation well and can see the way out of it. While our army was collected, Howe dared not risk a battle, and it is no credit to him that he decamped from the White Plains, and waited a mean opportunity to ravage the defenceless Jerseys; but it is great credit to us, that, with a handful of men, we sustained an orderly retreat for near an hundred miles, brought off our ammunition, all our field pieces, the greatest part of our stores, and had four rivers to pass. None can say that our retreat was precipitate, for we were near three weeks in performing it, that the country might have time to come in. Twice we marched back to meet the enemy, and remained out till dark. The sign of fear was not seen in our camp, and had not some of the cowardly and disaffected inhabitants spread false alarms through the country, the Jerseys had never been ravaged. Once more we are again collected and collecting, our new army at both ends of the continent is recruiting fast, and we shall be able to open the next campaign with sixty thousand men, well armed and clothed. This is our situation, and who will may know it. By perseverance and fortitude we have the prospect of a glorious issue; by cowardice and submission, the sad choice of a variety of evils—a ravaged country—a depopulated city—habitations without safety, and slavery without hope—our homes turned into barracks and bawdy-houses for Hessians, and a future race to provide for, whose fathers we shall doubt of. Look on this picture and weep over it! and if there yet remains one thoughtless wretch who believes it not, let him suffer it unlamented.

December 23, 1776 COMMON SENSE

☆ ☆ ☆

The Crisis

NUMBER IV

THOSE who expect to reap the blessings of freedom, must, like men, undergo the fatigues of supporting it. The event of yesterday was one of those kind of alarms which is just sufficient to rouse us to duty, without being of consequence enough to depress our fortitude. It is not a field of a few acres of ground, but a cause, that we are defending, and whether we defeat the enemy in one battle, or by degrees, the consequences will be the same.

Look back at the events of last winter and the present year, there you will find that the enemy's successes always contributed to reduce them. What they have gained in ground, they paid so dearly for in numbers, that their victories have in the end amounted to defeats. We have always been masters at the last push, and always shall be while we do our duty. Howe has been once on the banks of the Delaware, and from thence driven back with loss and disgrace: and why not be again driven from the Schuylkill? His condition and ours are very different. He has everybody to fight, we have only his *one* army to cope with, and which wastes away at every engagement: we can not only reinforce, but can redouble our numbers; he is cut off from all supplies, and must sooner or later inevitably fall into our hands.

Shall a band of ten or twelve thousand robbers, who are this day fifteen hundred or two thousand men less in strength than they were yesterday, conquer America, or subdue even a single state? The thing cannot be, unless we sit down and suffer them to do it. Another such a brush, notwithstanding we lost the ground, would, by still reducing the enemy, put them in a condition to be afterwards totally defeated.

Could our whole army have come up to the attack at one time, the consequences had probably been otherwise; but our having different parts of the Brandywine creek to guard, and the uncertainty which road to Philadelphia the enemy would attempt to take, naturally afforded them an opportunity of passing with their main body at a place where only a part of ours could be posted; for it must strike every thinking man with conviction, that it requires a much greater force to oppose an enemy in several places, than is sufficient to defeat him in any one place.

Men who are sincere in defending their freedom, will always feel concern at every circumstance which seems to make against them; it is the natural and honest consequence of all affectionate attachments, and the want of it is a vice. But the dejection lasts only for a moment; they soon rise out of it with additional vigor; the glow of hope, courage and fortitude, will, in a little time, supply the place of every inferior passion, and kindle the whole heart into heroism.

There is a mystery in the countenance of some causes, which we have not always present judgment enough to explain. It is distressing to see an enemy advancing into a country, but it is the only place in which we can beat them, and in which we have always beaten them, whenever they made the attempt. The nearer any disease approaches to a crisis, the nearer it is to a cure. Danger and deliverance make their advances together, and it is only the last push, in which one or the other takes the lead.

There are many men who will do their duty when it is not wanted; but a genuine public spirit always appears most when there is most occasion for it. Thank God! our army, though fatigued, is yet entire. The attack made by us yesterday, was under many disadvantages, naturally arising from the uncertainty of knowing which route the enemy would take; and, from that circumstance, the whole of our force could not be brought up together time enough to engage all at once. Our strength is yet reserved; and it is evident that Howe does not think himself a gainer by the affair, otherwise he would this morning have moved down and attacked General Washington.

Gentlemen of the city and country, it is in your power, by a spirited improvement of the present circumstance, to turn it to a real advantage. Howe is now weaker than before, and every shot will contribute to reduce him. You are more immediately interested than any other part of the continent: your all is at stake; it is not so with the general cause; you are devoted by the enemy to plunder and destruction: it is the encouragement which Howe, the chief of plunderers, has promised his army. Thus circumstanced, you may save yourselves by a manly resistance, but you can have no hope in any other conduct. I never yet knew our brave general, or any part of the army, officers or men, out of heart, and I have seen them in circumstances a thousand times more trying than the present. It is only those that are not in action, that feel languor and heaviness, and the best way to rub it off is to turn out, and make sure work of it.

Our army must undoubtedly feel fatigue, and want a reinforcement of rest though not of valour. Our own interest and happiness call upon us to give them every support in our power, and make the burden of the day, on which the safety of this city depends, as light as possible. Remember, gentlemen, that we have forces both to the northward and southward of Philadelphia, and if the enemy be but stopped till those can arrive, this city will be saved, and the enemy finally routed. You have too much at stake to hesitate. You ought not to think an hour upon the matter, but to spring to action at once. Other states have been invaded, have likewise driven off the invaders. Now our time and turn is come, and perhaps the finishing stroke is reserved for us. When we look back on the dangers we have been saved from, and reflect on the success we have been blessed with, it would be sinful either to be idle or to despair.

I close this paper with a short address to general Howe. You, sir, are only lingering out the period that shall bring with it your defeat. You have yet scarce began upon the war, and the further you enter, the faster will your troubles thicken. What you now enjoy is only a respite from ruin; an invitation to destruction; something that will lead on to our deliverance at your expense. We know the cause which we are engaged in, and though a passionate fondness for it may make us grieve at every injury which threatens it, yet, when the moment of concern is over, the determination to duty returns. We are not moved by the gloomy smile of a worthless king, but by the ardent glow of generous patriotism. We fight not to enslave, but to set a country free, and to make room upon the earth for honest men to live in. In such a case we are sure that we are right; and we leave to you the despairing reflection of being the tool of a miserable tyrant.

PHILADELPHIA, Sept. 12, 1777. COMMON SENSE

The Crisis

NUMBER V

TO GEN. SIR WILLIAM HOWE

To argue with a man who has renounced the use and authority of reason, and whose philosophy consists in holding humanity in contempt, is like administering medicine to the dead, or endeavoring to convert an atheist by scripture. Enjoy, sir, your insensibility of feeling and reflecting. It is the prerogative of animals. And no man will envy you these honors, in which a savage only can be your rival and a bear your master.

As the generosity of this country rewarded your brother's services last war, with an elegant monument in Westminster Abbey, it is consistent that she should bestow some mark of distinction upon you. You certainly deserve her notice, and a conspicuous place in the catalogue of extraordinary persons. Yet it would be a pity to pass you from the world in state, and consign you to magnificent oblivion among the tombs, without telling the future beholder why. Judas is as much known as John, yet history ascribes their fame to very different actions.

Sir William hath undoubtedly merited a monument; but of what kind, or with what inscription, where placed or how embellished, is a question that would puzzle all the heralds of St. James's in the profoundest mood of historical deliberation. We are at no loss, sir, to ascertain your real character, but somewhat perplexed how to perpetuate its identity, and preserve it uninjured from the transformations of time or mistake. A statuary may give a false expression to your bust, or decorate it with some equivocal emblems, by which you may happen to steal into reputation and impose upon the hereafter traditionary world. Ill nature or ridicule may conspire, or a variety of accidents combine to lessen, enlarge, or change Sir William's fame; and no doubt but he who has taken so much pains to be singular in his conduct, would choose to be just as singular in his exit, his monument and his epitaph.

The usual honours of the dead, to be sure, are not sufficiently sublime to escort a character like you to the republic of dust and ashes; for however men may differ in their ideas of grandeur or of government here, the grave is nevertheless a perfect republic. Death is not the monarch of the dead, but of the dying. The moment he obtains a conquest he loses a subject, and, like the foolish king you serve, will, in the end, war himself out of all his dominions.

As a proper preliminary towards the arrangement of your funeral honours, we readily admit of your new rank of *knighthood.* The title is perfectly in character, and is your own, more by merit than creation. There are knights of various orders, from the knight of the windmill to the knight of the post. The former is your patron for exploits, and the latter will assist you in settling your accounts. No honorary title could be more happily applied! The ingenuity is sublime! And your royal master hath discovered more genius in fitting you therewith, than in generating the most finished figure for a button, or descanting on the properties of a button mould.

But how, sir, shall we dispose of you? The invention of a statuary is exhausted, and Sir William is yet unprovided with a monument. America is anxious to bestow her funeral favours upon you, and wishes to do it in a manner that shall distinguish you from all the deceased heroes of the last war. The Egyptian method of embalming is not known to the present age, and hieroglyphical pageantry hath outlived the science of decyphering it. Some other method, therefore, must be thought of to immortalise the new knight of the windmill and post. Sir William, thanks to his stars, is not oppressed with very delicate ideas. He has no ambition of being wrapped up and handed about in myrrh, aloes and cassia. Less expensive odours will suffice; and it fortunately happens that the simple genius of America hath discovered the art of preserving bodies, and embellishing them too, with much greater frugality than the ancients. In balmage, sir, of humble tar, you will be as secure as Pharaoh, and in a hieroglyphic of feathers, rival in finery all the mummies of Egypt.

As you have already made your exit from the moral world, and by numberless acts both of passionate and deliberate injustice engraved an "*here lyeth*" on your deceased honour, it must be mere affectation in you to pretend concern at the humours or opinions of mankind respecting you. What remains of you may expire at any time. The sooner the better. For he who survives his reputation, lives out of despite of himself, like a man listening to his own reproach.

Thus entombed and ornamented, I leave you to the inspection of the curious, and return to the history of your yet surviving actions. The character of Sir William hath undergone some extraordinary revolutions since his arrival in America. It is now fixed and known; and we have nothing to hope from your candour or to fear from your capacity. Indolence and inability have too large a share in your composition, ever to suffer you to be anything more than the hero of little villainies and unfinished adventures. That, which to some persons appeared moderation in you at first, was not produced by any real virtue of your own, but by a contrast of passions, dividing and holding you in perpetual irresolution. One vice will frequently expel another, without the least merit in the man; as powers in contrary directions reduce each other to rest.

It became you to have supported a dignified solemnity of character; to have shown a superior liberality of soul; to have won respect by an obstinate perseverance in maintaining order, and to have exhibited on all occasions such an unchangeable graciousness of conduct, that while we beheld in you the resolution of an enemy, we might admire in you the sincerity of a man. You came to America under the high sounding titles of commander and commissioner; not only to suppress what you call rebellion, by arms, but to shame it out of countenance by the excellence of your example. Instead of which, you have been the patron of low and vulgar frauds, the encourager of Indian cruelties; and have imported a cargo of vices blacker than those which you pretend to suppress.

Mankind are not universally agreed in their determination of right and wrong; but there are certain actions which the consent of all nations and individuals hath branded with the unchangeable name of *meanness*. In the list of human vices we find some of such a refined constitution, they cannot be carried into practice without seducing some virtue to their assistance; but *meanness* hath neither alliance nor apology. It is generated in the dust and sweepings of other vices, and is of such a hateful figure that all the rest conspire to disown it. Sir William, the commissioner of George the third, hath at last vouchsafed to give it rank and pedigree. He has placed the fugitive at the council board, and dubbed it companion of the order of knighthood.

The particular act of meanness which I allude to in this description, is forgery. You, sir, have abetted and patronised the forging and uttering counterfeit continental bills. In the same New-York newspapers in which your own proclamation under your master's authority was published, offering, or pretending to offer, pardon and protection to these states, there were repeated advertisements of counterfeit money for sale, and persons who have come officially from you, and under the sanction of your flag, have been taken up in attempting to put them off.

A conduct so basely mean in a public character is without precedent or pretence. Every nation on earth, whether friends or enemies, will unite in despising you. 'Tis an incendiary war upon society, which nothing can excuse or palliate,—an improvement upon beggarly villainy—and shows an inbred wretchedness of heart made up between the venomous malignity of a serpent and the spiteful imbecility of an inferior reptile.

The laws of any civilized country would condemn you to the gibbet without regard to your rank or titles, because it is an action foreign to the usage and custom of war; and should you fall into our hands, which pray God you may, it will be a doubtful matter whether we are to consider you as a military prisoner or a prisoner for felony.

Besides, it is exceedingly unwise and impolitic in you, or any other persons in the English service, to promote or even encourage, or wink at the crime of forgery, in any case whatever. Because, as the riches of England, as a nation, are chiefly in paper, and the far greater part of trade among individuals is carried on by the same medium, that is, by notes and drafts on one another, they, therefore, of all people in the world, ought to endeavour to keep forgery out of sight, and, if possible, not to revive the idea of it. It is dangerous to make men familiar with a crime which they may afterwards practise to much greater advantage against those who first taught them. Several officers in the English army have made their exit at the gallows for forgery on their agents; for we all know, who know any thing of England, that there is not a more necessitous body of men, taking them generally, than what the English officers are. They contrive to make a show at the expense of the tailors, and appear clean at the charge of the washer-women.

England, hath at this time, nearly two hundred million pounds sterling of public money in paper, for which she hath no real property: besides a large circulation of bank notes, bank post bills, and promissory notes and drafts of private bankers, merchants and tradesmen. She hath the greatest quantity of paper currency and the least quantity of gold and silver of any nation in Europe; the real specie, which is about sixteen millions sterling, serves only as change in large sums, which are always made in paper, or for payment in small ones. Thus circumstanced, the nation is put to its wit's end, and obliged to be severe almost to criminality, to prevent the practice and growth of forgery. Scarcely a session passes at the Old Bailey, or an execution at Tyburn, but witnesseth this truth, yet you, sir, regardless of the policy which her necessity obliges her to adopt, have made your whole army intimate with the crime. And as all armies at the conclusion of a war, are too apt to carry into practice the vices of the campaign, it will probably happen, that England will hereafter abound in forgeries, to which art the practitioners were first initiated under your authority in America. You, sir, have the honour of adding a new vice to the military catalogue; and the reason, perhaps, why the invention was reserved for you, is, because no general before was mean enough even to think of it.

That a man whose soul is absorbed in the low traffic of vulgar vice, is incapable of moving in any superior region, is clearly shown in you by the event of every campaign. Your military exploits have been without plan, object or decision. Can it be possible that you or your employers suppose that the possession of Philadelphia will be any ways equal to the expense or expectation of the nation which supports you? What advantages does England derive from any achievements of yours? To *her* it is perfectly indifferent what place you are in, so long as the business of conquest is unperformed and the charge of maintaining you remains the same.

If the principal events of the three campaigns be attended to, the balance will appear against you at the close of each; but the last, in point of importance to us, has exceeded the former two. It is pleasant to look back on dangers past, and equally as pleasant to meditate on present ones when the way out begins to appear. That period is now arrived, and the long doubtful winter of war is changing to the sweeter prospects of victory and joy. At the close of the campaign, in 1775, you were obliged to retreat from Boston. In the summer of 1776, you appeared with a numerous fleet and army in the harbor of New-York. By what miracle the continent was preserved in that season of danger is a subject of admiration! If instead of wasting your time against Long-Island you had run up the North river, and landed any where above New-York, the consequence must have been, that either you would have compelled general Washington to fight you with very unequal numbers, or he must have suddenly evacuated the city with the loss of nearly all the stores of his army, or have surrendered for want of provisions; the situation of the place naturally producing one or the other of these events.

The preparations made to defend New-York were, nevertheless, wise and military; because your forces were then at sea, their numbrs uncertain; storms, sickness, or a variety of accidents might have disabled their coming, or so diminished them on their passage, that those which survived would have been incapable of opening the campaign with any prospect of success; in which case the defence would have been sufficient and the place preserved; for cities that have been raised from nothing with an infinitude of labour and expense, are not to be thrown away on the bare probability of their being taken. On these grounds the preparations made to maintain New-York were as judicious as the retreat afterwards. While you, in the interim, let slip the *very* opportunity which seemed to put conquest in your power.

Through the whole of that campaign you had nearly double the forces which general Washington immediately commanded. The principal plan at that time, on our part, was to wear away the season with as little loss as possible, and to raise the army for the next year. Long-Island, New-York, forts Washington and Lee were not defended after your superior force was known under any expectation of their being finally maintained, but as a range of outworks, in the attacking of which your time might be wasted, your numbers reduced, and your vanity amused by possessing them on our retreat. It was intended to have withdrawn the garrison from fort Washington after it had answered the former of those purposes, but the fate of that day put a prize into your hands without much honor to yourselves.

Your progress through the Jerseys was accidental; you had it not even in contemplation, or you would not have sent a principal part of your forces to Rhode-Island beforehand. The utmost hope of America in the year 1776, reached no higher than that she might not then be conquered. She had no expectation of defeating you in that campaign. Even the most cowardly tory allowed, that, could she withstand the shock of *that* summer, her independence would be past a doubt. You had *then* greatly the advantage of her. You were formidable. Your military knowledge was supposed to be complete. Your fleets and forces arrived without an accident. You had neither experience nor reinforcements to wait for. You had nothing to do but to begin, and your chance lay in the first vigorous onset.

America was young and unskilled. She was obliged to trust her defence to time and practice; and hath, by mere dint of perseverance, maintained her cause, and brought the enemy to a condition, in which she is now capable of meeting him on any grounds.

It is remarkable that in the campaign of 1776 you gained no more, notwithstanding your great force, than what was given you by consent of evacuation, except fort Washington; while every advantage obtained by us was by fair and hard fighting. The defeat of Sir Peter Parker was complete. The conquest of the Hessians at Trenton, by the remains of a retreating army, which but a few days before you affected to despise, is an instance of their heroic perseverance very seldom to be met with. And the victory over the British troops at Princeton, by a harassed and wearied party, who had been engaged the day before and marched all night without refreshment, is attended with such a scene of circumstances and superiority of generalship, as will ever give it a place in the first rank in the history of great actions.

When I look back on the gloomy days of last winter, and see America suspended by a thread, I feel a triumph of joy at the recollection of her delivery, and a reverence for the characters which snatched her from destruction. To doubt *now* would be a species of infidelity, and to forget the instruments which saved us *then* would be ingratitude.

The close of that campaign left us with the spirit of conquerors. The northern districts were relieved by the retreat of general Carleton over the lakes. The army under your command were hunted back and had their bounds prescribed. The continent began to feel its military importance, and the winter passed pleasantly away in preparations for the next campaign.

However confident you might be on your first arrival, the result of the year 1776 gave you some idea of the difficulty, if not impossibility of conquest. To this reason I ascribe your delay in opening the campaign of 1777. The face of matters, on the close of the former year, gave you no encouragement to pursue a discretionary war as soon as the spring admitted the taking the field; for though conquest, in that case, would have given you a double portion of fame, yet the experiment was too hazardous. The ministry, had you failed, would have shifted the whole blame upon you, charged you with having acted without orders, and condemned at once both your plan and execution.

To avoid the misfortunes, which might have involved you and your money accounts in perplexity and suspicion, you prudently waited the arrival of a plan of operations from England, which was that you should proceed for Philadelphia by way of the Chesapeake, and that Burgoyne, after reducing Ticonderoga, should take his route by Albany, and, if necessary, join you.

The splendid laurels of the last campaign have flourished in the north. In that quarter America has surprised the world, and laid the foundation of this year's glory. The conquest of Ticonderoga, (if it may be called a conquest) has, like all your other victories, led on to ruin. Even the provisions taken in that fortress (which by general Burgoyne's return was sufficient in bread and flour for nearly 5000 men for ten weeks, and in beef and pork for the same number of men for one month) served only to hasten his overthrow, by enabling him to proceed to Saratoga, the place of his destruction. A short review of the operations of the last campaign will show the condition of affairs on both sides.

You have taken Ticonderoga and marched into Philadelphia. These are all the events which the year hath produced on your part. A trifling campaign indeed, compared with the expenses of England and the conquest of the continent. On the other side, a considerable part of your northern force has been routed by the New-York militia under general Herkemer. Fort Stanwix has bravely survived a compound attack of soldiers and savages, and the besiegers have fled. The battle of Bennington has put a thousand prisoners into our hands, with all their arms, stores, artillery and baggage. General Burgoyne, in two engagements, has been defeated; himself, his army, and all that were his and theirs are now ours. Ticonderoga and Independence [forts] are retaken, and not the shadow of an enemy remains in all the northern districts. At this instant we have upwards of eleven thousand prisoners, between sixty and seventy [captured] pieces of brass ordnance, besides small arms, tents, stores, etc.

In order to know the real value of those advantages, we must reverse the scene, and suppose general Gates and the force he commanded, to be at your mercy as prisoners, and general Burgoyne, with his army of soldiers and savages, to be already joined to you in Pennsylvania. So dismal a picture can scarcely be looked at. It has all the tracings and colorings of horror and despair; and excites the most swelling emotions of gratitude by exhibiting the miseries we are so graciously preserved from.

I admire the distribution of laurels around the continent. It is the earnest of future union. South-Carolina has had her day of sufferings and of fame; and the other southern states have exerted themselves in proportion to the force that invaded or insulted them. Towards the close of the campaign, in 1776, these middle states were called upon and did their duty nobly. They were witnesses to the almost expiring flame of human freedom. It was the close struggle of life and death, the line of invisible division; and on which the unabated fortitude of a Washington prevailed, and saved the spark that has since blazed in the north with unrivalled lustre.

Let me ask, sir, what great exploits have you performed? Through all the variety of changes and opportunities which the war has produced, I know no one action of yours that can be styled masterly. You have moved in and out, backward and forward, round and round, as if valor consisted in a military jig. The history and figure of your movements would be truly ridiculous could they be justly delineated. They resemble the labours of a puppy pursuing his tail; the end is still at the same distance, and all the turnings round must be done over again.

The first appearance of affairs at Ticonderoga wore such an unpromising aspect, that it was necessary, in July, to detach a part of the forces to the support of that quarter, which were otherwise destined or intended to act against you; and this, perhaps, has been the means of postponing your downfall to another campaign. The destruction of one army at a time is work enough. We know, sir, what we are about, what we have to do, and how to do it.

Your progress from the Chesapeake, was marked by no capital stroke of policy or heroism. Your principal aim was to get general Washington between the Delaware and Schuylkill, and between Philadelphia and your army. In that situation, with a river on each of his flanks, which united about five miles below the city, and your army above him, you could have intercepted his reinforcements and supplies, cut off all his communication with the country, and, if necessary, have despatched assistance to open a passage for general Burgoyne. This scheme was too visible to succeed: for had general Washington suffered you to command the open country above him, I think it a very reasonable conjecture that the conquest of Burgoyne would not have taken place, because you could, in that case, have relieved him. It was therefore necessary, while that important victory was in suspense, to trepan *you* into a situation in which you could only be on the defensive, without the power of affording him assistance. The manœuvre had its effect, and Burgoyne was conquered.

There has been something unmilitary and passive in you from the time of your passing the Schuylkill and getting possession of Philadelphia, to the close of the campaign. You mistook a trap for a conquest, the probability of which had been made known to Europe, and the edge of your triumph taken off by our own information long before.

Having got you into this situation, a scheme for a general attack upon you at Germantown was carried into execution on the 4th of October and though the success was not equal to the excellence of the plan, yet the attempting it proved the genius of America to be on the rise, and her power approaching to superiority. The obscurity of the morning was your best friend, for a fog is always favourable to a hunted enemy. Some weeks after this you likewise planned an attack on general Washington while at Whitemarch. You marched out with infinite parade, but on finding him preparing to attack you next morning, you prudently turned about, and retreated to Philadelphia with all the precipitation of a man conquered in imagination.

Immediately after the battle of Germantown, the probability of Burgoyne's defeat gave a new policy to affairs in Pennsylvania, and it was judged most consistent with the general safety of America, to wait the issue of the northern campaign. Slow and sure is sound work. The news of that victory arrived in our camp on the 18th of October, and no sooner did that shout of joy, and the report of the thirteen cannon reach your ears, than you resolved upon a retreat, and the next day, that is, on the 19th, you withdrew your drooping army into Philadelphia. This movement was evidently dictated by fear; and carried with it a positive confession that you dreaded a second attack. It was hiding yourself among women and children, and sleeping away the choicest part of the campaign in expensive inactivity. An army in a city can never be a conquering army. The situation admits only of defence. It is mere shelter: and every military power in Europe will conclude you to be eventually defeated.

The time when you made this retreat was the very time you ought to have fought a battle, in order to put yourself in condition of recovering in Pennsylvania what you had lost in Saratoga. And the reason why you did not, must be either prudence or cowardice; the former supposes your inability, and the latter needs no explanation. I draw no conclusions, sir, but such as are naturally deduced from known and visible facts, and such as will always have a being while the facts which produced them remain unaltered.

After this retreat a new difficulty arose which exhibited the power of Britain in a very contemptible light; which was the attack and defence of Mud-Island. For several weeks did that little unfinished fortress stand out against all the attempts of admiral and general Howe. It was the fable of Bender realized on the Delaware. Scheme after scheme, and force upon force were tried and defeated. The garrison, with scarce anything to cover them but their bravery, survived in the midst of mud, shot and shells, and were at last obliged to give it up more to the powers of time and gunpowder than to military superiority of the besiegers.

It is my sincere opinion that matters are in much worse condition with you than what is generally known. Your master's speech at the opening of parliament, is like a soliloquy on ill luck. It shows him to be coming a little to his reason, for sense of pain is the first symptom of recovery, in profound stupefaction. His condition is deplorable. He is obliged to submit to all the insults of France and Spain, without daring to know or resent them; and thankful for the most trivial evasions to the most humble remonstrances. The time *was* when he could not deign an answer to a petition from America, and the time now *is* when he dare not give an answer to an affront from France. The capture of Burgoyne's army will sink his consequence as much in Europe as in America. In his speech he expresses his suspicions at the warlike preparations of France and Spain, and as he has only the one army which you command to support his character in the world with, it remains very uncertain when, or in what quartet it will be most wanted, or can be best employed; and this will partly account for the great care you take to keep it from action and attacks, for should Burgoyne's fate be yours, which it probably will, England may take her endless farewell not only of all America but of all the West-Indies.

Never did a nation invite destruction upon itself with the eagerness and the ignorance with which Britain has done. Bent upon the ruin of a young and unoffending country, she has drawn the sword that has wounded herself to the heart, and in the agony of her resentment has applied a poison for a cure. Her conduct towards America is a compound of rage and lunacy; she aims at the government of it, yet preserves neither dignity nor character in her methods to obtain it. Were government a mere manufacture or article of commerce, immaterial by whom it should be made or sold, we might as well employ her as another, but when we consider it as the fountain from whence the general manners and morality of a country take their rise, that the persons entrusted with the execution thereof are by their serious example an authority to support these principles, how abominably absurd is the idea of being hereafter governed by a set of men who have been guilty of forgery, perjury, treachery, theft and every species of villainy which the lowest wretches on earth could practise or invent. What greater public curse can befal any country than to be under such authority, and what greater blessing than to be delivered therefrom. The soul of any man of sentiment would rise in brave rebellion against them, and spurn them from the earth.

The malignant and venomous tempered general Vaughan has amused his savage fancy in burning the whole town of Kingston, in York government, and the late governor of that state, Mr. Tryon, in his letter to general Parsons, has endeavoured to justify it and declared his wish to burn the houses of every committeeman in the country. Such a confession from one who was once intrusted with the powers of civil government, is a reproach to the character. But it is the wish and the declaration of a man whom anguish and disappointment have driven to despair, and who is daily decaying into the grave with constitutional rottenness.

There is not in the compass of language a sufficiency of words to express the baseness of your king, his ministry and his army. They have refined upon villainy till it wants a name. To the fiercer vices of former ages they have added the dregs and scummings of the most finished rascality, and are so completely sunk in serpentine deceit, that there is not left among them *one* generous enemy.

From such men and such masters, may the gracious hand of Heaven preserve America! And though the sufferings she now endures are heavy, and severe, they are like straws in the wind compared to the weight of evils she would feel under the government of your king, and his pensioned parliament.

There is something in meanness which excites a species of resentment that never subsides, and something in cruelty which stirs up the heart to the highest agony of human hatred; Britain hath filled up both these characters till no addition can be made, and hath not reputation left with us to obtain credit for the slightest promise. The will of God hath parted us, and the deed is registered for eternity. When she shall be a spot scarcely visible among the nations, America shall flourish the favourite of heaven, and the friend of mankind.

For the domestic happiness of Britain and the peace of the world, I wish she had not a foot of land but what is circumscribed within her own island. Extent of dominion has been her ruin, and instead of civilizing others has brutalized herself. Her late reduction of India, under Clive and his successors, was not so properly a conquest as an extermination of mankind. She is the only power who could practise the prodigal barbarity of tying men to mouths of loaded cannon and blowing them away. It happens that general Burgoyne, who made the report of that horrid transaction, in the house of commons, is now a prisoner with us, and though an enemy, I can appeal to him for the truth of it, being confident that he neither can nor will deny it. Yet Clive received the approbation of the last parliament.

When we take a survey of mankind, we cannot help cursing the wretch, who, to the unavoidable misfortunes of nature, shall wilfully add the calamities of war. One would think there were evils enough in the world without studying to increase them, and that life is sufficiently short without shaking the sand that measures it. The histories of Alexander, and Charles of Sweden, are the histories of human devils; a good man cannot think of their actions without abhorrence, nor of their deaths without rejoicing. To see the bounties of heaven destroyed, the beautiful face of nature laid waste, and the choicest works of creation and art tumbled into ruin, would fetch a curse from the soul of piety itself. But in this country the aggravation is heightened by a new combination of affecting circumstances. America was young, and, compared with other countries, was virtuous. None but a Herod of uncommon malice would have made war upon infancy and innocence: and none but a people of the most finished fortitude, dared under those circumstances, have resisted the tyranny. The natives, or their ancestors, had fled from the former oppressions of England, and with the industry of bees had changed a wilderness into a habitable world. To Britain they were indebted for nothing. The country was the gift of heaven, and God alone is their Lord and Sovereign.

The time, sir, will come when you, in a melancholy hour, shall reckon up your miseries by your murders in America. Life, with you, begins to wear a clouded aspect. The vision of pleasurable delusion is wearing away, and changing to the barren wild of age and sorrow. The poor reflection of having served your king will yield you no consolation in your parting moments. He will crumble to the same undistinguished ashes with yourself, and have sins enough of his own to answer for. It is not the farcical benedictions of a bishop, nor the cringing hypocrisy of a court of chaplains, nor the formality of an act of parliament, that can change guilt into innocence, or make the punishment one pang the less. You may, perhaps, be unwilling to be serious, but this destruction of the goods of Providence, this havoc of the human race, and this sowing the world with mischief, must be accounted for to him who made and governs it. To us they are only present sufferings, but to him they are deep rebellions.

If there is a sin superior to every other, it is that of wilful and offensive war. Most other sins are circumscribed within narrow limits, that is, the power of *one* man cannot give them a very general extension, and many kinds of sins have only a mental existence from which no infection arises; but he who is the author of a war, lets loose the whole contagion of hell, and opens a vein that bleeds a nation to death. We leave it to England and Indians to boast of these honors; we feel no thirst for such savage glory; a nobler flame, a purer spirit animates America. She has taken up the sword of virtuous defence; she has bravely put herself between Tyranny and Freedom, between a curse and a blessing, determined to expel the one and protect the other.

It is the object only of war that makes it honourable. And if there was ever a *just* war since the world began, it is this in which America is now engaged. She invaded no land of yours. She hired no mercenaries to burn your towns, nor Indians to massacre their inhabitants. She wanted nothing from you, and was indebted for nothing to you: and thus circumstanced, her defence is honourable and her prosperity is certain.

Yet it is not on the *justice* only, but likewise on the *importance* of this cause that I ground my seeming enthusiastical confidence of our success. The vast extension of America makes her of too much value in the scale of Providence, to be cast like a pearl before swine, at the feet of an European island; and of much less consequence would it be that Britain were sunk in the sea than that America should miscarry. There has been such a chain of extraordinary events in the discovery of this country at first, in the peopling and planting it afterwards, in the rearing and nursing it to its present state, and in the protection of it through the present war, that no man can doubt, but Providence hath some nobler end to accomplish than the gratification of the petty elector of Hanover, or the ignorant and insignificant king of Britain.

As the blood of the martyrs hath been the seed of the Christian church, so the political persecutions of England will and have already enriched America with industry, experience, union, and importance. Before the present era she was a mere chaos of uncemented colonies, individually exposed to the ravages of the Indians and the invasion of any power that Britain should be at war with. She had nothing that she could call her own. Her felicity depended upon accident. The convulsions of Europe might have thrown her from one conquerer to another, till she had been the slave of all, and ruined by every one; for until she had spirit enough to become her own master, there was no knowing to which master she should belong. That period, thank God, is past, and she is no longer the dependant, disunited colonies of Britain, but the Independent and United States of America, knowing no master but heaven and herself. You, or your king, may call this "delusion," "rebellion," or what name you please. To us it is perfectly indifferent. The issue will determine the character, and time will give it a name as lasting as his own.

You have now, sir, tried the fate of three campaigns, and can fully declare to England, that nothing is to be got on your part, but blows and broken bones, and nothing on hers but waste of trade and credit, and an increase of poverty and taxes. You are now only where you might have been two years ago, without the loss of a single ship, and yet not a step more forward towards the conquest of the continent; because, as I have already hinted, "an army in a city can never be a conquering army." The full amount of your losses, since the beginning of the war, exceeds twenty thousand men, besides millions of treasure, for which you have nothing in exchange. Our expenses, though great, are circulated within ourselves. Yours is a direct sinking of money, and that from both ends at once; first, in hiring troops out of the nation, and in paying them afterwards, because the money in neither case can return to Britain. We are already in possession of the prize, you only in pursuit of it. To us it is a real treasure, to you it would be only an empty triumph. Our expenses will repay themselves with tenfold interest, while yours entail upon you everlasting poverty.

Take a review, sir, of the ground which you have gone over, and let it teach you policy, if it cannot honesty. You stand but on a very tottering foundation. A change of the ministry in England may probably bring your measures into question, and your head to the block. Clive, with all his successes, had some difficulty in escaping, and yours being all a war of losses, will afford you less pretensions, and your enemies more grounds for impeachment.

Go home, sir, and endeavour to save the remains of your ruined country, by a just representation of the madness of her measures. A few moments, well applied, may yet preserve her from political destruction. I am not one of those who wish to see Europe in a flame, because I am persuaded that such an event will not shorten the war. The rupture, at present, is confined between the two powers of America and England. England finds that she cannot conquer America, and America has no wish to conquer England. You are fighting for what you can never obtain, and we defending what we never mean to part with. A few words, therefore, settle the bargain. Let England mind her own business and we will mind ours. Govern yourselves, and we will govern ourselves. You may then trade where you please unmolested by us, and we will trade where we please unmolested by you; and such articles as we can purchase of each other better than elsewhere may be mutually done. If it were possible that you could carry on the war for twenty years you must still come to this point at last, or worse, and the sooner you think of it the better it will be for you.

My official situation enables me to know the repeated insults which Britain is obliged to put up with from foreign powers, and the wretched shifts that she is driven to, to gloss them over. Her reduced strength and exhausted coffers in a three years' war with America, hath given a powerful superiority to France and Spain. She is not now a match for them. But if neither councils can prevail on her to think, nor sufferings awaken her to reason, she must e'en go on, till the honour of England becomes a proverb of contempt, and Europe dub her the Land of Fools.

I am, Sir, with every wish for an honourable peace,

Your friend, enemy, and countryman,

COMMON SENSE.

TO THE INHABITANTS OF AMERICA

WITH all the pleasure with which a man exchanges bad company for good, I take my leave of Sir William and return to you. It is now nearly three years since the tyrrany of Britain received its first repulse by the arms of America. A period which has given birth to a new world, and erected a monument to the folly of the old.

I cannot help being sometimes surprised at the complimentary references which I have seen and heard made to ancient histories and transactions. The wisdom, civil governments, and sense of honor of the states of Greece and Rome, are frequently held up as objects of excellence and imitation. Mankind have lived to very little purpose, if, at this period of the world, they must go two or three thousand years back for lessons and examples. We do great injustice to ourselves by placing them in such a superior line. We have no just authority for it, neither can we tell why it is that we should suppose ourselves inferior.

Could the mist of antiquity be cleared away, and men and things be viewed as they really were, it is more than probable that they would admire us, rather than we them. America has surmounted a greater variety and combination of difficulties, than, I believe, ever fell to the share of any one people, in the same space of time, and has replenished the world with more useful knowledge and sounder maxims of civil government than were ever produced in any age before. Had it not been for America, there had been no such thing as freedom left throughout the whole universe. England hath lost hers in a long chain of right reasoning from wrong principles, and it is from this country, now, that she must learn the resolution to redress herself, and the wisdom how to accomplish it.

The Grecians and Romans were strongly possessed of the *spirit* of liberty but *not the principle,* for at the time that they were determined not to be slaves themselves, they employed their power to enslave the rest of mankind. But this distinguished era is blotted by no one misanthropical vice. In short, if the principle on which the cause is founded, the universal blessings that are to arise from it, the difficulties that accompanied it, the wisdom with which it has been debated, the fortitude by which it has been supported, the strength of the power which we had to oppose, and the condition in which we undertook it, be all taken in one view, we may justly style it the most virtuous and illustrious revolution that ever graced the history of mankind.

A good opinion of ourselves is exceedingly necessary in private life, but absolutely necessary in public life, and of the utmost importance in supporting national character. I have no notion of yielding the palm of the United States to any Grecians or Romans that were ever born. We have equalled the bravest in times of danger, and excelled the wisest in construction of civil governments.

From this agreeable eminence let us take a review of present affairs. The spirit of corruption is so inseparably interwoven with British politics, that their ministry suppose all mankind are governed by the same motives. They have no idea of a people submitting even to temporary inconvenience from an attachment to rights and privileges. Their plans of business are calculated *by* the hour and *for* the hour, and are uniform in nothing but the corruption which gives them birth. They never had, neither have they at this time, any regular plan for the conquest of America by arms. They know not how to go about it, neither have they power to effect it if they did know. The thing is not within the compass of human practicability, for America is too extensive either to be fully conquered or *passively* defended. But she may be *actively* defended by defeating or making prisoners of the army that invades her. And this is the only system of defence that can be effectual in a large country.

There is something in a war carried on by invasion which makes it differ in circumstances from any other mode of war, because he who conducts it cannot tell whether the ground he gains be for him, or against him, when he first obtains it. In the winter of 1776, general Howe marched with an air of victory through the Jerseys, the consequence of which was his defeat; and general Burgoyne at Saratoga experienced the same fate from the same cause. The Spaniards, about two years ago, were defeated by the Algerines in the same manner, that is, their first triumphs became a trap in which they were totally routed. And whoever will attend to the circumstances and events of a war carried on by invasion, will find, that any invader, in order to be finally conquered must first begin to conquer.

I confess myself one of those who believe the loss of Philadelphia to be attended with more advantages than injuries. The case stood thus: The enemy imagined Philadelphia to be of more importance to us than it really was; for we all know that it had long ceased to be a port: not a cargo of goods had been brought into it for near a twelvemonth, nor any fixed manufactories, nor even ship-building, carried on in it; yet as the enemy believed the conquest of it to be practicable, and to that belief added the absurd idea that the soul of all America was centred there, and would be conquered there, it naturally follows that their possession of it, by not answering the end proposed, must break up the plans they had so foolishly gone upon, and either oblige them to form a new one, for which their present strength is not sufficient, or to give over the attempt.

We never had so small an army to fight against, nor so fair an opportunity of final success as *now.* The death wound is already given. The day is ours if we follow it up. The enemy, by his situation, is within our reach, and by his reduced strength is within our power. The ministers of Britain may rage as they please, but our part is to conquer their armies. Let them wrangle and welcome, but let it not draw our attention from the *one* thing needful. *Here, in this spot* is our own business to be accomplished, our felicity secured. What we have now to do is as clear as light, and the way to do it is as straight as a line. It needs not to be commented upon, yet, in order to be perfectly understood I will put a case that cannot admit of a mistake.

Had the armies under generals Howe and Burgoyne been united, and taken post at Germantown, and had the northern army under general Gates been joined to that under general Washington, at Whitemarsh, the consequence would have been a general action; and if in that action we had killed and taken the same number of officers and men, that is, between nine and ten thousand, with the same quantity of artillery, arms, stores, etc. as have been taken at the northward, and obliged general Howe with the remains of his army, that is, with the same number he now commands, to take shelter in Philadelphia, we should certainly have thought ourselves the greatest heroes in the world; and should, as soon as the season permitted, have collected together all the force of the continent and laid siege to the city, for it requires a much greater force to besiege an enemy in a town than to defeat him in the field. The case *now* is just the same as if it had been produced by the means I have here supposed. Between nine and ten thousand have been killed and taken, all their stores are in our possession, and general Howe, in consequence of that victory, has thrown himself for shelter into Philadelphia. He, or his trifling friend Galloway, may form what pretences they please, yet no just reason can be given for their going into winter quarters so early as the 19th of October, but their apprehensions of a defeat if they continued out, or their conscious inability of keeping the field with safety. I see no advantage which can arise to America by hunting the enemy from state to state. It is a triumph without a prize, and wholly unworthy the attention of a people determined to conquer. Neither can any state promise itself security while the enemy remains in a condition to transport themselves from one part of the continent to another. Howe, likewise, cannot conquer where we have no army to oppose, therefore any such removals in him are mean and cowardly, and reduces Britain to a common pilferer. If he retreats from Philadelphia, he will be despised; if he stays, he may be shut up and starved out, and the country, if he advances into it, may become his Saratoga. He has his choice of evils and we of opportunities. If he moves early, it is not only a sign but a proof that he expects no reinforcement, and his delay will prove that he either waits for the arrival of a plan to go upon, or force to execute it, or both; in *which* case our strength will increase more than his, therefore in *any* case we cannot be wrong if we do but proceed.

The particular condition of Pennsylvania deserves the attention of all the other states. Her military strength must not be estimated by the number of inhabitants. Here are men of all nations, characters, professions and interests. Here are the firmest whigs, surviving, like sparks in the ocean, unquenched and uncooled in the midst of discouragement and disaffection. Here are men losing their all with cheerfulness, and collecting fire and fortitude from the flames of their own estates. Here are others skulking in secret, many making a market of the times, and numbers who are changing to whig or tory with the circumstances of every day.

It is by mere dint of fortitude and perseverance that the whigs of this state have been able to maintain so good a countenance, and do even what they have done. We want help, and the sooner it can arrive the more effectual it will be. The invaded state, be it which it may, will always feel an additional burden upon its back, and be hard set to support its civil power with sufficient authority; and this difficulty will rise or fall, in proportion as the other states throw in their assistance to the common cause.

The enemy will most probably make many manœuvres at the opening of this campaign, to amuse and draw off the attention of the several states from the *one thing needful*. We may expect to hear of alarms and pretended expeditions to *this* place and *that* place, to the southward, the eastward, and the northward, all intended to prevent our forming into one formidable body. The less the enemy's strength is, the more subtleties of this kind will they make use of. Their existence depends upon it, because the force of America, when collected, is sufficient to swallow their present army up. It is therefore our business to make short work of it, by bending our whole attention to *this one principal point*, for the instant that the main body under general Howe is defeated, all the inferior alarms throughout the continent, like so many shadows, will follow his downfall.

The only way to finish a war with the least possible bloodshed, or perhaps without any, is to collect an army, against the power of which the enemy shall have no chance. By not doing this, we prolong the war, and double both the calamities and expenses of it. What a rich and happy country would America be, were she, by a vigorous exertion, to reduce Howe as she has reduced Burgoyne. Her currency would rise to millions beyond its present value. Every man would be rich, and every man would have it in his power to be happy. And why not do these things? What is there to hinder? America is her own mistress and can do what she pleases.

If we had not at this time a man in the field, we could, nevertheless, raise an army in a few weeks sufficient to overwhelm all the force which general Howe at present commands. Vigor and determination will do any thing and every thing. We began the war with this kind of spirit, why not end it with the same? Here, gentlemen, is the enemy. Here is the army. The interest, the happiness of all America, is centred in this half ruined spot. Come and help us. Here are laurels, come and share them. Here are tories, come and help us to expel them. Here are whigs that will make you welcome, and enemies that dread your coming.

The worst of all policies is that of doing things by halves. Penny-wise and pound-foolish, has been the ruin of thousands. The present spring, if rightly improved, will free us from our troubles, and save us the expense of millions. We have now only one army to cope with. No opportunity can be fairer; no prospect more promising. I shall conclude this paper with a few outlines of a plan, either for filling up the battalions with expedition, or for raising an additional force, for any limited time, on any sudden emergency.

That in which every man is interested, is every man's duty to support. And any burden which falls equally on all men, and from which every man is to receive an equal benefit, is consistent with the most perfect ideas of liberty. I would wish to revive something of that virtuous ambition which first called America into the field. Then every man was eager to do his part, and perhaps the principal reason why we have in any degree fallen therefrom, is because we did not set a right value by it at first, but left it to blaze out of itself, instead of regulating and preserving it by just proportions of rest and service.

Suppose any state whose number of effective inhabitants was 80,000, should be required to furnish 3,200 men towards the defence of the continent on any sudden emergency.

1st, Let the whole number of effective inhabitants be divided into hundreds; then if each of those hundreds turn out four men, the whole number of 3,200 will be had.

2d, Let the name of each hundred men be entered in a book, and let four dollars be collected from each man, with as much more as any of the gentlemen, whose abilities can afford it, shall please to throw in, which gifts likewise shall be entered against the names of the donors.

3d, Let the sums so collected be offered as a present, over and above the bounty of twenty dollars, to any four who may be inclined to propose themselves as volunteers: if more than four offer, the majority of the subscribers present shall determine which; if none offer, then four out of the hundred shall be taken by lot, who shall be entitled to the said sums, and shall either go, or provide others that will, in the space of six days.

4th, As it will always happen, that in the space of ground on which an hundred men shall live, there will be always a number of persons who, by age and infirmity, are incapable of doing personal service, and as such persons are generally possessed of the greatest part of property in any country, their portion of service, therefore, will be to furnish each man with a blanket, which will make a regimental coat, jacket, and breeches, or clothes in lieu thereof, and another for a watch cloak, and two pair of shoes; for however choice people may be of these things matters not in cases of this kind; those who live always in houses can find many ways to keep themselves warm, but it is a shame and a sin to suffer a soldier in the field to want a blanket while there is one in the country.

Should the clothing not be wanted, the superannuated or infirm persons possessing property, may, in lieu thereof, throw in their money subscriptions towards increasing the bounty; for though age will naturally exempt a person from personal service, it cannot exempt him from his share of the charge, because the men are raised for the defence of property and liberty jointly.

There never was a scheme against which objections might not be raised. But this alone is not a sufficient reason for rejection. The only line to judge truly upon, is, to draw out and admit all the objections which can fairly be made, and place against them all the contrary qualities, conveniences and advantages, then by striking a balance you come at the true character of any scheme, principle or position.

The most material advantages of the plan here proposed are, ease, expedition, and cheapness; yet the men so raised get a much larger bounty than is any where at present given; because all the expenses, extravagance, and consequent idleness of recruiting are saved or prevented. The country incurs no new debt nor interest thereon; the whole matter being all settled at once and entirely done with. It is a subscription answering all the purposes of a tax, without either the charge or trouble of collecting. The men are ready for the field with the greatest possible expedition, because it becomes the duty of the inhabitants themselves, in every part of the country, to find their proportion of men instead of leaving it to a recruiting sergeant, who, be he ever so industrious, cannot know always where to apply.

I do not propose this as a regular digested plan, neither will the limits of this paper admit of any further remarks upon it. I believe it to be a hint capable of much improvement, and as such submit it to the public.

COMMON SENSE.

LANCASTER, March 21, 1778.

The Crisis

NUMBER IX

HAD America pursued her advantages with half the spirit that she resisted her misfortunes, she would, before now, have been a conquering and a peaceful people; but lulled in the lap of soft tranquillity, she rested on her hopes, and adversity only has convulsed her into action. Whether subtlety or sincerity at the close of the last year induced the enemy to an appearance for peace, is a point not material to know; it is sufficient that we see the effects it has had on our politics, and that we sternly rise to resent the delusion.

The war, on the part of America, has been a war of natural feelings. Brave in distress; serene in conquest; drowsy while at rest; and in every situation generously disposed to peace; a dangerous calm, and a most heightened zeal have, as circumstances varied, succeeded each other. Every passion but that of despair has been called to a tour of duty; and so mistaken has been the enemy, of our abilities and disposition, that when she supposed us conquered, we rose the conquerors. The extensiveness of the United States, and the variety of their resources; the universality of their cause, the quick operation of their feelings, and the similarity of their sentiments, have, in every trying situation, produced a *something*, which, favored by providence, and pursued with ardor, has accomplished in an instant the business of a campaign. We have never deliberately sought victory, but snatched it; and bravely undone in an hour the blotted operations of a season.

The reported fate of Charleston, like the misfortunes of 1776, has at last called forth a spirit, and kindled up a flame, which perhaps no other event could have produced. If the enemy has circulated a falsehood, they have unwisely aggravated us into life, and if they have told us the truth, they have unintentionally done us a service. We were returning with folded arms from the fatigues of war, and thinking and sitting leisurely down to enjoy repose. The dependence that has been put upon Charleston threw a drowsiness over America. We looked on the business done—the conflict over—the matter settled—or that all which remained unfinished would follow of itself. In this state of dangerous relaxation, exposed to the poisonous infusions of the enemy, and having no common danger to attract our attention, we were extinguishing, by stages, the ardor we began with, and surrendering by piece-meals the virtue that defended us.

Afflicting as the loss of Charleston may be, yet if it universally rouse us from the slumber of twelve months past, and renew in us the spirit of former days, it will produce an advantage more important than its loss. America ever *is* what she *thinks* herself to be. Governed by sentiment, and acting her own mind, she becomes, as she pleases, the victor or the victim.

It is not the conquest of towns, nor the accidental capture of garrisons, that can reduce a country so extensive as this. The sufferings of one part can never be relieved by the exertions of another, and there is no situation the enemy can be placed in that does not afford to us the same advantages which he seeks himself. By dividing his force, he leaves every post attackable. It is a mode of war that carries with it a confession of weakness, and goes on the principle of distress rather than conquest.

The decline of the enemy is visible, not only in their operations, but in their plans; Charleston originally made but a secondary object in the system of attack, and it is now become their principal one, because they have not been able to succeed elsewhere. It would have carried a cowardly appearance in Europe had they formed their grand expedition, in 1776, against a part of the continent where there was no army, or not a sufficient one to oppose them; but failing year after year in their impressions here, and to the eastward and northward, they deserted their capital design, and prudently contenting themselves with what they can get, give a flourish of honor to conceal disgrace.

But this piece-meal work is not conquering the continent. It is a discredit in them to attempt it, and in us to suffer it. It is now full time to put an end to a war of aggravations, which, on one side, has no possible object, and on the other has every inducement which honor, interest, safety and happiness can inspire. If we suffer them much longer to remain among us, we shall become as bad as themselves. An association of vice will reduce us more than the sword. A nation hardened in the practice of iniquity knows better how to profit by it, than a young country newly corrupted. We are not a match for them in the line of advantageous guilt, nor they for us on the principles which we bravely set out with. Our first days were our days of honour. They have marked the character of America wherever the story of her wars are told; and convinced of this, we have nothing to do but wisely and unitedly to tread the well known track. The progress of a war is often as ruinous to individuals, as the issue of it is to a nation; and it is not only necessary that our forces be such that we be conquerors in the end, but that by timely exertions we be secure in the interim. The present campaign will afford an opportunity which has never presented itself before, and the preparations for it are equally necessary, whether Charleston stand or fall. Suppose the first, it is in that case only a failure of the enemy, not a defeat. All the conquest that a besieged town can hope for, is, not to be conquered; and compelling an enemy to raise the siege, is to the besieged a victory. But there must be a probability amounting almost to a certainty, that would justify a garrison marching out to attack a retreat. Therefore should Charleston not be taken, and the enemy abandon the siege, every other part of the continent should prepare to meet them; and, on the contrary, should it be taken, the same preparations are necessary to balance the loss, and put ourselves in a position to co-operate with our allies, immediately on their arrival.

We are not now fighting our battles alone, as we were in 1776; England, from a malicious disposition to America, has not only not declared war against France and Spain, but, the better to prosecute her passions here, has afforded those powers no military object, and avoids them, to distress us. She will suffer her West India islands to be overrun by France, and her southern settlements to be taken by Spain, rather than quit the object that gratifies her revenge. This conduct, on the part of Britain, has pointed out the propriety of France sending a naval and land force to co-operate with America on the spot. Their arrival cannot be very distant, nor the ravages of the enemy long. The recruiting the army, and procuring the supplies, are the two things most necessary to be accomplished, and a capture of either of the enemy's divisions will restore to America peace and plenty.

At a crisis, big, like the present, with expectation and events, the whole country is called to unanimity and exertion. Not an ability ought now to sleep, that can produce but a mite to the general good, nor even a whisper to pass that militates against it. The necessity of the case, and the importance of the consequences, admit no delay from a friend, no apology from an enemy. To spare now, would be the height of extravagance, and to consult present ease, would be to sacrifice it perhaps forever.

America, rich in patriotism and produce, can want neither men nor supplies, when a serious necessity calls them forth. The slow operation of taxes, owing to the extensiveness of collection, and their depreciated value before they arrived in the treasury, have, in many instances, thrown a burden upon government, which has been artfully interpreted by the enemy into a general decline throughout the country. Yet this, inconvenient as it may at first appear, is not only remediable, but may be turned to an immediate advantage; for it makes no real difference, whether a certain number of men, or company of militia (and in this country every man is a militia-man), are directed by law to send a recruit at their own expense, or whether a tax is laid on them for that purpose, and the man hired by government afterwards. The first, if there is any difference, is both cheapest and best, because it saves the expense which would attend collecting it as a tax, and brings the man sooner into the field than the modes of recruiting formerly used; and, on this principle, a law has been passed in this state, for recruiting two men from each company of militia, which will add upwards of a thousand to the force of the country.

But the flame which has broke forth in this city since the report from New-York, of the loss of Charleston, not only does honor to the place, but, like the blaze of 1776, will kindle into action the scattered sparks throughout America. The valor of a country may be learned by the bravery of its soldiery, and the general cast of its inhabitants, but confidence of success is best discovered by the active measures pursued by men of property; and when the spirit of enterprise becomes so universal as to act at once on all ranks of men, a war may then, and not till then, be styled truly popular.

In 1776, the ardor of the enterprising part was considerably checked by the real revolt of some, and the coolness of others. But in the present case, there is a firmness in the substance and property of the country to the public cause. An association has been entered into by the merchants, tradesmen, and principal inhabitants of the city [Philadelphia], to receive and support the new state money at the value of gold and silver; a measure which, while it does them honor, will likewise contribute to their interest, by rendering the operations of the campaign convenient and effectual.

Nor has the spirit of exertion stopped here. A voluntary subscription is likewise begun, to raise a fund of hard money, to be given as bounties, to fill up the full quota of the Pennsylvania line. It has been the remark of the enemy, that every thing in America has been done by the force of government; but when she sees individuals throwing in their voluntary aid, and facilitating the public measures in concert with the established powers of the country, it will convince her that the cause of America stands not on the will of a few but on the broad foundation of property and popularity.

Thus aided and thus supported, disaffection will decline, and the withered head of tyranny expire in America. The ravages of the enemy will be short and limited, and like all their former ones, will produce a victory over themselves.

COMMON SENSE.

PHILADELPHIA, June 9, 1780.

At the time of writing this number of the Crisis, the loss of Charleston, though believed by some, was more confidently disbelieved by others. But there ought to be no longer a doubt upon the matter. Charleston is gone, and I believe for the want of a sufficient supply of provisions. The man that does not now feel for the honor of the best and noblest cause that ever a country engaged in, and exert himself accordingly, is no longer worthy of a peaceable residence among a people determined to be free.

C. S.

The Last Crisis

NUMBER XV

"The times that tried men's souls," are over—and the greatest and completest revolution the world over knew, gloriously and happily accomplished.

But to pass from the extremes of danger to safety—from the tumult of war to the tranquillity of peace, though sweet in contemplation, requires a gradual composure of the senses to receive it. Even calmness has the power of stunning, when it opens too instantly upon us. The long and raging hurricane that should cease in a moment, would leave us in a state rather of wonder than enjoyment; and some moments of recollection must pass, before we could be capable of tasting the felicity of repose. There are but few instances in which the mind is fitted for sudden transitions: it takes in its pleasures by reflection and comparison, and those must have time to act, before the relish for new scenes is complete.

In the present case the mighty magnitude of the object—the various uncertainties of fate it has undergone—the numerous and complicated dangers we have suffered or escaped—the eminence we now stand on, and the vast prospect before us, must all conspire to impress us with contemplation.

To see it in our power to make a world happy—to teach mankind the art of being so—to exhibit, on the theatre of the universe, a character hitherto unknown—and to have, as it were, a new creation intrusted to our hands, are honors that command reflection, and can neither be too highly estimated, nor too gratefully received.

In this pause then of recollection—while the storm is ceasing, and the long-agitated mind vibrating to a rest, let us look back on the scenes we have passed, and learn from experience what is yet to be done.

Never, I say, had a country so many openings to happiness as this. Her setting out in life, like the rising of a fair morning, was unclouded and promising. Her cause was good. Her principles just and liberal. Her temper serene and firm. Her conduct regulated by the nicest steps, and everything about her wore the mark of honor. It is not every country (perhaps there is not another in the world) that can boast so fair an origin. Even the first settlement of America corresponds with the character of the revolution. Rome, once the proud mistress of the universe, was originally a band of ruffians. Plunder and rapine made her rich, and her oppression of millions made her great. But America need never be ashamed to tell her birth, nor relate the stages by which she rose to empire.

The remembrance, then, of what is past, if it operates rightly, must inspire her with the most laudable of an ambition, that of adding to the fair fame she began with. The world has seen her great in adversity. Struggling without a thought of yielding, beneath accumulated difficulties. Bravely, nay proudly, encountering distress, and rising in resolution as the storm increased. All this is justly due to her for her fortitude has merited the character. Let then, the world see that she can bear prosperity: and that her honest virtue in time of peace, is equal to the bravest virtue in time of war.

She is now descending to the scenes of quiet and domestic life. Not beneath the cypress shade of disappointment, but to enjoy in her own land and under her own vine, the sweet of her labors, and the reward of her toil.—In this situation, may she never forget that a fair national reputation is of as much importance as independence. That it possesses a charm that wins upon the world, and makes even enemies civil.—That it gives a dignity which is often superior to power, and commands reverence where pomp and splendor fail.

It would be a circumstance ever to be lamented and never to be forgotten, were a single blot, from any cause whatever, suffered to fall on a revolution, which to the end of time must be an honor to the age that accomplished it: and which has contributed more to enlighten the world, and diffuse a spirit of freedom and liberality among mankind, than any human event (if this may be called one) that ever preceded it.

It is not among the least of the calamities of a long-continued war that it unhinges the mind from those nice sensations which at other times appear so amiable. The continued spectacle of woe blunts the finer feelings, and the necessity of bearing with the sight, renders it familiar. In like manner, are many of the moral obligations of society weakened, till the custom of acting by necessity becomes an apology, where it is truly a crime. Yet let but a nation conceive rightly of its character, and it will be chastely just in protecting it. None never began with a fairer than America, and none can be under a greater obligation to preserve it.

The debt which America has contracted, compared with the cause she has gained, and the advantages to flow from it, ought scarcely to be mentioned. She has it in her choice to do, and to live as happy as she pleases. The world is in her hands. She has no foreign power to monopolize her commerce, perplex her legislation, or control her prosperity. The struggle is over, which must one day have happened, and, perhaps, never could have happened at a better time. And instead of a domineering master, she has gained an *ally,* whose exemplary greatness, and universal liberality, have extorted a confession even from her enemies.

With the blessings of peace, independence, and an universal commerce, the states, individually and collectively, will have leisure and opportunity to regulate and establish their domestic concerns, and to put it beyond the power of calumny to throw the least reflection on their honor. Character is much easier kept than recovered, and that man, if any such there be, who, from sinister views, or littleness of soul, lends unseen his hand to injure it, contrives a wound it will never be in his power to heal.

As we have established an inheritance for posterity, let that inheritance descend with every mark of an honorable conveyance. The little it will cost, compared with the worth of the states, the greatness of the object, and the value of national character, will be a profitable exchange.

But that which must more forcibly strike a thoughtful penetrating mind, and which includes and renders easy all inferior concerns, is the *Union of the States.* On this our great national character depends. It is this which must give us importance abroad and security at home. It is through this only, that we are or can be nationally known in the world; it is the flag of the United States which renders our ships and commerce safe on the seas, or in a foreign port. Our Mediterranean passes must be obtained under the same style. All our treaties, whether of alliance, peace or commerce, are formed under the sovereignty of the United States, and Europe knows us by no other name or title.

The division of the empire into states is for our own convenience, but abroad this distinction ceases. The affairs of each state are local. They can go no further than to itself. And were the whole worth of even the richest of them expended in revenue, it would not be sufficient to support sovereignty against a foreign attack. In short, we have no other national sovereignty than as United States. It would even be fatal for us if we had—too expensive to be maintained, and impossible to be supported. Individuals, or individual states, may call themselves what they please; but the world, and especially the world of enemies, is not to be held in awe by the whistling of a name. Sovereignty must have power to protect all the parts that compose and constitute it; and as UNITED STATES we are equal to the importance of the title, but otherwise we are not. Our union, well and wisely regulated and cemented, is the cheapest way of being great—the easiest way of being powerful, and the happiest invention in government which the circumstances of America can admit of. Because it collects from each state, that which, by being inadequate, can be of no use to it, and forms an aggregate that serves for all.

The states of Holland are an unfortunate instance of the effects of individual sovereignty. Their disjointed condition exposes them to numerous intrigues, losses, calamities and enemies; and the almost impossibility of bringing their measures to a decision, and that decision into execution, is to them, and would be to us, a source of endless misfortune.

It is with confederated states as with individuals in society; something must be yielded up to make the whole secure. In this view of things we gain by what we give, and draw an annual interest greater than the capital.—I ever feel myself hurt when I hear the union, that great palladium of our liberty and safety, the least irreverently spoken of. It is the most sacred thing in the constitution of America, and that which every man should be most proud and tender of. Our citizenship in the United States is our national character. Our citizenship in any particular state is only our local distinction. By the latter we are known at home, by the former to the world. Our great title is AMERICANS—our inferior one varies with the place.

So far as my endeavors could go, they have all been directed to conciliate the affections, unite the interests, and draw and keep the mind of the country together; and the better to assist in this foundation work of the revolution, I have avoided all places of profit or office, either in the state I live in, or in the United States; kept myself at a distance from all parties and party connexions, and even disregarded all private and inferior concerns: and when we take into view the great work which we have gone through, and feel, as we ought to feel, the just importance of it, we shall then see, that the little wranglings and indecent contentions of personal parley, are as dishonorable to our characters as they are injurious to our repose.

It was the cause of America that made me an author. The force with which it struck my mind, and the dangerous condition the country appeared to me in, by courting an impossible and an unnatural reconciliation with those who were determined to reduce her, instead of striking out into the only line that could cement and save her, A DECLARATION OF INDEPENDENCE, made it impossible for me, feeling as I did, to be silent: and if, in the course of more than seven years, I have rendered her any service, I have likewise added something to the reputation of literature, by freely and disinterestedly employing it in the great cause of mankind, and showing that there may be genius without prostitution.

Independence always appeared to me practicable and probable; provided the sentiment of the country could be formed and held to the object: and there is no instance in the world, where a people so extended, and wedded to former habits of thinking, and under such a variety of circumstances, were so instantly and effectually pervaded by a turn in politics, as in the case of independence, and who supported their opinion, undiminished, through such a succession of good and ill fortune, till they crowned it with success.

But as the scenes of war are closed, and every man preparing for home and happier times, I therefore take my leave of the subject. I have most sincerely followed it from beginning to end, and through all its turns and windings, and whatever country I may hereafter be in, I shall always feel an honest pride at the part I have taken and acted, and a gratitude to nature and providence for putting it in my power to be of some use to mankind.

COMMON SENSE.

PHILADELPHIA, *April 19th, 1783*

☆ ☆ ☆

In the last of his *Crisis Papers,* Paine evaluates both America and his own work. To those who thoughtfully desire to understand the man who was Thomas Paine, I recommend a re-reading of the last *Crisis*. Here, for example, is his summing up:

"So far as my endeavors could go, they have all been directed to conciliate the affections, unite the interests, and draw and keep the mind of the country together; and the better to assist in this foundation work of the revolution, I have avoided all places of profit or office, either in the state I live in or in the United States; kept myself at a distance from all parties and party connexions, and even disregarded all private and inferior concerns."

Was there ever a clearer, wiser, or better balanced statement by a propagandist conscious of his own role in a time of crisis? This is an answer to those who regard Paine as a mystic; no mystic could so hard-headedly evaluate the need of a people fighting for their national liberation.

Also, this last *Crisis* is an answer to those who claim Paine was not completely conscious of his role in America. This is a completely conscious evaluation. All through the seven years, Paine worked as an objective revolutionist; he built, block by block. Even his slogans for unity were artfully and consciously constructed; witness that he starts the last *Crisis* with the slogan he had popularized seven years before. There, too, is an indication of the widespread popularity Paine's slogans must have gained.

In all, between 1776 and 1783, Paine wrote fifteen Crisis Papers, the five most pertinent of which are here included. Properly, the series finished with the one here indicated as the last—although nine months after the end of the Revolution, Paine wrote what some call the *Sixteenth Crisis,* a fierce and acute indictment of a colonial policy that would resist change with its last ounce of strength.

Paine, like Rush and certain other patriots, now sensed that the Revolution was not, as so many boasted and as he himself had written, finished—that certain battles still had to be fought. And, of course, that came about in the second war for national liberation which took place in 1812–1814.

Here, then, is his interesting though anticlimactic, warning to Americans:

A Warning

TO THE PEOPLE OF AMERICA

IN "Rivington's New York Gazette," of December 6th, is a publication, under the appearance of a letter from London, dated September 30th; and is on a subject which demands the attention of the United States.

The public will remember that a treaty of commerce between the United States and England was set on foot last spring, and that until the said treaty could be completed, a bill was brought into the British parliament by the then chancellor of the exchequer, Mr. Pitt, to admit and legalize (as the case then required) the commerce of the United States into the British ports and dominions. But neither the one nor the other has been completed. The commercial treaty is either broken off or remains as it began; and the bill in parliament has been thrown aside. And in lieu thereof a selfish system of English politics has started up, calculated to fetter the commerce of America, by engrossing to England the carrying trade of the American produce to the West India islands.

Among the advocates for this last measure is Lord Sheffield, a member of the British parliament, who has published a pamphlet entitled "Observations on the Commerce of the American States." The pamphlet has two objects; the one is to allure the Americans to purchase British manufactures; and the other to spirit up the British Parliament to prohibit the citizens of the United States from trading to the West India islands.

Viewed in this light, the pamphlet, though in some parts dexterously written, is an absurdity. It offends in the very act of endeavoring to ingratiate; and his lordship, as a politician, ought not to have suffered the two objects to have appeared together. The letter alluded to, contains extracts from the pamphlet, with high encomiums on Lord Sheffield, for laboriously endeavoring (as the letter styles it) "to show the mighty advantages of retaining the carrying trade."

Since the publication of this pamphlet in England, the commerce of the United States to the West Indies, in American vessels, has been prohibited; and all intercourse, except in British bottoms, the property of, and navigated by British subjects, cut off.

That a country has a right to be as foolish as it pleases, has been proved by the practice of England for many years past: in her island situation, sequestered from the world, she forgets that her whispers are heard by other nations; and in her plans of politics and commerce, she seems not to know, that other votes are necessary besides her own. America would be equally as foolish as Britain, were she to suffer so great a degradation on her flag, and such a stroke on the freedom of her commerce, to pass without a balance.

We admit the right of any nation to prohibit the commerce of another into its own dominions, where there are no treaties to the contrary; but as this right belongs to one side as well as the other, there is always a way left to bring avarice and insolence to reason.

But the ground of security which Lord Sheffield has chosen to erect his policy upon, is of a nature which ought, and I think must, awaken, in every American, a just and strong sense of national dignity. Lord Sheffield appears to be sensible, that in advising the British nation and parliament to engross to themselves so great a part of the carrying trade of America, he is attempting a measure which cannot succeed, if the politics of the United States be properly directed to counteract the assumption.

But, says he, in his pamphlet, "It will be a long time before the

American states can be brought to act as a nation, neither are they to be feared as such by us."

What is this more or less than to tell us, that while we have no national system of commerce, the British will govern our trade by their own laws and proclamations as they please. The quotation disclose a truth too serious to be overlooked, and too mischievous not to be remedied.

Among other circumstances which led them to this discovery, none could operate so effectually as the injudicious, uncandid and indecent opposition made by sundry persons in a certain state, to the recommendations of congress last winter, for an import duty of five per cent. It could not but explain to the British a weakness in the national power of America, and encourage them to attempt restrictions on her trade, which otherwise they would not have dared to hazard. Neither is there any state in the union, whose policy was more misdirected to its interest than the state I allude to, because her principal support is the carrying trade, which Britain, induced by the want of a well-centred power in the United States to protect and secure, is now attempting to take away. It fortunately happened (and to no state in the union more than the state in question) that the terms of peace were agreed on before the opposition appeared, otherwise, there cannot be a doubt, that if the same idea of the diminished authority of America had occurred to them at that time as has occurred to them since, but they would have made the same grasp at the fisheries, as they have done at the carrying trade.

It is surprising that an authority which can be supported with so much ease, and so little expense, and capable of such extensive advantages to the country should be cavilled at by those whose duty it is to watch over it, and whose existence as a people depends upon it. But this, perhaps, will ever be the case, till some misfortune awakens us into reason, and the instance now before us is but a gentle beginning of what America must expect, unless she guards her union with nicer care and stricter honor. United, she is formidable, and that with the least possible charge a nation can be so: separated, she is a medley of individual nothings, subject to the sport of foreign nations.

It is very probable that the ingenuity of commerce may have found out a method to evade and supersede the intentions of the British, in interdicting the trade with the West India islands. The language of both being the same, and their customs well understood, the vessels of one country may, by deception, pass for those of another. But this would be a practice too debasing for a sovereign people to stoop to, and too profligate not to be discountenanced. An illicit trade, under any shape it can be placed, cannot be carried on without a violation of truth. America is now sovereign and independent, and ought to conduct her affairs in a regular style of character. She has the same right to say that no British vessel shall enter her ports, or that no British manufactures shall be imported, but in American bottoms, the property of, and navigated by American subjects, as Britain has to say the same thing respecting the West Indies. Or she may lay a duty of ten, fifteen, or twenty shillings per ton (exclusive of other duties) on every British vessel coming from any port of the West Indies, where she is not permitted to trade, the said tonnage to continue as long on her side as the prohibition continues on the other.

But it is only by acting in union, that the usurpations of foreign nations on the freedom of trade can be counteracted, and security extended to the commerce of America. And when we view a flag, which to the eye is beautiful, and to contemplate its rise and origin inspires a sensation of sublime delight, our national honor must unite with our interest to prevent injury to the one, or insult to the other.

COMMON SENSE.

NEW YORK, *December 9, 1783.*

☆ ☆ ☆

From the first to the last paper, you have noted the political growth of Paine; he has matured both in his understanding of history and of his personal relationship to the world; he is humbly grateful that he has been allowed to participate in this wonderful drama of freedom, and he is superbly confident of mankind. His love of people has been confirmed, and the one-time outcast has found more good comrades than he can number. It is interesting to speculate on what Paine's role and future would have been had he stayed in America and become an American. Would he have become one of the great democratic leaders, along with Jefferson and Madison? Would he have been enshrined instead of hated? Would he have started a free press around which the democratic movement could have rallied? No one knows, and of course the speculation, while interesting, is fruitless. Paine was an Englishman; he remained one; his interest was not national, but international; and his belief in change, once confirmed, passed beyond the bounds of realism.

In one sense, the American Revolution was the most orderly in history. It finished clean, and although the fruits of the revolution were not fully realized until the administration of Madison, it seemed to Paine, in 1783, that the curtain had come down once and for all on the great drama. For the moment he was a man without employment. The spoils were spread, and he was invited to help himself generously.

When the revolution was over, Paine was forty-six years old and a person of consequence—both in America and in England. There was curiously little ill feeling against Americans in England when the war was done, and American patriots were welcomed and feted in the British Isles.

Much of this was due to the fact that the British masses had been against the war, and that most of the government had felt it was a stupid, even insane venture. Benjamin Franklin, who had lived in England for a decade before the war, was almost as admired there as in his homeland. This situation made Paine look forward to a return to England, but first he had a taste of comfort and victory in America. Congress was generous to him then, although not so generous as to others; he received some money and some land. The flame of revolt went out of him. Letters and science were the pursuits of an American gentleman of the time, and Paine, for all his diatribes against aristocracy could make his compromise with such aristocrats as Jefferson and Washington. He devised an iron bridge; he experimented; he wrote—pale, lifeless writing that traveled nowhere. He attended dinner parties and was a guest at many of the fine Georgian houses of the time.

Had the fiery belief in change gone out of him? Was the salvation of three million souls in America enough? What of the rest of the world, where mankind still groaned in bondage. He had finished his last *Crisis* with a prayer of gratitude that he had been of some use to mankind, not only to America. Was he to leave it there?

Thomas Paine, gentleman, became as restless and as angry as Thomas Paine, staymaker. Not quickly; but the cycle began again when he went to France in 1787, and then to England the following year.

THREE

Rights of Man

WELCOMED and honored in England, he even went to see the squire at Thetford; he consorted with the great—Romney, the painter; Blake, the poet; Burke, the statesman and one-time friend of America. He met lords and ladies, dukes and duchesses, all the people who were worth knowing. He was building his iron bridge in England, and it would make him famous. And sometimes, he even ventured into the abyss where the people lived; he considered things then, what these people might do if they awoke, determined, united, with guns in their hands. Such thoughts disturbed him, yet he could not shake them off; they coupled with the realization that now he wrote nothing worthwhile.

And then, from across the channel, came the smoke of a flame with which he was well familiar—revolution. We can imagine that it drew him like a loadstone. He was in France in 1789, the year the Bastille fell, and when Lafayette gave him the key to that monstrous old fortress, a key of liberty to unlock all doors, to present to George Washington, the sequestered and reasonable Paine who had existed for six years disappeared, and the old apostle of change returned.

The next two years of Paine's life are the least known as well as the least understood. We will never know how deeply he was concerned with the abortive working-class revolution that was growing in England and then was smashed in the bud. That he met and plotted, we do know; we know that arms were cached, and an equivalent of the New England minutemen formed. We know that men were quietly sentenced to death for their part in that plot. We know that Paine might well have been sentenced to death too, had he not fled England two steps ahead of the Crown's agents. And we know that he wrote a book called *Rights of Man* which shook England almost as much as *Common Sense* shook America.

It is one of history's curiosities that the volume, written by the foremost British statesman of the day, and to which *Rights of Man* was an answer, should be so nearly forgotten, while Paine's book has become a classic. After the opening phase of the French Revolution, Edmund Burke, the one-time friend of progress, wrote a scathing denunciation of the people's movement in France. He called this work *Reflections on the Revolution in France,* but it was as one-sided, as narrow, and as reactionary a set of reflections as ever a so-called liberal set down. He whitewashed the decadent French aristocracy and elevated them; he turned the people into a savage, frothing mob, the same heartless mob that Charles Dickens borrowed from Carlyle and in turn passed on to the Hollywood movie makers. Burke set a precedent in conscious, manufactured falsehood and calumny of a people's movement that has been dutifully followed even to this day.

It was this wretched piece of writing, happily forgotten today, that woke Tom Paine from his scribbling and set him to writing *Rights of Man,* one of the finest statements of eighteenth century democratic philosophy ever formulated.

When Paine wrote *Common Sense,* he was venturing into a new field. Not by the farthest stretch of imagination, as I have said, could he have imagined the consequences of his first published work. But settling down to *Rights of Man,* he had hindsight to aid him, and he proceeded deliberately to manufacture a document that would shake the whole fabric of England. It did.

It was a miracle that Paine should have succeeded twice in creating so influential a document; it would have been something more of a miracle if his second book touched off a revolution in a land so different from America.

The difference lay in the stages of development of the two countries; the psychology of the masses was different. The America to which Paine came had a revolutionary government, the Continental Congress, and this congress had already assumed many functions of the state. The British government was conservative, stable, and fully conscious of whatever revolutionary threat existed.

Paine finally found a courageous printer for his book. Aware of its content, the government allowed it to be printed with the belief that only the upper classes could afford to buy it. In that, however, they were mistaken. *Rights of Man* met with a response that was unique in English publishing history. The poor pooled pennies and dug into meagre savings to buy the book. Like an underground manifesto, it was passed from hand to hand, even when it became a crime to be found with *Rights of Man* in one's possession. It was published in two parts, each tremendously successful; but when we attempt to estimate the numbers of copies sold, we run into the same difficulties we encountered with *Common Sense*. I would guess that the expensive edition sold close to 100,000 copies. Cheap editions were gotten out in Scotland and Wales; extracts from the book were printed in pamphlet form.

The book became a bible to thousands of men who dreamed of a free England. In case after case in that period, when men were being tried for treason or for what was called treason by the British Crown, we find offered as damning evidence to the jury the fact that these men possessed a copy of *Rights of Man*.

Of Jordan, the man who published *Rights of Man* and stood by it when the government charged that it was seditious, too little is known. He must have been a brave and forthright man, one of the many Englishmen who believed in the things Paine said and loved him for what he was. He answered the government's charges, allowing Paine to escape to France. Undoubtedly, Paine hoped to return, to find the English populace ready and waiting; but he never returned; when he left England in 1792, he left it forever.

And the pitiful, abortive little revolution that Paine had brewed in England fell to pieces. Three generations would pass before even a small part of the things Paine pleaded for in his book came to that tight little isle.

Yet one cannot say that the book had no effect. It shook the government; it set thousands of people to thinking. It stirred the currents in what had been placid water, and once stirred, those currents never stilled themselves. And not only in England, but everywhere men longed for freedom, *Rights of Man* became an inspiration and a hope.

Just a word should be said about the fact that part one of *Rights of Man* was dedicated to George Washington. This dedication takes on added interest in light of the circumstance that years later Paine wrote a letter damning Washington in the strongest terms he knew. Note that here Paine gives ample evidence of the love and consideration in which he held the American President, and indeed there was no man on earth Paine considered more highly. Only when, after many years, separated from America by thousands of miles, Paine saw the rise of the party of reaction and the beginnings of the Federalist plot, did his esteem begin to waiver. And he finally lost faith when, in his hour of direst need, the American government abandoned him. Of that, more later.

So here is *Rights of Man,* a book which for more than a century and a half has pointed out paths in democratic government, and which even today would be considered radical by many.

Rights of Man

TO

GEORGE WASHINGTON

PRESIDENT OF THE UNITED STATES OF AMERICA

SIR,

I present you a small Treatise in defence of those Principles of Freedom which your exemplary Virtue hath so eminently contributed to establish. That the Rights of Man may become as universal as your Benevolence can wish, and that you may enjoy the Happiness of seeing the New World regenerate the Old, is the prayer of

Sir,
Your much obliged, and
Obedient humble Servant,

THOMAS PAINE.

PART THE FIRST

AMONG the incivilities by which nations or individuals provoke and irritate each other, Mr. Burke's pamphlet on the French Revolution is an extraordinary instance. Neither the people of France, nor the National Assembly, were troubling themselves about the affairs of England, or the English Parliament; and why Mr. Burke should commence an unprovoked attack upon them, both in Parliament and in public, is a conduct that cannot be pardoned on the score of manners, nor justified on that of policy.

There is scarcely an epithet of abuse to be found in the English language, with which Mr. Burke has not loaded the French Nation and the National Assembly. Everything which rancour, prejudice, ignorance or knowledge could suggest, is poured forth in the copious fury of near four hundred pages. In the strain and on the plan Mr. Burke was writing, he might have written on to as many thousands. When the tongue or the pen is let loose in a phrenzy of passion, it is the man, and not the subject, that becomes exhausted.

Hitherto Mr. Burke has been mistaken and disappointed in the opinions he had formed of the affairs of France; but such is the ingenuity of his hope, or the malignancy of his despair, that it furnishes him with new pretences to go on. There was a time when it was impossible to make Mr. Burke believe there would be any Revolution in France. His opinion then was, that the French had neither spirit to undertake it nor fortitude to support it; and now that there is one, he seeks an escape by condemning it.

Not sufficiently content with abusing the National Assembly, a great part of his work is taken up with abusing Dr. Price (one of the best-hearted men that lives) and the two societies in England known by the name of the Revolution Society and the Society for Constitutional Information.

Dr. Price had preached a sermon on the 4th of November, 1789, being the anniversary of what is called in England the Revolution, which took place 1688. Mr. Burke, speaking of this sermon, says, "The political Divine proceeds dogmatically to assert, that by the principles of the Revolution, the people of England have acquired three fundamental rights:

1. To choose their own governors.
2. To cashier them for misconduct.
3. To frame a government for ourselves."

Dr. Price does not say that the right to do these things exists in this or in that person, or in this or in that description of persons, but that it exists in the *whole;* that it is a right resident in the Nation. Mr. Burke, on the contrary, denies that such a right exists in the Nation, either in whole or in part, or that it exists anywhere; and, what is still more strange and marvellous, he says, "that the people of England utterly disclaim such a right, and that they will resist the practical assertion of it with their lives and fortunes." That men should take up arms and spend their lives and fortunes, *not* to maintain their rights, but to maintain they have *not* rights, is an entirely new species of discovery, and suited to the paradoxical genius of Mr. Burke.

The method which Mr. Burke takes to prove that the people of England have no such rights, and that such rights do not now exist in the Nation, either in whole or in part, or anywhere at all, is of the same marvellous and monstrous kind with what he has already said; for his arguments are that the persons, or the generation of persons, in whom they did exist, are dead, and with them the right is dead also. To prove this, he quotes a declaration made by parliament about a hundred years ago, to William and Mary, in these words: "The Lords Spiritual and Temporal, and Commons, do, in the name of the people aforesaid [meaning the people of England then living], most humbly and faithfully *submit* themselves, their *heirs* and *posterities,* for EVER." He also quotes a clause of another act of Parliament made in the same reign, the terms of which, he says, "bind us [meaning the people of that day], our *heirs* and our *posterity,* to *them,* their *heirs* and *posterity,* to the end of time."

Mr. Burke conceives his point sufficiently established by producing those clauses, which he enforces by saying that they exclude the right of the Nation for *ever.* And not yet content with making such declarations, repeated over and over again, he farther says, "that if the people of England possessed such a right before the Revolution [which he acknowledges to have been the case, not only in England, but throughout Europe, at an early period], yet that the *English Nation* did, at the time of the Revolution, most solemnly renounce and abdicate it, for themselves, and for *all their posterity, for ever.*"

As Mr. Burke occasionally applies the poison drawn from his horrid principles (if it is not prophanation to call them by the name of principles) not only to the English Nation, but to the French Revolution and the National Assembly, and charges that august, illuminated and illuminating body of men with the epithet of *usurpers,* I shall, *sans cérémonie,* place another system of principles in opposition to his.

The English Parliament of 1688 did a certain thing, which, for themselves and their constituents, they had a right to do, and which it appeared right should be done: but, in addition to this right, which they possessed by delegation, *they set up another right by assumption,* that of binding and controuling posterity to the end of time. The case, therefore, divides itself into two parts; the right which they possessed by delegation, and the right which they set up by assumption. The first is admitted; but with respect to the second, I reply—

There never did, there never will, and there never can, exist a Parliament, or any description of men, or any generation of men, in any country, possessed of the right or the power of binding and controuling posterity to the *"end of time,"* or of commanding for ever how the world shall be governed, or who shall govern it; and therefore all such clauses, acts or declarations by which the makers of them attempt to do what they have neither the right nor the power to do, nor the power to execute, are in themselves null and void. Every age and generation must be as free to act for itself *in all cases* as the ages and generations which preceded it. The vanity and presumption of governing beyond the grave is the most ridiculous and insolent of all tyrannies. Man has no property in man; neither has any generation a property in the generations which are to follow. The Parliament or the people of 1688, or of any other period, had no more right to dispose of the people of the present day, or to bind or to controul them *in any shape whatever,* than the Parliament or the people of the present day have to dispose of, bind or controul those who are to live a hundred or a thousand years hence. Every generation is, and must be, competent to all the purposes which its occasions require. It is the living, and not the dead, that are to be accommodated. When man ceases to be, his power and his wants cease with him; and having no longer any participation in the concerns of this world, he has no longer any authority in directing who shall be its governors, or how its Government shall be organised, or how administered.

I am not contending for nor against any form of Government, nor for nor against any party, here or elsewhere. That which a whole Nation chooses to do, it has a right to do. Mr. Burke says, No. Where, then, does the right exist? I am contending for the rights of the *living,* and against their being willed away, and controuled and contracted for, by the manuscript assumed authority of the dead; and Mr. Burke is contending for the authority of the dead over the rights and freedom of the living. There was a time when Kings disposed of their Crowns by will upon their deathbeds, and consigned the people, like beasts of the field, to whatever successor they appointed. This is now so exploded as scarcely to be remembered, and so monstrous as hardly to be believed; but the Parliamentary clauses upon which Mr. Burke builds his political church are of the same nature.

The laws of every country must be analogous to some common principle. In England no parent or master, nor all the authority of Parliament, omnipotent as it has called itself, can bind or controul the personal freedom even of an individual beyond the age of twenty-one years. On what ground of right, then, could the Parliament of 1688, or any other Parliament, bind all posterity for ever?

Those who have quitted the world, and those who are not yet arrived at it, are as remote from each other as the utmost stretch of mortal imagination can conceive. What possible obligation, then, can exist between them; what rule or principle can be laid down that of two non-entities, the one out of existence and the other not in, and who never can meet in this world, the one should controul the other to the end of time?

In England it is said that money cannot be taken out of the pockets of the people without their consent. But who authorised, or who could authorise, the Parliament of 1688 to controul and take away the freedom of posterity (who were not in existence to give or to withhold their consent), and limit and confine their right of acting in certain cases for ever?

A greater absurdity cannot present itself to the understanding of man than what Mr. Burke offers to his readers. He tells them, and he tells the world to come, that a certain body of men who existed a hundred years ago, made a law, and that there does not now exist in the Nation, nor ever will, nor ever can, a power to alter it. Under how many subtilties or absurdities has the divine right to govern been imposed on the credulity of mankind! Mr. Burke has discovered a new one, and he has shortened his journey to Rome by appealing to the power of this infallible Parliament of former days; and he produces what it has done as of divine authority, for that power must certainly be more than human which no human power to the end of time can alter.

But Mr. Burke has done some service, not to his cause, but to his country, by bringing those clauses into public view. They serve to demonstrate how necessary it is at all times to watch against the attempted encroachment of power, and to prevent its running to excess. It is somewhat extraordinary that the offence for which James II. was expelled, that of setting up power by *assumption,* should be re-acted, under another shape and form, by the Parliament that expelled him. It shows that the rights of man were but imperfectly understood at the Revolution; for certain it is that the right which that Parliament set up by *assumption* (for by delegation it had it not, and could not have it, because none could give it) over the persons and freedom of posterity for ever, was of the same tyrannical unfounded kind which James attempted to set up over the Parliament and the Nation, and for which he was expelled. The only difference is (for in principle they differ not) that the one was an usurper over the living, and the other over the unborn; and as the one has no better authority to stand upon than the other, both of them must be equally null and void, and of no effect.

From what, or from whence, does Mr. Burke prove the right of any human power to bind posterity for ever? He has produced his clauses, but he must produce also his proofs that such a right existed, and show how it existed. If it ever existed it must now exist, for whatever appertains to the nature of man cannot be annihilated by man. It is the nature of man to die, and he will continue to die as long as he continues to be born. But Mr. Burke has set up a sort of political Adam, in whom all posterity are bound for ever; he must, therefore, prove that his Adam possessed such a power, or such a right.

The weaker any cord is the less will it bear to be stretched, and the worse is the policy to stretch it, unless it is intended to break it. Had any one proposed the overthrow of Mr. Burke's positions, he would have proceeded as Mr. Burke has done. He would have magnified the authorities, on purpose to have called the *right* of them into question; and the instant the question of right was started, the authorities must have been given up.

It requires but a very small glance of thought to perceive that altho' laws made in one generation often continue in force through succeeding generations, yet that they continue to derive their force from the consent of the living. A law not repealed continues in force, not because it *cannot* be repealed, but because it *is not* repealed; and the non-repealing passes for consent.

But Mr. Burke's clauses have not even this qualification in their favour. They become null, by attempting to become immortal. The nature of them precludes consent. They destroy the right which they *might* have, by grounding it on a right which they *cannot* have. Immortal power is not a human right, and therefore cannot be a right of Parliament. The Parliament of 1688 might as well have passed an act to have authorized themselves to live for ever, as to make their authority live for ever. All, therefore, that can be said of those clauses is that they are a formality of words, of as much import as if those who used them had addressed a congratulation to themselves, and in the oriental stile of antiquity had said: O Parliament, live for ever!

The circumstances of the world are continually changing, and the opinions of men change also; and as Government is for the living, and not for the dead, it is the living only that has any right in it. That which may be thought right and found convenient in one age may be thought wrong and found inconvenient in another. In such cases, Who is to decide, the living, or the dead?

As almost one hundred pages of Mr. Burke's book are employed upon these clauses, it will consequently follow that if the clauses themselves, so far as they set up an *assumed usurped* dominion over posterity for ever, are unauthoritative, and in their nature null and void; that all his voluminous inferences, and declamation drawn therefrom, or founded thereon, are null and void also; and on this ground I rest the matter.

We now come more particularly to the affairs of France. Mr. Burke's book has the appearance of being written as instruction to the French Nation; but if I may permit myself the use of an extravagant metaphor, suited to the extravagance of the case, It is darkness attempting to illuminate light.

While I am writing this there are accidentally before me some proposals for a declaration of rights by the Marquis de la Fayette (I ask his pardon for using his former address, and do it only for distinction's sake) to the National Assembly, on the 11th of July, 1789, three days before the taking of the Bastille; and I cannot but remark with astonishment how opposite the sources are from which that gentleman and Mr. Burke draw their principles. Instead of referring to musty records and mouldy parchments to prove that the rights of the living are lost, "renounced and abdicated for ever," by those who are now no more, as Mr. Burke has done, M. de la Fayette applies to the living world, and emphatically says, "Call to mind the sentiments which Nature has engraved in the heart of every citizen, and which take a new force when they are solemnly recognised by all: For a Nation to love Liberty, it is sufficient that she knows it; and to be free, it is sufficient that she wills it." How dry, barren, and obscure is the source from which Mr. Burke labours; and how ineffectual, though gay with flowers, are all his declamation and his arguments compared with these clear, concise, and soul-animating sentiments! Few and short as they are, they lead to a vast field of generous and manly thinking, and do not finish, like Mr. Burke's periods, with music in the ear, and nothing in the heart.

As I have introduced M. de la Fayette, I will take the liberty of adding an anecdote respecting his farewell address to the Congress of America in 1783, which occurred fresh to my mind, when I saw Mr. Burke's thundering attack on the French Revolution. M. de la Fayette went to America at an early period of the war, and continued a volunteer in her service to the end. His conduct through the whole of that enterprise is one of the most extraordinary that is to be found in the history of a young man, scarcely then twenty years of age. Situated in a country that was like the lap of sensual pleasure, and with the means of enjoying it, how few are there to be found who would exchange such a scene for the woods and wildernesses of America, and pass the flowery years of youth in unprofitable danger and hardship! But such is the fact. When the war ended, and he was on the point of taking his final departure, he presented himself to Congress, and contemplating, in his affectionate farewell, the Revolution he had seen, expressed himself in these words: "May this great monument raised to Liberty, serve as a lesson to the oppressor, and an example to the oppressed!" When this address came to the hands of Dr. Franklin, who was then in France, he applied to Count Vergennes to have it inserted in the French Gazette, but never could obtain his consent. The fact was that Count Vergennes was an aristocratical despot at home, and dreaded the example of the American Revolution in France, as certain other persons now dread the example of the French Revolution in England; and Mr. Burke's tribute of fear (for in this light his book must be considered) runs parallel with Count Vergennes' refusal. But to return more particularly to his work—

"We have seen," says Mr. Burke, "the French rebel against a mild and lawful Monarch, with more fury, outrage, and insult, than any people has been known to rise against the most illegal usurper, or the most sanguinary tyrant." This is one among a thousand other instances, in which Mr. Burke shows that he is ignorant of the springs and principles of the French Revolution.

It was not against Louis XVI., but against the despotic principles of the government, that the Nation revolted. These principles had not their origin in him, but in the original establishment, many centuries back; and they were become too deeply rooted to be removed, and the Augean stable of parasites and plunderers too abominably filthy to be cleansed, by anything short of a complete and universal Revolution. When it becomes necessary to do a thing, the whole heart and soul should go into the measure, or not attempt it. That crisis was then arrived, and there remained no choice but to act with determined vigour, or not to act at all. The King was known to be the friend of the Nation, and this circumstance was favourable to the enterprise. Perhaps no man bred up in the style of an absolute King, ever possessed a heart so little disposed to the exercise of that species of power as the present King of France. But the principles of the Government itself still remained the same. The Monarch and the Monarchy were distinct and separate things; and it was against the established despotism of the latter, and not against the person or principles of the former, that the revolt commenced, and the Revolution has been carried.

Mr. Burke does not attend to the distinction between *men* and *principles;* and, therefore, he does not see that a revolt may take place against the despotism of the latter, while there lies no charge of despotism against the former.

The natural moderation of Louis XVI. contributed nothing to alter the hereditary despotism of the Monarchy. All the tyrannies of former reigns, acted under that hereditary despotism, were still liable to be revived in the hands of a successor. It was not the respite of a reign that would satisfy France, enlightened as she then was become. A casual discontinuance of the *practice* of despotism, is not a discontinuance of its *principles;* the former depends on the virtue of the individual who is in immediate possession of the power; the latter, on the virtue and fortitude of the nation. In the case of Charles I. and James II. of England, the revolt was against the personal despotism of the men; whereas in France, it was against the hereditary despotism of the established government. But men who can consign over the rights of posterity for ever on the authority of a mouldy parchment, like Mr. Burke, are not qualified to judge of this Revolution. It takes in a field too vast for their views to explore, and proceeds with a mightiness of reason they cannot keep pace with.

But there are many points of view in which this Revolution may be considered. When despotism has established itself for ages in a country, as in France, it is not in the person of the King only that it resides. It has the appearance of being so in show, and in nominal authority; but it is not so in practice and in fact. It has its standard everywhere. Every office and department has its despotism, founded upon custom and usage. Every place has its Bastille, and every Bastille its despot. The original hereditary despotism resident in the person of the King, divides and subdivides itself into a thousand shapes and forms, till at last the whole of it is acted by deputation. This was the case in France; and against this species of despotism, proceeding on through an endless labyrinth of office till the source of it is scarcely perceptible, there is no mode of redress. It strengthens itself by assuming the appearance of duty, and tyrannises under the pretence of obeying.

When a man reflects on the condition which France was in from the nature of her Government, he will see other causes for revolt than those which immediately connect themselves with the person or character of Louis XVI. There were, if I may so express it, a thousand despotisms to be reformed in France, which had grown up under the hereditary despotism of the monarchy, and became so rooted as to be in great measure independent of it. Between the Monarchy, the Parliament, and the Church, there was a *rivalship* of despotism; besides the feudal despotism operating locally, and the ministerial despotism operating everywhere. But Mr. Burke, by considering the King as the only possible object of a revolt, speaks as if France was a village, in which everything that passed must be known to its commanding officer, and no oppression could be acted but what he could immediately controul. Mr. Burke might have been in the Bastille his whole life, as well under Louis XVI. as Louis XIV., and neither the one nor the other have known that such a man as Mr. Burke existed. The despotic principles of the Government were the same in both reigns, though the dispositions of the men were as remote as tyranny and benevolence.

What Mr. Burke considers as a reproach to the French Revolution (that of bringing it forward under a reign more mild than the preceding ones) is one of its highest honours. The Revolutions that have taken place in other European countries, have been excited by personal hatred. The rage was against the man, and he became the victim. But, in the instance of France we see a revolution generated in the rational contemplation of the rights of man, and distinguishing from the beginning between persons and principles.

But Mr. Burke appears to have no idea of principles when he is contemplating Governments. "Ten years ago," says he, "I could have felicitated France on her having a Government, without inquiring what the nature of that Government was, or how it was administered." Is this the language of a rational man? Is it the language of a heart feeling as it ought to feel for the rights and happiness of the human race? On this ground, Mr. Burke must compliment all the Governments in the world, while the victims who suffer under them, whether sold into slavery, or tortured out of existence, are wholly forgotten. It is power, and not principles, that Mr. Burke venerates; and under this abominable depravity he is disqualified to judge between them. Thus much for his opinion as to the occasions of the French Revolution. I now proceed to other considerations.

I know a place in America called Point-no-Point, because as you proceed along the shore, gay and flowery as Mr. Burke's language, it continually recedes and presents itself at a distance before you; but when you have got as far as you can go, there is no point at all. Just thus it is with Mr. Burke's three hundred and fifty-six pages. It is therefore difficult to reply to him. But as the points he wishes to establish may be inferred from what he abuses, it is in his paradoxes that we must look for his arguments.

As to the tragic paintings by which Mr. Burke has outraged his own imagination, and seeks to work upon that of his readers, they are very well calculated for theatrical representation, where facts are manufactured for the sake of show, and accommodated to produce, through the weakness of sympathy, a weeping effect. But Mr. Burke should recollect that he is writing history, and not *plays,* and that his readers will expect truth, and not the spouting rant of high-toned exclamation.

When we see a man dramatically lamenting in a publication intended to be believed that *"The age of chivalry is gone!* that *The glory of Europe is extinguished for ever!* that *the unbought grace of life* (if any one knows what it is), *the cheap defence of nations, the nurse of manly sentiment and heroic enterprise is gone!"* and all this because the Quixote age of chivalry nonsense is gone, what opinion can we form of his judgment, or what regard can we pay to his facts? In the rhapsody of his imagination he has discovered a world of windmills, and his sorrows are that there are no Quixotes to attack them. But if the age of Aristocracy, like that of Chivalry, should fall (and they had originally some connection), Mr. Burke, the trumpeter of the order, may continue his parody to the end, and finish with exclaiming: *"Othello's occupation's gone!"*

Notwithstanding Mr. Burke's horrid paintings, when the French Revolution is compared with the Revolutions of other countries, the astonishment will be that it is marked with so few sacrifices; but this astonishment will cease when we reflect that *principles,* and not *persons,* were the meditated objects of destruction. The mind of the nation was acted upon by a higher stimulus than what the consideration of persons could inspire, and sought a higher conquest than could be produced by the downfall of an enemy. Among the few who fell there do not appear to be any that were intentionally singled out. They all of them had their fate in the circumstances of the moment, and were not pursued with that long, cold-blooded, unabated revenge which pursued the unfortunate Scotch in the affair of 1745.

Through the whole of Mr. Burke's book I do not observe that the Bastille is mentioned more than once, and that with a kind of implication as if he were sorry it was pulled down, and wished it were built up again. "We have rebuilt Newgate," says he, "and tenanted the mansion; and we have prisons almost as strong as the Bastille for those who dare to libel the Queens of France." As to what a madman like the person called Lord G—— G—— might say, to whom Newgate is rather a bedlam than a prison, it is unworthy a rational consideration. It was a madman that libelled, and that is sufficient apology; and it afforded an opportunity for confining him, which was the thing that was wished for. But certain it is that Mr. Burke, who does not call himself a madman (whatever other people may do), has libelled in the most unprovoked manner, and in the grossest stile of the most vulgar abuse, the whole representative authority of France, and yet Mr. Burke takes his seat in the British House of Commons! From his violence and his grief, his silence on some points and his excess on others, it is difficult not to believe that Mr. Burke is sorry, extremely sorry, that arbitrary power, the power of the Pope and the Bastille, are pulled down.

Not one glance of compassion, not one commiserating reflection that I can find throughout his book, has he bestowed on those who lingered out the most wretched of lives, a life without hope in the most miserable of prisons. It is painful to behold a man employing his talents to corrupt himself. Nature has been kinder to Mr. Burke than he is to her. He is not affected by the reality of distress touching his heart, but by the showy resemblance of it striking his imagination. He pities the plumage, but forgets the dying bird. Accustomed to kiss the aristocratical hand that hath purloined him from himself, he degenerates into a composition of art, and the genuine soul of nature forsakes him. His hero or his heroine must be a tragedy-victim expiring in show, and not the real prisoner of misery, sliding into death in the silence of a dungeon.

As Mr. Burke has passed over the whole transaction of the Bastille (and his silence is nothing in his favour), and has entertained his readers with reflections on supposed facts distorted into real falsehoods, I will give, since he has not, some account of the circumstances which preceded that transaction. They will serve to show that less mischief could scarcely have accompanied such an event when considered with the treacherous and hostile aggravations of the enemies of the Revolution.

The mind can hardly picture to itself a more tremendous scene than what the city of Paris exhibited at the time of taking the Bastille, and for two days before and after, nor conceive the possibility of its quieting so soon. At a distance this transaction has appeared only as an act of heroism standing on itself, and the close political connection it had with the Revolution is lost in the brilliancy of the achievement. But we are to consider it as the strength of the parties brought man to man, and contending for the issue. The Bastille was to be either the prize or the prison of the assailants. The downfall of it included the idea of the downfall of despotism, and this compounded image was become as figuratively united as Bunyan's Doubting Castle and Giant Despair.

The National Assembly, before and at the time of taking the Bastille, was sitting at Versailles, twelve miles distance from Paris. About a week before the rising of the Parisians, and their taking the Bastille, it was discovered that a plot was forming, at the head of which was the Count d'Artois, the king's youngest brother, for demolishing the National Assembly, seizing its members, and thereby crushing, by a *coup de main*, all hopes and prospects of forming a free government. For the sake of humanity, as well as of freedom, it is well this plan did not succeed. Examples are not wanting to show how dreadfully vindictive and cruel are all old Governments, when they are successful against what they call a revolt.

This plan must have been some time in contemplation; because, in order to carry it into execution, it was necessary to collect a large military force round Paris, and cut off the communication between that city and the National Assembly at Versailles. The troops destined for this service were chiefly the foreign troops in the pay of France, and who, for this particular purpose, were drawn from the distant provinces where they were then stationed. When they were collected to the amount of about twenty-five and thirty thousand, it was judged time to put the plan in execution. The ministry who were then in office, and who were friendly to the Revolution, were instantly dismissed and a new ministry formed of those who had concerted the project, among whom was Count de Broglio, and to his share was given the command of those troops. The character of this man as described to me in a letter which I communicated to Mr. Burke before he began to write his book, and from an authority which Mr. Burke well knows was good, was that of "a high-flying aristocrat, cool, and capable of every mischief."

While these matters were agitating, the National Assembly stood in the most perilous and critical situation that a body of men can be supposed to act in. They were the devoted victims, and they knew it. They had the hearts and wishes of their country on their side, but military authority they had none. The guards of Broglio surrounded the hall where the assemby sat, ready, at the word of command, to seize their persons, as had been done the year before to the Parliament of Paris. Had the National Assembly deserted their trust, or had they exhibited signs of weakness or fear, their enemies had been encouraged and the country depressed. When the situation they stood in, the cause they were engaged in and the crisis then ready to burst, which was to determine their personal and political fate and that of their country, and probably of Europe, are taken into one view, none but a heart callous with prejudice or corrupted by dependence can avoid interesting itself in their success.

The Archbishop of Vienne was at this time president of the National Assembly—a person too old to undergo the scene that a few days or a few hours might bring forth. A man of more activity and greater fortitude was necessary, and the National Assembly chose (under the form of a vice-president, for the presidency still resided in the Archbishop) M. de la Fayette; and this is the only instance of a vice-president being chosen. It was at the moment that this storm was pending (July 11th) that a declaration of rights was brought forward by M. de la Fayette; and is the same which is alluded to in page 17. It was hastily drawn up, and makes only a part of the more extensive declaration of rights agreed upon and adopted afterwards by the National Assembly. The particular reason for bringing it forward at this moment (M. de la Fayette has since informed me) was that if the National Assembly should fail in the threatened destruction that then surrounded it, some traces of its principles might have the chance of surviving the wreck.

Everything now was drawing to a crisis. The event was to be freedom or slavery. On one side, an army of nearly thirty thousand men; on the other, an unarmed body of citizens; for the citizens of Paris, on whom the National Assembly must then immediately depend, were as unarmed and as undisciplined as the citizens of London are now. The French guards had given strong symptoms of their being attached to the national cause; but their numbers were small, not a tenth part of the force that Broglio commanded, and their officers were in the interest of Broglio.

Matters being now ripe for execution, the new ministry made their appearance in office. The reader will carry in his mind that the Bastille was taken the 14th of July; the point of time I am now speaking to is the 12th. Immediately on the news of the change of ministry reaching Paris, in the afternoon, all the playhouses and places of entertainment, shops and houses, were shut up. The change of ministry was considered as the prelude of hostilities, and the opinion was rightly founded.

The foreign troops began to advance towards the city. The Prince de Lambesc, who commanded a body of German cavalry, approached by the Palace of Louis XV., which connects itself with some of the streets. In his march, he insulted and struck an old man with his sword. The French are remarkable for their respect to old age; and the insolence with which it appeared to be done, uniting with the general fermentation they were in, produced a powerful effect, and a cry of *"To arms! To arms!"* spread itself in a moment over the city.

Arms they had none, nor scarcely any who knew the use of them; but desperate resolution, when every hope is at stake, supplies, for a while, the want of arms. Near where the Prince de Lambesc was drawn up, were large piles of stones collected for building the new bridge, and with these the people attacked the cavalry. A party of the French guards, upon hearing the firing, rushed from their quarters and joined the people; and night coming on, the cavalry retreated.

The streets of Paris, being narrow, are favourable for defence, and the loftiness of the houses, consisting of many stories, from which great annoyance might be given, secured them against nocturnal enterprises; and the night was spent in providing themselves with every sort of weapon they could make or procure: guns, swords, blacksmiths' hammers, carpenters' axes, iron crows, pikes, halberts, pitchforks, spits, clubs, etc., etc. The incredible numbers in which they assembled the next morning, and the still more incredible resolution they exhibited, embarrassed and astonished their enemies. Little did the new ministry expect such a salute. Accustomed to slavery themselves, they had no idea that Liberty was capable of such inspiration, or that a body of unarmed citizens would dare to face the military force of thirty thousand men. Every moment of this day was employed in collecting arms, concerting plans, and arranging themselves into the best order which such an instantaneous movement could afford. Broglio continued lying round the city, but made no farther advances this day, and the succeeding night passed with as much tranquillity as such a scene could possibly admit.

But defence only was not the object of the citizens. They had a cause at stake, on which depended their freedom or their slavery. They every moment expected an attack, or to hear of one made on the National Assembly; and in such a situation, the most prompt measures are sometimes the best. The object that now presented itself was the Bastille;

and the *éclat* of carrying such a fortress in the face of such an army, could not fail to strike a terror into the new ministry, who had scarcely yet had time to meet. By some intercepted correspondence, it was discovered that the Mayor of Paris, M. Defflesselles, who appeared to be in the interest of the citizens, was betraying them; from this discovery, there remained no doubt that Broglio would reinforce the Bastille the ensuing evening. It was therefore necessary to attack it that day; but before this could be done, it was first necessary to procure a better supply of arms than they were then possessed of.

There was, adjoining to the city, a large magazine of arms deposited at the Hospital of the Invalids, which the citizens summoned to surrender; and as the place was not defensible, nor attempted much defence, they soon succeeded. Thus supplied, they marched to attack the Bastille; a vast mixed multitude of all ages, and of all degrees, armed with all sorts of weapons. Imagination would fail in describing to itself the appearance of such a procession, and of the anxiety for the events which a few hours or few minutes might produce. What plans the ministry was forming, were as unknown to the people within the city, as what the citizens were doing was unknown to the ministry; and what movements Broglio might make for the support or relief of the place, were to the citizens equally as unknown. All was mystery and hazard.

That the Bastille was attacked with an enthusiasm of heroism, such only as the highest animation of Liberty could inspire, and carried in the space of a few hours, is an event which the world is fully possessed of. I am not undertaking a detail of the attack, but bringing into view the conspiracy against the nation which provoked it, and which fell with the Bastille. The prison to which the new ministry were dooming the National Assembly, in addition to its being the high altar and castle of despotism, became the proper object to begin with. This enterprise broke up the new ministry, who began now to fly from the ruin they had prepared for others. The troops of Broglio dispersed, and himself fled also.

Mr. Burke has spoken a great deal about plots, but he has never once spoken of this plot against the National Assembly, and the liberties of the Nation; and that he might not, he has passed over all the circumstances that might throw it in his way. The exiles who have fled from France, whose case he so much interests himself in, and from whom he has had his lesson, fled in consequence of the miscarriage of this plot. No plot was formed against them; they were plotting against others; and those who fell, met, not unjustly, the punishment they were preparing to execute. But will Mr. Burke say, that if this plot, contrived with the subtilty of an ambuscade, had succeeded, the successful party would have restrained their wrath so soon? Let the history of all old Governments answer the question.

Whom has the National Assembly brought to the scaffold? None. They were themselves the devoted victims of this plot, and they have not retaliated; why, then, are they charged with revenge they have not acted? In the tremendous breaking forth of a whole people, in which all degrees, tempers, and characters are confounded, delivering themselves by a miracle of exertion from the destruction meditated against them, is it to be expected that nothing will happen? When men are sore with the sense of oppressions, and menaced with the prospect of new ones, is the calmness of philosophy or the palsy of insensibility to be looked for? Mr. Burke exclaims against outrage; yet the greatest is that which himself has committed. His book is a volume of outrage, not apologised for by the impulse of a moment, but cherished through a space of ten months; yet Mr. Burke had no provocation, no life, no interest at stake.

More of the citizens fell in this struggle than of their opponents; but four or five persons were seized by the populace and instantly put to death; the Governor of the Bastille, and the Mayor of Paris, who was detected in the act of betraying them; and afterwards Foulon, one of the new ministry, and Berthier, his son-in-law, who had accepted the office of intendant of Paris. Their heads were stuck upon spikes, and carried about the city; and it is upon this mode of punishment that Mr. Burke builds a great part of his tragic scenes. Let us therefore examine how men came by the idea of punishing in this manner.

They learn it from the Governments they live under, and retaliate the punishments they have been accustomed to behold. The heads stuck upon spikes, which remained for years upon Temple Bar, differed nothing in the horror of the scene from those carried about upon spikes at Paris; yet this was done by the English Government. It may perhaps be said that it signifies nothing to a man what is done to him after he is dead; but it signifies much to the living; it either tortures their feelings or hardens their hearts, and in either case it instructs them how to punish when power falls into their hands.

Lay then the axe to the root, and teach Governments humanity. It is their sanguinary punishments which corrupt mankind. In England the punishment in certain cases is by *hanging, drawing* and *quartering;* the heart of the sufferer is cut out and held up to the view of the populace. In France, under the former Government, the punishments were not less barbarous. Who does not remember the execution of Damien, torn to pieces by horses? The effect of those cruel spectacles exhibited to the populace is to destroy tenderness or excite revenge; and by the base and false idea of governing men by terror, instead of reason, they become precedents. It is over the lowest class of mankind that Government by terror is intended to operate, and it is on them that it operates to the worst effect. They have sense enough to feel they are the objects aimed at; and they inflict in their turn the examples of terror they have been instructed to practise.

There is in all European countries a large class of people of that description, which in England is called the *Mob*. Of this class were those who committed the burnings and devastations in London in 1780, and of this class were those who carried the heads upon spikes in Paris. Foulon and Berthier were taken up in the country, and sent to Paris, to undergo their examination at the Hotel de Ville; for the National Assembly, immediately on the new ministry coming into office, passed a decree, which they communicated to the King and Cabinet, that they (the National Assembly) would hold the ministry, of which Foulon was one, responsible for the measures they were advising and pursuing; but the mob, incensed at the appearance of Foulon and Berthier, tore them from their conductors before they were carried to the Hotel de Ville, and executed them on the spot. Why then does Mr. Burke charge outrages of this kind on a whole people? As well may he charge the riots and outrages of 1780 on all the people of London, or those in Ireland on all his countrymen.

But everything we see or hear offensive to our feelings and derogatory to the human character should lead to other reflections than those of reproach. Even the beings who commit them have some claim to our consideration. How then is it that such vast classes of mankind as are distinguished by the appellation of the vulgar, or the ignorant mob, are so numerous in all old countries? The instant we ask ourselves this question, reflection feels an answer. They arise, as an unavoidable consequence, out of the ill construction of all old Governments in Europe, England included with the rest. It is by distortedly exalting some men, that others are distortedly debased, till the whole is out of nature. A vast mass of mankind are degradedly thrown into the background of the human picture, to bring forward, with greater glare, the puppet-show of State and Aristocracy. In the commencement of a Revolution, those men are rather the followers of the *camp* than of the *standard* of Liberty, and have yet to be instructed how to reverence it.

I give to Mr. Burke all his theatrical exaggerations for facts, and I then ask him if they do not establish the certainty of what I here lay down? Admitting them to be true, they show the necessity of the French Revolution, as much as any one thing he could have asserted. These outrages were not the effect of the principles of the Revolution, but of the degraded mind that existed before the Revolution, and which the Revolution is calculated to reform. Place them then to their proper cause, and take the reproach of them to your own side.

It is to the honour of the National Assembly and the city of Paris that, during such a tremendous scene of arms and confusion, beyond the controul of all authority, they have been able, by the influence of example and exhortation, to restrain so much. Never were more pains taken to instruct and enlighten mankind, and to make them see that their interest consisted in their virtue, and not in their revenge, than have been displayed in the Revolution of France. I now proceed to make some remarks on Mr. Burke's account of the expedition to Versailles, October the 5th and 6th.

I cannot consider Mr. Burke's book in any other light than a dramatic performance; and he must, I think, have considered it in the same light himself, by the poetical liberties he has taken of omitting some facts, distorting others, and making the whole machinery bend to produce a stage effect. Of this kind is his account of the expedition to Versailles. He begins this account by omitting the only facts which as causes are known to be true; everything beyond these is conjecture even in Paris; and he then works up a tale accommodated to his own passions and prejudices.

It is to be observed throughout Mr. Burke's book that he never speaks of plots *against* the Revolution; and it is from those plots that all the mischiefs have arisen. It suits his purpose to exhibit the consequences without their causes. It is one of the arts of the drama to do so. If the crimes of men were exhibited with their sufferings, the stage effect would sometimes be lost, and the audience would be inclined to approve where it was intended they should commiserate.

After all the investigations that have been made into this intricate affair (the expedition to Versailles), it still remains enveloped in all that kind of mystery which ever accompanies events produced more from a concurrence of awkward circumstances than from fixed design. While the characters of men are forming, as is always the case in Revolutions, there is a reciprocal suspicion, and a disposition to misinterpret each other; and even parties directly opposite in principle will sometimes concur in pushing forward the same movement with very different views, and with the hopes of its producing very different consequences. A great deal of this may be discovered in this embarrassed affair, and yet the issue of the whole was what nobody had in view.

The only things certainly known are that considerable uneasiness was at this time excited at Paris by the delay of the King in not sanctioning and forwarding the decrees of the National Assembly, particularly that of the *Declaration of the Rights of Man,* and the decrees of the *fourth of August,* which contained the foundation principles on which the constitution was to be erected. The kindest, and perhaps the fairest conjecture upon this matter is, that some of the ministers intended to make remarks and observations upon certain parts of them before they were finally sanctioned and sent to the provinces; but be this as it may, the enemies of the Revolution derived hope from the delay, and the friends of the Revolution uneasiness.

During this state of suspense, the *Garde du Corps,* which was composed, as such regiments generally are, of persons much connected with the Court, gave an entertainment at Versailles (October 1) to some foreign regiments then arrived; and when the entertainment was at the height, on a signal given the *Garde du Corps* tore the national cockade from their hats, trampled it under foot, and replaced it with a counter-cockade prepared for the purpose. An indignity of this kind amounted to defiance. It was like declaring war; and if men will give challenges they must expect consequences. But all this Mr. Burke has carefully kept out of sight. He begins his account by saying: "History will record that on the morning of the 6th of October, 1789, the King and Queen of France, after a day of confusion, alarm, dismay, and slaughter, lay down under the pledged security of public faith to indulge nature in a few hours of respite, and troubled melancholy repose." This is neither the sober stile of history, nor the intention of it. It leaves everything to be guessed at and mistaken. One would at least think there had been a battle; and a battle there probably would have been had it not been for the moderating prudence of those whom Mr. Burke involves in his censures. By his keeping the *Garde du Corps* out of sight Mr. Burke has afforded himself the dramatic licence of putting the King and Queen in their places, as if the object of the expedition was against them. But to return to my account—

This conduct of the *Garde du Corps,* as might well be expected, alarmed and enraged the Parisians. The colours of the cause, and the cause itself, were become too united to mistake the intention of the insult, and the Parisians were determined to call the *Garde du Corps* to an account. There was certainly nothing of the cowardice of assassination in marching in the face of day to demand satisfaction, if such a phrase may be used, of a body of armed men who had voluntarily given defiance. But the circumstance which serves to throw this affair into embarrassment is, that the enemies of the Revolution appear to have encouraged it as well as its friends. The one hoped to prevent a civil war by checking it in time, and the other to make one. The hopes of those opposed to the Revolution rested in making the King of their party, and getting him from Versailles to Metz, where they expected to collect a force and set up a standard. We have, therefore, two different objects presenting themselves at the same time, and to be accomplished by the same means; the one to chastise the *Garde du Corps,* which was the object of the Parisians; the other to render the confusion of such a scene an inducement to the King to set off for Metz.

On the 5th of October a very numerous body of women, and men in the disguise of women, collected round the Hotel de Ville or town-hall at Paris, and set off for Versailles. Their professed object was the *Garde du Corps;* but prudent men readily recollect that mischief is more easily begun than ended; and this impressed itself with the more force from the suspicions already stated, and the irregularity of such a cavalcade. As soon, therefore, as a sufficient force could be collected, M. de la Fayette, by orders from the civil authority of Paris, set off after them at the head of twenty thousand of the Paris militia. The Revolution could derive no benefit from confusion, and its opposers might. By an amiable and spirited manner of address he had hitherto been fortunate in calming disquietudes, and in this he was extraordinarily successful; to frustrate, therefore, the hopes of those who might seek to improve this scene into a sort of justifiable necessity for the King's quitting Versailles and withdrawing to Metz, and to prevent at the same time the consequences that might ensue between the *Garde du Corps* and this phalanx of men and women, he forwarded expresses to the King, that he was on his march to Versailles, by the orders of the civil authority of Paris, for the purpose of peace and protection, expressing at the same time the necessity of restraining the *Garde du Corps* from firing upon the people.

He arrived at Versailles between ten and eleven at night. The *Garde du Corps* was drawn up, and the people had arrived some time before, but everything had remained suspended. Wisdom and policy now consisted in changing a scene of danger into a happy event. M. de la Fayette became the mediator between the enraged parties; and the King, to remove the uneasiness which had arisen from the delay already stated, sent for the President of the National Assembly, and signed the Declaration of the

Rights of Man, and such other parts of the Constitution as were in readiness.

It was now about one in the morning. Everything appeared to be composed, and a general congratulation took place. By the beat of drum a proclamation was made that the citizens of Versailles would give the hospitality of their houses to their fellow-citizens of Paris. Those who could not be accommodated in this manner remained in the streets, or took up their quarters in the churches; and at two o'clock the King and Queen retired.

In this state matters passed till the break of day, when a fresh disturbance arose from the censurable conduct of some of both parties, for such characters there will be in all such scenes. One of the *Garde du Corps* appeared at one of the windows of the palace, and the people who had remained during the night in the streets accosted him with reviling and provocative language. Instead of retiring, as in such a case prudence would have dictated, he presented his musket, fired, and killed one of the Paris militia. The peace being thus broken, the people rushed into the palace in quest of the offender. They attacked the quarters of the *Garde du Corps* within the palace, and pursued them throughout the avenues of it, and to the apartments of the King. On this tumult, not the Queen only, as Mr. Burke has represented it, but every person in the palace was awakened and alarmed; and M. de la Fayette had a second time to interpose between the parties, the event of which was that the *Garde du Corps* put on the national cockade, and the matter ended as by oblivion, after the loss of two or three lives.

During the latter part of the time in which this confusion was acting, the King and Queen were in public at the balcony, and neither of them concealed for safety's sake, as Mr. Burke insinuates. Matters being thus appeased, and tranquillity restored, a general acclamation broke forth of *Le Roi à Paris—Le Roi à Paris*—The King of Paris. It was the shout of peace, and immediately accepted on the part of the King. By this measure all future projects of trepanning the King to Metz, and setting up the standard of opposition to the Constitution, were prevented, and the suspicions extinguished. The King and his family reached Paris in the evening, and were congratulated on their arrival by M. Bailley, the Mayor of Paris, in the name of the citizens. Mr. Burke, who throughout his book confounds things, persons, and principles, as in his remarks on M. Bailley's address, confounded time also. He censures M. Bailley for calling it *"un bon jour,"* a good day. Mr. Burke should have informed himself that this scene took up the space of two days, the day on which it began with every appearance of danger and mischief, and the day on which it terminated without the mischiefs that threatened; and that it is to this peaceful termination that M. Bailley alludes, and to the arrival of the King at Paris. Not less than three hundred thousand persons arranged themselves in the procession from Versailles to Paris, and not an act of molestation was committed during the whole march.

Mr. Burke, on the authority of M. Lally Tollendal, a deserter from the National Assembly, says, that on entering Paris, the people shouted "*Tous les évèques à la lanterne.*" All Bishops to be hanged at the lanthorn or lamp-posts. It is surprising that nobody could hear this but Lally Tollendal, and that nobody should believe it but Mr. Burke. It has not the least connection with any part of the transaction, and is totally foreign to every circumstance of it. The Bishops had never been introduced before into any scene of Mr. Burke's drama: why then are they, all at once, and altogether, *tout à coup, et tous ensemble,* introduced now? Mr. Burke brings forward his bishops and his lanthorn-like figures in a magic lanthorn, and raises his scenes by contrast instead of connection. But it serves to show, with the rest of his book, what little credit ought to be given where even probability is set at defiance, for the purpose of defaming; and with this reflection, instead of a soliloquy in praise of chivalry, as Mr. Burke has done, I close the account of the expedition to Versailles.

I have now to follow Mr. Burke through a pathless wilderness of rhapsodies, and a sort of descant upon Governments, in which he asserts whatever he pleases, on the presumption of its being believed, without offering either evidence or reasons for so doing.

Before anything can be reasoned upon to a conclusion, certain facts, principles, or data, to reason from, must be established, admitted, or denied. Mr. Burke, with his usual outrage, abuses the *Declaration of the Rights of Man,* published by the National Assembly of France as the basis on which the constitution of France is built. This he calls "paltry and blurred sheets of paper about the rights of man." Does Mr. Burke mean to deny that *man* has any rights? If he does, then he must mean that there are no such things as rights anywhere, and that he has none himself; for who is there in the world but man? But if Mr. Burke means to admit that man has rights, the question then will be: What are those rights, and how came man by them originally?

The error of those who reason by precedents drawn from antiquity, respecting the rights of man, is that they do not go far enough into antiquity. They do not go the whole way. They stop in some of the intermediate stages of an hundred or a thousand years, and produce what was then done, as a rule for the present day. This is not authority at all. If we travel still farther into antiquity, we shall find a direct contrary opinion and practice prevailing; and if antiquity is to be authority, a thousand such authorities may be produced, successively contradicting each other; but if we proceed on, we shall at last come out right; we shall come to the time when man came from the hand of his Maker. What was he then? Man. Man was his high and only title, and a higher cannot be given him. But of titles I shall speak hereafter.

We are now got at the origin of man, and at the origin of his rights. As to the manner in which the world has been governed from that day to this, it is no farther any concern of ours than to make a proper use of the errors or the improvements which the history of it presents. Those who lived a hundred or a thousand years ago, were then moderns, as we are now. They had *their* ancients, and those ancients had others, and we also shall be ancients in our turn. If the mere name of antiquity is to govern in the affairs of life, the people who are to live an hundred or a thousand years hence, may as well take us for a precedent, as we make a precedent of those who lived an hundred or a thousand years ago. The fact is, that portions of antiquity, by proving everything, establish nothing. It is authority against authority all the way, till we come to the divine origin of the rights of man at the creation. Here our inquiries find a resting-place, and our reason finds a home. If a dispute about the rights of man had arisen at the distance of an hundred years from the creation, it is to this source of authority they must have referred, and it is to this same source of authority that we must now refer.

Though I mean not to touch upon any sectarian principle of religion, yet it may be worth observing, that the genealogy of Christ is traced to Adam. Why then not trace the rights of man to the creation of man? I will answer the question. Because there have been upstart Governments, thrusting themselves between and presumptuously working to *un-make* man.

If any generation of men ever possessed the right of dictating the mode by which the world should be governed for ever, it was the first generation that existed; and if that generation did it not, no succeeding generation can show any authority for doing it, nor can set any up. The illuminating and divine principle of the equal rights of man (for it has its origin from the Maker of man) relates, not only to the living individuals, but to generations of men succeeding each other. Every generation is equal in rights to the generations which preceded it, by the same rule that every individual is born equal in rights with his contemporary.

Every history of the creation, and every traditionary account, whether from the lettered or unlettered world, however they may vary in their opinion or belief of certain particulars, all agree in establishing one point, *the unity of man;* by which I mean that men are all of *one degree,* and consequently that all men are born equal, and with equal natural rights, in the same manner as if posterity had been continued by *creation* instead of *generation,* the latter being only the mode by which the former is carried forward; and consequently every child born into the world must be considered as deriving its existence from God. The world is as new to him as it was to the first man that existed, and his natural right in it is of the same kind.

The Mosaic account of the creation, whether taken as divine authority or merely historical, is fully up to this point, *the unity or equality of man.* The expressions admit of no controversy. "And God said, Let us make man in our own image. In the image of God created he him; male and female created he them." The distinction of sexes is pointed out, but no other distinction is even implied. If this be not divine authority, it is at least historical authority, and shows that the equality of man, so far from being a modern doctrine, is the oldest upon record.

It is also to be observed that all the religions known in the world are founded, so far as they relate to man, one the *unity of man,* as being all of one degree. Whether in heaven or in hell, or in whatever state man may be supposed to exist hereafter, the good and the bad are the only distinctions. Nay, even the laws of Governments are obliged to slide into this principle, by making degrees to consist in crimes and not in persons.

It is one of the greatest of all truths, and of the highest advantage to cultivate. By considering man in this light, and by instructing him to consider himself in this light, it places him in a close connection with all his duties, whether to his Creator or to the creation, of which he is a part; and it is only when he forgets his origin, or, to use a more fashionable phrase, his *birth and family,* that he becomes dissolute. It is not among the least of the evils of the present existing Governments in all parts of Europe that man, considered as man, is thrown back to a vast distance from his Maker, and the artificial chasm filled up by a succession of barriers, or sort of turnpike gates, through which he has to pass. I will quote Mr. Burke's catalogue of barriers that he has set up between Man and his Maker. Putting himself in the character of a herald, he says: *We fear God—we look with* AWE *to kings—with affection to Parliaments—with duty to magistrates—with reverence to priests, and with respect to nobility*. Mr. Burke has forgotten to put in "*chivalry*." He has also forgotten to put in Peter.

The duty of man is not a wilderness of turnpike gates, through which he is to pass by tickets from one to the other. It is plain and simple, and consists but of two points. His duty to God, which every man must feel; and with respect to his neighbour, to do as he would be done by. If those to whom power is delegated do well, they will be respected; if not, they will be despised; and with regard to those to whom no power is delegated, but who assume it, the rational world can know nothing of them.

Hitherto we have spoken only (and that but in part) of the natural rights of man. We have now to consider the civil rights of man, and to show how the one originates from the other. Man did not enter into society to become *worse* than he was before, not to have fewer rights than he had before, but to have those rights better secured. His natural rights are the foundation of all his civil rights. But in order to pursue this distinction with more precision, it will be necessary to mark the different qualities of natural and civil rights.

A few words will explain this. Natural rights are those which appertain to man in right of his existence. Of this kind are all the intellectual rights, or rights of the mind, and also all those rights of acting as an individual for his own comfort and happiness, which are not injurious to the natural rights of others. Civil rights are those which appertain to man in right of his being a member of society. Every civil right has for its foundation some natural right pre-existing in the individual, but to the enjoyment of which his individual power is not, in all cases, sufficiently competent. Of this kind are all those which relate to security and protection.

From this short view it will be easy to distinguish between that class of natural rights which man retains after entering into society and those which he throws into the common stock as a member of society.

The natural rights which he retains are all those in which the *power* to execute it is as perfect in the individual as the right itself. Among this class, as is before mentioned, are all the intellectual rights, or rights of the mind; consequently religion is one of those rights. The natural rights which are not retained, are all those in which, though the right is perfect in the individual, the power to execute them is defective. They answer not his purpose. A man, by natural right, has a right to judge in his own cause; and so far as the right of the mind is concerned, he never surrenders it. But what availeth it him to judge, if he has not power to redress? He therefore deposits this right in the common stock of society, and takes the arm of society, of which he is a part, in preference and in addition to his own. Society *grants* him nothing. Every man is a proprietor in society, and draws on the capital as a matter of right.

From these premisses two or three certain conclusions will follow:

First, *That every civil right grows out of a natural right; or, in other words, is a natural right exchanged.*

Secondly, *That civil power properly considered as such is made up of the aggregate of that class of the natural rights of man, which becomes defective in the individual in point of power, and answers not his purpose, but when collected to a focus becomes competent to the purpose of every one.*

Thirdly, *That the power produced from the aggregate of natural rights, imperfect in power in the individual, cannot be applied to invade the natural rights which are retained in the individual, and in which the power to execute is as perfect as the right itself.*

We have now, in a few words, traced man from a natural individual to a member of society, and shown, or endeavoured to show, the quality of the natural rights retained, and of those which are exchanged for civil rights. Let us now apply these principles to Governments.

In casting our eyes over the world, it is extremely easy to distinguish the Governments which have arisen out of society, or out of the social compact, from those which have not; but to place this in a clearer light than what a single glance may afford, it will be proper to take a review of the several sources from which Governments have arisen and on which they have been founded.

They may be all comprehended under three heads.

First, *Superstition.*

Secondly, *Power.*

Thirdly, *The common interest of society and the common rights of man.*

The first was a Government of Priestcraft, the second of Conquerors, and the third of Reason.

When a set of artful men pretended, through the medium of oracles, to hold intercourse with the Deity, as familiarly as they now march up the back-stairs in European Courts, the world was completely under the government of superstition. The oracles were consulted, and whatever they were made to say became the law; and this sort of Government lasted as long as this sort of superstition lasted.

After these a race of conquerors arose, whose Government, like that of William the Conqueror, was founded in power, and the sword assumed the name of a sceptre. Governments thus established last as long as the power to support them lasts; but that they might avail themselves of every engine in their favour, they united fraud to force, and set up an idol which they called *Divine Right,* and which, in imitation of the Pope, who affects to be spiritual and temporal, and in contradiction to the Founder of the Christian religion, twisted itself afterwards into an idol of another shape, called *Church and State.* The key of St. Peter and the key of the Treasury became quartered on one another, and the wondering cheated multitude worshipped the invention.

When I contemplate the natural dignity of man, when I feel (for Nature has not been kind enough to me to blunt my feelings) for the honour and happiness of its character, I become irritated at the attempt to govern mankind by force and fraud, as if they were all knaves and fools and can scarcely avoid disgust at those who are thus imposed upon.

We have now to review the governments which arise out of society, in contradistinction to those which arose out of superstition and conquest.

It has been thought a considerable advance towards establishing the principles of Freedom to say that Government is a compact between those who govern and those who are governed; but this cannot be true, because it is putting the effect before the cause; for as man must have existed before Governments existed, there necessarily was a time when Governments did not exist, and consequently there could originally exist no governors to form such a compact with. The fact therefore must be that the *individuals themselves,* each in his own personal and sovereign right, *entered into a compact with each other* to produce a Government: and this is the only mode in which Governments have a right to arise, and the only principle on which they have a right to exist.

To possess ourselves of a clear idea of what Government is, or ought to be, we must trace it to its origin. In doing this we shall easily discover that Governments must have arisen either *out* of the people or *over* the people. Mr. Burke has made no distinction. He investigates nothing to its source, and therefore he confounds everything; but he has signified his intention of undertaking, at some future opportunity, a comparison between the Constitutions of England and France. As he thus renders it a subject of controversy by throwing the gauntlet, I take him up on his own ground. It is in high challenges that high truths have the right of appearing; and I accept it with the more readiness because it affords me, at the same time, an opportunity of pursuing the subject with respect to Governments arising out of society.

But it will be first necessary to define what is meant by a *Constitution.* It is not sufficient that we adopt the word; we must fix also a standard signification to it.

A Constitution is not a thing in name only, but in fact. It has not an ideal, but a real existence; and wherever it cannot be produced in a visible form, there is none. A Constitution is a thing *antecedent* to a Government, and a Government is only the creature of a Constitution. The Constitution of a country is not the act of its Government, but of the people constituting a Government. It is the body of elements, to which you can refer, and quote article by article; and which contains the principles on which the Government shall be established, the manner in which it shall be organised, the powers it shall have, the mode of elections, the duration of Parliaments, or by what other name such bodies may be called; the powers which the executive part of the Government shall have; and in fine, everything that relates to the complete organisation of a civil Government, and the principles on which it shall act, and by which it shall be bound. A Constitution, therefore, is to a Government what the laws made afterwards by that Government are to a Court of Judicature. The Court of Judicature does not make the laws, neither can it alter them; it only acts in conformity to the laws made: and the Government is in like manner governed by the Constitution.

Can, then, Mr. Burke produce the English Constitution? If he cannot, we may fairly conclude that though it has been so much talked about, no such thing as a Constitution exists, or ever did exist, and consequently that the people have yet a Constitution to form.

Mr. Burke will not, I presume, deny the position I have already advanced—namely, that Governments arise either *out* of the people or *over* the people. The English Government is one of those which arose out of a conquest, and not out of society, and consequently it arose over the people; and though it has been much modified from the opportunity of circumstances since the time of William the Conqueror, the country has never yet regenerated itself, and is therefore without a Constitution.

I readily perceive the reason why Mr. Burke declined going into the comparison between the English and French Constitutions, because he could not but perceive, when he sat down to the task, that no such thing as a Constitution existed on his side the question. His book is certainly bulky enough to have contained all he could say on this subject, and it would have been the best manner in which people could have judged of their separate merits. Why then has he declined the only thing that was worth while to write upon? It was the strongest ground he could take, if the advantages were on his side, but the weakest if they were not; and his declining to take it is either a sign that he could not possess it or could not maintain it.

Mr. Burke said, in a speech last winter in Parliament, that *when the National Assembly first met in three Orders* (the Tiers Etats, the Clergy, and the Noblesse), *France had then a good constitution.* This shows among numerous other instances, that Mr. Burke does not understand what a constitution is. The persons so met were not a *Constitution,* but a *Convention,* to make a Constitution.

The present National Assembly of France is, strictly speaking, the *personal social compact.* The members of it are the delegates of the Nation in its *original* character; future assemblies will be the delegates of the Nation in its *organised* character. The authority of the present assembly is different to what the authority of future assemblies will be. The authority of the present one is to form a Constitution; the authority of future assemblies will be to legislate according to the principles and forms prescribed in that Constitution; and if experience should hereafter show that alterations, amendments, or additions are necessary, the Constitution will point out the mode by which such things shall be done, and not leave it to the discretionary power of the future Government.

A Government on the principles on which constitutional Governments arising out of society are established, cannot have the right of altering itself. If it had, it would be arbitrary. It might make itself what it pleased; and wherever such a right is set up, it shows there is no Constitution. The act by which the English Parliament empowered itself to sit seven years, shows there is no Constitution in England. It might, by the same self-authority, have sat any greater number of years, or for life. The bill which the present Mr. Pitt brought into Parliament some years ago, to reform Parliament, was on the same erroneous principle. The right of reform is in the nation in its original character, and the constitutional method would be by a general convention elected for the purpose. There is, moreover, a paradox in the idea of vitiated bodies reforming themselves.

From these preliminaries I proceed to draw some comparisons. I have already spoken of the declaration of rights; and as I mean to be as concise as possible, I shall proceed to other parts of the French Constitution.

The Constitution of France says, *That every man who pays a tax of sixty sous per annum* (2s. 6d. English) *is an elector.* What article will Mr. Burke place against this? Can anything be more limited, and at the same time more capricious, than the qualifications of electors are in England? Limited—because not one man in an hundred (I speak much within compass) is admitted to vote. Capricious—because the lowest character that can be supposed to exist, and who has not so much as the visible means of an honest livelihood, is an elector in some places: while in other places, the man who pays very large taxes, and has a known fair character, and the farmer who rents to the amount of three or four hundred pounds a year, with a property on that farm to three or four times that amount, is not admitted to be an elector.

Everything is out of nature, as Mr. Burke says on another occasion. in this strange chaos, and all sorts of follies are blended with all sorts of crimes.

William the Conqueror and his descendants parcelled out the country in this manner, and bribed some parts of it by what they called charters to hold the other parts of it the better subjected to their will. This is the reason why so many of those charters abound in Cornwall; the people were averse to the Government established at the conquest, and the towns were garrisoned and bribed to enslave the country. All the old charters are the badges of this conquest, and it is from this source that the capriciousness of elections arises.

The French Constitution says, *that the number of representatives for any place shall be in a ratio to the number of taxable inhabitants or electors.*

What article will Mr. Burke place against this? The county of Yorkshire, which contains nearly a million of souls, sends two county members; and so does the county of Rutland, which contains not an hundredth part of that number. The town of Old Sarum, which contains not three houses, sends two members; and the town of Manchester, which contains upwards of sixty thousand souls, is not admitted to send any. Is there any principle in these things? Is there anything by which you can trace the marks of freedom, or discover those of wisdom? No wonder then Mr. Burke has declined the comparison, and endeavoured to lead his readers from the point by a wild, unsystematical, display of paradoxical rhapsodies.

The French Constitution says, *that the National Assembly shall be elected every two years.*

What article will Mr. Burke place against this? Why, that the Nation has no right at all in the case; that the Government is perfectly arbitrary with respect to this point; and he can quote for his authority the precedent of a former Parliament.

The French Constitution says, *there shall be no game laws, that the farmer on whose lands wild game shall be found (for it is by the produce of his lands they are fed) shall have a right to what he can take; that there shall be no monopolies of any kind—that all trade shall be free and every man free to follow any occupation by which he can procure an honest livelihood, and in any place, town, or city throughout the Nation.*

What will Mr. Burke say to this? In England, game is made the property of those at whose expense it is not fed; and with respect to monopolies, the country is cut up into monopolies. Every chartered town is an aristocratical monopoly in itself, and the qualification of electors proceeds out of those chartered monopolies. Is this freedom? Is this what Mr. Burke means by a Constitution?

In these chartered monopolies, a man coming from another part of the country is hunted from them as if he were a foreign enemy. An Englishman is not free of his own country; every one of those places presents a barrier in his way, and tells him he is not a freeman—that he has no rights. Within these monopolies are other monopolies. In a city, such for instance as Bath, which contains between twenty and thirty thousand inhabitants, the right of electing representatives to Parliament is monopolized by about thirty-one persons. And within these monopolies are still others. A man even of the same town, whose parents were not in circumstances to give him an occupation, is debarred, in many cases, from the natural right of acquiring one, be his genius or industry what it may.

Are these things examples to hold out to a country regenerating itself from slavery, like France? Certainly they are not, and certain am I, that when the people of England come to reflect upon them they will, like France, annihilate those badges of ancient oppression, those traces of a conquered nation. Had Mr. Burke possessed talents similar to the author of "On the Wealth of Nations," he would have comprehended all the parts which enter into, and, by assemblage, form a constitution. He would have reasoned from minutiæ to magnitude. It is not from his prejudices only, but from the disorderly cast of his genius, that he is unfitted for the subject he writes upon. Even his genius is without a Constitution. It is a genius at random, and not a genius constituted. But he must say something. He has therefore mounted in the air like a balloon, to draw the eyes of the multitude from the ground they stand upon.

Much is to be learned from the French Constitution. Conquest and tyranny transplanted themselves with William the Conqueror from Normandy into England, and the country is yet disfigured with the marks.

May, then, the example of all France contribute to regenerate the freedom which a province of it destroyed!

The French Constitution says *that to preserve the national representation from being corrupt no member of the National Assembly shall be an officer of the Government, a placeman or a pensioner.*

What will Mr. Burke place against this? I will whisper his answer—Loaves and Fishes. Ah! this Government of loaves and fishes has more mischief in it than people have yet reflected on. The National Assembly has made the discovery, and it holds out the example to the world. Had Governments agreed to quarrel on purpose to fleece their countries by taxes, they could not have succeeded better than they have done.

Many things in the English Government appear to me the reverse of what they ought to be and what they are said to be. The Parliament, imperfectly and capriciously elected as it is, is nevertheless *supposed* to hold the national purse in *trust* for the nation; but in the manner in which an English Parliament is constructed it is like a man being both mortgager and mortgagee, and in the case of misapplication of trust it is the criminal sitting in judgment upon himself. If those who vote the supplies are the same persons who receive the supplies when voted, and are to account for the expenditure of those supplies to those who voted them, it is *themselves accountable to themselves,* and the Comedy of Errors concludes with the Pantomime of Hush. Neither the ministerial party nor the Opposition will touch upon this case. The national purse is the common hack which each mounts upon. It is like what the country people call "Ride and tie—You ride a little way, and then I." They order these things better in France.

The French Constitution says *that the right of war and peace is in the nation.*

Where else should it reside but in those who are to pay the expence?

In England this right is said to reside in a *metaphor* shown at the Tower for sixpence or a shilling a piece: so are the lions; and it would be a step nearer to reason to say it resided in them, for any inanimate metaphor is no more than a hat or a cap. We can all see the absurdity of worshipping Aaron's molten calf, or Nebuchadnezzar's golden image; but why do men continue to practise themselves the absurdities they despise in others?

It may with reason be said that in the manner the English Nation is represented it signifies not where this right resides, whether in the Crown or in the Parliament. War is the common harvest of all those who participate in the division and expenditure of public money, in all countries. It is the art of *conquering at home;* the object of it is an increase of revenue; and as revenue cannot be increased without taxes, a pretence must be made for expenditures. In reviewing the history of the English Government, its wars and its taxes, a bystander, not blinded by prejudice nor warped by interest, would declare that taxes were not raised to carry on wars, but that wars were raised to carry on taxes.

Mr. Burke, as a member of the House of Commons, is a part of the English Government; and though he professes himself an enemy to war, he abuses the French Constitution, which seeks to explode it. He holds up the English Government as a model, in all its parts, to France; but he should first know the remarks which the French make upon it. They contend in favour of their own, that the portion of liberty enjoyed in England is just enough to enslave a country by more productively than by despotism, and that as the real object of all despotism is revenue, a Government so formed obtains more than it could do either by direct despotism, or in a full state of freedom, and is, therefore, on the ground of interest, opposed to both. They account also for the readiness which always appears in such Governments for engaging in wars by remarking on the different motives which produce them. In despotic Governments wars are the effect of pride; but in those Governments in which they become the means of taxation, they acquire thereby a more permanent promptitude.

The French Constitution, therefore, to provide against both these evils, has taken away the power of declaring war from kings and ministers, and placed the right where the expence must fall.

When the question of the right of war and peace was agitating in the National Assembly, the people of England appeared to be much interested in the event, and highly to applaud the decision. As a principle it applies as much to one country as another. William the Conqueror, *as a conqueror,* held this power of war and peace in himself, and his descendants have ever since claimed it under him as a right.

Although Mr. Burke has asserted the right of the Parliament at the Revolution to bind and control the Nation and posterity *for ever,* he denies at the same time that the Parliament or the nation had any right to alter what he calls the succession of the Crown in anything but in part, or by a sort of modification. By his taking this ground he throws the case back to the *Norman Conquest,* and by thus running a line of succession springing from William the Conqueror to the present day, he makes it necessary to inquire who and what William the Conqueror was, and where he came from, and into the origin, history and nature of what are called prerogatives. Everything must have had a beginning, and the fog of time and antiquity should be penetrated to discover it. Let, then, Mr. Burke bring forward his William of Normandy, for it is to this origin that his argument goes. It also unfortunately happens, in running this line of succession, that another line parallel thereto presents itself, which is, that if the succession runs in the line of the conquest, the Nation runs in the line of being conquered, and it ought to rescue itself from this reproach.

But it will perhaps be said that tho' the power of declaring war descends in the heritage of the conquest, it is held in check by the right of the Parliament to withhold the supplies. It will always happen when a thing is originally wrong that amendments do not make it right, and it often happens that they do as much mischief one way as good the other, and such is the case here, for if the one rashly declares war as a matter of right, and the other peremptorily withholds the supplies as a matter of right, the remedy becomes as bad, or worse, than the disease. The one forces the Nation to a combat, and the other ties its hands; but the more probable issue is that the contest will end in a collusion between the parties, and be made a screen to both.

On this question of war, three things are to be considered. First, the right of declaring it; secondly, the expence of supporting it; thirdly, the mode of conducting it after it is declared. The French Constitution places the *right* where the *expence* must fall, and this union can be only in the Nation. The mode of conducting it after it is declared, it consigns to the executive department. Were this the case in all countries, we should hear but little more of wars.

Before I proceed to consider other parts of the French Constitution, and by way of relieving the fatigue of argument, I will introduce an anecdote which I had from Dr. Franklin.

While the Doctor resided in France as Minister from America during the war, he had numerous proposals made to him by projectors of every country and of every kind, who wished to go to the land that floweth with milk and honey, America; and among the rest, there was one who offered himself to be King. He introduced his proposal to the Doctor by letter, which is now in the hands of M. Beaumarchais, of Paris—stating first, that as the Americans had dismissed or sent away their King, that they would want another. Secondly, that himself was a Norman. Thirdly, that he was of a more ancient family than the Dukes of Normandy, and of a more honourable descent, his line having never been bastardised. Fourthly, that there was already a precedent in England of Kings coming out of Normandy, and on these grounds he rested his offer, *enjoining* that the Doctor would forward it to America. But as the Doctor neither did this, nor yet sent him an answer, the projector wrote a second letter in which he did not, it is true, threaten to go over and conquer America, but only with great dignity proposed that if his offer was not accepted, an acknowledgment of about £30,000 might be made to him for his generosity! Now, as all arguments respecting succession must necessarily connect that succession with some beginning, Mr. Burke's arguments on this subject go to show that there is no English origin of Kings, and that they are descendants of the Norman line in right of the Conquest. It may, therefore, be of service to his doctrine to make this story known and to inform him, that in case of that natural extinction to which all mortality is subject, Kings may again be had from Normandy, on more reasonable terms than William the Conqueror; and consequently that the good people of England at the Revolution of 1688, *might have done much better,* had such a generous Norman as *this* known *their* wants, and they had known *his!* The chivalry character which Mr. Burke so much admires, is certainly much easier to make a bargain with than a *hard dealing Dutchman.* But to return to the matters of the Constitution.

The French Constitution says, *There shall be no titles;* and, of consequence, all that class of equivocal generation which in some countries is called "*aristocracy*" and in others "*nobility,*" is done away, and the *peer* is exalted into MAN.

Titles are but nicknames, and every nickname is a title. The thing is perfectly harmless in itself, but it marks a sort of foppery in the human character, which degrades it. It reduces man into the diminutive of man in things which are great, and the counterfeit of woman in things which are little. It talks about its fine *blue ribbon* like a girl, and shows its new *garter* like a child. A certain writer, of some antiquity, says: "*When I was a child, I thought as a child; but when I became a man, I put away childish things.*"

It is, properly, from the elevated mind of France that the folly of titles has fallen. It has outgrown the baby cloaths of *Count* and *Duke,* and breeched itself in manhood. France has not levelled, it has exalted. It has put down the dwarf, to set up the man. The punyism of a senseless word like *Duke* or *Count* or *Earl* has ceased to please. Even those who possessed them have disowned the gibberish, and as they outgrew the rickets, have despised the rattle. The genuine mind of man, thirsting for its native home, society, contemns the gewgaws that separate him from it. Titles are like circles drawn by the magician's wand, to contract the sphere of man's felicity. He lived immured within the Bastille of a word, and surveys at a distance the envied life of man.

Is it, then, any wonder that titles should fall in France? Is it not a greater wonder they should be kept up anywhere? What are they? What is their worth, and "what is their amount"?

When we think or speak of a *Judge* or a *General,* we associate with it the ideas of office and character; we think of gravity in the one and bravery in the other; but when we use a word *merely as a title,* no ideas associate with it. Through all the vocabulary of Adam there is not such an animal as a Duke or a Count; neither can we connect any certain idea with the words. Whether they mean strength or weakness, wisdom or folly, a child or a man, or the rider or the horse, is all equivocal. What respect then can be paid to that which describes nothing, and which means nothing? Imagination has given figure and character to centaurs, satyrs, and down to all the fairy tribe; but titles baffle even the powers of fancy, and are a chimerical nondescript.

But this is not all. If a whole country is disposed to hold them in contempt, all their value is gone, and none will own them. It is common opinion only that makes them anything or nothing, or worse than nothing. There is no occasion to take titles away, for they take themselves away when society concurs to ridicule them. This species of imaginary consequence has visibly declined in every part of Europe, and it hastens to its exit as the world of reason continues to rise. There was a time when the lowest class of what are called *nobility* was more thought of than the highest is now, and when a man in armour riding through Christendom in quest of adventures was more stared at than a modern Duke. The world has seen this folly fall, and it has fallen by being laughed at, and the farce of titles will follow its fate. The patriots of France have discovered in good time that rank and dignity in society must take a new ground. The old one has fallen through. It must now take the substantial ground of character, instead of chimerical ground of titles; and they have brought their titles to the altar, and made of them a burnt-offering to Reason.

If no mischief had annexed itself to the folly of titles they would not have been worth a serious and formal destruction, such as the National Assembly have decreed them; and this makes it necessary to inquire farther into the nature and character of Aristocracy.

That, then, which is called Aristocracy in some countries and Nobility in others arose out of the Governments founded upon conquest. It was originally a military order for the purpose of supporting military Government (for such were all Governments founded in conquest); and to keep up a succession of this order for the purpose for which it was established, all the younger branches of those families were disinherited and the law of *primogenitureship* set up.

The nature and character of Aristocracy shows itself to us in this law. It is a law against every law of nature, and Nature herself calls for its destruction. Establish family justice and Aristocracy falls. By the aristocratical law of primogenitureship, in a family of six children five are exposed. Aristocracy has never more than one child. The rest are begotten to be devoured. They are thrown to the cannibal for prey, and the natural parent prepares the unnatural repast.

As everything which is out of nature in man affects, more or less, the interest of society, so does this. All the children which the Aristocracy disowns (which are all except the eldest) are, in general, cast like orphans on a parish, to be provided for by the public, but at a greater charge. Unnecessary offices and places in Governments and Courts are created at the expence of the public to maintain them.

With what kind of parental reflections can the father or mother contemplate their younger offspring? By Nature they are children, and by Marriage they are heirs; but by Aristocracy they are bastards and orphans. They are the flesh and blood of their parents in one line, and nothing akin to them in the other. To restore, therefore, parents to their children, and children to their parents—relations to each other, and man to society—and to exterminate the monster Aristocracy, root and branch—the French Constitution has destroyed the law of PRIMOGENITURESHIP. Here then lies the monster; and Mr. Burke, if he pleases, may write its epitaph.

Hitherto we have considered Aristocracy chiefly in one point of view. We have now to consider it in another. But whether we view it before or behind, or sideways, or any way else, domestically or publicly, it is still a monster.

In France Aristocracy had one feature less in its countenance than what it has in some other countries. It did not compose a body of hereditary legislators. It was not a *"Corporation of Aristocracy,"* for such I have heard M. de la Fayette describe an English House of Peers. Let us then examine the grounds upon which the French Constitution has resolved against having such a House in France.

Because, in the first place, as is already mentioned, Aristocracy is kept up by family tyranny and injustice.

Secondly, because there is an unnatural unfitness in an Aristocracy to be legislators for a Nation. Their ideas of *distributive justice* are corrupted at the very source. They begin life by trampling on all their younger brothers and sisters, and relations of every kind, and are taught and educated so to do. With what ideas of justice or honour can that man enter a house of legislation, who absorbs in his own person the inheritance of a whole family of children or doles out to them some pitiful portion with the insolence of a gift?

Thirdly, because the idea of hereditary legislators is as inconsistent as that of hereditary judges, or hereditary juries; and as absurd as an hereditary mathematician, or an hereditary wise man; and as ridiculous as an hereditary poet-laureate.

Fourthly, because a body of men, holding themselves accountable to nobody, ought not to be trusted by any body.

Fifthly, because it is continuing the uncivilised principle of Governments founded in conquest, and the base idea of man having property in man, and governing him by personal right.

Sixthly, because Aristocracy has a tendency to degenerate the human species. By the universal œconomy of nature it is known, and by the instance of the Jews it is proved, that the human species has a tendency to degenerate, in any small number of persons, when separated from the general stock of society, and inter-marrying constantly with each other. It defeats even its pretended end, and becomes in time the opposite of what is noble in man. Mr. Burke talks of nobility; let him show what it is. The greatest characters the world have known have risen on the democratic floor. Aristocracy has not been able to keep a proportionate pace with Democracy. The artificial NOBLE shrinks into a dwarf before the NOBLE of Nature; and in the few instances of those (for there are some in all countries) in whom nature, as by a miracle, has survived in Aristocracy, THOSE MEN DESPISE IT. But it is time to proceed to a new subject.

The French Constitution has reformed the condition of the clergy. It has raised the income of the lower and middle classes, and taken from the higher. None is now less than twelve hundred livres (fifty pounds sterling) nor any higher than about two or three thousand pounds. What will Mr. Burke place against this? Hear what he says. He says—

"That the people of England can see without pain or grudging, an archbishop precede a duke; they can see a Bishop of Durham, or a Bishop of Winchester in possession of £10,000 a-year; and cannot see why it is in worse hands than estates to the like amount, in the hands of this earl or that 'squire."

And Mr. Burke offers this as an example to France.

As to the first part, whether the Archbishop precedes the Duke, or the Duke the Bishop, it is, I believe, to the people in general, somewhat like *Sternhold* and *Hopkins,* or *Hopkins* and *Sternhold;* you may put which you please first; and as I confess that I do not understand the merits of this case, I will not contend it with Mr. Burke.

But with respect to the latter, I have something to say:—Mr. Burke has not put the case right. The comparison is out of order, by being put between the bishop and the earl or the 'squire. It ought to be put between the bishop and the curate, and then it will stand thus:—

"The people of England can see without pain or grudging, a Bishop of Durham, or a Bishop of Winchester, in possession of ten thousand pounds a-year, and a curate on thirty or forty pounds a-year, or less."

No, sir, they certainly do not see those things without great pain or grudging. It is a case that applies itself to every man's sense of justice, and is one among many that calls aloud for a Constitution.

In France the cry of *"the Church! the Church!"* was repeated as often as in Mr. Burke's book, and as loudly as when the Dissenters' Bill was before the English Parliament; but the generality of the French clergy were not to be deceived by this cry any longer. They knew that whatever the pretence might be it was themselves who were one of the principal objects of it. It was the cry of the high beneficed clergy, to prevent any regulation of income taking place between those of ten thousand pounds a-year and the parish priest. They therefore joined their case to those of every other oppressed class of men, and by this union obtained redress.

The French Constitution *has abolished Tythes,* that source of perpetual discontent between the tythe-holder and the parishioner. When land is held on tythe, it is in the condition of an estate held between two parties; the one receiving one-tenth, and the other nine-tenths of the produce: and consequently, on principles of equity, if the estate can be improved, and made to produce by that improvement double or treble what it did before, or in any other ratio, the expense of such improvement ought to be borne in like proportion between the parties who are to share the produce. But this is not the case in tythes; the farmer bears the whole expence, and the tythe-holder takes a tenth of the improvement, in addition to the original tenth, and by this means gets the value of two-tenths instead of one. This is another case that calls for a Constitution.

The French Constitution hath abolished or renounced *Toleration* and *Intoleration* also, and hath established UNIVERSAL RIGHT OF CONSCIENCE.

Toleration is not the *opposite* of Intolerance, but is the *counterfeit* of it. Both are despotisms. The one assumes to itself the right of withholding Liberty of Conscience, and the other of granting it. The one is the Pope armed with fire and faggot, and the other is the Pope selling or granting indulgences. The former is Church and State, and the latter is Church and traffic.

But Toleration may be viewed in a much stronger light. Man worships not himself, but his Maker; and the liberty of conscience which he claims is not for the service of himself, but of his God. In this case, therefore, we must necessarily have the associated idea of two beings; the *mortal* who renders the worship, and the IMMORTAL BEING who is worshipped. Toleration, therefore, places itself, not between man and man, nor between Church and Church, nor between one denomination of religion and another, but between God and man; between the being who worships, and the BEING who is worshipped; and by the same act of assumed authority by which it tolerates man to pay his worship, it presumptuously and blasphemously sets itself up to tolerate the Almighty to receive it.

Were a Bill brought into any Parliament, entitled, *"An Act to tolerate or grant liberty to the Almighty to receive the worship of a Jew or a Turk,"* or "to prohibit the Almighty from receiving it," all men would startle and call it blasphemy. There would be an uproar. The presumption of toleration in religious matters would then present itself unmasked; but the presumption is not the less because the name of "Man" only appears to those laws, for the associated idea of the *worshipped* and the *worshipper* cannot be separated. Who then art thou, vain dust and ashes! by whatever name thou art called, whether a King, a Bishop, a Church, or a State, a Parliament, or anything else, that obtrudest thine insignificance between the soul of man and its maker? Mind thine own concerns. If he believes not as thou believest, it is a proof that thou believest not as he believeth, and there is no earthly power can determine between you.

With respect to what are called denominations of religion, if every one is left to judge of his own religion, there is no such thing as a religion that is wrong; but if they are to judge of each other's religion, there is no such thing as a religion that is right; and therefore all the world is right, or all the world is wrong. But with respect to religion itself, without regard to names, and as directing itself from the universal family of mankind to the Divine object of all adoration, *it is man bringing to his Maker the fruits of his heart;* and though those fruits may differ from each other like the fruits of the earth, the grateful tribute of every one is accepted.

A Bishop of Durham, or a Bishop of Winchester, or the Archbishop who heads the Dukes, will not refuse a tythe-sheaf of wheat because it is not a cock of hay, nor a cock of hay because it is not a sheaf of wheat; nor a pig, because it is neither one nor the other; but these same persons, under the figure of an established church, will not permit their Maker to receive the varied tythes of man's devotion.

One of the continual choruses of Mr. Burke's book is "Church and State." He does not mean some one particular Church, or some one particular State, but any Church and State; and he uses the term as a general figure to hold forth the political doctrine of always uniting the Church with the State in every country, and he censures the National Assembly for not having done this in France. Let us bestow a few thoughts on this subject.

All religions are in their nature kind and benign, and united with principles of morality. They could not have made proselytes at first by professing anything that was vicious, cruel, persecuting, or immoral. Like everything else, they had their beginning; and they proceeded by persuasion, exhortation, and example. How then is it that they lose their native mildness, and become morose and intolerant?

It proceeds from the connection which Mr. Burke recommends. By engendering the Church with the State, a sort of mule-animal, capable only of destroying, and not of breeding up, is produced, called *The Church established by Law*. It is a stranger, even from its birth, to any parent mother, on whom it is begotten, and whom in time it kicks out and destroys.

The Inquisition in Spain does not proceed from the religion originally professed but from this mule-animal engendered between the Church and the State. The burnings in Smithfield proceeded from the same heterogeneous production; and it was the regeneration of this strange animal in England afterwards that renewed rancour and irreligion among the inhabitants, and that drove the people called Quakers and Dissenters to America. Persecution is not an original feature in *any* religion; but it is always the strongly-marked feature of all law-religions, or religions established by law. Take away the law-establishment and every religion reassumes its original benignity. In America a Catholic priest is a good citizen, a good character, and a good neighbour; an Episcopalian minister is of the same description; and this proceeds, independently of the men, from there being no law establishment in America.

If also we view this matter in a temporal sense we shall see the ill effects it has had on the prosperity of nations. The union of Church and State has impoverished Spain. The revoking the Edict of Nantes drove the silk manufacture from France into England; and Church and State are driving the cotton manufacture from England to America and France. Let then Mr. Burke continue to preach his antipolitical doctrine of Church and State. It will do some good. The National Assembly will not follow his advice, but will benefit by his folly. It was by observing the ill effects of it in England, that America has been warned against it; and it is by experiencing them in France, that the National Assembly have abolished it, and, like America, have established UNIVERSAL RIGHT OF CONSCIENCE AND UNIVERSAL RIGHT OF CITIZENSHIP.

I will here cease the comparison with respect to the principles of the French Constitution, and conclude this part of the subject with a few observations on the organisation of the formal parts of the French and English Governments.

The executive power in each country is in the hands of a person stiled the King; but the French Constitution distinguishes between the King and the Sovereign. It considers the station of King as official, and places Sovereignty in the Nation.

The representatives of the Nation who compose the National Assembly, and who are the legislative power, originate in and from the people by election, as an inherent right in the people. In England it is otherwise; and this arises from the original establishment of what is called its monarchy; for as by the Conquest all the rights of the people or the Nation were absorbed into the hands of the Conqueror, and who added the title of King to that of Conqueror, those same matters which in France are now held as rights in the people, or in the Nation, are held in England as grants from what is called the Crown. The Parliament in England, in both its branches, was erected by patents from the descendants of the Conqueror. The House of Commons did not originate as a matter of right in the people to delegate or elect, but as a grant or boon.

By the French Constitution the Nation is always named before the King. The third article of the Declaration of Rights says: *"The Nation is essentially the source (or fountain) of all sovereignty."* Mr. Burke argues that in England a King is the fountain—that he is the fountain of all honour. But as this idea is evidently descended from the Conquest I shall make no other remark upon it, than that it is the nature of conquest to turn everything upside down; and as Mr. Burke will not be refused the privilege of speaking twice, and as there are but two parts in the figure, the *fountain* and the *spout,* he will be right the second time.

The French Constitution puts the legislative before the executive, the Law before the King; *la Loi, le Roi.* This also is in the natural order of things, because laws must have existence before they can have execution.

A King in France does not, in addressing himself to the National Assembly, say "My Assembly," similar to the phrase used in England of "*my* Parliament"; neither can he use it consistently with the Constitution, nor could it be admitted. There may be propriety in the use of it in England, because as is before mentioned, both Houses of Parliament originated from what is called the Crown by patent or boon—and not from the inherent rights of the people, as the National Assembly does in France, and whose name designates its origin.

The President of the National Assembly does not ask the King *to grant to the Assembly liberty of speech,* as is the case with the English House of Commons. The constitutional dignity of the National Assembly cannot debase itself. Speech is, in the first place, one of the natural rights of man always retained; and with respect to the National Assembly the use of it is their *duty,* and the nation is their *authority.* They were elected by the greatest body of men exercising the right of election the European world ever saw. They sprung not from the filth of rotten boroughs, nor are they the vassal representatives of aristocratical ones. Feeling the proper dignity of their character, they support it. Their parliamentary language, whether for or against the question, is free, bold and manly, and extends to all the parts and circumstances of the case. If any matter or subject respecting the executive department or the person who presides in it (the King) comes before them it is debated on with the spirit of men, and the language of gentlemen; and their answer or their address is returned in the same stile. They stand not aloof with the gaping vacuity of vulgar ignorance, nor bend with the cringe of sycophantic insignificance. The graceful pride of truth knows no extremes, and preserves, in every latitude of life, the right-angled character of man.

Let us now look to the other side of the question. In the addresses of the English Parliaments to their Kings we see neither the intrepid spirit of the old Parliaments of France, nor the serene dignity of the present National Assembly; neither do we see in them anything of the style of English manners, which borders somewhat on bluntness. Since then they are neither of foreign extraction, nor naturally of English production, their origin must be sought for elsewhere, and that origin is the Norman Conquest. They are evidently of the vassalage class of manners, and emphatically mark the prostrate distance that exists in no other condition of men than between the conqueror and the conquered. That this vassalage idea and stile of speaking was not got rid of even at the Revolution of 1688, is evident from the declaration of Parliament to William and Mary in these words: "We do most humbly and faithfully *submit* ourselves, our heirs and posterities, for ever." Submission is wholly a vassalage term, repugnant to the dignity of freedom, and an echo of the language used at the Conquest.

As the estimation of all things is by comparison, the Revolution of 1688, however from circumstances it may have been exalted beyond its value, will find its level. It is already on the wane, eclipsed by the enlarging orb of reason, and the luminous Revolutions of America and France. In less than another century it will go, as well as Mr. Burke's labours, "to the family vault of all the Capulets." Mankind will then scarcely believe that a country calling itself free would send to Holland for a man, and cloath him with power on purpose to put themselves in fear of him, and give him almost a million sterling a year for leave to *submit* themselves and their posterity, like bondmen and bondwomen, for ever.

But there is a truth that ought to be made known: I have had the opportunity of seeing it; which is, *that notwithstanding appearances, there is not any description of men that despise monarchy so much as courtiers.* But they well know, that if it were seen by others, as it is seen by them, the juggle could not be kept up. They are in the condition of men who get their living by a show, and to whom the folly of that show is so familiar that they ridicule it; but were the audience to be made as wise in this respect as themselves, there would be an end to the show and the profits with it. The difference between a republican and a courtier with respect to monarchy, is that the one opposes monarchy, believing it to be something; and the other laughs at it, knowing it to be nothing.

As I used sometimes to correspond with Mr. Burke believing him then to be a man of sounder principles than his book shows him to be, I wrote to him last winter from Paris, and gave him an account how prosperously matters were going on. Among other subjects in that letter, I referred to the happy situation the National Assembly were placed in; that they had taken a ground on which their moral duty and their political interest were united. They have not to hold out a language which they do not themselves believe, for the fraudulent purpose of making others believe it. Their station requires no artifice to support it, and can only be maintained by enlightening mankind. It is not their interest to cherish ignorance, but to dispel it. They are not in the case of a ministerial or an opposition party in England, who, though they are opposed, are still united to keep up the common mystery. The National Assembly must throw open a magazine of light. It must show man the proper character of man; and the nearer it can bring him to that standard, the stronger the National Assembly becomes.

In contemplating the French Constitution, we see in it a rational order of things. The principles harmonize with the forms, and both with their origin. It may perhaps be said as an excuse for bad forms, that they are nothing more than forms; but this is a mistake. Forms grow out of principles, and operate to continue the principles they grow from. It is impossible to practise a bad form on anything but a bad principle. It cannot be ingrafted on a good one; and wherever the forms in any government are bad, it is a certain indication that the principles are bad also.

I will here finally close this subject. I began it by remarking that Mr. Burke had *voluntarily* declined going into a comparison of the English and French Constitutions. He apologises for not doing it, by saying that he had not time. Mr. Burke's book was upwards of eight months in hand, and is extended to a volume of three hundred and sixty-six pages. As his omission does injury to his cause, his apology makes it worse; and men on the English side of the water will begin to consider, whether there is not some radical defect in what is called the English Constitution, that made it necessary for Mr. Burke to suppress the comparison, to avoid bringing it into view.

As Mr. Burke has not written on Constitutions so neither has he written on the French Revolution. He gives no account of its commencement or its progress. He only expresses his wonder. "It looks," says he, "to me, as if I were in a great crisis, not of the affairs of France alone, but of all Europe, perhaps of more than Europe. All circumstances taken together, the French Revolution is the most astonishing that has hitherto happened in the world."

As wise men are astonished at foolish things, and other people at wise ones, I know not on which ground to account for Mr. Burke's astonishment; but certain it is, that he does not understand the French Revolution. It has apparently burst forth like a creation from a chaos, but it is no more the consequence of a mental Revolution priorily existing in France. The mind of the Nation had changed beforehand, and the new order of things has naturally followed the new order of thoughts. I will here, as concisely as I can, trace out the growth of the French Revolution, and mark the circumstances that have contributed to produce it.

The despotism of Louis XIV., united with the gaiety of his Court, and the gaudy ostentation of his character had so humbled, and at the same time so fascinated the mind of France, that the people appear to have lost all sense of their own dignity, in contemplating that of their Grand Monarch; and the whole reign of Louis XV., remarkable only for weakness and effeminacy, made no other alteration than that of spreading a sort of lethargy over the nation, from which it showed no disposition to rise.

The only signs which appeared of the spirit of Liberty during those periods, are to be found in the writings of the French philosophers. Montesquieu, President of the Parliament of Bordeaux, went as far as a writer under a despotic Government could well proceed; and being obliged to divide himself between principle and prudence, his mind often appears under a veil, and we ought to give him credit for more than he has expressed.

Voltaire, who was both the flatterer and the satirist of despotism, took another line. His forte lay in exposing and ridiculing the superstitions which priestcraft, united with statecraft, had interwoven with Governments. It was not from the purity of his principles, or his love of mankind (for satire and philanthropy are not naturally concordant), but from his strong capacity of seeing folly in its true shape, and his irresistible propensity to expose it, that he made those attacks. They were, however, as formidable as if the motives had been virtuous; and he merits the thanks rather than the esteem of mankind.

On the contrary, we find in the writings of Rousseau, and the Abbé Raynal, a loveliness of sentiment in favour of liberty, that excites respect, and elevates the human faculties; but having raised this animation, they do not direct its operations, and leave the mind in love with an object, without describing the means of possessing it.

The writings of Quesnay, Turgot, and the friends of those authors, are of the serious kind; but they laboured under the same disadvantage with Montesquieu; their writings abound with moral maxims of Government, but are rather directed to œconomise and reform the administration of the Government, than the Government itself.

But all those writings and many others had their weight; and by the different manner in which they treated the subject of Government, Montesquieu by his judgment and knowledge of laws, Voltaire by his wit, Rousseau and Raynal by their animation, and Quesnay and Turgot by their moral maxims and systems of œconomy, readers of every class met with something to their taste, and a spirit of political inquiry began to diffuse itself through the Nation at the time the dispute between England the then colonies of America broke out.

In the war which France afterwards engaged in, it is very well known that the nation appeared to be beforehand with the French ministry. Each of them had its view: but those views were directed to different objects; the one sought liberty, and the other retaliation on England. The French officers and soldiers, who after this went to America, were eventually placed in the school of Freedom, and learned the practice as well as the principles of it by heart.

As it was impossible to separate the military events which took place in America from the principles of the American Revolution, the publication of those events in France necessarily connected themselves with the principles which produced them. Many of the facts were in themselves principles; such as the Declaration of American Independence, and the treaty of alliance between France and America, which recognised the natural right of man, and justified resistance to oppression. The then Minister of France, Count Vergennes, was not the friend of America; and it is both justice and gratitude to say, that it was the Queen of France who gave the cause of America a fashion at the French Court. Count Vergennes was the personal and social friend of Dr. Franklin; and the Doctor had obtained, by his sensible gracefulness, a sort of influence over him; but with respect to principles Count Vergennes was a despot.

The situation of Dr. Franklin, as Minister from America to France, should be taken into the chain of circumstances. The diplomatic character is of itself the narrowest sphere of society that man can act in. It forbids intercourse by the reciprocity of suspicion; and a diplomatic is a sort of unconnected atom, continually repelling and repelled. But this was not the case with Dr. Franklin. He was not the diplomatic of a Court, but of MAN. His character as a philosopher had been long established, and his circle of society in France was universal. Count Vergennes resisted for a considerable time the publication in France of the American Constitutions, translated into the French language: but even in this he was obliged to give way to public opinion, and a sort of propriety in admitting to appear what he had undertaken to defend. The American Constitutions were to Liberty what a grammar is to language: they define its parts of speech, and practically construct them into syntax. The peculiar situation of the then Marquis de la Fayette is another link in the great chain. He served in America as an American officer under a commission of Congress, and by the universality of his acquaintance was in close friendship with the civil government of America, as well as with the military line. He spoke the language of the country, entered into the discussions on the principles of Government, and was always a welcome friend at any election.

When the war closed, a vast reinforcement to the cause of Liberty spread itself over France, by the return of the French officers and soldiers. A knowledge of the practice was then joined to the theory; and all that was wanting to give it real existence was opportunity. Man cannot, properly speaking, make circumstances for his purpose, but he always has it in his power to improve them when they occur, and this was the case in France.

M. Neckar was displaced in May, 1781; and by the ill-management of the finances afterwards, and particularly during the extravagant administration of M. Calonne, the revenue of France, which was nearly twenty-four millions sterling per year, was become unequal to the expenditure, not because the revenue had decreased, but because the expences had increased; and this was a circumstance which the Nation laid hold of to bring forward a Revolution. The English Minister, Mr. Pitt, has frequently alluded to the state of the French finances in his budgets, without understanding the subject. Had the French Parliaments been as ready to register edicts for new taxes as an English Parliament is to grant them, there had been no derangement in the finances, nor yet any Revolution; but this will better explain itself as I proceed. It will be necessary here to show how taxes were formerly raised in France. The King, or rather the Court or Ministry acting under the use of that name, framed the edicts for taxes at their own discretion, and sent them to the Parliaments to be registered; for until they were registered by the Parliaments they were not operative. Disputes had long existed between the Court and the Parliaments with respect to the extent of the Parliaments' authority on this head. The Court insisted that the authority of Parliaments went no farther than to remonstrate or show reasons against the tax, reserving to itself the right of determining whether the reasons were well or ill-founded; and in consequence thereof, either to withdraw the edict as a matter of choice, or to *order* it to be enregistered as a matter of authority. The Parliaments on their part insisted that they had not only a right to remonstrate, but to reject; and on this ground they were always supported by the Nation. But to return to the order of my narrative M. Calonne wanted money: and as he knew the sturdy disposition of the Parliaments with respect to new taxes, he ingeniously sought either to approach them by a more gentle means than that of direct authority, or to get over their heads by a manœuvre; and for this purpose he revived the project of assembling a body of men from the several provinces, under the style of an "Assembly of the Notables," or men of note, who met in 1787, and who were either to recommend taxes to the Parliaments, or to act as a Parliament themselves. An assembly under this name had been called in 1617.

As we are to view this as the first practical step towards the Revolution, it will be proper to enter into some particulars respecting it. The Assembly of the Notables has in some places been mistaken for the States-General, but was wholly a different body, the States-General being always by election. The persons who composed the Assembly of the Notables were all nominated by the King, and consisted of one hundred and forty members. But as M. Calonne could not depend upon a majority of this Assembly in his favour, he very ingeniously arranged them in such a manner as to make forty-four a majority of one hundred and forty; to effect this he disposed of them into seven separate committees, of twenty members each. Every general question was to be decided, not by a majority of persons, but by a majority of committees; and as eleven votes would make a majority in a committee, and four committees a majority of seven, M. Calonne, had good reason to conclude that as forty-four would determine any general question he could not be outvoted. But all his plans deceived him, and in the event became his overthrow. The then Marquis de la Fayette was placed in the second committee, of which the Count D'Artois was president, and as money matters were the object, it naturally brought into view every circumstance connected with it. M. de la Fayette made a verbal charge against Calonne for selling crown lands to the amount of two millions of livres, in a manner that appeared to be unknown to the King. The Count D'Artois (as if to intimidate, for the Bastille was then in being) asked the Marquis if he would render the charge in writing? He replied that he would. The Count D'Artois did not demand it, but brought a message from the King to that purport. M. de la Fayette then delivered in his charge in writing, to be given to the King, undertaking to support it. No farther proceedings were had upon this affair, but M. Calonne was soon after dismissed by the King and sent off to England.

As M. de la Fayette, from the experience of what he had seen in America, was better acquainted with the science of civil Government than the generality of the members who composed the Assembly of the Notables could then be, the brunt of the business fell considerably to his share. The plan of those who had a Constitution in view was to contend with the Court on the ground of taxes, and some of them openly professed their object. Disputes frequently arose between Count D'Artois and M. de la

Fayette upon various subjects. With respect to the arrears already incurred the latter proposed to remedy them by accommodating the expences to the revenue instead of the revenue to the expences; and as objects of reform he proposed to abolish the Bastille and all the State prisons throughout the Nation (the keeping of which was attended with great expense), and to suppress *lettres de cachet;* but those matters were not then much attended to, and with respect to *lettres de cachet, a majority of the nobles appeared to be in favour of them.*

On the subject of supplying the Treasury by new taxes the Assembly declined taking the matter on themselves, concurring in the opinion that they had not authority. In a debate on this subject M. de la Fayette said that raising money by taxes could only be done by a National Assembly, freely elected by the people, and acting as their representatives. Do you mean, said the Count D'Artois, the *States-General?* M. de la Fayette replied that he did. Will you, said the Count D'Artois, sign what you say to be given to the King? The other replied that he would not only do this but that he would go farther, and say that the effectual mode would be for the King to agree to the establishment of a Constitution.

As one of the plans had thus failed, that of getting the Assembly to act as a Parliament, the other came into view, that of recommending. On this subject the Assembly agreed to recommend two new taxes to be enregistered by the Parliament: the one a stamp-tax and the other a territorial or sort of land-tax. The two have been estimated at about five millions sterling per annum. We have now to turn our attention to the Parliaments, on whom the business was again devolving.

The Archbishop of Toulouse (since Archbishop of Sens, and now a Cardinal) was appointed to the administration of the finances soon after the dismission of Calonne. He was also made Prime Minister, an office that did not always exist in France. When this office did not exist, the chiefs of the principal departments transacted business immediately with the King, but when a Prime Minister was appointed they did business only with him. The Archbishop arrived to more state-authority than any Minister since the Duke de Choiseul, and the Nation was strongly disposed in his favour; but by a line of conduct scarcely to be accounted for he perverted every opportunity, turned out a despot, and sunk into disgrace, and a Cardinal.

The Assembly of the Notables having broken up, the new Minister sent the edicts for the two taxes recommended by the Assembly to the Parliaments to be enregistered. They of course came first before the Parliament of Paris, who returned for answer, *That with such a revenue as the na-*

tion then supported the name of taxes ought not to be mentioned but for the purpose of reducing them, and threw both the edicts out.

On this refusal the Parliament was ordered to Versailles, where, in the usual form, the King held what under the old Government was called a Bed of Justice; and the two edicts were enregistered in presence of the Parliament by an order of State.

On this the Parliament immediately returned to Paris, renewed their session in form, and ordered the enregistering to be struck out, declaring that everything done at Versailles was illegal. All the members of the Parliament were then served with *Lettres de Cachet,* and exiled to Trois; but as they continued as inflexible in exile as before, and as vengeance did not supply the place of taxes, they were after a short time recalled to Paris.

The edicts were again tendered to them, and the Count D'Artois undertook to act as representative of the King. For this purpose he came from Versailles to Paris, in a train of procession; and the Parliament were assembled to receive him. But show and parade had lost their influence in France; and whatever ideas of importance he might set off with, he had to return with those of mortification and disappointment. On alighting from his carriage to ascend the steps of the Parliament House, the crowd (which was numerously collected) threw out trite expressions saying: "This is Monsieur D'Artois, who wants more of our money to spend." The marked disapprobation which he saw impressed him with apprehensions, and the word *Aux armes!* (*To arms!*) was given out by the officer of the guard who attended him. It was so loudly vociferated, that it echoed through the avenues of the House, and produced a temporary confusion. I was then standing in one of the apartments through which he had to pass, and could not avoid reflecting how wretched was the condition of a disrespected man.

He endeavoured to impress the Parliament by great words, and opened his authority by saying, "The King, our Lord and Master." The Parliament received him very coolly and with their usual determination not to register the taxes; and in this manner the interview ended.

After this a new subject took place: In the various debates and contests which arose between the Court and the Parliaments on the subject of taxes, the Parliament of Paris at last declared that although it had been customary for Parliaments to enregister edicts for taxes as a matter of convenience, the right belonged only to the *States-General;* and that, therefore, the Parliament could go longer with propriety continue to debate on what it had not authority to act. The King after this came to

Paris and held a meeting with the Parliament, in which he continued from ten in the morning till about six in the evening, and, in a manner that appeared to proceed from him as if unconsulted upon with the Cabinet or Ministry, gave his word to the Parliament that the States-General should be convened.

But after this another scene arose, on a ground different from all the former. The Minister and the Cabinet were averse to calling the States-General. They well knew that if the States-General were assembled, themselves must fall; and as the King had not mentioned *any time,* they hit on a project calculated to elude, without appearing to oppose.

For this purpose, the Court set about making a sort of Constitution itself. It was principally the work of M. Lamoignon, Keeper of the Seals, who afterwards shot himself. This new arrangement consisted in establishing a body under the name of a *Cour Plénière,* or full Court, in which were invested all the powers that the Government might have occasion to make use of. The persons composing this Court were to be nominated by the King. The contended right of taxation was given up on the part of the King, and a new criminal code of laws and law proceedings was substituted in the room of the former. The thing, in many points, contained better principles than those upon which the Government had hitherto been administered; but with respect to the *Cour Plénière,* it was no other than a medium through which despotism was to pass, without appearing to act directly from itself.

The Cabinet had high expectations from their new contrivance. The persons who were to compose the *Cour Plénière* were already nominated; and as it was necessary to carry a fair appearance, many of the best characters in the Nation were appointed among the number. It was to commence on the 8th of May, 1788; but an opposition arose to it on two grounds—the one as to principle, the other as to form.

On the ground of principle it was contended that Government had not a right to alter itself, and that if the practice was once admitted it would grow into a principle and be made a precedent for any future alterations the Government might wish to establish; that the right of altering the Government was a national right, and not a right of Government. And on the ground of form it was contended that the *Cour Plénière* was nothing more than a larger Cabinet.

The then Duke de la Rouchefoucault, Luxembourg, De Noailles, and many others, refused to accept the nomination, and strenuously opposed the whole plan. When the edict for establishing this new Court was sent to the Parliaments to be enregistered and put into execution, they resisted also. The Parliament of Paris not only refused, but denied the authority; and the contest renewed itself between the Parliament and the Cabinet more strongly than ever. While the Parliament were sitting in debate on this subject, the Ministry ordered a regiment of soldiers to surround the House and form a blockade. The members sent out for beds and provisions, and lived as in a besieged citadel; and as this had no effect, the commanding officer was ordered to enter the Parliament House and seize them, which he did, and some of the principal members were shut up in different prisons. About the same time a deputation of persons arrived from the province of Brittany to remonstrate against the establishment of the *Cour Plénière,* and those the Archbishop sent to the Bastille. But the spirit of the Nation was not to be overcome, and it was so fully sensible of the strong ground it had taken, that of withholding taxes, that it contented itself with keeping up a sort of quiet resistance, which effectually overthrew all the plans at that time formed against it. The project of the *Cour Plénière* was at last obliged to be given up, and the Prime Minister not long afterwards followed its fate, and M. Neckar was recalled into office.

The attempt to establish the *Cour Plénière* had an effect upon the Nation which itself did not perceive. It was a sort of new form of Government that insensibly served to put the old one out of sight and to unhinge it from the superstitious authority of antiquity. It was Government dethroning Government; and the old one, by attempting to make a new one, made a chasm.

The failure of this scheme renewed the subject of convening the States-General; and this gave rise to a new series of politics.

There was no settled form for convening the States-General; all that it positively meant was a deputation from what was then called the Clergy, the Noblesse, and the Commons; but their numbers or their proportions had not been always the same. They had been convened only on extraordinary occasions, the last of which was in 1614; their numbers were then in equal proportions, and they voted by orders.

It could not well escape the sagacity of M. Neckar, that the mode of 1614 would answer neither the purpose of the then Government nor of the Nation. As matters were at that time circumstanced it would have been too contentious to agree upon anything. The debates would have been endless upon privileges and exemptions, in which neither the wants of the Government nor the wishes of the Nation for a Constitution would have been attended to. But as he did not choose to take the decision upon himself, he summoned again the *Assembly of the Notables* and referred it to them. This body was in general interested in the decision, being chiefly of the Aristocracy and the high-paid Clergy, and they decided in favour of the mode of 1614. This decision was against the sense of the Nation, and also against the wishes of the Court; for the Aristocracy opposed itself to both and contended for privileges independent of either. The subject was then taken up by the Parliament, who recommended that the number of the Commons should be equal to the other two: and they should all sit in one house and vote in one body. The number finally determined on was 1200; 600 to be chosen by the Commons (and this was less than their proportion ought to have been when their worth and consequence is considered on a national scale), 300 by the Clergy, and 300 by the Aristocracy; but with respect to the mode of assembling themselves, whether together or apart, or the manner in which they should vote, these matters were referred.

The election that followed was not a contested election, but an animated one. The candidates were not men, but principles. Societies were formed in Paris, and committees of correspondence and communication established throughout the Nation, for the purpose of enlightening the people, and explaining to them the principles of civil Government; and so orderly was the election conducted, that it did not give rise even to the rumour of tumult.

The States-General were to meet at Versailles in April, 1789, but did not assemble till May. They situated themselves in three separate chambers, or rather the Clergy and the Aristocracy withdrew each into a separate chamber.

The majority of the Aristocracy claimed what they called the privilege of voting as a separate body, and of giving their consent or their negative in that manner; and many of the Bishops and the high-beneficed Clergy claimed the same privilege on the part of their Order.

The *Tiers Etat* (as they were then called) disowned any knowledge of artificial Orders and artificial privileges; and they were not only resolute on this point, but somewhat disdainful. They began to consider Aristocracy as a kind of fungus growing out of the corruption of society, that could not be admitted even as a branch of it; and from the disposition the Aristocracy had shown by upholding *Lettres de Cachet* and in sundry other instances, it was manifest that no Constitution could be formed by admitting men in any other character than as National Men.

After various altercations on this head, the *Tiers Etat* or Commons (as they were then called) declared themselves (on a motion made for that purpose by the Abbé Sieyes) "THE REPRESENTATIVES OF THE NATION; and that the two Orders could be considered but as deputies of corporations, and could only have a deliberative voice when they assembled in a national character with the national representatives."

This proceeding extinguished the stile of *Etats Généraux,* or States-General, and erected it into the stile it now bears, that of *L'Assemblée Nationale,* or National Assembly.

This motion was not made in a precipitate manner. It was the result of cool deliberation, and concerted between the national representatives and the patriotic members of the two chambers, who saw into the folly, mischief and injustice of artificial privileged distinctions.

It was become evident, that no Constitution, worthy of being called by that name, could be established on anything less than a national ground. The Aristocracy had hitherto opposed the despotism of the Court, and affected the language of patriotism; but it opposed it as its rival (as the English Barons opposed King John), and it now opposed the nation from the same motives.

On carrying this motion, the national representatives, as had been concerted, sent an invitation to the two chambers, to unite with them in a National character, and proceed to business.

A majority of the Clergy, chiefly of the parish priests, withdrew from the clerical chamber, and joined the Nation; and forty-five from the other chamber joined in like manner.

There is a sort of secret history belonging to this last circumstance, which is necessary to its explanation; it was not judged prudent that all the patriotic members of the chamber stiling itself the Nobles, should quit it at once; and in consequence of this arrangement, they drew off by degrees, always leaving some, as well to reason the case, as to watch the suspected.

In a little time the numbers increased from forty-five to eighty, and soon after to a greater number; which, with the majority of the clergy, and the whole of the national representatives, put the malcontents in a very diminutive condition.

The King, who, very different from the general class called by that name, is a man of a good heart, showed himself disposed to recommend a union of the three chambers, on the ground the National Assembly had taken; but the malcontents exerted themselves to prevent it, and began now to have another project in view.

Their numbers consisted of a majority of the aristocratical chamber and a minority of the clerical chamber, chiefly of Bishops and high-beneficed Clergy; and these men were determined to put everything to issue, as well by strength as by stratagem.

They had no objection to a Constitution; but it must be such a one as themselves should dictate, and suited to their own views and particular situations.

On the other hand, the Nation disowned knowing anything of them but as citizens, and was determined to shut out all such upstart pretensions. The more Aristocracy appeared, the more it was despised; there was a visible imbecility and want of intellects in the majority—a sort of *je ne sais quoi,* that while it affected to be more than citizen, was less than man. It lost ground from contempt more than from hatred; and was rather jeered at as an ass than dreaded as a lion. This is the general character of Aristocracy, or what are called Nobles or Nobility, or rather No-ability, in all countries.

The plan of the malcontents consisted now of two things; either to deliberate and vote by chambers (or orders), more especially on all questions respecting a Constitution (by which the aristocratical chamber would have had a negative on any article of the Constitution); or, in case they could not accomplish this object, to overthrow the National Assembly entirely.

To effect one or other of these objects they began now to cultivate a friendship with the despotism they had hitherto attempted to rival, and the Count D'Artois became their chief.

The King (who has since declared himself deceived into their measures) held, according to the old form, a *Bed of Justice,* in which he accorded to the deliberation and vote *par tête* (by head) upon several subjects; but reserved the deliberation and vote upon all questions respecting a Constitution to the three chambers separately.

This declaration of the King was made against the advice of M. Neckar, who now began to perceive that he was growing out of fashion at Court, and that another Minister was in contemplation.

As the form of sitting in separate chambers was yet apparently kept up, though essentially destroyed, the national representatives immediately after this declaration of the King resorted to their own chambers to consult on a protest against it; and the minority of the chamber (calling itself the Nobles), who had joined the national cause, retired to a private house to consult in like manner.

The malcontents had by this time concerted their measures with the Court, which Count D'Artois undertook to conduct; and as they saw from the discontent which the declaration excited, and the opposition making against it, that they could not obtain a control over the intended Constitution by a separate vote, they prepared themselves for their final object—that of conspiring against the National Assembly, and overthrowing it.

The next morning the door of the chamber of the National Assembly was shut against them, and guarded by troops; and the members were refused admittance. On this they withdrew to a tennis-ground in the neighbourhood of Versailles, as the most convenient place they could find, and, after renewing their session, took an oath never to separate from each other, under any circumstance whatever, death excepted, until they had established a Constitution. As the experiment of shutting up the house had no other effect than that of producing a closer connection in the members, it was opened again the next day, and the public business recommenced in the usual place.

We now are to have in view the forming of the new Ministry, which was to accomplish the overthrow of the National Assembly. But as force would be necessary, orders were issued to assemble thirty thousand troops, the command of which was given to Broglio, one of the new-intended Ministry, who was recalled from the country for this purpose. But as some management was necessary to keep this plan concealed till the moment it should be ready for execution, it is to this policy that a declaration made by Count D'Artois must be attributed, and which is here proper to be introduced.

It could not but occur, while the malcontents continued to resort to their chambers separate from the National Assembly, that more jealousy would be excited than if they were mixed with it, and that the plot might be suspected. But as they had taken their ground, and wanted a pretence for quitting it, it was necessary that one should be devised. This was effectually accomplished by a declaration made by the Count D'Artois: "That if they took not a part in the National Assembly, the life of the King would be endangered;" on which they quitted their chambers, and mixed with the Assembly, in one body.

At the time this declaration was made, it was generally treated as a piece of absurdity in Count D'Artois, and calculated merely to relieve the outstanding members of the two chambers from the diminutive situation they were put in; and if nothing more had followed, this conclusion would have been good. But as things best explain themselves by their events, this apparent union was only a cover to the machinations which were secretly going on; and the declaration accommodated itself to answer that purpose. In a little time the National Assembly found itself surrounded by troops, and thousands more were daily arriving. On this a very strong declaration was made by the National Assembly to the King, remonstrating on the impropriety of the measure, and demanding the reason. The King, who was not in the secret of this business, as himself afterwards declared, gave substantially for answer, that he had no other object in view than to preserve the public tranquillity, which appeared to be much disturbed.

But in a few days from this time the plot unravelled itself. M. Neckar and the Ministry were displaced, and a new one formed of the enemies of the Revolution; and Broglio, with between twenty-five and thirty thousand foreign troops, was arrived to support them. The mask was now thrown off, and matters were come to a crisis. The event was that in a space of three days the new Ministry and their abettors found it prudent to fly the Nation; the Bastille was taken, and Broglio and his foreign troops dispersed, as is already related in the former part of this work.

There are some curious circumstances in the history of this short-lived Ministry, and this short-lived attempt at a counter-revolution. The Palace of Versailles, where the Court was sitting, was not more than four hundred yards distant from the hall where the National Assembly was sitting. The two places were at this moment like the separate headquarters of two combatant armies; yet the Court was as perfectly ignorant of the information which had arrived from Paris to the National Assembly, as if it had resided at a hundred miles distance. The then Marquis de la Fayette, who (as has been already mentioned) was chosen to preside in the National Assembly on this particular occasion, named by order of the Assembly three successive deputations to the King, on the day and up to the evening on which the Bastille was taken, to inform and confer with him on the state of affairs; but the Ministry, who knew not so much as that it was attacked, precluded all communication, and were solacing themselves how dexterously they had succeeded; but in a few hours the accounts arrived so thick and fast that they had to start from their desks and run. Some set off in one disguise, and some in another, and none in their own character. Their anxiety now was to outride the news, lest they should be stopped, which, though it flew fast, flew not so fast as themselves.

It is worth relating that the National Assembly neither pursued those fugitive conspirators, nor took any notice of them, nor sought to retaliate in any shape whatever.

Occupied with establishing a Constitution founded on the Rights of

Man and the Authority of the People, the only authority on which Government has a right to exist in any country, the National Assembly felt none of those mean passions which mark the character of impertinent Governments, founding themselves on their own authority, or on the absurdity of hereditary succession. It is the faculty of the human mind to become what it contemplates, and to act in unison with its object.

The conspiracy being thus dispersed, one of the first works of the National Assembly, instead of vindictive proclamations, as has been the case with other Governments, published a Declaration of the Rights of Man, as the basis on which the new Constitution was to be built, and which is here subjoined.

Declaration of the Rights of Man and of Citizens

by the National Assembly of France

The representatives of the people of France, formed into a National Assembly, considering that ignorance, neglect, or contempt of human rights, are the sole causes of public misfortunes and corruptions of Government, have resolved to set forth in a solemn declaration, these natural, imprescriptible, and inalienable rights; that this declaration being constantly present to the minds of the members of the body social, they may be ever kept attentive to their rights and their duties; that the acts of the legislative and executive powers of Government, being capable of being every moment compared with the end of political institutions, may be more respected; and also, that the future claims of the citizens, being directed by simple and incontestable principles, may always tend to the maintenance of the Constitution, and the general happiness.

For these reasons the National Assembly doth recognise and declare, in the presence of the Supreme Being, and with the hope of his blessing and favour, the following *sacred* rights of men and of citizens:

I. Men are born, and always continue, free and equal in respect of their rights. Civil distinctions, therefore, can be founded only on public utility.

II. The end of all political associations is the preservation of the natural and imprescriptible rights of man; and these rights are Liberty, Property, Security, and Resistance of Oppression.

III. The Nation is essentially the source of all sovereignty; nor can any individual, or any body of men, be entitled to any authority which is not expressly derived from it.

IV. Political Liberty consists in the power of doing whatever does not injure another. The exercise of the natural rights of every man, has no other limits than those which are necessary to secure to every *other* man the free exercise of the same rights; and these limits are determinable only by the law.

V. The law ought to prohibit only actions hurtful to society. What is not prohibited by the law should not be hindered; nor should any one be compelled to that which the law does not require.

VI. The law is an expression of the will of the community. All citizens have a right to concur, either personally or by their representatives, in its formation. It should be the same to all, whether it protects or punishes; and all being equal in its sight, are equally eligible to all honours, places, and employments, according to their different abilities, without any other distinction than that created by their virtues and talents.

VII. No man should be accused, arrested, or held in confinement, except in cases determined by the law, and according to the forms which it has prescribed. All who promote, solicit, execute, or cause to be executed, arbitrary orders, ought to be punished, and every citizen called upon, or apprehended by virtue of the law, ought immediately to obey, and renders himself culpable by resistance.

VIII. The law ought to impose no other penalties but such as are absolutely and evidently necessary; and no one ought to be punished, but in virtue of a law promulgated before the offence, and legally applied.

IX. Every man being presumed innocent till he has been convicted, whenever his detention becomes indispensable, all rigour to him, more than is necessary to secure his person, ought to be provided against by the law.

X. No man ought to be molested on account of his opinions, not even on account of his religious opinions, provided his avowal of them does not disturb the public order established by the law.

XI. The unrestrained communication of thoughts and opinions being one of the most precious Rights of Man, every citizen may speak, write, and publish freely, provided he is responsible for the abuse of this liberty, in cases determined by the law.

XII. A public force being necessary to give security to the Rights of Men and of citizens, that force is instituted for the benefit of the community and not for the particular benefit of the persons with whom it is intrusted.

XIII. A common contribution being necessary for the support of the public force, and for defraying the other expenses of Government, it ought to be divided equally among the members of the community, according to their abilities.

XIV. Every citizen has a right, either by himself or his representative, to a free voice in determining the necessity of public contributions, the appropriation of them, and their amount, mode of assessment, and duration.

XV. Every community has a right to demand of all its agents an account of their conduct.

XVI. Every community in which a separation of powers and a security of rights is not provided for, wants a Constitution.

XVII. The right to property being inviolable and sacred, no one ought to be deprived of it, except in cases of evident public necessity, legally ascertained, and on condition of a previous just indemnity.

Observations on the Declaration of Rights

The first three articles comprehend in general terms the whole of a Declaration of Rights; all the succeeding articles either originate from them or follow as elucidations. The 4th, 5th, and 6th define more particularly what is only generally expressed in the 1st, 2nd, and 3rd.

The 7th, 8th, 9th, 10th, and 11th articles are declaratory of principles upon which laws shall be constructed, conformable to rights already declared.

But it is questioned by some very good people in France, as well as in other countries, whether the 10th article sufficiently guarantees the right it is intended to accord with; besides which it takes off from the divine dignity of religion, and weakens its operative force upon the mind, to make it a subject of human laws. It then presents itself to man like light intercepted by a cloudy medium, in which the source of it is obscured from his sight, and he sees nothing to reverence in the dusky ray.

The remaining articles, beginning with the twelfth, are substantially contained in the principles of the preceding articles; but in the particular situation which France then was, having to undo what was wrong, as well as to set up what was right, it was proper to be more particular than what in another condition of things would be necessary.

While the Declaration of Rights was before the National Assembly some of its members remarked that if a Declaration of Rights was published it should be accompanied by a declaration of duties. The observation discovered a mind that reflected, and it only erred by not reflecting far enough. A Declaration of Rights is, by reciprocity, a declaration of duties also. Whatever is my right as a man is also the right of another; and it becomes my duty to guarantee as well as to possess.

The first three articles are the basis of Liberty, as well individual as national; nor can any country be called free whose Government does not take its beginning from the principles they contain, and continue to preserve them pure; and the whole of the Declaration of Rights is of more value to the world, and will do more good, than all the laws and statutes that have yet been promulgated.

In the declaratory exordium which prefaces the Declaration of Rights we see the solemn and majestic spectacle of a Nation opening its commission, under the auspices of its Creator, to establish a Government, a scene so new, and so transcendently unequalled by anything in the European world, that the name of a Revolution is diminutive of its character, and it rises into a REGENERATION OF MAN. What are the present Governments of Europe but a scene of iniquity and oppression? What is that of England? Do not its own inhabitants say it is a market where every man has his price, and where corruption is common traffic at the expence of a deluded people? No wonder, then, that the French Revolution is traduced. Had it confined itself merely to the destruction of flagrant despotism perhaps Mr. Burke and some others had been silent. Their cry now is, "It has gone too far"—that is, it has gone too far for them. It stares corruption in the face, and the venal tribe are all alarmed. Their fear discovers itself in their outrage, and they are but publishing the groans of a wounded vice. But from such opposition the French Revolution, instead of suffering, receives an homage. The more it is struck the more sparks it will emit; and the fear is it will not be struck enough. It has nothing to dread from attacks: Truth has given it an establishment, and Time will record it with a name as lasting as his own.

Having now traced the progress of the French Revolution through most of its principal stages, from its commencement to the taking of the Bastille, and its establishment by the Declaration of Rights, I will close the subject with the energetic apostrophe of M. de la Fayette—MAY THIS GREAT MONUMENT, RAISED TO LIBERTY, SERVE AS A LESSON TO THE OPPRESSOR, AND AN EXAMPLE TO THE OPPRESSED!

MISCELLANEOUS CHAPTER

TO PREVENT interrupting the argument in the preceding part of this work, or the narrative that follows it, I reserved some observations to be thrown together into a miscellaneous chapter; by which variety might not be censured for confusion.

Mr. Burke's book is *all* miscellany. His intention was to make an attack on the French Revolution; but instead of proceeding with an orderly arrangement, he has stormed it with a mob of ideas tumbling over and destroying one another.

But this confusion and contradiction in Mr. Burke's book is easily accounted for. When a man in a long cause attempts to steer his course by anything else than some polar truth or principle, he is sure to be lost. It is beyond the compass of his capacity to keep all the parts of an argument together, and make them unite in one issue, by any other means than having this guide always in view. Neither memory nor invention will supply the want of it. The former fails him, and the latter betrays him.

Notwithstanding the nonsense, for it deserves no better name, that Mr. Burke has asserted about hereditary succession, and that a Nation has not a right to form a Government for itself; it happened to fall in his way to give some account of what Government is.

"Government," says he, "is a contrivance of human wisdom."

Admitting that Government is a contrivance of human *wisdom*, it must necessarily follow, that hereditary succession and hereditary rights (as they are called), can make no part of it, because it is impossible to make wisdom hereditary; and on the other hand, that cannot be a wise contrivance, which in its operation may commit the Government of a Nation to the wisdom of an idiot.

The ground which Mr. Burke now takes is fatal to every part of his cause. The argument changes from hereditary rights to hereditary wisdom; and the question is, Who is the wisest man?

He must now shew that every one in the line of hereditary succession was a Solomon, or his title is not good to be a King.

What a stroke has Mr. Burke now made! To use a sailor's phrase, he has swabbed the deck, and scarcely left a name legible in the list of Kings; and he has mowed down and thinned the House of Peers, with a scythe as formidable as Death and Time.

But Mr. Burke appears to have been aware of this retort; and he has taken care to guard against it, by making Government to be not only a contrivance of human wisdom, but a monopoly of wisdom.

He puts the Nation as fools on one side, and places his Government of wisdom, all wise men of Gotham, on the other side; and he then proclaims and says that "Men have a RIGHT that their WANTS should be provided for by this wisdom." Having thus made proclamation, he next proceeds to explain to them what their *wants* are, and also what their *rights* are.

In this he has succeeded dexterously, for he makes their wants to be a *want* of wisdom; but as this is but cold comfort, he then informs them, that they have a *right*—not to any of the wisdom, but to be governed by it; and in order to impress them with a solemn reverence for this monopoly-government of wisdom, and of its vast capacity for all purposes, possible or impossible, right or wrong, he proceeds with astrological mysterious importance, to tell them its powers in these words: "The rights of men in Government are their advantages; and these are often in balance between differences of good; and in compromises sometimes between *good* and *evil,* and sometimes between *evil* and *evil.* Political reason is a *computing principle;* adding—subtracting—multiplying—and dividing, morally and not metaphysically or mathematically, true moral demonstrations."

As the wondering audience, whom Mr. Burke supposes himself talking to, may not understand all this learned jargon, I will undertake to be its interpreter. The meaning, then, good people, of all this, is, That Government is governed by no principle whatever; that it can make evil good, or good evil, just as it pleases. In short, that Government is *arbitrary power.*

But there are some things which Mr. Burke has forgotten.

First, he has not shewn where the wisdom originally came from.

And *Secondly,* he has not shewn by what authority it first began to act.

In the manner he introduces the matter, it is either Government stealing wisdom, or wisdom stealing Government. It is without an origin, and its powers without authority. In short, it is usurpation.

Whether it be from a sense of shame, or from a consciousness of some radical defect in a Government necessary to be kept out of sight, or from both, or from any other cause, I undertake not to determine, but so it is, that a monarchical reasoner never traces Government to its source, or from its source. It is one of the *shibboleths* by which he may be known. A thousand years hence, those who shall live in America or in France, will look back with contemplative pride on the origin of their Governments, and say, *This was the work of our glorious ancestors!* But what can a monarchical talker say? What has he to exult in? Alas! he has nothing. A certain something forbids him to look back to a beginning, lest some robber, or some Robin Hood, should rise from the long obscurity of time and say, *I am the origin.* Hard as Mr. Burke laboured the Regency Bill and hereditary succession two years ago, and much as he dived for precedents, he still had not boldness enough to bring up William of Normandy, and say, *There is the head of the list, there is the fountain of honour;* the son of a prostitute and the plunderer of the English Nation.

The opinions of men with respect to Government are changing fast in all countries. The Revolutions of America and France have thrown a beam of light over the world, which reaches into man. The enormous expense of Governments has provoked people to think, by making them feel; and when once the veil begins to rend, it admits not of repair. Ignorance is of a peculiar nature: and once dispelled, it is impossible to re-establish it. It is not originally a thing of itself, but is only the absence of knowledge; and though man may be *kept* ignorant, he cannot be *made* ignorant.

The mind, in discovering truth, acts in the same manner as it acts through the eye in discovering objects; when once any object has been seen, it is impossible to put the mind back to the same condition it was in before it saw it.

Those who talk of a counter-revolution in France, show how little they understand of man. There does not exist in the compass of language an arrangement of words to express so much as the means of effecting a counter-revolution. The means must be an obliteration of knowledge; and it has never yet been discovered how to make man *unknow* his knowledge, or *unthink* his thoughts.

Mr. Burke is labouring in vain to stop the progress of knowledge; and it comes with the worse grace from him, as there is a certain transaction known in the city which renders him suspected of being a pensioner in a fictitious name. This may account for some strange doctrine he has advanced in his book, which though he points it at the Revolution Society, is effectually directed against the whole Nation.

"The King of England," says he, "holds *his* Crown" (for it does not belong to the Nation, according to Mr. Burke) "in *contempt* of the choice of the Revolution Society, who have not a single vote for a King among them either *individually* or *collectively;* and his Majesty's heirs each in their time and order, will come to the Crown *with the same contempt* of their choice with which his Majesty has succeeded to that which he now wears."

As to who is King in England or elsewhere, or whether there is any King at all, or whether the people choose a Cherokee chief, or a Hessian hussar for a King, it is not a matter that I trouble myself about, be that to themselves; but with respect to the doctrine, so far as it relates to the rights of Men and Nations, it is as abominable as anything ever uttered in the most enslaved country under heaven. Whether it sounds worse to my ear, by not being accustomed to hear such despotism, than what it does to the ear of another person, I am not so well a judge of; but of its abominable principle I am at no loss to judge.

It is not the Revolution Society that Mr. Burke means; it is the Nation, as well in its *original* as in its *representative* character; and he has taken care to make himself understood, by saying that they have not a vote either *collectively* or *individually*. The Revolution Society is composed of citizens of all denominations, and of members of both the Houses of Parliament; and consequently, if there is not a right to a vote in any of the characters, there can be no right to any either in the Nation or in its Parliament. This ought to be a caution to every country how it imports foreign families to be Kings. It is somewhat curious to observe, that although the people of England have been in the habit of talking about Kings, it is always a foreign house of Kings, hating foreigners yet governed by them. It is now the House of Brunswick, one of the petty tribes of Germany.

It has hitherto been the practice of the English Parliaments to regulate what was called the succession (taking it for granted that the Nation then continued to accord to the form of annexing a monarchical branch to its Government; for without this the Parliament could not have had authority to have sent either to Holland or to Hanover, or to impose a King upon the Nation against its will). And this must be the utmost limit to which Parliament can go upon the case; but the right of the Nation goes to the *whole* case, because it has the right of changing its *whole* form of Government. The right of a Parliament is only a right in trust, a right by delegation, and that but from a very small part of the Nation; and one of its Houses has not even this. But the right of the Nation is an original right, as universal as taxation. The Nation is the paymaster of everything, and everything must conform to its general will.

I remember taking notice of a speech in what is called the English House of Peers, by the then Earl of Shelburne, and I think it was at the time he was Minister, which is applicable to this case. I do not directly charge my memory with every particular; but the words and the purport, as nearly as I remember, were these: *That the form of a Government was a matter wholly at the will of a Nation at all times, that if it chose a monarchical form, it had a right to have it so; and if it afterwards chose to be a Republic, it had a right to be a Republic, and to say to a King, "We have no longer any occasion for you."*

When Mr. Burke says that "his Majesty's heirs and successors, each in their time and order, will come to the Crown with the *same contempt* of their choice with which his Majesty has succeeded to that he wears," it is saying too much even to the humblest individual in the country, part of whose daily labour goes towards making up the million sterling a-year, which the country gives the person it stiles a King. Government with insolence is despotism; but when contempt is added it becomes worse; and to pay for contempt is the excess of slavery. This species of Government comes from Germany; and reminds me of what one of the Brunswick soldiers told me, who was taken prisoner by the Americans in the late war: "Ah!" said he, "America is a fine free country, it is worth the people's fighting for; I know the difference by knowing my own; in my country, if the prince says eat straw, we eat straw." God help that country, thought I, be it England or elsewhere, whose liberties are to be protected by German principles of Government, and Princes of Brunswick!

As Mr. Burke sometimes speaks of England, sometimes of France, and sometimes of the world, and of Government in general, it is difficult to answer his book without apparently meeting him on the same ground. Although principles of Government are general subjects, it is next to impossible, in many cases, to separate them from the idea of place and circumstance, and the more so when circumstances are put for arguments, which is frequently the case with Mr. Burke.

In the former part of his book, addressing himself to the people of France, he says: "No experience has taught us (meaning the English), that in any other course or method than that of a *hereditary crown,* can our liberties be regularly perpetuated and preserved sacred as our *hereditary right.*" I asked Mr. Burke, Who is to take them away? M. de la Fayette, in speaking to France, says: "For a Nation to be free, it is sufficient that she wills it." But Mr. Burke represents England as wanting capacity to take care of itself, and that its liberties must be taken care of by a King holding it in "contempt." If England is sunk to this, it is preparing itself to eat straw, as in Hanover, or in Brunswick. But besides the folly of the declaration, it happens that the facts are all against Mr. Burke. It was by the Government *being hereditary,* that the liberties of the people were endangered. Charles I. and James II. are instances of this truth; yet neither of them went so far as to hold the Nation in contempt.

As it is sometimes of advantage to the people of one country to hear what those of other countries have to say respecting it, it is possible that the people of France may learn something from Mr. Burke's book, and that the people of England may also learn something from the answers it will occasion. When Nations fall out about freedom, a wide field of debate is opened. The argument commences with the rights of war, without its evils; and as knowledge is the object contended for, the party that sustains the defeat obtains the prize.

Mr. Burke talks about what he calls an hereditary crown, as if it were some production of Nature; or as if, like time, it had a power to operate, not only independently, but in spite of man; or as if it were a thing or a subject universally consented to. Alas! it has none of those properties, but is the reverse of them all. It is a thing in imagination, the propriety of which is more than doubted, and the legality of which in a few years will be denied.

But, to arrange this matter in a clearer view than what general expression can convey, it will be necessary to state the distinct heads under which (what is called) an hereditary crown, or more properly speaking, an hereditary succession to the Government of a Nation, can be considered; which are—

First, the right of a particular Family to establish itself.

Secondly, the right of a Nation to establish a particular Family.

With respect to the first of these heads, that of a Family establishing itself with hereditary powers on its own authority, and independent of the consent of a Nation, all men will concur in calling it despotism, and it would be trespassing on their understanding to attempt to prove it.

But the second head, that of a Nation establishing a particular Family with hereditary powers, does not present itself as despotism on the first reflection; but if men will permit a second reflection to take place, and carry that reflection forward but one remove out of their own persons to that of their offspring, they will then see that hereditary succession becomes in its consequences the same despotism to others, which they reprobated for themselves. It operates to preclude the consent of the succeeding generations; and the preclusion of consent is despotism. When the person who at any time shall be in possession of a Government, or those who stand in succession to him, shall say to a Nation, I hold this power in "contempt" of you, it signifies not on what authority he pretends to say it. It is no relief, but an aggravation to a person in slavery, to reflect that he was sold by his parent; and as that which heightens the criminality of an act cannot be produced to prove the legality of it, hereditary succession cannot be established as a legal thing.

In order to arrive at a more perfect decision on this head, it will be proper to consider the generation which undertakes to establish a family with hereditary powers, apart and separate from the generations which are to follow; and also to consider the character in which the first generation acts with respect to succeeding generations.

The generation which first selects a person, and puts him at the head of its Government, either with the title of King, or any other distinction, acts its own choice, be it wise or foolish, as a free agent for itself.

The person so set up is not hereditary, but selected and appointed; and the generation who sets him up, does not live under an hereditary Government, but under a Government of its own choice and establishment.

Were the generation who sets him up, and the person so set up, to live for ever, it never could become hereditary succession; and of consequence hereditary succession can only follow on the death of the first parties.

As, therefore, hereditary succession is out of the question with respect to the *first* generation, we have now to consider the character in which *that* generation acts with respect to the commencing generation, and to all succeeding ones.

It assumes a character, to which it has neither right nor title. It changes itself from a legislator to a testator, and affects to make its WILL, which is to have operation after the demise of the makers, to bequeath the Government: and it not only attempts to bequeath, but to establish on the succeeding generation, a new and different form of Government under which itself lived. Itself, as already observed, lived not under a hereditary Government, but under a Government of its own choice and establishment; and it now attempts, by virtue of a will and testament (and which it has not authority to make), to take from the commencing generation, and all future ones, the rights and free agency by which itself acted.

But, exclusive of the right which any generation has to act collectively as a testator, the objects to which it applies itself in this case, are not within the compass of any law, or of any will or testament.

The rights of men in society, are neither devisable or transferable, nor annihilable, but are descendable only, and it is not in the power of any generation to intercept finally, and cut off the descent.

If the present generation, or any other, are disposed to be slaves, it does not lessen the right of the succeeding generation to be free. Wrongs cannot have a legal descent.

When Mr. Burke attempts to maintain that the English Nation did at the Revolution of 1688, most solemnly renounce and abdicate their rights for themselves, and for all their posterity for ever, he speaks a language that merits not reply, and which can only excite contempt for his prostitute principles, or pity for his ignorance.

In whatever light hereditary succession, as growing out of the will and testament of some former generation, presents itself, it is an absurdity. A cannot make a will to take from B the property of B, and give it to C; yet this is the manner in which (what is called) hereditary succession by law operates. A certain former generation made a will to take away the rights of the commencing generation, and all future ones, and convey those rights to a third person, who afterwards comes forward, and tells them, in Mr. Burke's language, that they have *no rights,* that their rights are already bequeathed to him and that he will govern in *contempt* of them. From such principles, and such ignorance, Good Lord deliver the world!

But, after all, what is the metaphor called a Crown, or rather what is Monarchy? Is it a thing, or is it a name, or is it a fraud? Is it a "contrivance of human wisdom," or of human craft to obtain money from a Nation under specious pretences? Is it a thing necessary to a Nation? If it is, in what does that necessity consist, what services does it perform, what is its business, and what are its merits? Does the virtue consist in the metaphor, or in the man? Doth the goldsmith that makes the crown, make the virtue also? Doth it operate like Fortunatus's wishing-cap, or Harlequin's wooden sword? Doth it make a man a conjuror? In fine, what is it? It appears to be a something going much out of fashion, falling into ridicule, and rejected in some countries both as unnecessary and expensive. In America it is considered as an absurdity; and in France it has so far declined, that the goodness of the man and the respect for his personal character, are the only things that preserve the appearance of its existence.

If Government be what Mr. Burke describes it, "a contrivance of human wisdom," I might ask him, if wisdom was at such a low ebb in England, that it was become necessary to import it from Holland and from Hanover? But I will do the country the justice to say, that was not the case; and even if it was, it mistook the cargo. The wisdom of every country, when properly exerted, is sufficient for all its purposes; and there could exist no more real occasion in England to have sent for a Dutch stadtholder, or a German elector, than there was in America to have done a similar thing. If a country does not understand its own affairs, how is a foreigner to understand them, who knows neither its laws, its manners, nor its language? If there existed a man so transcendently wise above all others, that his wisdom was necessary to instruct a Nation, some reason might be offered for Monarchy; but when we cast our eyes about a country, and observe how every part understands its own affairs; and when we look around the world, and see that of all men in it, the race of Kings are the most insignificant in capacity, our reason cannot fail to ask us—What are those men kept for?

If there be anything in Monarchy which we people of America do not understand, I wish Mr. Burke would be so kind as to inform us. I see in America, a Government extending over a country ten times as large as England, and conducted with regularity, for a fortieth part of the expence which Government costs in England. If I ask a man in America if he wants a King, he retorts, and asks me if I take him for an idiot? How is it that this difference happens? are we more or less wise than others? I see in America the generality of people living in a stile of plenty unknown in monarchical countries; and I see that the principle of its Government, which is that of the *equal Rights of Man,* is making a rapid progress in the world.

If Monarchy is a useless thing, why is it kept up anywhere? and if a necessary thing, how can it be dispensed with? That *civil Government* is necessary, all civilised Nations will agree: but civil Government is republican Government. All that part of the Government of England which begins with the office of constable, and proceeds through the department of magistrate, quarter-sessions, and general assize, including trial by jury, is republican Government. Nothing of Monarchy appears in any part of it, except the name which William the Conqueror imposed upon the English, that of obliging them to call him "Their Sovereign Lord the King."

It is easy to conceive that a band of interested men, such as placemen, pensioners, lords of the bedchamber, lords of the kitchen, lords of the necessary-house, and the Lord knows what besides, can find as many reasons for Monarchy as their salaries, paid at the expence of the country, amount to; but if I ask the farmer, the manufacturer, the merchant, the tradesman, and down through all the occupations of life to the common labourer, what service Monarchy is to him? he can give me no answer. If I ask him what Monarchy is, he believes it is something like a sinecure.

Notwithstanding the taxes of England amount to almost seventeen millions a year, said to be for the expences of Government, it is still evident that the sense of the nation is left to govern itself, and does govern itself, by magistrates and juries, almost at its own charge, on republican principles, exclusive of the expence of taxes. The salaries of the judges are almost the only charge that is paid out of the revenue. Considering that all the internal Government is executed by the people, the taxes of England ought to be the lightest of any nation in Europe; instead of which, they are the contrary. As this cannot be counted on the score of civil Government, the subject necessarily extends itself to the Monarchical part.

When the people of England sent for George the First, (and it would puzzle a wiser man than Mr. Burke to discover for what he could be wanted, or what service he could render) they ought at least to have conditioned for the abandonment of Hanover. Besides the endless German intrigues that must follow from a German Elector being King of England, there is a natural impossibility of uniting in the same person the principles of freedom and the principles of despotism, or as it is usually called in England arbitrary power. A German Elector is in his electorate a despot; how then could it be expected that he should be attached to principles of liberty in one country while his interest in another was to be supported by despotism? The union cannot exist; and it might easily have been foreseen that German electors would make German Kings, or in Mr. Burke's words, would assume Government with "contempt." The English have been in the habit of considering a King of England only in the character in which he appears to them; whereas the same person, while the connection lasts, has a home-seat in another country, the interest of which is different to their own, and the principles of the Governments in opposition to each other. To such a person England will appear as a town-residence, and the electorate as the estate. The English may wish, as I believe they do, success to the principles of liberty in France, or in Germany; but a German Elector trembles for the fate of despotism in his electorate; and the Dutchy of Mecklenburg, where the present Queen's family governs, is under the same wretched state of arbitrary power, and the people in slavish vassalage.

There never was a time when it became the English to watch continental intrigues more circumspectly than at the present moment, and to distinguish the politics of the electorate from the politics of the Nation. The Revolution of France has entirely changed the ground with respect to England and France, as Nations; but the German despots, with Prussia at their head, are combining against Liberty; and the fondness of Mr. Pitt for office, and the interest which all his family connections have obtained, do not give sufficient security against this intrigue.

As everything which passes in the world becomes matter for history,

I will now quit this subject, and take a concise review of the state of parties and politics in England, as Mr. Burke has done in France.

Whether the present reign commenced with contempt, I leave to Mr. Burke; certain, however, it is that it had strongly that appearance. The animosity of the English Nation, it is very well remembered, ran high; and, had the true principles of Liberty been as well understood then as they now promise to be, it is probable the Nation would not have patiently submitted to so much. George the First and Second were sensible of a rival in the remains of the Stuarts; and as they could not but consider themselves as standing on their good behaviour, they had prudence to keep their German principles of Government to themselves; but as the Stuart family wore away, the prudence became less necessary.

The contest between rights, and what were called prerogatives, continued to heat the Nation till some time after the conclusion of the American War—when all at once it fell a calm—execration exchanged itself for applause, and Court popularity sprang up like a mushroom in a night.

To account for this sudden transition, it is proper to observe that there are two distinct species of popularity; the one excited by merit, and the other by resentment. As the Nation had formed itself into two parties, and each was extolling the merits of its parliamentary champions for and against prerogative, nothing could operate to give a more general shock than an immediate coalition of the champions themselves. The partisans of each being thus suddenly left in the lurch, and mutually heated with disgust at the measure, felt no other relief than uniting in a common execration against both. A higher stimulus of resentment being thus excited than what the contest on prerogatives occasioned, the Nation quitted all former objects of rights and wrongs, and sought only that of gratification. The indignation at the Coalition so effectually superseded the indignation against the Court as to extinguish it; and without any change of principles on the part of the Court, the same people who had reprobated its despotism united with it to revenge themselves on the Coalition Parliament. The case was not, which they liked best, but which they hated most; and the least hated passed for love. The dissolution of the Coalition Parliament, as it afforded the means of gratifying the resentment of the Nation, could not fail to be popular: and from hence arose the popularity of the Court.

Transitions of this kind exhibit a Nation under the Government of temper, instead of a fixed and steady principle; and having once committed itself, however rashly, it feels itself urged along to justify, by continuance, its first proceeding. Measures which at other times it would censure, it now approves, and acts persuasion upon itself to suffocate its judgment.

On the return of a new Parliament, the new Minister, Mr. Pitt, found himself in a secure majority; and the Nation gave him credit, not out of regard to himself, but because it had resolved to do it out of resentment to another. He introduced himself to public notice by a proposed reform of Parliament, which in its operation would have amounted to a public justification of corruption. The Nation was to be at the expence of buying up the rotten boroughs, whereas it ought to punish the persons who deal in the traffic.

Passing over the two bubbles of the Dutch business and the million a-year to sink the national debt, the matter which most presents itself, is the affair of the Regency. Never, in the course of my observation, was delusion more successfully acted, nor a Nation more completely deceived. But, to make this appear, it will be necessary to go over the circumstances.

Mr. Fox had stated in the House of Commons, that the Prince of Wales, as heir in succession, had a right in himself to assume the Government. This was opposed by Mr. Pitt; and, so far as the opposition was confined to the doctrine, it was just. But the principles which Mr. Pitt maintained on the contrary side were as bad, or worse in their extent, than those of Mr. Fox; because they went to establish an Aristocracy over the Nation, and over the small representation it has in the House of Commons.

Whether the English form of Government be good or bad, is not in this case the question; but, taking it as it stands, without regard to its merits or demerits, Mr. Pitt was farther from the point than Mr. Fox.

It is supposed to consist of three parts: while therefore the Nation is disposed to continue this form, the parts have a *national standing,* independent of each other, and are not the creatures of each other. Had Mr. Fox passed through Parliament, and said that the person alluded to claimed on the ground of the Nation, Mr. Pitt must then have contended (what he called) the right of the Parliament against the right of the Nation.

By the appearance which the contest made, Mr. Fox took the hereditary ground, and Mr. Pitt the parliamentary ground; but the fact is, they both took hereditary ground, and Mr. Pitt took the worse of the two.

What is called the Parliament is made up of two Houses, one of which is more hereditary, and more beyond the controul of the Nation than what the Crown (as it is called) is supposed to be. It is an hereditary Aristocracy, assuming and asserting indefeasible, irrevocable rights and authority, wholly independent of the Nation. Where, then, was the merited popularity of exalting this hereditary power over another hereditary power less independent of the Nation than what itself assumed to be, and of absorbing the rights of the Nation into a House over which it has neither election nor controul?

The general impulse of the Nation was right; but it acted without reflection. It approved the opposition made to the right set up by Mr. Fox, without perceiving that Mr. Pitt was supporting another indefeasible right more remote from the Nation in opposition to it.

With respect to the House of Commons, it is elected but by a small part of the Nation; but were the election as universal as taxation, which it ought to be, it would still be only the organ of the Nation, and cannot possess inherent rights. When the National Assembly of France resolves a matter, the resolve is made in right of the Nation; but Mr. Pitt, on all national questions, so far as they refer to the House of Commons, absorbs the rights of the nation into the organ, and makes the organ into a Nation, and the Nation itself into a cypher.

In a few words, the question on the Regency was a question of a million a-year, which is appropriated to the executive department; and Mr. Pitt could not possess himself of any management of this sum, without setting up the supremacy of Parliament; and when this was accomplished, it was indifferent who should be Regent, as he must be Regent at his own cost. Among the curiosities which this contentious debate afforded, was that of making the Great Seal into a King, the affixing of which to an act was to be royal authority. If, therefore, Royal Authority is a Great Seal, it consequently is in itself nothing; and a good Constitution would be of infinitely more value to the Nation than what the three nominal powers, as they now stand, are worth.

The continual use of the word *Constitution* in the English Parliament shews there is none; and that the whole is merely a form of Government without a Constitution, and constituting itself with what powers it pleases. If there were a Constitution it certainly could be referred to; and the debate on any constitutional point would terminate by producing the Constitution. One member says this is constitution, and another says that is constitution—to-day it is one thing, to-morrow it is something else—while the maintaining the debate proves there is none. Constitution is now the cant word of Parliament, tuning itself to the ear of the Nation. Formerly it was the *universal supremacy of Parliament—the omnipotence of Parliament:* but since the progress of Liberty in France, those phrases have a despotic harshness in their note; and the English Parliament have catched the fashion from the National Assembly, but without the substance, of speaking of *Constitution.*

As the present generation of people in England did not make the Government, they are not accountable for any of its defects; but, that sooner or later, it must come into their hands to undergo a constitutional reformation, is as certain as that the same thing has happened in France. If France, with a revenue of nearly twenty-four millions sterling, with an extent of rich and fertile country above four times larger than England, with a population of twenty-four millions of inhabitants to support taxation, with upwards of ninety millions sterling of gold and silver circulating in the Nation, and with a debt less than the present debt of England —still found it necessary, from whatever cause, to come to a settlement of its affairs, it solves the problem of funding for both countries.

It is out of the question to say how long what is called the English Constitution has lasted, and to argue from thence how long it is to last; the question is, how long can the funding system last? It is a thing but of modern invention, and has not yet continued beyond the life of a man; yet in that short space it has so far accumulated, that, together with the current expences, it requires an amount of taxes at least equal to the whole landed rental of the Nation in acres to defray the annual expenditure. That a Government could not have always gone on by the same system which has been followed for the last seventy years, must be evident to every man; and for the same reason it cannot always go on.

The funding system is not money; neither is it, properly speaking, credit. It, in effect, creates upon paper the sum which it appears to borrow, and lays on a tax to keep the imaginary capital alive by the payment of interest and sends the annuity to market, to be sold for paper already in circulation. If any credit is given, it is to the disposition of the people to pay the tax, and not to the government, which lays it on. When this disposition expires, what is supposed to be the credit of Government expires with it. The instance of France under the former Government, shews that it is impossible to compel the payment of taxes by force, when a whole Nation is determined to take its stand upon that ground.

Mr. Burke, in his review of the finances of France, states the quantity of gold and silver in France, at about eighty-eight millions sterling. In doing this, he has, I presume, divided by the difference of exchange, instead of the standard of twenty-four livres to a pound sterling; for

M. Neckar's statement, from which Mr. Burke's is taken, is *two thousand two hundred millions of livres,* which is upwards of ninety-one millions and a half sterling.

M. Neckar in France, and Mr. George Chalmers of the Office of Trade and Plantation in England, of which Lord Hawkesbury is president, published nearly about the same time (1786) an account of the quantity of money in each Nation, from the returns of the Mint of each Nation. Mr. Chalmers, from the returns of the English Mint at the Tower of London, states the quantity of money in England, including Scotland and Ireland, to be twenty millions sterling.

M. Neckar says that the amount of money in France, re-coined from the old coin which was called in, was two thousand five hundred millions of livres (upwards of one hundred and four millions sterling); and, after deducting for waste, and what may be in the West Indies and other possible circumstances, states the circulation quantity at home to be ninety-one millions and a half sterling; but taking it as Mr. Burke has put it, it is sixty-eight millions more than the national quantity in England.

That the quantity of money in France cannot be under this sum, may at once be seen from the state of the French Revenue, without referring to the records of the French Mint for proofs. The Revenue of France, prior to the Revolution, was nearly twenty-four millions sterling; and as paper had then no existence in France the whole revenue was collected in gold and silver; and it would have been impossible to have collected such a quantity of revenue upon a less national quantity than M. Neckar has stated. Before the establishment of paper in England, the revenue was about a fourth part of the national amount of gold and silver, as may be known by referring to the revenue prior to King William and the quantity of money stated to be in the Nation at that time, which was nearly as much as it is now.

It can be of no real service to a Nation, to impose upon itself, or to permit itself to be imposed upon; but the prejudices of some, and the imposition of others, have always represented France as a Nation possessing but little money—whereas the quantity is not only more than four times what the quantity is in England, but is considerably greater on a proportion of numbers. To account for this deficiency on the part of England, some reference should be had to the English system of funding. It operates to multiply paper, and to substitute it in the room of money, in various shapes; and the more paper is multiplied, the more opportunities are afforded to export the specie; and it admits of a possibility (by extending it to small notes) of increasing paper till there is no money left.

I know this is not a pleasant subject to English readers; but the matters I am going to mention, are so important in themselves, as to require the attention of men interested in money transactions of a public nature. There is a circumstance stated by M. Neckar, in his treatise on the administration of the finances, which has never been attended to in England, but which forms the only basis whereon to estimate the quantity of money (gold and silver) which ought to be in every Nation in Europe, to preserve a relative proportion with other nations.

Lisbon and Cadiz are the two ports into which money, gold and silver, from South America are imported, and which afterwards divide and spread themselves over Europe by means of commerce, and increase the quantity of money in all parts of Europe. If, therefore, the amount of the annual importation into Europe can be known, and the relative proportion of the foreign commerce of the several nations by which it can be distributed can be ascertained, they give a rule sufficiently true, to ascertain the quantity of money which ought to be found in any Nation, at any given time.

M. Neckar shows from the registers of Lisbon and Cadiz, that the importation of gold and silver into Europe, is five millions sterling annually. He has not taken it on a single year, but on an average of fifteen succeeding years, from 1763 to 1777, both inclusive; in which time the amount was one thousand eight hundred million livres, which is seventy-five millions sterling.

From the commencement of the Hanover succession in 1714 to the time Mr. Chalmers published is seventy-two years; and the quantity imported into Europe, in that time, would be three hundred and sixty millions sterling.

If the foreign commerce of Great Britain be stated at a sixth part of what the whole foreign commerce of Europe amounts to (which is probably an inferior estimation to what the gentlemen at the exchange would allow) the proportion which Britain should draw by commerce of this sum, to keep herself on a proportion with the rest of Europe, would be also a sixth part, which is sixty millions sterling; and if the same allowance for waste and accident be made for England which M. Neckar makes for France, the quantity remaining after these deductions would be fifty-two millions; and this sum ought to have been in the Nation (at the time Mr. Chalmers published), in addition to the sum which was in the Nation at the commencement of the Hanover succession, and to have made in the whole at least sixty-six millions sterling; instead of which there were but twenty millions, which is forty-six millions below its proportionate quantity.

As the quantity of gold and silver imported into Lisbon and Cadiz is more exactly ascertained than that of any commodity imported into England, and as the quantity of money coined at the Tower of London is still more positively known, the leading facts do not admit of controversy. Either, therefore, the commerce of England is unproductive of profit, or the gold and silver which it brings in leak continually away by unseen means at the average rate of about three-quarters of a million a year, which, in the course of seventy-two years, accounts for the deficiency; and its absence is supplied by paper.

The Revolution of France is attended with many novel circumstances, not only in the political sphere, but in the circle of money transactions. Among others, it shews that a Government may be in a state of insolvency and a Nation rich. So far as the fact is confined to the late Government of France, it was insolvent; because the Nation would no longer support its extravagance, and therefore it could no longer support itself—but with respect to the Nation all the means existed. A Government may be said to be insolvent every time it applies to the Nation to discharge its arrears. The insolvency of the late Government of France and the present Government of England differed in no other respect than as the disposition of the people differ. The people of France refused their aid to the old Government; and the people of England submit to taxation without enquiry. What is called the Crown in England has been insolvent several times; the last of which, publicly known, was in May, 1777, when it applied to the nation to discharge upwards of £600,000 private debts, which otherwise it could not pay.

It was the error of Mr. Pitt, Mr. Burke, and all those who were unacquainted with the affairs of France, to confound the French Nation with the French Government. The French Nation, in effect, endeavoured to render the late Government insolvent for the purpose of taking Government into its own hands: and it reserved its means for the support of the new Government. In a country of such vast extent and population as France the natural means cannot be wanting; and the political means appear the instant the Nation is disposed to permit them. When Mr. Burke, in a speech last winter in the British Parliament, *cast his eyes over the map of Europe, and saw a chasm that once was France,* he talked like a dreamer of dreams. The same natural France existed as before, and all the natural means existed with it. The only chasm was that which the extinction of despotism had left, and which was to be filled up with a Constitution more formidable in resources than the power which had expired.

Although the French Nation rendered the late Government insolvent, it did not permit the insolvency to act towards the creditors; and the creditors, considering the Nation as the real pay-master, and the Government only as the agent, rested themselves on the Nation, in preference to the Government. This appears greatly to disturb Mr. Burke, as the precedent is fatal to the policy by which Governments have supposed themselves secure. They have contracted debts, with a view of attaching what is called the monied interest of a Nation to their support; but the example in France shews that the permanent security of the creditor is in the Nation, and not in the Government; and that in all possible Revolutions that may happen in Governments, the means are always with the Nation, and the Nation always in existence. Mr. Burke argues that the creditors ought to have abided the fate of the Government which they trusted; but the National Assembly considered them as the creditors of the Nation, and not of the Government—of the master, and not of the steward.

Notwithstanding the late Government could not discharge the current expences, the present Government has paid off a great part of the capital. This has been accomplished by two means; the one by lessening the expences of Government, and the other by the sale of the monastic and ecclesiastical landed estates. The devotees and penitent debauchees, extortioners and misers of former days, to ensure themselves a better world than that which they were about to leave, had bequeathed immense property in trust to the priesthood, for *pious uses;* and the priesthood kept it for themselves. The National Assembly has ordered it to be sold for the good of the whole Nation, and the priesthood to be decently provided for.

In consequence of the Revolution, the annual interest of the debt of France will be reduced at least six millions sterling, by paying off upwards of one hundred millions of the capital; which, with lessening the former expences of Government at least three millions, will place France in a situation worthy the imitation of Europe.

Upon a whole review of the subject, how vast is the contrast! While Mr. Burke has been talking of a general bankruptcy in France, the National Assembly has been paying off the capital of its debt; and while taxes have increased near a million a year in England, they have lowered several millions a year in France. Not a word has either Mr. Burke or Mr. Pitt said about the French affairs, or the state of the French finances, in the present session of Parliament. The subject begins to be too well understood, and imposition serves no longer.

There is a general enigma running through the whole of Mr. Burke's book. He writes in a rage against the National Assembly; but what is he enraged about? If his assertions were as true as they are groundless, and that France, by her Revolution, had annihilated her power, and become what he calls a *chasm,* it might excite the grief of a Frenchman (considering himself as a national man), and provoke his rage against the National Assembly; but why should it excite the rage of Mr. Burke? Alas! it is not the Nation of France that Mr. Burke means, but the COURT; and every Court in Europe, dreading the same fate, is in mourning. He writes neither in the character of a Frenchman nor an Englishman, but in the fawning character of that creature known in all countries, and a friend to none, a COURTIER. Whether it be the Court of Versailles, or the Court of St. James, or of Carlton House, or the Court in expectation, signifies not; for the caterpillar principle of all courts and courtiers are alike. They form a common policy throughout Europe, detached and separate from the interest of Nations; and while they appear to quarrel, they agree to plunder. Nothing can be more terrible to a Court or courtier than the Revolution of France. That which is a blessing to Nations is bitterness to them: and as their existence depends on the duplicity of a country, they tremble at the approach of principles, and dread the precedent that threatens their overthrow.

CONCLUSION

REASON and Ignorance, the opposite to each other, influence the great bulk of mankind. If either of these can be rendered sufficiently extensive in a country, the machinery of Government goes easily on. Reason obeys itself; and Ignorance submits to whatever is dictated to it.

The two modes of Government which prevail in the world, are—

First, Government by election and representation.

Secondly, Government by hereditary succession.

The former is generally known by the name of Republic; the latter by that of Monarchy and Aristocracy.

Those two distinct and opposite forms erect themselves on the two distinct and opposite bases of Reason and Ignorance.

As the exercise of Government requires talents and abilities, and as talents and abilities cannot have hereditary descent, it is evident that hereditary succession requires a belief from man to which his reason cannot subscribe, and which can only be established upon his ignorance; and the more ignorant any country is, the better it is fitted for this species of Government.

On the contrary, Government, in a well-constituted Republic, requires no belief from man beyond what his reason can give.

He sees the *rationale* of the whole system, its origin and its operation; and as it is best supported when best understood, the human faculties act with boldness, and acquire under this form of Government a gigantic manliness.

As, therefore, each of those forms acts on a different base, the one moving freely by the aid of reason, the other by ignorance, we have next to consider, what it is that gives motion to that species of Government which is called Mixed Government, or, as it is sometimes ludicrously stiled, *a Government of this, that, and t'other.*

The moving power in this species of Government is of necessity Corruption. However imperfect election and representation may be in Mixed Governments, they still give exercise to a greater portion of reason than is convenient to the hereditary part; and therefore it becomes necessary to buy the reason up.

A Mixed Government is an imperfect everything, cementing and soldering the discordant parts together by corruption, to act as a whole. Mr. Burke appears highly disgusted that France, since she had resolved on a Revolution, did not adopt what he calls *"A British Constitution;"* and the regretful manner in which he expresses himself on this occasion implies a suspicion that the British Constitution needed something to keep its defects in countenance.

In Mixed Governments there is no responsibility: the parts cover each other till responsibility is lost; and the Corruption which moves the machine, contrives at the same time its own escape. When it is laid down as a maxim, that *a King can do no wrong,* it places him in a state of similar security with that of idiots and persons insane, and responsibility is out of the question with respect to himself.

It then descends upon the Minister, who shelters himself under a majority in Parliament, which by places, pensions, and corruption, he can always command; and that majority justifies itself by the same authority with which it protects the Minister. In this rotatory motion, responsibility is thrown off from the parts, and from the whole.

When there is part in a Government which can do no wrong, it implies that it does nothing; and is only the machine of another power, by whose advice and direction it acts.

What is supposed to be the King in a Mixed Government is the Cabinet; and as the Cabinet is always a part of the Parliament, and the members justifying in one character what they advise and act in another, a Mixed Government becomes a continual enigma; entailing upon a country, by the quantity of corruption necessary to solder the parts, the expence of supporting all the forms of Government at once, and finally resolving them into a Government by committee; in which the advisers, the actors, the approvers, the justifiers, the persons responsible, and the persons not responsible, are the same persons.

By this pantomimical contrivance, and change of scene and character, the parts help each other out in matters which neither of them singly would assume to act.

When money is to be obtained, the mass of variety apparently dissolves, and a profusion of parliamentary praises passes between the parts. Each admires with astonishment, the wisdom, the liberality, and disinterestedness of the other; and all of them breathe a pitying sigh at the burdens of the Nation.

But in a well-constituted Republic, nothing of this soldering, praising, and pitying, can take place; the representation being equal throughout the country, and compleat in itself, however it may be arranged into legislative and executive, they have all one and the same natural source. The parts are not foreigners to each other, like Democracy, Aristocracy, and Monarchy. As there are no discordant distinctions, there is nothing to corrupt by compromise, nor confound by contrivance. Public measures appeal of themselves to the understanding of the Nation, and resting on their own merits, disown any flattering applications to vanity. The continual whine of lamenting the burden of taxes, however successfully it may be practised in Mixed Governments, is inconsistent with the sense and spirit of a Republic. If taxes are necessary, they are of course advantageous, but if they require an apology, the apology itself implies an impeachment. Why, then, is man imposed upon, or why does he impose upon himself?

When men are spoken of as Kings and subjects, or when Government is mentioned under the distinct or combined heads of Monarchy, Aristocracy, and Democracy, what is it that *reasoning* man is to understand by the terms? If there really existed in the world two or more distinct and separate *elements* of human power, we should then see the several origins to which those terms would descriptively apply; but as there is but one species of man, there can be but one element of human power, and that element is man himself. Monarchy, Aristocracy, and Democracy, are but creatures of imagination; and a thousand such may be contrived as well as three.

From the Revolutions of America and France, and the symptoms that have appeared in other countries, it is evident that the opinion of the world is changed with respect to systems of Government, and that Revolutions are not within the compass of political calculations.

The progress of time and circumstances, which men assign to the accomplishment of great changes, is too mechanical to measure the force of the mind, and the rapidity of reflection, by which Revolutions are generated: All the old Governments have received a shock from those that already appear, and which were once more improbable, and are a greater subject of wonder, than a general Revolution in Europe would be now.

When we survey the wretched condition of Man, under the monarchical and hereditary systems of Government, dragged from his home by one power, or driven by another, and impoverished by taxes more than by enemies, it becomes evident that those systems are bad, and that a general Revolution in the principle and construction of Governments is necessary.

What is Government more than the management of the affairs of a Nation? It is not, and from its nature cannot be, the property of any particular man or family, but of the whole community, at whose expence it is supported; and though by force and contrivance it has been usurped into an inheritance, the usurpation cannot alter the right of things. Sovereignty, as a matter of right, appertains to the Nation only, and not to any individual; and a Nation has at all times an inherent, indefeasible right to abolish any form of Government it finds inconvenient, and to establish such as accords with its interest, disposition, and happiness. The romantic and barbarous distinction of men into Kings and subjects, though it may suit the conditions of courtiers, cannot that of citizens; and is exploded by the principle upon which Governments are now founded. Every citizen is a member of the sovereignty; and, as such, can acknowledge no personal subjection: and his obedience can be only to the laws.

When men think of what Government is, they must necessarily suppose it to possess a knowledge of all the objects and matters upon which its authority is to be exercised. In this view of Government, the Republican system, as established by America and France, operates to embrace the whole of a Nation; and the knowledge necessary to the interest of all the parts, is to be found in the centre, which the parts by representation form; but the old Governments are on a construction that excludes knowledge as well as happiness; Government by monks, who know nothing of the world beyond the walls of a convent, is as inconsistent as Government by Kings.

What we formerly called Revolutions, were little more than a change of persons, or an alteration of local circumstances. They rose and fell like things of course, and had nothing in their existence or their fate that could influence beyond the spot that produced them. But what we now see in the world, from the Revolutions of America and France, are a renovation of the natural order of things, a system of principles as universal as truth and the existence of man, and combining moral with political happiness and national prosperity.

I. *Men are born, and always continue, free and equal in respect of their rights. Civil distinctions, therefore, can be founded only on public utility.*

II. *The end of all political associations is the preservation of the natural and imprescriptible rights of man; and these rights are liberty, property, security, and resistance of oppression.*

III. *The Nation is essentially the source of all sovereignty; nor can* ANY INDIVIDUAL, *or* ANY BODY OF MEN, *be entitled to any authority which is not expressly derived from it.*"

In these principles there is nothing to throw a Nation into confusion by inflaming ambition. They are calculated to call forth wisdom and abilities, and to exercise them for the public good, and not for the emolument or aggrandisement of particular descriptions of men or families. Monarchical sovereignty, the enemy of mankind, and the source of misery, is abolished; and sovereignty itself is restored to its natural and original place, the Nation. Were this the case throughout Europe, the cause of wars would be taken away.

It is attributed to Henry the Fourth of France, a man of enlarged and benevolent heart, that he proposed, about the year 1610, a plan for abolishing war in Europe: the plan consisted in constituting an European Congress, or as the French authors stile it, a Pacific Republic, by appointing delegates from the several Nations who were to act as a Court of Arbitration in any disputes that might arise between Nation and Nation.

Had such a plan been adopted at the time it was proposed, the taxes of England and France, as two of the parties, would have been at least ten millions sterling annually to each nation less than they were at the commencement of the French Revolution.

To conceive a cause why such a plan has not been adopted (and that instead of a Congress for the purpose of *preventing* war, it has been called only to *terminate* a war, after a fruitless expence of several years), it will be necessary to consider the interest of Governments as a distinct interest to that of Nations.

Whatever is the cause of taxes to a Nation, becomes also the means of revenue to a Government. Every war terminates with an addition of taxes, and consequently with an addition of revenue; and in any event of war, in the manner they are now commenced and concluded, the power and interest of Governments are increased. War, therefore, from its productiveness, as it easily furnishes the pretence of necessity for taxes and appointments to places and offices, becomes a principal part of the system of old Governments; and to establish any mode to abolish war, however advantageous it might be to Nations, would be to take from such Government the most lucrative of its branches. The frivolous matters upon which war is made shew the disposition and avidity of Governments to uphold the system of war, and betray the motives upon which they act.

Why are not Republics plunged into war, but because the nature of their Government does not admit of an interest distinct from that of the Nation? Even Holland, though an ill-constructed Republic, and with a commerce extending over the world, existed nearly a century without war; and the instant the form of Government was changed in France the republican principles of peace and domestic prosperity and economy arose with the new Government; and the same consequences would follow the same causes in other nations.

As war is the system of Government on the old construction, the animosity which Nations reciprocally entertain is nothing more than what the policy of their Governments excites to keep up the spirit of the system. Each Government accuses the other of perfidy, intrigue, and ambition, as a means of heating the imagination of their respective Nations, and incensing them to hostilities. Man is not the enemy of Man, but through the medium of a false system of Government. Instead, therefore, of exclaiming against the ambition of Kings, the exclamation should be directed against the principle of such Governments; and instead of seeking to reform the individual, the wisdom of a Nation should apply itself to reform the system.

Whether the forms and maxims of Governments which are still in practice were adapted to the condition of the world at the period they were established is not in this case the question. The older they are the less correspondence can they have with the present state of things.

Time, and change of circumstances and opinions, have the same progressive effect in rendering modes of Government obsolete as they have upon customs and manners. Agriculture, commerce, manufactures, and the tranquil arts, by which the prosperity of Nations is best promoted, require a different system of Government, and a different species of knowledge to direct its operations, than what might have been required in the former condition of the world.

As it is not difficult to perceive, from the enlightened state of mankind, that hereditary Governments are verging to their decline, and that Revolutions on the broad basis of national sovereignty and Government by representation, are making their way in Europe, it would be an act of wisdom to anticipate their approach, and produce Revolutions by reason and accommodation, rather than commit them to the issue of convulsions.

From what we now see, nothing of reform in the political world ought to be held improbable. It is an age of Revolutions, in which everything may be looked for.

The intrigue of Courts, by which the system of war is kept up, may provoke a confederation of Nations to abolish it; and an European Congress to patronize the progress of free Government, and promote the civilisation of Nations with each other, is an event nearer in probability than once were the Revolutions and Alliance of France and America.

Rights of Man

PART THE SECOND

To M. de la Fayette

After an acquaintance of nearly fifteen years in difficult situations in America, and various consultations in Europe, I feel a pleasure in presenting to you this small treatise in gratitude for your services to my beloved America, and as a testimony of my esteem for the virtues, public and private, which I know you to possess.

The only point upon which I could ever discover that we differed was not as to principles of Government, but as to time. For my own part I think it equally as injurious to good principles to permit them to linger, as to push them on too fast. That which you suppose accomplishable in fourteen or fifteen years I may believe practicable in a much shorter period. Mankind, as it appears to me, are always ripe enough to understand their true interest, provided it be presented clearly to their understanding, and that in a manner not to create suspicion by anything like self-design, nor offend by assuming too much. Where we would wish to reform we must not reproach.

When the American Revolution was established I felt a disposition to sit serenely down and enjoy the calm. It did not appear to me that any object could afterwards arise great enough to make me quit tranquillity and feel as I had felt before. But when principle, and not place, is the energetic cause of action, a man, I find, is everywhere the same.

I am now once more in the public world; and as I have not a right to contemplate on so many years of remaining life as you have, I am resolved to labour as fast as I can; and as I am anxious for your aid and your company, I wish you to hasten your principles and overtake me.

If you make a campaign the ensuing spring, which it is most probable there will be no occasion for, I will come and join you. Should the campaign commence, I hope it will terminate in the extinction of German despotism, and in establishing the freedom of all Germany. When France shall be surrounded with Revolutions she will be in peace and safety, and her taxes, as well as those of Germany, will consequently become less.

Your sincere,

Affectionate friend,

THOMAS PAINE.

LONDON, *February* 9, 1792.

PREFACE

WHEN I began the chapter entitled the *Conclusion* in the former part of the RIGHTS OF MAN, published last year, it was my intention to have extended it to a greater length; but in casting the whole matter in my mind which I wish to add, I found that it must either make the work too bulky, or contract my plan too much. I therefore brought it to a close as soon as the subject would admit, and reserved what I had further to say to another opportunity.

Several other reasons contributed to produce this determination. I wished to know the manner in which a work, written in a style of thinking and expression different to what had been customary in England, would be received before I proceeded farther. A great field was opening to the view of mankind by means of the French Revolution. Mr. Burke's outrageous opposition thereto brought the controversy into England. He attacked principles which he knew (from information) I would contest with him, because they are principles I believe to be good, and which I have contributed to establish, and conceive myself bound to defend. Had he not urged the controversy, I had most probably been a silent man.

Another reason for deferring the remainder of the work was, that Mr. Burke promised in his first publication to renew the subject at another opportunity, and to make a comparison of which he called the English and French Constitutions. I therefore held myself in reserve for him. He has published two works since, without doing this: which he certainly would not have omitted, had the comparison been in his favour.

In his last work, his "*Appeal from the new to the old Whigs,*" he has quoted about ten pages from the *Rights of Man,* and having given himself the trouble of doing this, says he shall "not attempt in the smallest degree to refute them," meaning the principles therein contained. I am enough acquainted with Mr. Burke to know that he would if he could. But instead of contesting them, he immediately after consoles himself with saying that "he has done his part." He has not done his part. He has not performed his promise of a comparison of Constitutions. He started the controversy, he gave the challenge, and has fled from it; and he is now a *case in point* with his own opinion that "*the age of chivalry is gone!*"

The title as well as the substance of his last work, his "*Appeal,*" is his condemnation. Principles must stand on their own merits, and if they are good they certainly will. To put them under the shelter of other men's authority, as Mr. Burke has done, serves to bring them into suspicion. Mr. Burke is not very fond of dividing his honours, but in this case he is artfully dividing the disgrace.

But who are those to whom Mr. Burke has made his appeal? A set of childish thinkers, and half-way politicians born in the last century, men who went no farther with any principle than as it suited their purpose as a party; the Nation was always left out of the question; and this has been the character of every party from that day to this. The nation sees nothing in such works, or such politics, worthy its attention. A little matter will move a party, but it must be something great that moves a Nation.

Though I see nothing in Mr. Burke's *Appeal* worth taking much notice of, there is, however, one expression upon which I shall offer a few remarks. After quoting largely from the *Rights of Man,* and declining to contest the principles contained in that work, he says: "This will most probably be done (*if such writings shall be thought to deserve any other refutation than that of criminal justice*) by others, who may think with Mr. Burke and with the same zeal."

In the first place, it has not yet been done by anybody. Not less, I believe, than eight or ten pamphlets intended as answers to the former part of the *Rights of Man* have been published by different persons, and not one of them to my knowledge has extended to a second edition, nor are even the titles of them so much as generally remembered. As I am averse to unnecessarily multiplying publications, I have answered none of them. And as I believe that a man may write himself out of reputation when nobody else can do it, I am careful to avoid that rock.

But as I would decline unnecessary publications on the one hand, so would I avoid everything that might appear like sullen pride on the other. If Mr. Burke, or any person on his side the question, will produce an answer to the *Rights of Man* that shall extend to a half, or even to a fourth part of the number of copies to which the *Rights of Man* extended, I will reply to his work. But until this be done, I shall so far take the sense of the public for my guide (and the world knows I am not a flatterer) that what they do not think worth while to read, is not worth mine to answer. I suppose the number of copies to which the first part of the *Rights of Man* extended, taking England, Scotland, and Ireland, is not less than between forty and fifty thousand.

I now come to remark on the remaining part of the quotation I have made from Mr. Burke.

"If," says he, "such writing shall be thought to deserve any other refutation than that of *criminal* justice."

Pardoning the pun, it must be *criminal* justice indeed that should condemn a work as a substitute for not being able to refute it. The greatest condemnation that could be passed upon it would be a refutation. But in proceeding by the method Mr. Burke alludes to, the condemnation would, in the final event, pass upon the criminality of the process and not upon the work, and in this case, I had rather be the author, than be either the judge or the jury that should condemn it.

But to come at once to the point. I have differed from some professional gentlemen on the subject of prosecutions, and I since find they are falling into my opinion, which I will here state as fully, but as concisely as I can.

I will first put a case with respect to any law, and then compare it with a Government, or with what in England is, or has been, called a Constitution.

It would be an act of despotism, or what in England is called arbitrary power, to make a law to prohibit investigating the principles, good or bad, on which such a law, or any other, is founded.

If a law be bad it is one thing to oppose the practice of it, but it is quite a different thing to expose its errors, to reason on its defects, and to shew cause how it should be repealed, or why another ought to be substituted in its place. I have always held it an opinion (making it also my practice) that it is better to obey a bad law, making use at the same time of every argument to show its errors and procure its repeal, than forcibly to violate it; because the precedent of breaking a bad law might weaken the force, and lead to a discretionary violation of those which are good.

The case is the same with respect to principles and forms of Government, or to what are called Constitutions and the parts of which they are composed.

It is for the good of Nations and not for the emolument or aggrandisement of particular individuals, that Government ought to be established, and that mankind are at the expence of supporting it. The defects of every Government and Constitution, both as to principle and form, must on a parity of reasoning, be as open to discussion as the defects of a law, and it is a duty which every man owes to society to point them out. When those defects, and the means of remedying them, are generally seen by a Nation, that Nation will reform its Government or its Constitution in the one case, as the Government repealed or reformed the law in the other. The operation of Government is restricted to the making and the administering of laws; but it is to a Nation that the right of forming or reforming, generating or regenerating, Constitutions and Governments belong; and consequently those subjects, as subjects of investigation, are always before a country *as a matter of right,* and cannot, without invading the general rights of that country, be made subjects for prosecution. On this ground I will meet Mr. Burke whenever he pleases. It is better that the whole argument should come out than to seek to stifle it. It was himself that opened the controversy, and he ought not to desert it.

I do not believe that Monarchy and Aristocracy will continue seven years longer in any of the enlightened countries in Europe. If better reasons can be shewn for them than against them, they will stand; if the contrary, they will not. Mankind are not now to be told they shall not think or they shall not read; and publications that go no further than to investigate principles of Government, to invite men to reason and to reflect and to shew the errors and excellencies of different systems, have a right to appear. If they do not excite attention, they are not worth the trouble of a prosecution, and if they do the prosecution will amount to nothing, since it cannot amount to a prohibition of reading. This would be a sentence on the public instead of the author, and would also be the most effectual mode of making or hastening Revolutions.

On all cases that apply universally to a Nation with respect to systems of Government, a jury of *twelve* men is not competent to decide. Where there are no witnesses to be examined, no facts to be proved, and where the whole matter is before the whole public, and the merits or demerits of it resting on their opinion; and where there is nothing to be known in a court, but what everybody knows out of it, any twelve men is equally as good a jury as the other, and would most probably reverse another's verdict; or, from the variety of their opinions, not be able to form one. It is one case whether a Nation approve a work or a plan: but it is quite another case whether it will commit to any such jury the power of determining whether that Nation have a right to or shall reform its Government or not. I mention those cases that Mr. Burke may see I have not written on Government without reflecting on what is Law, as well as on what are Rights. The only effectual jury in such cases would be a convention of the whole Nation fairly elected; for in all such cases the whole Nation is the vicinage. If Mr. Burke will propose such a jury I will waive all privileges of being the citizen of another country, and, defending its principles, abide the issue, provided he will do the same; for my opinion is that his work and his principles would be condemned instead of mine.

As to the prejudices which men have from education and habit, in favour of any particular form or system of Government, those prejudices have yet to stand the test of reason and reflection. In fact, such prejudices are nothing. No man is prejudiced in favour of a thing knowing it to be wrong. He is attached to it on the belief of its being right, and when he sees it is not so, the prejudice will be gone. We have but a defective idea of what prejudice is. It might be said that until men think for themselves the whole is prejudice, and *not opinion:* for that only is opinion which is the result of reason and reflection. I offer this remark that Mr. Burke may not confide too much in what have been the customary prejudices of the country.

I do not believe that the people of England have ever been fairly and candidly dealt by. They have been imposed on by parties and by men assuming the character of leaders. It is time that the Nation should rise above those trifles. It is time to dismiss that inattention which has so long been the encouraging cause of stretching taxation to excess. It is time to dismiss all those songs and toasts which are calculated to enslave, and operate to suffocate reflection. On all such subjects men have but to think and they will neither act wrong nor be misled. To say that any people are not fit for freedom is to make poverty their choice, and to say they had rather be loaded with taxes than not. If such a case could be proved it would equally prove that those who govern are not fit to govern them, for they are a part of the same national mass.

But admitting Governments to be changed all over Europe; it certainly may be done without convulsion or revenge. It is not worth making changes or Revolutions, unless it be for some great national benefit: and when this shall appear to a Nation the danger will be as in America and France, to those who oppose; and with this reflection I close my preface.

THOMAS PAINE.

LONDON, *February* 9, 1792.

INTRODUCTION

WHAT Archimedes said of the mechanical powers may be applied to reason and liberty. *"Had we,"* said he, *"a place to stand upon, we might raise the world."*

The Revolution of America presented in politics what was only theory in mechanics. So deeply rooted were all the Governments of the old world, and so effectually had the tyranny and the antiquity of habit established itself over the mind, that no beginning could be made in Asia, Africa, or Europe, to reform the political condition of man. Freedom had been hunted round the globe; reason was considered as rebellion; and the slavery of fear had made men afraid to think.

But such is the irresistible nature of truth that all it asks, and all it wants, is the liberty of appearing. The sun needs no inscription to distinguish him from darkness; and no sooner did the American Governments display themselves to the world than despotism felt a shock and man began to contemplate redress.

The Independence of America, considered merely as a separation from England, would have been a matter of but little importance, had it not been accompanied by a Revolution in the principles and practice of Governments. She made a stand, not for herself only, but for the world, and looked beyond the advantages herself could receive. Even the Hessian, though hired to fight against her, may live to bless his defeat; and England, condemning the viciousness of its Government, rejoice in its miscarriage.

As America was the only spot in the political world where the principles of universal reformation could begin, so also was it the best in the natural world. An assemblage of circumstances conspired not only to give birth, but to add gigantic maturity to its principles. The scene which that country presents to the eye of a spectator has something in it which generates and encourages great ideas. Nature appears to him in magnitude. The mighty objects he beholds act upon his mind by enlarging it, and he partakes of the greatness he contemplates. Its first settlers were emigrants from different European Nations, and of diversified professions of religion, retiring from the governmental persecutions of the old world, and meeting in the new, not as enemies, but as brothers. The wants which necessarily accompany the cultivation of a wilderness produced among them a state of society which countries long harassed by the quarrels and intrigues of Governments had neglected to cherish. In such a situation man becomes what he ought. He sees his species, not with the inhuman idea of a natural enemy, but as kindred; and the example shows to the artificial world that man must go back to nature for information.

From the rapid progress which America makes in every species of improvement, it is rational to conclude that, if the Governments of Asia, Africa, and Europe had begun on a principle similar to that of America, or had not been very early corrupted therefrom, those countries must by this time have been in a far superior condition to what they are. Age after age has passed away, for no other purpose than to behold their wretchedness. Could we suppose a spectator who knew nothing of the world, and who was put into it merely to make his observations, he would take a great part of the old world to be new, just struggling with the difficulties and hardships of an infant settlement. He could not suppose that the hordes of miserable poor with which old countries abound could be any other than those who had not yet had time to provide for themselves. Little would he think they were the consequence of what in such countries is called Government.

If, from the more wretched parts of the old world, we look at those which are in an advanced stage of improvement, we still find the greedy hand of Government thrusting itself into every corner and crevice of industry, and grasping the spoil of the multitude. Invention is continually exercised to furnish new pretences for revenue and taxation. It watches prosperity as its prey, and permits none to escape without a tribute.

As Revolutions have begun (and as the probability is always greater against a thing beginning than of proceeding after it has begun), it is natural to expect that other Revolutions will follow. The amazing and still increasing expences with which old Governments are conducted, the numerous wars they engage in or provoke, the embarrassments they throw in the way of universal civilization and commerce, and the oppression and usurpation they practise at home, have wearied out the patience and exhausted the property of the world. In such a situation and with the examples already existing, Revolutions are to be looked for. They are become subjects of universal conversation, and may be considered as the *Order of the Day.*

If systems of Government can be introduced less expencive and more productive of general happiness than those which have existed, all attempts to oppose their progress will in the end be fruitless. Reason, like time, will make its own way, and prejudice will fall in a combat with interest. If universal peace, civilization, and commerce are ever to be the happy lot of man, it cannot be accomplished but by a Revolution in the system of Governments. All the monarchical Governments are military. War is their trade, plunder and revenue their objects. While such Governments continue, peace has not the absolute security of a day. What is the history of all monarchical Governments but a disgustful picture of human wretchedness, and the accidental respite of a few years' repose? Wearied with war, and tired with human butchery, they sat down to rest, and called it peace. This certainly is not the condition that heaven intended for man; and if *this be Monarchy,* well might Monarchy be reckoned among the sins of the Jews.

The Revolutions which formerly took place in the world had nothing in them that interested the bulk of mankind. They extended only to a change of persons and measures, but not of principles, and rose or fell among the common transactions of the moment. What we now behold may not improperly be called a *"counter Revolution."* Conquest and tyranny, at some early period, dispossessed man of his rights, and he is now recovering them. And as the tide of all human affairs has its ebb and flow in directions contrary to each other, so also is it in this. Government founded on a *moral theory, on a system of universal peace, on the indefeasible hereditary Rights of Man,* is now revolving from west to east by a stronger impulse than the Government of the sword revolved from east to west. It interests not particular individuals, but Nations in its progress, and promises a new era to the human race.

The danger to which the success of Revolutions is most exposed is that of attempting them before the principles on which they proceed, and the advantages to result from them, are sufficiently seen and understood. Almost everything appertaining to the circumstances of a Nation, has been absorbed and confounded under the general and mysterious word *Government*. Though it avoids taking to its account the errors it commits, and the mischiefs it occasions, it fails not to arrogate to itself whatever has the appearance of prosperity. It robs industry of its honours, by pedanticly making itself the cause of its effects; and purloins from the general character of man, the merits that appertain to him as a social being.

It may therefore be of use in this day of Revolutions to discriminate between those things which are the effect of Government, and those which are not. This will best be done by taking a review of society and civilisation, and the consequences resulting therefrom, as things distinct from what are called Governments. By beginning with this investigation, we shall be able to assign effects to their proper cause and analyze the mass of common errors.

Of Society and Civilisation

Great part of that order which reigns among mankind is not the effect of Government. It has its origin in the principles of society and the natural constitution of man. It existed prior to Government, and would exist if the formality of Government was abolished. The mutual dependence and reciprocal interest which man has upon man, and all the parts of a civilised community upon each other, create that great chain of connection which holds it together. The landholder, the farmer, the manufacturer, the merchant, the tradesman, and every occupation, prospers by the aid which each receives from the other, and from the whole. Common interest regulates their concerns, and forms their law; and the laws which common usage ordains, have a greater influence than the laws of Government. In fine, society performs for itself almost everything which is ascribed to Government.

To understand the nature and quantity of Government proper for man, it is necessary to attend to his character. As nature created him for social life, she fitted him for the station she intended. In all cases she made his natural wants greater than his individual powers. No one man is capable, without the aid of society, of supplying his own wants; and those wants, acting upon every individual, impel the whole of them into society, as naturally as gravitation acts to a centre.

But she has gone further. She has not only forced man into society by a diversity of wants which the reciprocal aid of each other can supply, but she has implanted in him a system of social affections, which, though not necessary to his existence, are essential to his happiness. There is no period in life when this love for society ceases to act. It begins and ends with our being.

If we examine with attention the composition and constitution of man, the diversity of his wants and talents in different men for reciprocally accommodating the wants of each other, his propensity to society, and consequently to preserve the advantages resulting from it, we shall easily discover that a great part of what is called Government is mere imposition.

Government is no farther necessary than to supply the few cases to which society and civilisation are not conveniently competent; and instances are not wanting to show, that everything which Government can usefully add thereto, has been performed by the common consent of society, without Government.

For upwards of two years from the commencement of the American War, and to a longer period in several of the American States, there were no established forms of Government. The old Governments had been abolished, and the country was too much occupied in defence to employ its attention in establishing new Governments; yet during this interval order and harmony were preserved as inviolate as in any country in Europe. There is a natural aptness in man, and more so in society, because it embraces a greater variety of abilities and resources, to accommodate itself to whatever situation it is in. The instant formal Government is abolished, society begins to act: a general association takes place, and common interest produces common security.

So far is it from being true, as has been pretended, that the abolition of any formal Government is the dissolution of society, that it acts by a contrary impulse, and brings the latter the closer together. All that part of its organization which it had committed to its Government, devolves again upon itself, and acts through its medium. When men, as well from natural instinct as from reciprocal benefits, have habituated themselves to social and civilised life, there is always enough of its principles in practice to carry them through any changes they may find necessary or convenient to make in their Government. In short, man is so naturally a creature of society that it is almost impossible to put him out of it.

Formal Government makes but a small part of civilised life; and when even the best that human wisdom can devise is established, it is a thing more in name and idea than in fact. It is to the great and fundamental principles of society and civilisation—to the common usage universally consented to, and mutually and reciprocally maintained—to the unceasing circulation of interest, which passing through its million channels, invigorates the whole mass of civilised man—it is to these things, infinitely more than to anything which even the best instituted Government can perform, that the safety and prosperity of the individual and of the whole depends.

The more perfect civilisation is, the less occasion has it for Government, because the more it does regulate its own affairs, and govern itself; but so contrary is the practice of old Governments to the reason of the case, that the expences of them increase in the proportion they ought to diminish. It is but few general laws that civilised life requires, and those of such common usefulness, that whether they are enforced by the forms of government or not, the effect will be nearly the same. If we consider what the principles are that first condense men into society, and what the motives that regulate their mutual intercourse afterwards, we shall find, by the time we arrive at what is called Government, that nearly the whole of the business is performed by the natural operation of the parts upon each other.

Man, with respect to all those matters, is more a creature of consistency than he is aware, or that Governments would wish him to believe. All the great laws of society are laws of nature. Those of trade and commerce, whether with respect to the intercourse of individuals or of nations, are laws of mutual and reciprocal interests. They are followed and obeyed, because it is the interest of the parties so to do, and not on account of any formal laws their Governments may impose or interpose.

But how often is the natural propensity to society disturbed or destroyed by the operations of Government! When the latter, instead of being ingrafted on the principles of the former, assumes to exist for itself, and acts by partialities of favour and oppression, it becomes the cause of the mischiefs it ought to prevent.

If we look back to the riots and tumults which at various times have happened in England, we shall find that they did not proceed from the want of a Government, but that Government was itself the generating cause: instead of consolidating society it divided it; it deprived it of its natural cohesion, and engendered discontents and disorders which otherwise would not have existed. In those associations, which men promiscuously form for the purpose of trade, or of any concern in which Government is totally out of the question, and in which they act merely on the principles of society, we see how naturally the various parties unite; and this shows, by comparison, that Governments, so far from being always the cause or means of order, are often the destruction of it. The riots of 1780 had no other source than the remains of those prejudices which the Government of itself had encouraged. But with respect to England there are also other causes.

Excess and inequality of taxation, however disguised in the means, never fail to appear in their effects. As a great mass of the community are thrown thereby into poverty and discontent, they are constantly on the brink of commotion; and deprived, as they unfortunately are, of the means of information, are easily heated to outrage. Whatever the apparent cause of any riots may be, the real one is always want of happiness. It shows that something is wrong in the system of Government that injures the felicity by which society is to be preserved.

But as fact is superior to reasoning, the instance of America presents itself to confirm these observations. If there is a country in the world where concord, according to common calculation, would be least expected, it is America. Made up as it is of people from different nations, accustomed to different forms and habits of Government, speaking different languages, and more different in their modes of worship, it would appear that the union of such a people was impracticable; but by the simple operation of constructing Government on the principles of Society and the rights of man, every difficulty retires, and all the parts are brought into cordial unison. There the poor are not oppressed, the rich are not privileged. Industry is not mortified by the splendid extravagance of a Court rioting at its expence. Their taxes are few, because their Government is just: and as there is nothing to render them wretched, there is nothing to engender riots and tumults.

A metaphysical man, like Mr. Burke, would have tortured his invention to discover how such a people could be governed. He would have supposed that some must be managed by fraud, others by force, and all by some contrivance; that genius must be hired to impose upon ignorance, and show and parade to fascinate the vulgar. Lost in the abundance of his researches, he would have resolved and re-resolved, and finally overlooked the plain and easy road that lay directly before him.

One of the great advantages of the American Revolution has been, that it led to a discovery of the principles, and laid open the imposition of Governments. All the Revolutions till then had been worked within the small sphere of a Court, and never on the great floor of a Nation. The parties were always of the class of courtiers; and whatever was their rage for reformation, they carefully preserved the fraud of the profession.

In all cases they took care to represent Government as a thing made up of mysteries, which only themselves understood; and they hid from the understanding of the Nation the only thing that was beneficial to know, namely, *that Government is nothing more than a national association acting on the principles of society.*

Having thus endeavoured to show that the social and civilised state of man is capable of performing within itself almost everything necessary to its protection and Government, it will be proper, on the other hand, to take a review of the present old Governments, and examine whether their principles and practice are correspondent thereto.

Of the Origin of the Present Old Governments

It is impossible that such Governments as have hitherto existed in the world, would have commenced by any other means than a total violation of every principle, sacred and moral. The obscurity in which the origin of all the present old Governments is buried, implies the iniquity and disgrace with which they began. The origin of the present Government of America and France will ever be remembered, because it is honourable to record it; but with respect to the rest, even flattery has consigned them to the tomb of time, without an inscription.

It could have been no difficult thing in the early and solitary ages of the world, while the chief employment of men was that of attending flocks and herds, for a banditti of ruffians to overrun a country and lay it under contributions. Their power being thus established the chief of the band contrived to lose the name of Robber in that of Monarch; and hence the origin of Monarchy and Kings.

The origin of the Government of England, so far as relates to what is called its line of Monarchy, being one of the latest, is perhaps the best recorded. The hatred which the Norman invasion and tyranny begat, must have been deeply rooted in the nation, to have outlived the contrivance to obliterate it. Though not a courtier will talk of the curfeu-bell, not a village in England has forgotten it.

Those bands of robbers having parcelled out the world, and divided it into dominions, began, as is naturally the case, to quarrel with each other. What at first was obtained by violence was considered by others as lawful to be taken, and a second plunderer succeeded the first. They alternately invaded the dominions which each had assigned to himself, and the brutality with which they treated each other explains the original character of monarchy. It was ruffian torturing ruffian. The conqueror considered the conquered, not as his prisoner, but his property. He led him in triumph rattling in chains, and doomed him, at pleasure, to slavery or death. As time obliterated the history of their beginning, their successors assumed new appearances, to cut off the entail of their disgrace, but their principles and objects remained the same. What at first was plunder, assumed the softer name of revenue; and the power originally usurped, they affected to inherit.

From such beginning of Governments, what could be expected but a continual system of war and extortion? It has established itself into a trade. The vice is not peculiar to one more than to another, but is the common principle of all. There does not exist within such Governments sufficient stamina whereon to engraft reformation; and the shortest, easiest, and most effectual remedy is to begin anew on the ground of the oration.

What scenes of horror, what perfection of iniquity, present themselves in contemplating the character and reviewing the history of such Governments! If we would delineate human nature with a baseness of heart and hypocrisy of countenance that reflection would shudder at and humanity disown, it is Kings, Courts, and Cabinets that must sit for the portrait. Man, naturally as he is, with all his faults about him, is not up to the character.

Can we possibly suppose that if Governments had originated in a right principle, and had not an interest in pursuing a wrong one, the world could have been in the wretched and quarrelsome condition we have seen it? What inducement has the farmer, while following the plough, to lay aside his peaceful pursuits, and go to war with the farmer of another country? or what inducement has the manufacturer? What is dominion to them, or to any class of men in a nation? Does it add an acre to any man's estate, or raise its value? Are not conquest and defeat each of the same price, and taxes the never-failing consequence? Though this reasoning may be good to a Nation, it is not so to a Government. War is the Pharo table of Governments, and Nations the dupes of the games.

If there is anything to wonder at in this miserable scene of Governments more than might be expected, it is the progress which the peaceful arts of agriculture, manufacture and commerce have made beneath such a long accumulating load of discouragement and oppression. It serves to show that instinct in animals does not act with stronger impulse than the principles of society and civilization operate in man. Under all discouragements, he pursues his object, and yields to nothing but impossibilities.

Of the Old and New Systems of Government

Nothing can appear more contradictory than the principles on which the old Governments began, and the condition to which society, civilization and commerce are capable of carrying mankind. Government, on the old system, is an assumption of power, for the aggrandizement of itself; on the new a delegation of power for the common benefit of society. The former supports itself by keeping up a system of war; the latter promotes a system of peace, as the true means of enriching a Nation. The one encourages national prejudices; the other promotes universal society, as the means of universal commerce. The one measures its prosperity by the quantity of revenue it extorts; the other proves its excellence by the small quantity of taxes it requires.

Mr. Burke has talked of old and new whigs. If he can amuse himself with childish names and distinctions, I shall not interrupt his pleasure. It is not to him, but to the Abbé Sieyes, that I address this chapter. I am already engaged to the latter gentleman to discuss the subject of monarchical Government; and as it naturally occurs in comparing the old and new systems, I make this the opportunity of presenting to him my observations. I shall occasionally take Mr. Burke in my way.

Though it might be proved that the system of Government now called the NEW is the most ancient in principle of all that have existed, being founded on the original inherent Rights of Man; yet, as tyranny and the sword have suspended the exercise of those rights for many centuries past, it serves better the purpose of distinction to call it the *new* than to claim the right of calling it the old.

The first general distinction between those two systems is that the one now called the old is *hereditary,* either in whole or in part; and the new is entirely *representative.* It rejects all hereditary Government:

First, As being an imposition on mankind.

Secondly, As inadequate to the purposes for which Government is necessary.

With respect to the first of these heads—It cannot be proved by what right hereditary Government could begin; neither does there exist within the compass of mortal power a right to establish it. Man has no authority over posterity in matters of personal right; and, therefore, no man or body of men had, or can have, a right to set up hereditary Government. Were even ourselves to come again into existence, instead of being succeeded by posterity, we have not now the right of taking from ourselves the rights which would then be ours. On what ground, then, do we pretend to take them from others?

All hereditary Government is in its nature tyranny. An heritable crown, or an heritable throne, or by what other fanciful name such things may be called, have no other significant explanation than that mankind are heritable property. To inherit a Government, is to inherit the people, as if they were flocks and herds.

With respect to the second head, that of being inadequate to the purposes for which Government is necessary, we have only to consider what Government essentially is, and compare it with the circumstances to which hereditary succession is subject.

Government ought to be a thing always in full maturity. It ought to be so constructed as to be superior to all the accidents to which individual man is subject; and, therefore, hereditary succession, by being *subject to them all,* is the most irregular and imperfect of all the systems of Government.

We have heard the *Rights of Man* called a *levelling* system; but the only system to which the word *levelling* is truly applicable, is the hereditary monarchical system. It is a system of *mental levelling*. It indiscriminately admits every species of character to the same authority. Vice and virtue, ignorance and wisdom, in short, every quality, good or bad, is put on the same level. Kings succeed each other, not as rationals, but as animals. It signifies not what their mental or moral characters are. Can we then be surprised at the abject state of the human mind in monarchical countries, when the Government itself is formed on such an abject levelling system? It has no fixed character. To-day it is one thing; to-morrow it is something else. It changes with the temper of every succeeding individual, and is subject to all the varieties of each. It is Government through the medium of passions and accidents. It appears under all the various characters of childhood, decrepitude, dotage; a thing at nurse, in leading-strings, or in crutches. It reverses the wholesome order of nature. It occasionally puts children over men, and the conceits of nonage over wisdom and experience. In short, we cannot conceive a more ridiculous figure of Government, than hereditary succession, in all its cases, presents.

Could it be made a decree in nature, or an edict registered in heaven, and man could know it, that virtue and wisdom should invariably appertain to hereditary succession, the objections to it would be removed; but when we see that nature acts as if she disowned and sported with the hereditary system; that the mental characters of successors, in all countries, are below the average of human understanding; that one is a tyrant, another an idiot, a third insane, and some all three together, it is impossible to attach confidence to it, when reason in man has power to act.

It is not to the Abbé Sieyes that I need apply this reasoning; he has already saved me that trouble by giving his own opinion upon the case. "If it be asked," says he, "what is my opinion with respect to hereditary right, I answer, without hesitation, that, in good theory, an hereditary transmission of any power or office, can never accord with the laws of a true representation. Hereditaryship is, in this sense, as much an attaint upon principle, as an outrage upon society. But let us," continues he, "refer to the history of all elective monarchies and principalities: is there one in which the elective mode is not worse than the hereditary succession?"

As to debating on which is the worse of the two, it is admitting both to be bad: and herein we are agreed. The preference which the Abbé has given is a condemnation of the thing that he prefers. Such a mode of reasoning on such a subject is inadmissible, because it finally amounts to an accusation upon Providence, as if she had left to man no other choice with respect to Government than between two evils, the best of which he admits to be "an attaint upon principle, and an outrage upon society."

Passing over for the present all the evils and mischiefs which monarchy has occasioned in the world, nothing can more effectually prove its uselessness in a state of *civil government*, than making it hereditary. Would we make any office hereditary that required wisdom and abilities to fill it? and where wisdom and abilities are not necessary, such an office, whatever it may be, is superfluous or insignificant.

Hereditary succession is a burlesque upon monarchy. It puts it in the most ridiculous light, by presenting it as an office which any child or idiot may fill. It requires some talents to be a common mechanic; but to be a King requires only the animal figure of man—a sort of breathing automaton. This sort of superstition may last a few years more, but it cannot long resist the awakened reason and interest of man.

As to Mr. Burke, he is a stickler for monarchy, not altogether as a pensioner, if he is one, which I believe, but as a political man. He has taken up a contemptible opinion of mankind, who, in their turn, are taking up the same of him. He considers them as a herd of beings that must be governed by fraud, effigy, and show; and an idol would be as good a figure of monarchy with him as a man. I will, however, do him the justice to say that, with respect to America, he has been very complimentary. He always contended, at least in my hearing, that the people of America were more enlightened than those of England, or of any country in Europe; and that therefore the imposition of shew was not necessary in their Governments.

Though the comparison between hereditary and elective monarchy, which the Abbé has made, is unnecessary to the case, because the representative system rejects both; yet, were I to make the comparison, I should decide contrary to what he has done.

The civil wars which have originated from contested hereditary claims are more numerous, and have been more dreadful, and of longer continuance, than those which have been occasioned by election. All the civil wars in France arose from the hereditary system; they were either produced by hereditary claims, or by the imperfection of the hereditary form, which admits of regencies, or monarchy at nurse. With respect to England, its history is full of the same misfortunes. The contests for succession between the houses of York and Lancaster, lasted a whole century; and others of a similar nature have renewed themselves since that period. Those of 1715 and 1745 were of the same kind. The succession war for the crown of Spain embroiled almost half Europe. The disturbances in Holland are generated from the hereditaryship of the Stadtholder. A Government calling itself free, with an hereditary office, is like a thorn in the flesh, that produces a fermentation which endeavours to discharge it.

But I might go further, and place also foreign wars, of whatever kind, to the same cause. It is by adding the evil of hereditary succession to that of monarchy, that a permanent family interest is created, whose constant objects are dominion and revenue. Poland, though an elective monarchy, has had fewer wars than those which are hereditary; and it is the only Government that has made a voluntary essay, though but a small one, to reform the condition of the country.

Having thus glanced at a few of the defects of the old, or hereditary systems of Government, let us compare it with the new, or representative system.

The representative system takes society and civilisation for its basis; nature, reason, and experience for its guide.

Experience, in all ages and in all countries, has demonstrated that it is impossible to controul nature in her distribution of mental powers. She gives them as she pleases. Whatever is the rule by which she, apparently to us, scatters them among mankind, that rule remains a secret to man. It would be as ridiculous to attempt to fix the hereditaryship of human beauty as of wisdom. Whatever wisdom constituently is, it is like a seedless plant; it may be reared when it appears, but it cannot be voluntarily produced. There is always a sufficiency somewhere in the general mass of society for all purposes; but with respect to the parts of society, it is continually changing its place. It rises in one to-day, in another to-morrow, and has most probably visited in rotation every family of the earth, and again withdrawn.

As this is in the order of nature, the order of Government must necessarily follow it, or Government will, as we see it does, degenerate into ignorance. The hereditary system, therefore, is as repugnant to human wisdom as to human rights; and is as absurd as it is unjust.

As the republic of letters brings forward the best literary productions, by giving to genius a fair and universal chance; so the representative system of Government is calculated to produce the wisest laws, by collecting wisdom from where it can be found. I smile to myself when I contemplate the ridiculous insignificance into which literature and all the sciences would sink, were they made hereditary; and I carry the same idea into Governments. An hereditary governor is as inconsistent as an hereditary author. I know not whether Homer or Euclid had sons; but I will venture an opinion that if they had, and had left their works unfinished, those sons could not have completed them.

Do we need a stronger evidence of the absurdity of hereditary Government than is seen in the descendants of those men, in any line of life, who once were famous? Is there scarcely an instance in which there is not a total reverse of the character? It appears as if the tide of mental faculties flowed as far as it could in certain channels, and then forsook its course and arose in others. How irrational then is the hereditary system, which establishes channels of power, in company with which wisdom refuses to flow! By continuing this absurdity, man is perpetually in contradiction with himself; he accepts, for a King, or a chief magistrate, or a legislator, a person whom he would not elect for a constable.

It appears to general observation that Revolutions create genius and talents; but those events do no more than bring them forward. There is existing in man a mass of sense lying in a dormant state, and which, unless something excites to action, will descend with him, in that condition, to the grave. As it is to the advantage of society that the whole of the faculties should be employed, the construction of Government ought to be such as to bring forward by a quiet and regular operation, all that extent of capacity which never fails to appear in Revolutions.

This cannot take place in the insipid state of hereditary Government, not only because it prevents, but because it operates to benumb. When the mind of a Nation is bowed down by any political superstition in its Government, such as hereditary succession is, it loses a considerable portion of its powers on all other subjects and objects. Hereditary succession requires the same obedience to ignorance as to wisdom; and when once the mind can bring itself to pay this indiscriminate reverence, it descends below the stature of mental manhood. It is fit to be great only in little things. It acts a treachery upon itself, and suffocates the sensations that urge to detection.

Though the ancient Governments present to us a miserable picture of the condition of man, there is one which above all others exempts itself from the general description. I mean the democracy of Athenians. We see more to admire, and less to condemn, in that great, extraordinary people than in anything which history affords.

Mr. Burke is so little acquainted with constituent principles of Government, that he confounds democracy and representation together. Representation was a thing unknown in the ancient democracies. In those the mass of the people met and enacted laws (grammatically speaking) in the first person. Simple democracy was no other than the common hall of the ancients. It signifies the *form* as well as the public principle of the Government. As those democracies increased in population, and the territory extended, the simple democratical form became unwieldy and impracticable; and as the system of representation was not known, the consequence was, they either degenerated convulsively into monarchies or became absorbed into such as then existed. Had the system of representation been then understood, as it now is, there is no reason to believe that those forms of Government now called monarchical or aristocratical would ever have taken place. It was the want of some method to consolidate the parts of society after it became too populous and too expensive for the simple democratical form, and also the lax and solitary condition of shepherds and herdsmen in other parts of the world, that afforded opportunities to those unnatural modes of Government to begin.

As it is necessary to clear away the rubbish of errors into which the subject of Government has been thrown, I shall proceed to remark on some others.

It has always been the political craft of courtiers and court-governments to abuse something which they called republicanism; but what republicanism was or is they never attempt to explain. Let us examine a little into this case.

The only forms of Government are the democratical, the aristocratical, the monarchical, and what is now called the representative.

What is called a *Republic* is not any *particular form* of Government. It is wholly characteristical of the purport, matter or object for which Government ought to be instituted, and on which it is to be employed: RES-PUBLICA, the public affairs, or the public good; or, literally translated, the *public thing*. It is a word of a good original, referring to what ought to be the character and business of Government; and in this sense it is naturally opposed to the word *monarchy*, which has a base original signification. It means arbitrary power in an individual person; in the exercise of which, *himself*, and not the *res-publica*, is the object.

Every Government that does not act on the principle of a *Republic*, or, in other words, that does not make the *res-publica* its whole and sole object, is not a good Government. Republican Government is no other than Government established and conducted for the interest of the public, as well individually as collectively. It is not necessarily connected with any particular form, but it most naturally associates with the representative form, as being best calculated to secure the end for which a Nation is at the expense of supporting it.

Various forms of Government have affected to stile themselves a Republic. Poland calls itself a Republic which is an hereditary Aristocracy, with what is called an elective Monarchy. Holland calls itself a Republic which is chiefly aristocratical, with an hereditary stadtholdership. But the Government of America, which is wholly on the system of representation, is the only real Republic, in character and in practice, that now exists. Its Government has no other object than the public business of the Nation, and therefore it is properly a Republic; and the Americans have taken care that THIS, and no other, shall always be the object of their Government, by their rejecting everything hereditary, and establishing Government on the system of representation only.

Those who have said that a Republic is not a *form* of Government calculated for countries of great extent, mistook, in the first place, the *business* of a Government, for a *form* of Government; for the *res-publica* equally appertains to every extent of territory and population. And, in the second place, if they meant anything with respect to *form*, it was the simple democratical form, such as was the mode of Government in the ancient democracies, in which there was no representation. The case, therefore, is not that a Republic cannot be extensive, but that it cannot be extensive on the simple democratical form; and the question naturally presents itself, *what is the best form of Government for conducting the* RES-PUBLICA, *or the* PUBLIC BUSINESS *of a nation, after it becomes too extensive and populous for the simple democratical form?*

It cannot be Monarchy, because Monarchy is subject to an objection of the same amount to which the simple democratical form was subject.

It is possible that an individual may lay down a system of principles, on which Government shall be constitutionally established to any extent of territory. This is no more than an operation of the mind, acting by its own powers. But the practice upon those principles, as applying to the various and numerous circumstances of a Nation, its agriculture, manufacture, trade, commerce, etc., etc., requires a knowledge of a different kind, and which can be had only from the various parts of society. It is an assemblage of practical knowledge, which no one individual can possess; and therefore the monarchical form is as much limited, in useful practice, from the incompetency of knowledge, as was the democratical form from the multiplicity of population. The one degenerates, by extension, into confusion; the other into ignorance and incapacity, of which all the great monarchies are an evidence. The monarchical form, therefore, could not be a substitute for the democratical, because it has equal inconveniences.

Much less could it when made hereditary. This is the most effectual of all forms to preclude knowledge. Neither could the high democratical mind have voluntarily yielded itself to be governed by children and idiots, and all the motley insignificance of character which attends such a mere animal system, the disgrace and the reproach of reason and of man.

As to the aristocratical form, it has the same vices and defects with the monarchical, except that the chance of abilities is better from the proportion of numbers, but there is still no security for the right use and application of them.

Referring then to the original simple Democracy, it affords the true data from which Government on a large scale can begin. It is incapable of extension, not from its principle, but from the inconvenience of its form; and Monarchy and Aristocracy, from their incapacity. Retaining, then, Democracy as the ground, and rejecting the corrupt systems of Monarchy and Aristocracy, the representative system naturally presents itself; remedying at once the defects of the simple Democracy as to form, and the incapacity of the other two with respect to knowledge.

Simple Democracy was society governing itself without the aid of secondary means. By ingrafting representation upon Democracy, we arrive at a system of Government capable of embracing and confederating all the various interests and every extent of territory and population; and that also with advantages as much superior to hereditary Government, as the Republic of Letters is to hereditary literature.

It is on this system that the American Government is founded. It is representation ingrafted upon Democracy. It has fixed the form by a scale parallel in all cases to the extent of the principle. What Athens was in miniature, America will be in magnitude. The one was the wonder of the ancient world; the other is becoming the admiration, the model of the present. It is the easiest of all the forms of Government to be understood and the most eligible in practice, and excludes at once the ignorance and insecurity of the hereditary mode, and the inconvenience of the simple Democracy.

It is impossible to conceive a system of Government capable of acting over such an extent of territory, and such a circle of interests, as is immediately produced by the operation of representation. France, great and populous as it is, is but a spot in the capaciousness of the system. It is preferable to simple Democracy even in small territories. Athens, by representation, would have outrivalled her own Democracy.

That which is called Government, or rather that which we ought to conceive Government to be, is no more than some common centre, in which all the parts of society unite. This cannot be accomplished by any method so conducive to the various interests of the community as by the representative system. It concentrates the knowledge necessary to the interest of the parts, and of the whole. It places Government in a state of constant maturity. It is, as has already been observed, never young, never old. It is subject neither to nonage nor dotage. It is never in the cradle nor on crutches. It admits not of a separation between knowledge and power, and is superior, as Government always ought to be, to all the accidents of individual man, and is therefore superior to what is called Monarchy.

A Nation is not a body, the figure of which is to be represented by the human body, but is like a body contained within a circle, having a common centre in which every radius meets; and that centre is formed by representation. To connect representation with what is called Monarchy is eccentric Government. Representation is of itself the delegated Monarchy of a Nation, and cannot debase itself by dividing it with another.

Mr. Burke has two or three times, in his parliamentary speeches, and in his publication, made use of a jingle of words that convey no ideas. Speaking of Government, he says: "It is better to have Monarchy for its basis, and Republicanism for its corrective, than Republicanism for its basis, and Monarchy for its corrective." If he means that it is better to correct folly with wisdom than wisdom with folly, I will not otherwise contend with him, than that it would be much better to reject the folly entirely.

But what is this thing which Mr. Burke calls Monarchy? Will he explain it? All men can understand what representation is; and that it must necessarily include a variety of knowledge and talents. But what security is there for the same qualities on the part of Monarchy? or, when this Monarchy is a child, where then is the wisdom? What does it know about Government? Who then is the Monarch, or where is the Monarchy? If it is to be performed by Regency, it proves to be a farce. A Regency is a mock species of Republic, and the whole of Monarchy deserves no better description. It is a thing as various as imagination can paint. It has none of the stable character that Government ought to possess. Every succession is a Revolution, and every regency a counter-revolution. The whole of it is a scene of perpetual court cabal and intrigue, of which Mr. Burke is himself an instance. To render Monarchy consistent with Government, the next in succession should not be born a child, but a man at once, and that man a Solomon. It is ridiculous that Nations are to wait and Government be interrupted till boys grow to be men.

Whether I have too little sense to see, or too much to be imposed upon; whether I have too much or too little pride, or of anything else, I leave out of the question; but certain it is, that what is called Monarchy always appears to me a silly contemptible thing. I compare it to something kept behind a curtain, about which there is a great deal of bustle and fuss, and a wonderful air of seeming solemnity; but when, by an accident, the curtain happens to be opened, and the company see what it is, they burst into laughter.

In the representative system of Government, nothing of this can happen. Like the Nation itself, it possesses a perpetual stamina, as well of body as of mind, and presents itself on the open theatre of the world in a fair and manly manner. Whatever are its excellencies or defects, they are visible to all. It exists not by fraud and mystery; it deals not in cant and sophistry; but inspires a language that, passing from heart to heart, is felt and understood.

We must shut our eyes against reason, we must basely degrade our understanding, not to see the folly of what is called Monarchy. Nature is orderly in all her works; but this is a mode of Government that counteracts nature. It turns the progress of the human faculties upside down. It subjects age to be governed by children, and wisdom by folly.

On the contrary, the representative system is always parallel with the order and immutable laws of nature, and meets the reason of man in every part. For example:—

In the American federal Government, more power is delegated to the President of the United States than to any other individual member of Congress. He cannot, therefore, be elected to this office under the age of thirty-five years. By this time the judgment of man becomes matured, and he has lived long enough to be acquainted with man and things, and the country with him. But on the monarchical plan (exclusive of the numerous chances there are against every man born into the world, of drawing a prize in the lottery of human faculties), the next in succession, whatever he may be, is put at the head of a Nation, and of a Government, at the age of eighteen years. Does this appear like an act of wisdom? Is it consistent with the proper dignity and manly character of a Nation? Where is the propriety of calling such a lad the father of the people? In all other cases, a person is a minor until the age of twenty-one years. Before this period, he is not entrusted with the management of an acre of land, or with the heritable property of a flock of sheep or an herd of swine; but wonderful to tell! he may at the age of eighteen years be trusted with a Nation.

That Monarchy is all a bubble, a mere court artifice to procure money, is evident (at least to me) in every character in which it can be viewed. It would be impossible, on the rational system of representative Government, to make out a bill of expences to such an enormous amount as this deception admits. Government is not of itself a very chargeable institution. The whole expence of the federal Government of America, founded, as I have already said, on the system of representation, and extending over a country nearly ten times as large as England, is but six hundred thousand dollars, or one hundred and thirty-five thousand pounds sterling.

I presume that no man in his sober sense will compare the character of the Kings of Europe with that of General Washington. Yet in France, and also in England, the expence of the civil list only, for the support of one man, is eight times greater than the whole expence of the federal Government in America. To assign a reason for this appears almost impossible. The generality of the people of America, especially the poor, are more able to pay taxes than the generality of people either in France or England.

But the case is, that the representative system diffuses such a body of knowledge throughout a Nation, on the subject of Government, as to explode ignorance and preclude imposition. The craft of courts cannot be acted on that ground. There is no place for mystery; nowhere for it to begin. Those who are not in the representation know as much of the nature of business as those who are. An affectation of mysterious importance would there be scouted. Nations can have no secrets; and the secrets of courts, like those of individuals, are always their defects.

In the representative system, the reason for everything must publicly appear. Every man is a proprietor in Government, and considers it a necessary part of his business to understand. It concerns his interest, because it affects his property. He examines the cost, and compares it with the advantages; and above all, he does not adopt the slavish custom of following what in other Governments are called LEADERS.

It can only be by blinding the understanding of man, and making him believe that Government is some wonderful mysterious thing, that excessive revenues are obtained. Monarchy is well calculated to ensure this end. It is the popery of Government, a thing kept up to amuse the ignorant and quiet them into taxes.

The Government of a free country, properly speaking, is not in the persons, but in the laws. The enacting of those requires no great expence; and when they are administered the whole of civil Government is performed—the rest is all court contrivance.

Of Constitutions

THAT men mean distinct and separate things when they speak of Constitutions and of Governments, is evident; or why are those terms distinctly and separately used? A Constitution is not the act of a Government, but of a people constituting a Government; and Government without a Constitution is power without a right.

All power exercised over a Nation must have some beginning. It must either be delegated or assumed. There are no other sources. All delegated power is trust, and all assumed power is usurpation. Time does not alter the nature and quality of either.

In viewing this subject, the case and circumstances of America present themselves as in the beginning of a world; and our enquiry into the origin of Government is shortened by referring to the facts that have arisen in our own day. We have no occasion to roam for information into the obscure field of antiquity, nor hazard ourselves upon conjecture. We are brought at once to the point of seeing Government begin, as if we had lived in the beginning of time. The real volume, not of history, but of fact, is directly before us, unmutilated by contrivance or the errors of tradition.

I will here concisely state the commencement of the American Constitutions: by which the difference between Constitutions and Governments will sufficiently appear.

It may not be improper to remind the reader that the United States of America consist of thirteen separate states, each of which established a Government for itself, after the Declaration of Independence, done the 4th of July, 1776. Each state acted independently of the rest, in forming its Government; but the same general principle pervades the whole. When the several state Governments were formed, they proceeded to form the federal Government that acts over the whole in all matters which concern the interest of the whole, or which relate to the intercourse of the several states with each other, or with foreign Nations. I will begin with giving an instance from one of the state Governments (that of Pennsylvania), and then proceed to the federal Government.

The state of Pennsylvania, though nearly of the same extent of territory as England, was then divided into only twelve counties. Each of these counties had elected a committee at the commencement of the dispute with the English Government; and as the city of Philadelphia, which also had its committee, was the most central for intelligence, it became the centre of communication to the several county committees. When it became necessary to proceed to the formation of a Government, the committee of Philadelphia proposed a conference of all the committees, to be held in that city, and which met the latter end of July, 1776.

Though these committees had been elected by the people, they were not elected expressly for the purpose, nor invested with the authority, of forming a Constitution; and as they could not, consistently with the American ideas of right, assume such a power, they could only confer upon the matter, and put it into a train of operation. The conferees, therefore, did no more than state the case, and recommend to the several counties to elect six representatives for each county, to meet in convention at Philadelphia, with powers to form a Constitution, and propose it for public consideration.

This convention, of which Benjamin Franklin was President, having met and deliberated, and agreed upon a Constitution, they next ordered it to be published, not as a thing established, but for the consideration of the whole people, their approbation or rejection, and then adjourned to a stated time. When the time of adjournment was expired, the convention re-assembled, and as the general opinion of the people in approbation of it was then known, the Constitution was signed, sealed, and proclaimed, on the *authority of the people,* and the original instrument deposited as a public record. The convention then appointed a day for the general election of the representatives who were to compose the Government, and the time it should commence; and having done this they dissolved, and returned to their several homes and occupations.

In this Constitution were laid down, first, a declaration of rights; then followed the form which the Government should have, and the powers which it should possess—the authority of the courts of judicature and of juries—the manner in which elections should be conducted, and the proportion of representatives to the number of electors—the time which each succeeding assembly should continue, which was one year—the mode of levying, and the accounting for the expenditure, of public money—of appointing public officers, etc., etc.

No article of this Constitution could be altered or infringed at the discretion of the Government that was to ensue. It was to the Government a law. But as it would have been unwise to preclude the benefit of experience, and in order also to prevent the accumulation of errors, if any should be found, and to preserve a unison of Government with the circumstances of the state to all times, the Constitution provided that at the expiration of every seven years, a convention should be elected for the express purpose of revising the Constitution and making alterations, additions, or abolitions therein, if any such should be found necessary.

Here we see a regular process—a Government issuing out of a Constitution, formed by the people in their original character; and that Constitution serving not only as an authority, but as a law of controul to the Government. It was the political Bible of the state. Scarcely a family was without it. Every member of the Government had a copy; and nothing was more common when any debate arose on the principle of a bill, or on the extent of any species of authority, than for the members to take the printed Constitution out of their pocket and read the chapter with which such matter in debate was connected.

Having thus given an instance from one of the states, I will show the proceedings by which the federal Constitution of the United States arose and was formed.

Congress, at its first two meetings, in September, 1774, and May, 1775, was nothing more than a deputation from the legislatures of the several provinces, afterwards states; and had no other authority than what arose from common consent, and the necessity of its acting as a public body. In everything which related to the internal affairs of America, Congress went no further than to issue recommendations to the several provincial assemblies, who at discretion adopted them or not. Nothing on the part of Congress was compulsive; yet in this situation, it was more faithfully and affectionately obeyed than was any Government in Europe. This instance, like that of the National Assembly of France, sufficiently shews, that the strength of Government does not consist of anything *within* itself, but in the attachment of a Nation, and the interest which the people feel in supporting it. When this is lost Government is but a child in power, and though like the old Government of France it may harass individuals for a while, it but facilitates its own fall.

After the Declaration of Independence it became consistent with the principle on which representative Government is founded, that the authority of Congress should be defined and established. Whether that authority should be more or less than Congress then discretionarily exercised, was not the question. It was merely the rectitude of the measure.

For this purpose, the act called the Act of Confederation (which was a sort of imperfect federal Constitution) was proposed, and after long deliberation was concluded in the year 1781. It was not the Act of Congress, because it is repugnant to the principles of representative Government that a body should give power to itself. Congress first informed the several states of the powers which it conceived were necessary to be invested in the union, to enable it to perform the duties and services required from it; and the states severally agreed with each other, and concentrated in Congress those powers.

It may not be improper to observe that in both those instances (the one of Pennsylvania, and the other of the United States) there is no such thing as an idea of a compact between the people on one side and the Government on the other. The compact was that of the people with each other to produce and constitute a Government. To suppose that any Government can be a party in a compact with the whole people is to suppose it to have existence before it can have a right to exist. The only instance in which a compact can take place between the people and those who exercise the Government is, that the people shall pay them while they choose to employ them.

Government is not a trade which any man, or any body of men, has a right to set up and exercise for his own emolument, but is altogether a trust in right of those by whom the trust is delegated, and by whom it is always resumable. It has of itself no rights; they are altogether duties.

Having thus given two instances of the original formation of a Constitution, I will shew the manner in which both have been changed since their first establishment.

The powers vested in the Governments of the several states, by the state Constitutions, were found upon experience to be too great, and those vested in the federal Government by the Act of Confederation, too little. The defect was not in the principle but in the distribution of power.

Numerous publications, in pamphlets and in newspapers, appeared on the propriety and necessity of new modelling the federal Government. After some time of public discussion, carried on through the channel of the press, and in conversations, the state of Virginia, experiencing some inconvenience with respect to commerce, proposed holding a continental conference; in consequence of which, a deputation from five or six of the state assemblies met at Annapolis, in Maryland, 1786. This meeting, not conceiving itself sufficiently authorised to go into the business of a reform, did no more than state their general opinions of the propriety of the measure, and recommend that a convention of all the states should be held the year following.

The convention met at Philadelphia in May, 1787, of which General Washington was elected President. He was not at that time connected with any of the state Governments, or with Congress. He delivered up his commission when the war ended, and since then had lived a private citizen.

The convention went deeply into all the subjects; and having, after a variety of debate and investigation, agreed among themselves upon the several parts of a federal Constitution, the next question was, the manner of giving it authority and practice.

For this purpose they did not, like a cabal of courtiers, send for a Dutch Stadtholder, or a German Elector; but they referred the whole matter to the sense and interests of the country.

They first directed that the proposed Constitution should be published. Secondly, that each state should elect a convention expressly for the purpose of taking it into consideration, and of ratifying or rejecting it; and that as soon as the approbation and ratification of any nine states should be given, that those states should proceed to the election of their proportion of members to the new federal Government; and that the operation of it should then begin, and the federal Government cease.

The several states proceeded accordingly to elect their conventions. Some of those conventions ratified the Constitution by very large majorities, and two or three unanimously. In others there were much debate and division of opinion. In the Massachusetts convention, which met at Boston, the majority was not above nineteen or twenty in about three hundred members; but such is the nature of representative Government, that it quietly decides all matters by majority. After the debate in the

Massachusetts convention was closed, and the vote taken, the objecting members rose and declared: "*That though they had argued and voted against it because certain parts appeared to them in a different light to what they appeared to other members; yet, as the vote had decided in favour of the Constitution as proposed, they should give it the same practical support as if they had voted for it.*"

As soon as nine states had concurred (and the rest followed in the order their conventions were elected), the old fabric of the federal Government was taken down, and the new erected, of which General Washington is President. In this place I cannot help remarking that the character and services of this gentleman are sufficient to put all those men called Kings to shame. While they are receiving from the sweat and labours of mankind a prodigality of pay, to which neither their abilities nor their services can entitle them, he is rendering every service in his power, and refusing every pecuniary reward. He accepted no pay as commander-in-chief; he accepts none as President of the United States.

After the new federal Constitution was established, the state of Pennsylvania, conceiving that some parts of its own Constitution required to be altered, elected a convention for that purpose. The proposed alterations were published, and the people concurring therein, they were established.

In forming those Constitutions, or in altering them, little or no inconvenience took place. The ordinary course of things was not interrupted, and the advantages have been much. It is always the interest of a far greater number of people in a Nation to have things right than to let them remain wrong; and when public matters are open to debate, and the public judgment free, it will not decide wrong, unless it decides too hastily.

In the two instances of changing the Constitutions, the Governments then in being were not actors either way. Government has no right to make itself a party in any debate respecting the principles or modes of forming, or of changing, Constitutions. It is not for the benefit of those who exercise the powers of Government that Constitutions, and the Governments issuing from them, are established. In all those matters the right of judging and acting are in those who pay, and not in those who receive.

A Constitution is the property of a Nation, and not of those who exercise the Government. All the Constitutions of America are declared to be established on the authority of the people. In France, the word Nation is used instead of the people; but in both cases a Constitution is a thing antecedent to the Government, and always distinct therefrom.

In England it is not difficult to perceive that everything has a Constitution, except the Nation. Every society and association that is established first agreed upon a number of original articles, digested into form, which are its Constitution. It then appointed its officers, whose powers and authorities are described in that Constitution, and the Government of that society then commenced. Those officers, by whatever name they are called, have no authority to add to, alter, or abridge the original articles. It is only to the constituting power that this right belongs.

From the want of understanding the difference between a Constitution and a Government, Dr. Johnson and all writers of his description have always bewildered themselves. They could not but perceive that there must necessarily be a *controuling* power existing somewhere, and they placed this in the discretion of the persons exercising the Government, instead of placing it in a Constitution formed by the Nation. When it is in a Constitution it has the Nation for its support, and the natural and the political controuling powers are together. The laws which are enacted by Governments controul men only as individuals, but the Nation, through its Constitution, controuls the whole Government, and has a natural ability so to do. The final controuling power, therefore, and the original constituting power, are one and the same power.

Dr. Johnson could not have advanced such a position in any country where there was a Constitution; and he is himself an evidence that no such thing as a Constitution exists in England. But it may be put as a question, not improper to be investigated, That if a Constitution does not exist how came the idea of its existence so generally established.

In order to decide this question, it is necessary to consider a Constitution in both its cases:—First, as creating a Government and giving it powers. Secondly, as regulating and restraining the powers so given.

If we begin with William of Normandy, we find that the Government of England was originally a tyranny, founded on an invasion and conquest of the country. This being admitted, it will then appear that the exertion of the Nation at different periods to abate that tyranny and render it less intolerable, has been credited for a Constitution.

Magna Charta, as it was called (it is now like an almanack of the same date), was no more than compelling the Government to renounce a part of its assumptions. It did not create and give powers to Government in the manner a Constitution does; but was, as far as it went, of the nature of a re-conquest, and not a Constitution; for could the Nation have totally expelled the usurpation as France has done its despotism, it would then have had a Constitution to form.

The history of the Edwards and the Henries, and up to the commencement of the Stuarts, exhibits as many instances of tyranny as could be acted within the limits to which the Nation had restricted it. The Stuarts endeavoured to pass those limits, and their fate is well known. In all those instances we see nothing of a Constitution, but only of restrictions on assumed power.

After this, another William, descended from the same stock, and claiming from the same origin, gained possession; and of the two evils, *James* and *William*, the nation preferred what it thought the least; since, from circumstances, it must take one. The act, called the Bill of Rights, comes here into view. What is it but a bargain which the parts of the Government made with each other, to divide powers, profits, and privileges? You shall have so much, and I will have the rest; and with respect to the Nation, it said, for *your share* YOU *shall have the right of petitioning.* This being the case, the Bill of Rights is more properly the bill of wrongs and of insult. As to what is called the convention Parliament, it was a thing that made itself, and then made the authority by which it acted. A few persons got together, and called themselves by that name. Several of them had never been elected, and none of them for the purpose.

From the time of William a species of Government arose, issuing out of this coalition Bill of Rights; and more so since the corruption introduced at the Hanover succession, by the agency of Walpole, that can be described by no other name than a despotic legislation. Though the parts may embarrass each other, the whole has no bounds; and the only right it acknowledges out of itself is the right of petitioning. Where then is the Constitution that either gives or restrains power?

It is not because a part of the Government is elective, that makes it less a despotism, if the persons so elected possess afterwards, as a Parliament, unlimited powers. Election in this case becomes separated from representation, and the candidates are candidates for despotism.

I cannot believe that any Nation, reasoning on its own right, would have thought of calling those things *a Constitution,* if the cry of Constitution had not been set up by the Government. It has got into circulation like the words *bore* and *quiz,* by being chalked up in the speeches of Parliament, as those words were on window-shutters and door-posts; but whatever the Constitution may be in other respects, it has undoubtedly been *the most productive machine of taxation that was ever invented.*

The taxes in France, under the new Constitution, are not quite thirteen shillings per head, and the taxes in England, under what is called its present Constitution, are forty-eight shillings and sixpence per head—men, women, and children—amounting to nearly seventeen millions sterling, besides the expence of collecting, which is upwards of a million more.

In a country like England, where the whole of the civil Government is executed by the people of every town and county by means of parish officers, magistrates, quarterly sessions, juries, and assize, without any trouble to what is called the Government or any other expence to the revenue than the salary of the judges, it is astonishing how such a mass of taxes can be employed. Not even the internal defence of the country is paid out of the revenue. On all occasions, whether real or contrived, recourse is continually had to new loans and new taxes. No wonder, then, that a machine of Government so advantageous to the advocates of a Court should be so triumphantly extolled. No wonder, that St. James' or St. Stephen's should echo with the continual cry of Constitution! No wonder, that the French Revolution should be reprobated, and the *res-publica* treated with reproach! The *red book* of England, like the red book of France, will explain the reason.

I will now, by way of relaxation, turn a thought or two to Mr. Burke. I ask his pardon for neglecting him so long.

"America," says he (in his speech on the Canada Constitution Bill), "never dreamed of such absurd doctrine as the *Rights of Man*."

Mr. Burke is such a bold presumer, and advances his assertions and his premises with such a deficiency of judgment, that without troubling ourselves about the principles of philosophy or politics, the mere logical conclusions they produce are ridiculous. For instance:

If Governments, as Mr. Burke asserts, are not founded on the Rights of MAN, and are founded on *any rights* at all, they consequently must be founded on the right of *something* that is *not man*. What then is that something?

Generally speaking, we know of no other creatures that inhabit the earth than man and beast; and in all cases where only two things offer themselves, and one must be admitted, a negation proved on any one amounts to an affirmative on the other; and therefore, Mr. Burke, by proving against the Rights of *Man* proves in behalf of the *beast;* and consequently, proves that Government is a beast; and as difficult things sometimes explain each other, we now see the origin of keeping wild beasts in the Tower; for they certainly can be of no other use than to shew the origin of the Government. They are in the place of a Constitution. O, John Bull, what honours thou hast lost by not being a wild beast. Thou mightest, on Mr. Burke's system, have been in the Tower for life.

If Mr. Burke's arguments have not weight enough to keep one serious, the fault is less mine than his; and as I am willing to make an apology to the reader for the liberty I have taken, I hope Mr. Burke will also make his for giving the cause.

Having thus paid Mr. Burke the compliment of remembering him, I return to the subject.

From the want of a Constitution in England to restrain and regulate the wild impulse of power, many of the laws are irrational and tyrannical, and the administration of them vague and problematical.

The attention of the Government of England (for I rather chuse to call it by this name than the English Government) appears since its political connection with Germany to have been so completely engrossed and absorbed by foreign affairs, and the means of raising taxes, that it seems to exist for no other purposes. Domestic concerns are neglected; and with respect to regular law there is scarcely such a thing.

Almost every case now must be determined by some precedent, be that precedent good or bad, or whether it properly applies or not; and the practice is become so general as to suggest a suspicion that it proceeds from a deeper policy than at first sight appears.

Since the Revolution of America, and more so since that of France, this preaching up the doctrines of precedents, drawn from times and circumstances antecedent to those events, has been the studied practice of the English Government. The generality of those precedents are founded on principles and opinions, the reverse of what they ought; and the greater distance of time they are drawn from the more they are to be suspected. But by associating those precedents with a superstitious reverence for ancient things, as monks shew relics and call them holy, the generality of mankind are deceived into the design. Governments now act as if they were afraid to awaken a single reflection in man. They are softly leading him to the sepulchre of precedents to deaden his faculties and call attention from the scene of Revolutions. They feel that he is arriving at knowledge faster than they wish, and their policy of precedents is the barometer of their fears. This political popery, like the ecclesiastical popery of old, has had its day, and is hastening to its exit. The ragged relic and the antiquated precedent, the monk and the monarch, will moulder together.

Government by precedent, without any regard to the principle of the precedent, is one of the vilest systems that can be set up. In numerous instances the precedent ought to operate as a warning, and not as an example, and requires to be shunned instead of imitated; but instead of this, precedents are taken in the lump, and put at once for Constitution and for law.

Either the doctrine of precedents is policy to keep man in a state of ignorance, or it is a practical confession that wisdom degenerates in Governments as Governments increase in age, and can only hobble along by the stilts and crutches of precedents. How is it that the same persons who would proudly be thought wiser than their predecessors appear at the same time only as the ghosts of departed wisdom? How strangely is antiquity treated! To answer some purposes it is spoken of as the times of darkness and ignorance, and to answer others, it is put for the light of the world.

If the doctrine of precedents is to be followed, the expences of Government need not continue the same. Why pay men extravagantly who have but little to do? If everything that can happen is already in precedent, legislation is at an end, and precedent, like a dictionary, determines every case. Either, therefore, Government has arrived at its dotage, and requires to be renovated, or all the occasions for exercising its wisdom have already occurred.

We now see all over Europe, and particularly in England, the curious phænomenon of a nation looking one way, and the Government the other —the one forward and the other backward. If Governments are to go on by precedent, while Nations go on by improvement, they must at last come to a final separation; and the sooner, and the more civilly they determine this point, the better.

Having thus spoken of Constitutions generally, as things distinct from actual Governments, let us proceed to consider the parts of which a Constitution is composed.

Opinions differ more on this subject than with respect to the whole. That a Nation ought to have a Constitution, as a rule, for the conduct of its Government is a simple question in which all men not directly courtiers, will agree. It is only on the component parts that questions and opinions multiply.

But this difficulty, like every other, will diminish when put into a train of being rightly understood.

The first thing is, that a Nation has a right to establish a Constitution.

Whether it exercises this right in the most judicious manner at first is quite another case. It exercises it agreeably to the judgment it possesses; and by continuing to do so, all errors will at last be exploded.

When this right is established in a Nation, there is no fear that it will be employed to its own injury. A Nation can have no interest in being wrong.

Though all the Constitutions of America are on one general principle, yet no two of them are exactly alike in their component parts or in the distribution of the powers which they give to the actual Governments. Some are more, and others less complex.

In forming a Constitution, it is first necessary to consider what are the ends for which Government is necessary? Secondly, what are the best means, and the least expencive, for accomplishing those ends?

Government is nothing more than a national association; and the object of this association is the good of all, as well individually as collectively. Every man wishes to pursue his occupation, and to enjoy the fruits of his labours and the produce of his property in peace and safety, and with the least possible expence. When these things are accomplished, all the objects for which Government ought to be established are answered.

It has been customary to consider Government under three distinct general heads. The legislative, the executive, and the judicial.

But if we permit our judgment to act unencumbered by the habit of multiplied terms, we can perceive no more than two divisions of power, of which civil Government is composed, namely that of legislating or enacting laws, and that of executing or administering them. Everything, therefore, appertaining to civil Government, classes itself under one or other of these two divisions.

So far as regards the execution of the laws, that which is called the judicial power, is strictly and properly the executive power of every country. It is that power to which every individual has to appeal, and which causes the law to be executed; neither have we any other clear idea with respect to the official execution of the laws. In England, and also in America and France, this power begins with the magistrate, and proceeds up through all the courts of judicature.

I leave to courtiers to explain what is meant by calling Monarchy the executive power. It is merly a name in which acts of Government are done; and any other, or none at all, would answer the same purpose. Laws have neither more nor less authority on this account. It must be from the justness of their principles, and the interest which a Nation feels therein, that they derive support; if they require any other than this, it is a sign that something in the system of Government is imperfect. Laws difficult to be executed cannot be generally good.

With respect to the organization of the *legislative power,* different modes have been adopted in different countries. In America it is generally composed of two houses. In France it consists but of one, but in both countries it is wholly by representation.

The case is, that mankind (from the long tyranny of assumed power) have had so few opportunities of making the necessary trials on modes and principles of Government, in order to discover the best, *that Government is but now beginning to be known,* and experience is yet wanting to determine many particulars.

The objections against two houses are, first, that there is an inconsistency in any part of a whole legislature, coming to a final determination by vote on any matter, whilst *that matter,* with respect to *that whole,* is yet only in a train of deliberation, and consequently open to new illustrations.

Secondly. That by taking the vote on each, as a separate body, it always admits of the possibility, and is often the case in practice, that the minority governs the majority, and that in some instances to a degree of great inconsistency.

Thirdly. That two houses arbitrarily checking or controuling each other is inconsistent; because it cannot be proved on the principles of just representation, that either should be wiser or better than the other. They may check in the wrong as well as in the right—and therefore to give the power where we cannot give the wisdom to use it, nor be assured of its being rightly used, renders the hazard at least equal to the precaution.

The objection against a single house is, that it is always in a condition of committing itself too soon. But it should at the same time be remembered, that when there is a Constitution which defines the power, and establishes the principles within which a legislature shall act, there is already a more effectual check provided, and more powerfully operating, than any other check can be. For example:

Were a Bill to be brought into any of the American legislatures similar to that which was passed into an act by the English Parliament, at the commencement of George the First, to extend the duration of the assemblies to a longer period than they now sit, the check is in the Constitution, which in effect says, *Thus far shalt thou go and no further.*

But in order to remove the objection against a single house, that of acting with too quick an impulse, and at the same time to avoid the inconsistencies, in some cases absurdities, arising from two houses, the following method has been proposed as an improvement upon both.

First, to have but one representation.

Secondly, to divide that representation, by lot, into two or three parts.

Thirdly, that every proposed Bill shall be first debated in those parts by succession, that they may become the hearers of each other, but without taking any vote. After which the whole representation to assemble for a general debate and determination by vote.

To this proposed improvement has been added another, for the purpose of keeping the representation in the state of constant renovation; which is that one-third of the representation of each country shall go out at the expiration of one year, and the number be replaced by new elections. Another third at the expiration of the second year replaced in like manner, and every third year to be a general election.

But in whatever manner the separate parts of a Constitution may be arranged there is *one* general principle that distinguishes freedom from slavery, which is, *that all hereditary Government over a people is to them a species of slavery, and representative Government is freedom.*

Considering Government in the only light in which it should be considered, that of a National Association, it ought to be so constructed as not to be disordered by any accident happening among the parts; and, therefore, no extraordinary power, capable of producing such an effect, should be lodged in the hands of any individual. The death, sickness, absence or defection, of any one individual in a Government, ought to be a matter of no more consequence, with respect to the Nation, than if the same circumstance had taken place in a member of the English Parliament, or the French National Assembly.

Scarcely anything presents a more degrading character of national greatness, than its being thrown into confusion, by anything happening to or acted by any individual; and the ridiculousness of the scene is often increased by the natural insignificance of the person by whom it is occasioned. Were a Government so constructed, that it could not go on unless a goose or a gander were present in the senate, the difficulties would be just as great and as real, on the flight or sickness of the goose, or the gander, as if it were called a King. We laugh at individuals for the silly difficulties they make to themselves, without perceiving that the greatest of all ridiculous things are acted in Governments.

All the Constitutions of America are on a plan that excludes the childish embarrassments which occur in monarchical countries. No suspension of Government can there take place for a moment, from any circumstances whatever. The system of representation provides for everything, and is the only system in which Nations and Governments can always appear in their proper character.

As extraordinary power ought not to be lodged in the hands of any individual, so ought there to be no appropriations of public money to any person, beyond what his services in a state may be worth. It signifies not whether a man be called a president, a king, an emperor, a senator, or by any other name which propriety or folly may devise or arrogance assume, it is only a certain service he can perform in the state; and the service of any such individual in the routine of office, whether such office be called monarchical, presidential, senatorial, or by any other name or title, can never exceed the value of ten thousand pounds a year. All the great services that are done in the world are performed by volunteer characters, who accept nothing for them; but the routine of office is always regulated to such a general standard of abilities as to be within the compass of numbers in every country to perform, and therefore cannot merit very extraordinary recompence. *Government,* says Swift, *is a plain thing, and fitted to the capacity of many heads.*

It is inhuman to talk of a million sterling a year, paid out of the public taxes of any country, for the support of an individual, whilst thousands who are forced to contribute thereto, are pining with want, and struggling with misery. Government does not consist in a contrast between prisons and palaces, between poverty and pomp; it is not instituted to rob the needy of his mite, and increase the wretchedness of the wretched. But of this part of the subject I shall speak hereafter, and confine myself at present to political observations.

When extraordinary power and extraordinary pay are allotted to any individual in a Government, he becomes the centre, round which every kind of corruption generates and forms. Give to any man a million a-year, and add thereto the power of creating and disposing of places, at the expence of a country, and the liberties of that country are no longer secure. What is called the splendour of a throne is no other than the corruption of the state. It is made up of a band of parasites living in luxurious indolence out of the public taxes.

When once such a vicious system is established it becomes the guard and protection of all inferior abuses. The man who is in the receipt of a million a year is the last person to promote a spirit of reform, lest, in the event, it should reach to himself. It is always his interest to defend inferior abuses, as so many outworks to protect the citadel; and on this species of political fortification, all the parts have such a common dependence that it is never to be expected they will attack each other.

Monarchy would not have continued so many ages in the world had it not been for the abuses it protects. It is the master-fraud, which shelters all others. By admitting a participation of the spoil, it makes itself friends; and when it ceases to do this it will cease to be the idol of courtiers.

As the principle on which Constitutions are now formed rejects all hereditary pretensions to Government, it also rejects all that catalogue of assumptions known by the name of prerogatives.

If there is any Government where prerogatives might with apparent safety be entrusted to any individual, it is in the federal Government of America. The President of the United States of America is elected only for four years. He is not only responsible in the general sense of the word, but a particular mode is laid down in the Constitution for trying him. He cannot be elected under thirty-five years of age; and he must be a native of the country.

In a comparison of these cases with the Government of England, the difference when applied to the latter amounts to an absurdity. In England the person who exercises prerogative is often a foreigner; always half a foreigner, and always married to a foreigner. He is never in full natural or political connection with the country, is not responsible for anything, and becomes of age at eighteen years; yet such a person is permitted to form foreign alliances, without even the knowledge of the Nation, and to make war and peace without its consent.

But this is not all. Though such a person cannot dispose of the Government in the manner of a testator, he dictates the marriage connections, which, in effect, accomplish a great part of the same end. He cannot directly bequeath half the Government to Prussia, but he can form a marriage partnership that will produce almost the same thing. Under such circumstances, it is happy for England that she is not situated on the Continent, or she might, like Holland, fall under the dictatorship of Prussia. Holland, by marriage, is as effectually governed by Prussia, as if the whole tyranny of bequeathing the Government had been the means.

The presidency in America (or, as it is sometimes called, the executive) is the only office from which a foreigner is excluded, and in England it is the only one to which he is admitted. A foreigner cannot be a member of Parliament, but he may be what is called a King. If there is any reason for excluding foreigners, it ought to be from those offices where mischief can be most acted, and where, by uniting every bias of interest and attachment, the trust is best secured. But as Nations proceed in the great business of forming Constitutions, they will examine with more precision into the nature and business of that department which is called executive. What the legislative and judicial departments are every one can see; but with respect to what, in Europe, is called the executive, as distinct from those two, it is either a political superfluity or a chaos of unknown things.

Some kind of official department, to which reports shall be made from the different parts of a Nation, or from abroad, to be laid before the national representatives, is all that is necessary; but there is no consistency in calling this the executive; neither can it be considered in any other light than as inferior to the legislative. The sovereign authority in any country is the power of making laws, and everything else is an official department.

Next to the arrangement of the principles and the organization of the several parts of a Constitution, is the provision to be made for the support of the persons to whom the Nation shall confide the administration of the Constitutional powers.

A nation can have no right to the time and services of any person at his own expence, whom it may choose to employ or entrust in any department whatever; neither can any reason be given for making provision for the support of any one part of a Government and not for the other.

But admitting that the honour of being entrusted with any part of a Government is to be considered a sufficient reward, it ought to be so to every person alike. If the members of the legislature of any country are to serve at their own expence, that which is called the executive, whether monarchical or by any other name, ought to serve in like manner. It is inconsistent to pay the one, and accept the service of the other gratis.

In America, every department in the Government is decently provided for; but no one is extravagantly paid. Every member of Congress, and of the assemblies, is allowed a sufficiency for his expences. Whereas in England, a most prodigal provision is made for the support of one part of the Government and none for the other, the consequence of which is that the one is furnished with the means of corruption and the other is put into the condition of being corrupted. Less than a fourth part of such expence, applied as it is in America, would remedy a great part of the corruption.

Another reform in the American Constitutions is the exploding of all oaths of personality. The oath of allegiance in America is to the nation only. The putting any individual as a figure for a Nation is improper. The happiness of a Nation is the superior object, and therefore the intention of an oath of allegiance ought not to be obscured by being figuratively taken to, or in the name of, any person. The oath, called the civic oath, in France, viz., the "*Nation, the Law, and the King,*" is improper. If taken at all, it ought to be as in America, to the nation only. The law may or may not be good; but in this place it can have no other meaning than as being conducive to the happiness of the nation, and therefore is included in it. The remainder of the oath is improper on the ground that all personal oaths ought to be abolished. They are the remains of tyranny on one part and slavery on the other; and the name of the CREATOR ought not to be introduced to witness the degradation of his creation; or if taken, as is already mentioned, as figurative of the Nation, it is in this place redundant. But whatever apology may be made for oaths at the first establishment of a Government, they ought not to be permitted afterwards. If a Government requires the support of oaths, it is a sign that it is not worth supporting, and ought not to be supported. Make Government what it ought to be, and it will support itself.

To conclude this part of the subject:—One of the greatest improvements that has been made for the perpetual security and progress of constitutional liberty, is the provision which the new Constitutions make for occasionally revising, altering, and amending them.

The principle upon which Mr. Burke formed his political creed, that of *binding and controlling posterity to the end of time, and of renouncing and abdicating the rights of all posterity for ever,* is now become too detestable to be made a subject of debate; and therefore I pass it over with no other notice than exposing it.

Government is but now beginning to be known. Hitherto it has been the mere exercise of power which forbade all effectual enquiry into rights, and grounded itself wholly on possession. While the enemy of liberty was its judge, the progress of its principles must have been small indeed.

The Constitutions of America, and also that of France, have either affixed a period for their revision, or laid down the mode by which improvement shall be made. It is perhaps impossible to establish anything that combines principles with opinions and practice, which the progress of circumstances, through a length of years, will not in some measure derange, or render inconsistent; and, therefore, to prevent inconveniences accumulating, till they discourage reformations or provoke Revolutions, it is best to provide the means of regulating them as they occur. The Rights of Man are the rights of all generations of men, and cannot be monopolized by any. That which is worth following will be followed for the sake of its worth, and it is in this that its security lies, and not in any conditions with which it may be encumbered. When a man leaves property to his heirs, he does not connect it with an obligation that they shall accept it. Why, then, should we do otherwise with respect to Constitutions?

The best Constitution that could now be devised, consistent with the condition of the present moment, may be far short of that excellence which a few years may afford. There is a morning of reason rising upon man on the subject of Government that has not appeared before. As the barbarism of the present old Governments expires, the moral condition of Nations with respect to each other will be changed. Man will not be brought up with the savage idea of considering his species as his enemy, because the accident of birth gave the individuals existence in countries distinguished by different names; and as Constitutions have always some relation to external as well as to domestic circumstances, the means of benefiting by every change, foreign or domestic, should be a part of every Constitution.

We already see an alteration in the national disposition of England and France towards each other, which, when we look back to only a few years, is itself a Revolution. Who could have foreseen, or who would have believed, that a French National Assembly would ever have been a popular toast in England, or that a friendly alliance of the two Nations should become the wish of either? It shews that man, were he not corrupted by Governments, is naturally the friend of man, and that human nature is not of itself vicious. That spirit of jealousy and ferocity, which the Governments of the two countries inspired, and which they rendered subservient to the purpose of taxation, is now yielding to the dictates of reason, interest, and humanity. The trade of courts is beginning to be understood, and the affectation of mystery, with all the artificial sorcery by which they imposed upon mankind, is on the decline. It has received its death wound; and though it may linger, it will expire.

Government ought to be as much open to improvement as anything which appertains to man, instead of which it has been monopolized from age to age, by the most ignorant and vicious of the human race. Need we any other proof of their wretched management, than the excess of debts and taxes with which every nation groans, and the quarrels into which they have precipitated the world?

Just emerging from such a barbarous condition, it is too soon to determine to what extent of improvement Government may yet be carried.

For what we can foresee, all Europe may form but one great Republic, and man be free of the whole.

Ways and Means of Improving the Condition of Europe, Interspersed with Miscellaneous Observations

In contemplating a subject that embraces with equatorial magnitude the whole region of humanity it is impossible to confine the pursuit in one single direction. It takes ground on every character and condition that appertains to man, and blends the individual, the nation, and the world.

From a small spark, kindled in America, a flame has arisen not to be extinguished. Without consuming, like the *Ultima Ratio Regum,* it winds its progress from Nation to Nation and conquers by a silent operation. Man finds himself changed, he scarcely perceives how. He acquires a knowledge of his rights by attending justly to his interest, and discovers in the event that the strength and powers of despotism consist wholly in the fear of resisting it, and that in order *"to be free it is sufficient that he wills it."*

Having in all the preceding parts of this work endeavoured to establish a system of principles as a basis on which Governments ought to be erected, I shall proceed in this to the ways and means of rendering them into practice. But in order to introduce this part of the subject with more propriety and stronger effect, some preliminary observations, deducible from, or connected with those principles, are necessary.

Whatever the form or Constitution of Government may be, it ought to have no other object than the *general* happiness. When instead of this it operates to create and increase wretchedness, in any of the parts of society, it is on a wrong system and reformation is necessary.

Customary language has classed the condition of man under the two descriptions of civilized and uncivilized life. To the one it has ascribed felicity and affluence: to the other hardship and want. But, however our imagination may be impressed by painting and comparison, it is nevertheless true, that a great portion of mankind, in what are called civilized countries, are in a state of poverty and wretchedness, far below the condition of an Indian. I speak not of one country, but of all. It is so in England, it is so all over Europe. Let us enquire into the cause.

It lies not in any natural defect in the principles of civilization, but in preventing those principles having an universal operation; the consequence of which is a perpetual system of war and expence, that drains the country and defeats the general felicity of which civilization is capable.

All the European Governments (France now excepted) are constructed not on the principle of universal civilization, but on the reverse of it. So far as those Governments relate to each other they are in the same condition as we conceive of savage uncivilized life, they put themselves beyond the law as well of God as of man, and are with respect to principle and reciprocal conduct like so many individuals in a state of nature.

The inhabitants of every country, under the civilization of laws, easily civilize together, but Governments being yet in an uncivilized state, and almost continually at war, they pervert the abundance which civilized life produces to carry on the uncivilized part to a greater extent. By thus engrafting the barbarism of Government upon the internal civilization of a country, it draws from the latter, and more especially from the poor, a great portion of those earnings which should be applied to their own subsistence and comfort. Apart from all reflections of morality and philosophy, it is a melancholy fact that more than one-fourth of the labour of mankind is annually consumed by this barbarous system.

What has served to continue this evil is the pecuniary advantage which all the Governments of Europe have found in keeping up this state of uncivilization. It affords to them pretences for power and revenue, for which there would be neither occasion nor apology if the circle of civilization were rendered complete. Civil Government alone, or the Government of laws, is not productive of pretences for many taxes; it operates at home, directly under the eye of the country, and precludes the possibility of much imposition. But when the scene is laid in the uncivilized contention of Governments, the field of pretences is enlarged, and the country being no longer a judge, is open to every imposition which Governments please to act.

Not a thirtieth, scarcely a fortieth, part of the taxes which are raised in England are either occasioned by, or applied to, the purposes of civil Government. It is not difficult to see that the whole which the actual Government does in this respect is to enact laws, and that the country administers and executes them, at its own expense, by means of magistrates, juries, sessions, and assize, over and above the taxes which it pays.

In this view of the case, we have two distinct characters of Government; the one the civil Government, or the Government of laws, which operates at home, the other the Court or Cabinet Government, which operates abroad, on the rude plan of uncivilized life; the one attended with little charge, the other with boundless extravagance; and so distinct are the two, that if the latter were to sink, as it were, by a sudden opening of the earth, and totally disappear, the former would not be deranged. It would still proceed, because it is the common interest of the Nation that it should, and all the means are in practice.

Revolutions, then, have for their object a change in the moral condition of Governments, and with this change the burden of public taxes will lessen, and civilization will be left to the enjoyment of that abundance of which it is now deprived.

In contemplating the whole of this subject, I extend my views into the department of commerce. In all my publications, where the matter would admit, I have been an advocate for commerce, because I am a friend to its effects. It is a pacific system, operating to cordialise mankind, by rendering Nations, as well as individuals, useful to each other. As to the mere theoretical reformation, I have never preached it up. The most effectual process is that of improving the condition of man by means of his interest; and it is on this ground that I take my stand.

If commerce were permitted to act to the universal extent it is capable, it would extirpate the system of war, and produce a Revolution in the uncivilized state of Governments. The invention of commerce has arisen since those Governments began, and it is the greatest approach towards universal civilization that has yet been made by any means not immediately flowing from moral principles.

Whatever has a tendency to promote the civil intercourse of Nations by an exchange of benefits, is a subject as worthy of philosophy as of politics. Commerce is no other than the traffic of two individuals, multiplied on a scale of number; and the same rule that nature intended the intercourse of two, she intended for all. For this purpose she has distributed the materials of manufactures and commerce in various and distant parts of a Nation and of the world; and as they cannot be procured by war so cheaply or so commodiously as by commerce, she has rendered the latter the means of extirpating the former.

As the two are nearly the opposites of each other, consequently, the uncivilized state of the European Governments is injurious to commerce. Every kind of destruction or embarrassment serves to lessen the quantity, and it matters but little in what part of the commercial world the reduction begins. Like blood, it cannot be taken from any of the parts, without being taken from the whole mass in circulation, and all partake of the loss. When the ability in any Nation to buy is destroyed, it equally involves the seller. Could the Government of England destroy the commerce of all other Nations, she would most effectually ruin her own.

It is possible that a Nation may be the carrier for the world, but she cannot be the merchant. She cannot be the seller and buyer of her own merchandize. The ability to buy must reside out of herself; and, therefore, the prosperity of any commercial Nation is regulated by the prosperity of the rest. If they are poor she cannot be rich, and her condition, be it what it may, is an index of the height of the commercial tide in other Nations.

That the principles of commerce, and its universal operation, may be understood, without understanding the practice, is a position that reason will not deny; and it is on this ground only that I argue the subject. It is one thing in the counting-house, in the world it is another. With respect to its operation it must necessarily be contemplated as a reciprocal thing; that only one-half of its power resides within the Nation, and that the whole is as effectually destroyed by destroying the half that resides without, as if the destruction had been committed on that which is within; for neither can act without the other.

When in the last, as well as in the former wars, the commerce of England sunk, it was because the general quantity was lessened everywhere; and it now rises, because commerce is in a rising state in every Nation. If England, at this day, imports and exports more than at any former period, the Nation with which she trades must necessarily do the same; her imports are their exports, and *vice versa.*

There can be no such thing as a Nation flourishing alone in commerce; she can only participate; and the destruction of it in any part must necessarily affect all. When, therefore, Governments are at war, the attack is made upon the common stock of commerce, and the consequence is the same as if each had attacked his own.

The present increase of commerce is not to be attributed to ministers, or to any political contrivances, but to its own natural operations in consequence of peace. The regular markets had been destroyed, the channels of trade broken up, the high road of the seas infested with robbers of every Nation, and the attention of the world called to other objects. Those interruptions have ceased, and peace has restored the deranged condition of things to their proper order.

It is worth remarking, that every Nation reckons the balance of trade in its own favour; and therefore something must be irregular in the common ideas upon this subject.

The fact, however, is true, according to what is called a balance; and it is from this cause that commerce is universally supported. Every Nation feels the advantage, or it would abandon the practice; but the deception lies in the mode of making up the accounts, and in attributing what are called profits to a wrong cause.

Mr. Pitt has sometimes amused himself, by showing what he called a balance of trade from the custom-house books. This mode of calculation, not only affords no rule that is true, but one that is false.

In the first place, Every cargo that departs from the custom-house, appears on the books as an export; and according to the custom-house balance, the losses at sea, and by foreign failures, are all reckoned on the side of profit because they appear as exports.

Secondly, Because the importation by the smuggling trade does not appear on the custom-house books, to arrange against the exports.

No balance, therefore, as applying to superior advantages, can be drawn from those documents: and if we examine the natural operation of commerce, the idea is fallacious, and if true, would soon be injurious. The great support of commerce consists in the balance being a level of benefits among all Nations.

Two merchants of different Nations trading together, will both become rich, and each makes the balance in his own favour; consequently they do not get rich out of each other; and it is the same with respect to the Nations in which they reside. The case must be, that each Nation must get rich out of its own means, and encrease that riches by something which it procures from another in exchange.

If a merchant in England sends an article of English manufacture abroad which costs him a shilling at home and imports something which sells for two, he makes a balance of one shilling in his own favour; but this is not gained out of the foreign Nation or the foreign merchant, for he also does the same by the articles he receives, and neither has a balance of advantage upon the other. The original value of the two articles in their proper countries was but two shillings, but by changing their places, they acquire a new idea of value equal to double what they had at first, and that encreased value is equally divided.

There is no otherwise a balance on foreign than on domestic commerce. The merchants of London and Newcastle trade on the same principles, as if they resided in different Nations, and make their balances in the same manner; yet London does not get rich out of Newcastle, any more than Newcastle out of London; but coals, the merchandize of Newcastle, have an additional value at London, and London merchandize has the same at Newcastle.

Though the principle of all commerce is the same, the domestic, in a national view, is the part the most beneficial; because the whole of the advantages, on both sides, rests within the Nation; whereas, in foreign commerce, it is only participation of one-half.

The most unprofitable of all commerce is that connected with foreign dominion. To a few individuals it may be beneficial, merely because it is commerce; but to the Nation it is a loss. The expence of maintaining dominion more than absorbs the profits of any trade. It does not encrease the general quantity in the world, but operates to lessen it, and as a greater mass would be afloat by relinquishing dominion, the participation without the expence would be more valuable than a greater quantity with it.

But it is impossible to engross commerce by dominion; and therefore it is still more fallacious. It cannot exist in confined channels, and necessarily breaks out by regular or irregular means, that defeat the attempt; and to succeed would be still worse. France, since the Revolution, has been more than indifferent as to foreign possessions, and other Nations will become the same when they investigate the subject with respect to commerce.

To the expence of dominion is to be added that of navies, and when the amount of the two are subtracted from the profits of commerce, it will appear that what is called the balance of trade, even admitting it to exist, is not enjoyed by the Nation, but absorbed by the Government.

The idea of having navies for the protection of commerce is delusive. It is putting the means of destruction for the means of protection. Commerce needs no other protection than the reciprocal interest which every nation feels in supporting it—it is common stock—it exists by a balance of advantages to all; and the only interruption it meets, is from the present uncivilized state of Governments, and which it is common interest to reform.

Quitting this subject, I now proceed to other matters. As it is necessary to include England in the prospect of a general reformation, it is proper to enquire into the defects of its Government. It is only by each Nation reforming its own, that the whole can be improved, and the full benefit of reformation enjoyed. Only partial advantages can flow from partial reforms.

France and England are the only two countries in Europe where a reformation in Government could have successfully begun. The one secure by the ocean, and the other by the immensity of its internal strength, could defy the malignancy of foreign despotism. But it is with Revolutions as with commerce, the advantages increase by their becoming general, and double to either what each would receive alone.

As a new system is now opening to the view of the world, the European courts are plotting to counteract it. Alliances, contrary to all former systems, are agitating, and a common interest of Courts is forming against the common interest of man. This combination draws a line that runs throughout Europe, and presents a cause so entirely new as to exclude all calculations from former circumstances. While despotism warred with despotism, man had no interest in the contest; but in a cause that unites the soldier with the citizen, and Nation with Nation, the despotism of Courts, though it feels the danger, and meditates revenge, is afraid to strike.

No question has arisen within the records of history that pressed with the importance of the present. It is not whether this or that party shall be in or not, or Whig or Tory, or high or low shall prevail; but whether man shall inherit his rights, and universal civilization take place? Whether the fruits of his labours shall be enjoyed by himself or consumed by the profligacy of Governments? Whether robbery shall be banished from Courts, and wretchedness from countries?

When, in countries that are called civilized, we see age going to the workhouse and youth to the gallows, something must be wrong in the system of Government. It would seem, by the exterior appearances of such countries, that all was happiness; but there lies hidden from the eye of common observation, a mass of wretchedness that has scarcely any other chance, than to expire in poverty or infamy. Its entrance into life is marked with the presage of its fate; and until this is remedied, it is in vain to punish.

Civil Government does not consist in executions; but in making that provision for the instruction of youth and the support of age, as to exclude, as much as possible, profligacy from the one and despair from the other. Instead of this, the resources of a country are lavished upon kings, upon Courts, upon hirelings, imposters and prostitutes; and even the poor themselves, with all their wants upon them, are compelled to support the fraud that oppresses them.

Why is it that scarcely any are executed but the poor? The fact is a proof, among other things, of a wretchedness in their condition. Bred up without morals, and cast upon the world without a prospect, they are the exposed sacrifice of vice and legal barbarity. The millions that are superfluously wasted upon Governments are more than sufficient to reform those evils, and to benefit the condition of every man in a Nation, not included within the purlieus of a Court. This I hope to make appear in the progress of this work.

It is the nature of compassion to associate with misfortune. In taking up this subject I seek no recompence—I fear no consequence. Fortified with that proud integrity that disdains to triumph or to yield, I will advocate the Rights of Man.

It is to my advantage that I have served an apprenticeship to life. I know the value of moral instruction, and I have seen the danger of the contrary.

At an early period, little more than sixteen years of age, raw and adventurous, and heated with the false heroism of a master who had served in a man-of-war, I began the carver of my own fortune, and entered on board the Terrible Privateer, Captain Death. From this adventure I was happily prevented by the affectionate and moral remonstrance of a good father, who, from his own habits of life, being of the Quaker profession, must begin to look upon me as lost. But the impression, much as it affected at the time, began to wear away, and I entered afterwards in the King of Prussia Privateer, Captain Mendez, and went with her to sea. Yet from such a beginning, and with all the inconvenience of early life against me, I am proud to say that with a perseverence undismayed by difficulties, a disinterestedness that compelled respect, I have not only contributed to raise a new empire in the world, founded on a new system of Government, but I have arrived at an eminence in political literature, the most difficult of all lines to succeed and excel in, which Aristocracy with all its aids has not been able to reach or to rival.

Knowing my own heart and feeling myself as I now do, superior to all the skirmish of party, the inveteracy of interested or mistaken opponents, I answer not to falsehood or abuse, but proceed to the defects of the English Government.

I begin with charters and corporations.

It is a perversion of terms to say that a charter gives rights. It operates by a contrary effect—that of taking rights away. Rights are inherently in all the inhabitants; but charters, by annulling those rights in the majority, leave the right, by exclusion, in the hands of a few. If charters were constructed so as to express in direct terms, *"that every inhabitant, who is not a member of a corporation, shall not exercise the right of voting,"* such charters would, in the face, be charters not of rights, but of exclusion. The effect is the same under the form they now stand; and the only persons on whom they operate are the persons whom they exclude. Those whose rights are guaranteed, by not being taken away, exercise no other rights than as members of the community they are entitled to without a charter; and, therefore, all charters have no other than an indirect negative operation. They do not give rights to A, but they make a difference in favour of A by taking away the right of B, and consequently are instruments of injustice.

But charters and corporations have a more extensive evil effect than what relates merely to elections. They are sources of endless contentions in the places where they exist, and they lessen the common rights of national society. A native of England, under the operation of these charters and corporations, cannot be said to be an Englishman in the full sense of the word. He is not free of the Nation in the same manner that a Frenchman is free of France, and an American of America. His rights are circumscribed to the town, and in some cases to the parish of his birth; and all other parts, though in his native land, are to him as a foreign country. To acquire a residence in these he must undergo a local naturalization by purchase, or he is forbidden or expelled the place. This species of feudality is kept up to aggrandize the corporations at the ruin of towns; and the effect is visible.

The generality of corporation towns are in a state of solitary decay, and prevented from further ruin only by some circumstance in their situation, such as a navigable river, or a plentiful surrounding country. As population is one of the chief sources of wealth (for without it land itself has no value), everything which operates to prevent it must lessen the value of property; and as corporations have not only this tendency, but directly this effect, they cannot be but injurious. If any policy were to be followed, instead of that of general freedom to every person to settle where he choose (as in France or America) it would be more consistent to give encouragement to new comers than to preclude their admission by exacting premiums from them.

The persons most immediately interested in the abolition of corporations are the inhabitants of the towns where corporations are established. The instances of Manchester, Birmingham, and Sheffield shew, by contrast, the injury which those Gothic institutions are to property and commerce. A few examples may be found, such as that of London, whose natural and commercial advantages, owing to its situation on the Thames, is capable of bearing up against the political evils of a corporation; but in almost all other cases the fatality is too visible to be doubted or denied.

Though the whole Nation is not so directly affected by the depression of property in corporation towns as the inhabitants themselves, it partakes of the consequence. By lessening the value of property, the quantity of national commerce is curtailed. Every man is a customer in proportion to his ability; and as all parts of the Nation trade with each other, whatever affects any of the parts must necessarily communicate to the whole.

As one of the houses of the English Parliament is, in a great measure, made up of elections from these corporations; and as it is unnatural that a pure stream should flow from a foul fountain, its vices are but a continuation of the vices of its origin. A man of moral honour and good political principles cannot submit to the mean drudgery and disgraceful arts by which such elections are carried. To be a successful candidate he must be destitute of the qualities that constitute a just legislator; and being thus disciplined to corruption by the mode of entering into Parliament, it is not to be expected that the representative should be better than the man.

Mr. Burke, in speaking of the English representation, has advanced as bold a challenge as ever was given in the days of chivalry. "Our representation," says he, "has been found *perfectly adequate to all the purposes* for which a representation of the people can be desired or devised. I defy," continues he, "the enemies of our Constitution to shew the contrary." This declaration from a man who has been in constant opposition to all the measures of Parliament the whole of his political life, a year or two excepted, is most extraordinary; and, comparing him with himself, admits of no other alternative than that he acted against his judgment as a member, or has declared contrary to it as an author.

But it is not in the representation only that the defects lie, and therefore I proceed in the next place to the Aristocracy.

What is called the House of Peers is constituted on a ground very similar to that against which there is a law in other cases. It amounts to a combination of persons in one common interest. No reason can be given why a house of legislation should be composed entirely of men whose occupation consists in letting landed property, than why it should be composed of those who hire, or of brewers, or bakers, or any other separate class of men.

Mr. Burke calls this house *"the great ground and pillar of security to the landed interest."* Let us examine this idea.

What pillar of security does the landed interest require more than any other interest in the state, or what right has it to a distinct and separate representation from the general interest of a Nation? The only use to be made of this power (and which it has always made) is to ward off taxes from itself, and throw the burden upon such articles of consumption by which itself would be least affected.

That this has been the consequence (and will always be the consequence) of constructing Governments on combinations, is evident with respect to England from the history of its taxes.

Notwithstanding taxes have encreased and multiplied upon every article of common consumption, the land-tax, which more particularly affects this "pillar," has diminished. In 1788 the amount of the land-tax was £1,950,000, which is half-a-million less than it produced almost a hundred years ago, notwithstanding the rentals are in many instances doubled since that period.

Before the coming of the Hanoverians, the taxes were divided in nearly equal proportions between the land and articles of consumption, the land bearing rather the largest share; but since that æra nearly thirteen millions annually of new taxes have been thrown upon consumption; the consequence of which has been a constant encrease in the number and wretchedness of the poor, and in the amount of the poor rates. Yet here again the burden does not fall in equal proportions on the Aristocracy with the rest of the community. Their residences, whether in town or country, are not mixed with the habitations of the poor. They live apart from distress and the expence of relieving it. It is in manufacturing towns and labouring villages that those burdens press the heaviest, in many of which it is one class of poor supporting another.

Several of the most heavy and productive taxes are so contrived as to give an exemption to this pillar, thus standing in its own defence. The tax upon beer brewed for sale does not affect the Aristocracy, who brew their own beer free of this duty. It falls only on those who have not conveniency or ability to brew, and who must purchase it in small quantities. But what will mankind think of the justice of taxation when they know that this tax alone, from which the Aristocracy are from circumstances exempt, is nearly equal to the whole of the land-tax, being in the year 1788, and it is not less now, £1,666,152, and with its proportion of the taxes on malt and hops, it exceeds it. That a single article, thus partially consumed, and that chiefly by the working part, should be subject to a tax, equal to that on the whole rental of a Nation, is, perhaps, a fact not to be paralleled in the histories of revenues.

This is one of the consequences resulting from a house of legislation composed on the ground of a combination of common interest; for whatever their separate politics as to parties may be, in this they are united. Whether a combination acts to raise the price of any article for sale, or the rate of wages, or whether it acts to throw taxes from itself upon another class of the community, the principle and the effect are the same;

and if the one be illegal, it will be difficult to shew that the other ought to exist.

It is to no use to say that taxes are first proposed in the House of Commons; for as the other House has always a negative it can always defend itself; and it would be ridiculous to suppose that its acquiescence in the measures to be proposed were not understood beforehand. Besides which it has obtained so much influence by borough-traffic, and so many of its relations and connections are distributed on both sides of the Commons, as to give it, besides an absolute negative in one House, a preponderancy in the other in all matters of common concern.

It is difficult to discover what is meant by the *landed interest,* if it does not mean a combination of aristocratical landholders opposing their own pecuniary interest to that of the farmer, and every branch of trade, commerce, and manufacture. In all other respects it is the only interest that needs no partial protection. It enjoys the general protection of the world. Every individual, high or low, is interested in the fruits of the earth; men, women, and children, of all ages and degrees, will turn out to assist the farmer, rather than a harvest should not be got in; and they will not act thus by any other property. It is the only one for which the common prayer of mankind is put up, and the only one that can never fail from the want of means. It is the interest, not of the policy, but of the existence of man, and when it ceases he must cease to be.

No other interest in a Nation stands on the same united support. Commerce, manufactures, arts, sciences, and everything else, compared with this, are supported but in parts. Their prosperity or their decay has not the same universal influence. When the vallies laugh and sing it is not the farmer only but all creation that rejoices. It is a prosperity that excludes all envy; and this cannot be said of anything else.

Why, then, does Mr. Burke talk of his House of Peers as the pillar of the landed interest? Were that pillar to sink into the earth, the same landed property would continue, and the same ploughing, sowing, and reaping would go on. The Aristocracy are not the farmers who work the land and raise the produce, but are the mere consumers of the rent; and when compared with the active world, are the drones, a seraglio of males, who neither collect the honey nor form the hive, but exist only for lazy employment.

Mr. Burke, in his first essay, called Aristocracy *"the Corinthian capital of polished society."* Towards compleating the figure he has now added the *pillar;* but still the base is wanting: and whenever a Nation chuse to act a Samson, not blind, but bold, down go the temple of Dagon, the Lords and the Philistines.

If a house of legislation is to be composed of men of one class for the purpose of protecting a distinct interest, all the other interests should have the same. The inequality as well as the burden of taxation arises from admitting it in one case and not in all. Had there been a house of farmers, there had been no game laws; or a house of merchants and manufacturers, the taxes had neither been so unequal nor so excessive. It is from the power of taxation being in the hands of those who can throw so great a part of it from their own shoulders, that it has raged without a check.

Men of small or moderate estates are more injured by the taxes being thrown on articles of consumption than they are eased by warding it from landed property for the following reasons:

First, They consume more of the productive taxable articles, in proportion to their property, than those of large estates.

Secondly, their residence is chiefly in towns, and their property in houses; and the encrease of the poor-rates, occasioned by taxes on consumption, is in much greater proportion than the land-tax has been favoured. In Birmingham, the poor-rates are not less than seven shillings in the pound. From this, as already observed, the Aristocracy are in a great measure exempt.

These are but a part of the mischiefs flowing from the wretched scheme of a House of Peers.

As a combination, it can always throw a considerable portion of taxes from itself; and as an hereditary house, accountable to nobody, it resembles a rotten borough, whose consent is to be courted by interest. There are but a few of its members, who are not in some mode or other participators, or disposers of the public money. One turns a candleholder, or a lord in waiting; another a lord of the bed-chamber, a groom of the stole, or any insignificant nominal office to which a salary is annexed, paid out of the public taxes, and which avoids the direct appearance of corruption. Such situations are derogatory to the character of man; and where they can be submitted to, honour cannot reside.

To all these are to be added the numerous dependants, the long list of younger branches and distant relations, who are to be provided for at the public expence; in short, were an estimation to be made of the charge of Aristocracy to a Nation, it will be found nearly equal to that of supporting the poor. The Duke of Richmond alone (and there are cases similar to his) takes away as much for himself as would maintain two thousand poor and aged persons. Is it, then, any wonder that under such a system of Government, taxes and rates have multiplied to their present extent?

In stating these matters, I speak an open and disengaged language dictated by no passion but that of humanity. To me, who have not only refused offers because I thought them improper; but have declined rewards I might with reputation have accepted, it is no wonder that meanness and imposition appear disgustful. Independence is my happiness, and I view things as they are, without regard to place or person; my country is the world, and my religion is to do good.

Mr. Burke, in speaking of the aristocratical law of primogeniture, says: "It is the standing law of our landed inheritance; and which, without question, has a tendency, and I think," continues he, "a happy tendency, to preserve a character of weight and consequence."

Mr. Burke may call this law what he pleases, but humanity and impartial reflection will denounce it a law of brutal injustice. Were he not accustomed to the daily practice, and did we only hear of that as the law of some distant part of the world, we should conclude that the legislators of such countries had not yet arrived at a state of civilization.

As to its preserving a character of *weight and consequence,* the case appears to me directly the reverse. It is an attaint upon character; a sort of privateering on family property. It may have weight among dependent tenants, but it gives none on a scale of national, and much less of universal, character. Speaking for myself, my parents were not able to give me a shilling beyond what they gave me in education; and to do this they distressed themselves; yet I possess more of what is called consequence in the world, than any one in Mr. Burke's catalogue of aristocrats.

Having thus glanced at some of the defects of the two Houses of Parliament, I proceed to what is called the Crown, upon which I shall be very concise.

It signifies a nominal office of a million sterling a-year, the business of which consists in receiving the money. Whether the person be wise or foolish, sane or insane, a native or a foreigner, matters not. Every Ministry acts upon the same idea that Mr. Burke writes, namely, that the people must be hood-winked, and held in superstitious ignorance by some bugbear or other; and what is called the Crown answers this purpose, and therefore it answers all the purposes to be expected from it. This is more than can be said of the other two branches.

The hazard to which this office is exposed in all countries is not from anything that can happen to the man, but from what may happen to the Nation—the danger of its coming to its senses.

It has been customary to call the Crown the executive power, and the custom is continued, though the reason has ceased.

It was called the *executive,* because the person whom it signified used formerly to sit in the character of a judge, in administering or executing the laws. The tribunals were then a part of the Court. The power, therefore, which is now called the judicial, is what was called the executive; and, consequently, one or other of the terms is redundant, and one of the offices useless. We speak of the Crown now, it means nothing; it signifies neither a judge nor a general; besides which it is the laws that govern, and not the man. The old terms are kept up, to give an appearance of consequence to empty forms; and the only effect they have is that of encreasing expences.

Before I proceed to the means of rendering Governments more conducive to the general happiness of mankind than they are at present, it will not be improper to take a review of the progress of taxation in England.

It is a general idea, that when taxes are once laid on, they are never taken off. However true this may have been of late, it was not always so. Either, therefore, the people of former times were more watchful over Government than those of the present, or Government was administered with less extravagance.

It is now seven hundred years since the Norman Conquest, and the establishment of what is called the Crown. Taking this portion of time in seven separate periods of one hundred years each, the amount of the annual taxes, at each period, will be as follows:—

Annual amount of taxes levied by William the Conqueror, beginning in the year 1066	£400,000
Annual amount of taxes at one hundred years from the Conquest (1166)	200,000
Annual amount of taxes at two hundred years from the Conquest (1266)	150,000
Annual amount of taxes at three hundred years from the Conquest (1366)	130,000
Annual amount of taxes at four hundred years from the Conquest (1466)	100,000

These statements and those which follow, are taken from Sir John Sinclair's *History of the Revenue;* by which it appears, that taxes continued decreasing for four hundred years, at the expiration of which time they were reduced three-fourths, viz., from four hundred thousand pounds to one hundred thousand. The people of England of the present day, have a traditionary and historical idea of the bravery of their ancestors; but whatever their virtues or their vices might have been, they certainly were a people who would not be imposed upon, and who kept Government in awe as to taxation, if not as to principle. Though they were not able to expel the monarchical usurpation, they restricted it to a republican œconomy of taxes.

Let us now review the remaining three hundred years.

Annual amount of taxes at five hundred years from the Conquest (1566)................................	£500,000
Annual amount of taxes at six hundred years from the Conquest (1666)................................	1,800,000
Annual amount of taxes at the present time (1791)	17,000,000

The difference between the first four hundred years and the last three is so astonishing, as to warrant an opinion that the national character of the English has changed. It would have been impossible to have dragooned the former English into the excess of taxation that now exists; and when it is considered that the pay of the army, the navy, and of all the revenue officers, is the same now as it was above a hundred years ago, when the taxes were not above a tenth part of what they are at present, it appears impossible to account for the enormous expenditure on any other ground than extravagance, corruption and intrigue.

With the Revolution of 1688, and more so since the Hanover succession, came the destructive system of continental intrigues, and the rage for foreign wars and foreign dominion; systems of such secure mystery that the expences admit of no accounts; a single line stands for millions. To what excess taxation might have extended, had not the French Revolution contributed to break up the system, and put an end to pretences, is impossible to say. Viewed, as that Revolution ought to be, as the fortunate means of lessening the load of taxes of both countries, it is of as much importance to England as to France; and, if properly improved to all the advantages of which it is capable, and to which it leads, deserves as much celebration in one country as the other.

In pursuing this subject, I shall begin with the matter that first presents itself, that of lessening the burden of taxes; and shall then add such matters and propositions, respecting the three countries of England, France and America, as the present prospect of things appears to justify. I mean, an alliance of the three, for the purposes that will be mentioned in their proper place.

What has happened may happen again. By the statement before shown of the progress of taxation, it is seen that taxes have been lessened to a fourth part of what they had formerly been. Though the present circumstances do not admit of the same reduction, yet it admits of such a beginning as may accomplish that end in less time than in the former case.

The amount of taxes for the year ending at Michaelmas, 1788, was as follows:—

Land tax	£1,950,000
Customs	3,789,274
Excise (including old and new malt)	6,751,727
Stamps	1,278,214
Miscellaneous taxes and incidents	1,803,755
	£15,572,970

Since the year 1788 upwards of one million of new taxes have been laid on, besides the produce from the lotteries, and as the taxes have in general been more productive since than before, the amount may be taken in round numbers at £17,000,000.

N.B.—The expence of collection and the drawbacks, which together amount to nearly two millions, are paid out of the gross amount, and the above is the nett sum paid into the exchequer.

This sum of seventeen millions is applied to two different purposes, the one to pay the interest of the national debt, the other to the current expences of each other. About nine millions are appropriated to the former, and the remainder, being nearly eight millions, to the latter. As to the million said to be applied to the reduction of the debt, it is so much like paying with one hand and taking out with the other as not to merit much notice.

It happened fortunately for France that she possessed national domains for paying off her debt, and thereby lessening her taxes; but as this is not the case in England, her reduction of taxes can only take place by reducing the current expences, which may now be done to the amount of four or five millions annually, as will hereafter appear. When this is accomplished it will more than counterbalance the enormous charge of the American War, and the saving will be from the same source from whence the evil arose.

As to the national debt, however heavy the interest may be in taxes, yet as it serves to keep alive a capital useful to commerce, it balances by its effects a considerable part of its own weight; and as the quantity of gold and silver in England, is by some means or other, short of its proper proportion (being not more than twenty millions whereas it should be sixty) it would, besides the injustice, be bad policy to extinguish a capital that serves to supply that defect. But with respect to the current expence whatever is saved therefrom is gain. The excess may serve to keep corruption alive, but it has no reaction on credit and commerce like the interest of the debt.

It is now very probable that the English Government (I do not mean the Nation) is unfriendly to the French Revolution. Whatever serves to expose the intrigue and lessen the influence of courts by lessening taxation will be unwelcome to those who feed upon the spoil. Whilst the clamour of French intrigue, arbitrary power, Popery, and wooden shoes could be kept up the Nation was easily allured and alarmed into taxes. Those days are now past; deception, it is to be hoped, has reaped its last harvest, and better times are in prospect for both countries and for the world.

Taking it for granted that an alliance may be formed between England, France and America for the purposes hereafter to be mentioned, the national expences of France and England may consequently be lessened. The same fleets and armies will no longer be necessary to either, and the reduction can be made ship for ship on each side. But to accomplish these objects the Governments must necessarily be fitted to a common and correspondent principle. Confidence can never take place while an hostile disposition remains in either, or where mystery and secrecy on one side is opposed to candour and openness on the other.

These matters admitted, the national expences might be put back *for the sake of a precedent,* to what they were at some period when France and England were not enemies. This, consequently, must be prior to the Hanover succession, and also to the Revolution of 1688. The first instance that presents itself, antecedent to those dates, is in the very wasteful and profligate times of Charles the Second; at which time England and France acted as allies. If I have chosen a period of great extravagance it will serve to show modern extravagance in a still worse light; especially as the pay of the navy, the army, and the revenue officers has not encreased since that time.

The peace establishment was then as follows (see Sir John Sinclair's "History of the Revenue"):—

Navy	£300,000
Army	212,000
Ordnance	40,000
Civil List	462,115
	£1,014,115

The Parliament, however, settled the whole annual peace establishment at £1,200,000. If we go back to the time of Elizabeth the amount of all the taxes was but half a million, yet the Nation sees nothing during that period that reproaches it with want of consequence.

All circumstances, then, taken together, arising from the French Revolution, from the approaching harmony and reciprocal interest of the two nations, the abolition of our Court intrigue on both sides, and the progress of knowledge in the science of Government, the annual expenditure might be put back to one million and a half, viz.:—

Navy	£500,000
Army	500,000
Expences of government	500,000
	£1,500,000

Even this sum is six times greater than the expences of Government are in America, yet the civil internal Government in England (I mean that administered by means of quarter sessions, juries, and assize, and which, in fact, is nearly the whole, and performed by the Nation), is less expence upon the revenue than the same species and portion of Government is in America.

It is time that Nations should be rational, and not be governed like animals, for the pleasure of their riders. To read the history of Kings, a man would be almost inclined to suppose that Government consisted in stag-hunting, and that every Nation paid a million a-year to a huntsman. Man ought to have pride or shame enough to blush at being thus imposed upon, and when he feels his proper character he will. Upon all subjects of this nature, there is often passing in the mind a train of ideas he has not yet accustomed himself to encourage and communicate. Restrained by something that puts on the character of prudence, he acts the hypocrite upon himself as well as to others. It is, however, curious to observe how soon this spell can be dissolved. A single expression, boldly conceived and uttered, will sometimes put a whole company into their proper feelings: and whole Nations are acted upon in the same manner.

As to the offices of which any civil Government may be composed, it matters but little by what names they are described. In the routine of business, as before observed, whether a man be styled a president, a King, an Emperor, a senator, or anything else, it is impossible that any service he can perform can merit from a Nation more than ten thousand pounds a year; and as no man should be paid beyond his services, so every man of a proper heart will not accept more. Public money ought to be touched with the most scrupulous consciousness of honour. It is not the produce of riches only, but of the hard earnings of labour and poverty. It is drawn even from the bitterness of want and misery. Not a beggar passes, or perishes in the streets, whose mite is not in that mass.

Were it possible that the Congress of America could be so lost to their duty, and to the interest of their constituents, as to offer General Washington, as President of America, a million a year, he would not, and he could not, accept it. His sense of honour is of another kind. It has cost England almost seventy millions sterling to maintain a family imported from abroad, of very inferior capacity to thousands in the nation; and scarcely a year has passed that has not produced some new mercenary application. Even the physicians' bills have been sent to the public to be paid. No wonder that jails are crowded, and taxes and poor rates increased. Under such systems, nothing is to be looked for but what has already happened; and as to reformation, whenever it comes, it must be from the Nation, and not from the Government.

To show that the sum of five hundred thousand is more than sufficient to defray all the expences of Government, exclusive of navies and armies, the following estimate is added, for any country of the same extent as England.

In the first place, three hundred representatives fairly selected, are sufficient for all the purposes to which legislation can apply, and preferable to a larger number. They may be divided into two or three houses, or meet in one, as in France, or in any manner a Constitution shall direct.

As representation is always considered in free countries as the most honourable of all stations, the allowance made to it is merely to defray the expence which the representatives incur by that service, and not to it as an office.

If an allowance, at the rate of five hundred pounds per annum, be made to every representative, deducting for non-attendance, the expence, if the whole number attended for six months each year would be	£75,000
The official departments cannot reasonably exceed the following number, with the salaries annexed:—	
Three offices at ten thousand pounds each	£30,000
Ten ditto, at five thousand pounds each	50,000
Twenty ditto, at two thousand pounds each	40,000
Forty ditto, at one thousand pounds each	40,000
Two hundred ditto, at five hundred pounds each	100,000
Three hundred ditto, at two hundred pounds each	60,000
Five hundred ditto, at one hundred pounds each	50,000
Seven hundred ditto, at seventy-five pounds each	52,500
	£497,500

If a Nation chuse, it can deduct four per cent. from all offices, and make one of twenty thousand per annum.

All revenue officers are paid out of the monies they collect, and therefore are not in this estimation.

The foregoing is not offered as an exact detail of offices, but to show the number and rate of salaries which five hundred thousand pounds will support; and it will, on experience, be found impracticable to find business sufficient to justify even this expence. As to the manner in which office business is now performed, the chiefs in several offices, such as the post office and certain offices in the exchequer, etc., do little more than sign their names three or four times a year; and the whole duty is performed by under-clerks.

Taking, therefore, one million and a half as a sufficient peace establishment for all the honest purposes of Government, which is three hundred thousand pounds more than the peace establishment in the profligate and prodigal times of Charles the Second (notwithstanding, as has been already observed, the pay and salaries of the army, navy, and revenue officers continue the same as at that period), there will remain a surplus of upwards of six millions out of the present current expences. The question then will be, how to dispose of this surplus?

Whoever has observed the manner in which trade and taxes twist themselves together, must be sensible of the impossibility of separating them suddenly.

First. Because the articles now on hand are already charged with the duty; and the reduction cannot take place on the present stock.

Secondly. Because, on all those articles on which the duty is charged on the gross, such as per barrel, hogshead, hundredweight or ton, the abolition of the duty does not admit of being divided down so as fully to relieve the consumer, who purchases by the pint, or the pound. The last duty on strong beer and ale, was three shillings per barrel, which, if taken off, would lessen the purchase only half a farthing per pint, and consequently, would not reach to practical relief.

This being the condition of a great part of the taxes, it will be necessary to look for such others as are free from this embarrassment and where the relief will be direct and visible, and capable of immediate operation.

In the first place, then, the poor-rates are a direct tax which every housekeeper feels, and who knows also, to a farthing, the sum which he pays. The national amount of the whole of the poor-rates is not positively known, but can be procured. Sir John Sinclair, in his *History of the Revenue,* has stated it at £2,100,587. A considerable part of which is expended in litigations, in which the poor, instead of being relieved are tormented. The expence, however, is the same to the parish from whatever cause it arises.

In Birmingham the amount of the poor-rates is fourteen thousand pounds a year. This, though a large sum, is moderate compared with the population. Birmingham is said to contain seventy thousand souls, and on a proportion of seventy thousand to fourteen thousand pounds poor-rates, the national amount of poor-rates, taking the population of England at seven millions, would be but one million four hundred thousand pounds. It is, therefore, most probable, that the population of Birmingham is over-rated. Fourteen thousand pounds is the proportion upon fifty thousand souls, taking two millions of poor-rates, as the national amount.

Be it, however, what it may, it is no other than the consequence of the excessive burden of taxes, for, at the time when the taxes were very low, the poor were able to maintain themselves; and there were no poor-rates. In the present state of things a labouring man, with a wife and two or three children, does not pay less than between seven and eight pounds a year in taxes. He is not sensible of this, because it is disguised to him in the articles which he buys, and he thinks only of their dearness; but as the taxes take from him, at least, a fourth of his yearly earnings, he is consequently disabled from providing for a family, especially if himself or any of them are afflicted with sickness.

The first step, therefore, of practical relief, would be to abolish the poor-rates entirely, and in lieu thereof, to make a remission of taxes to the poor of double the amount of the present poor-rates, viz., four millions annually, out of the surplus taxes. By this measure, the poor will be benefited two millions, and the housekeepers two millions. This alone would be equal to a reduction of one hundred and twenty millions of the National Debt, and consequently equal to the whole expence of the American War.

It will then remain to be considered, which is the most effectual mode of distributing this remission of four millions.

It is easily seen, that the poor are generally composed of large families of children, and old people past their labour. If these two classes are provided for, the remedy will so far reach to the full extent of the case, that what remains will be incidental, and in a great measure, fall within the compass of benefit clubs, which, though of humble invention, merit to be ranked among the best of modern institutions.

Admitting England to contain seven millions of souls; if one-fifth thereof are of that class of poor which need support, the number will be one million four hundred thousand. Of this number, one hundred and forty thousand will be aged poor, as will be hereafter shown, and for which a distinct provision will be proposed.

There will remain one million two hundred and sixty thousand which, at five souls to each family, amount to two hundred and fifty-two thousand families, rendered poor from the expence of children and the weight of taxes.

The number of children under fourteen years of age, in each of those families, will be found to be about five to every two families; some having two, and others three; some one, and others four: some none, and others five; but it rarely happens that more than five are under fourteen years of age, and after this age they are capable of service or of being apprenticed.

Allowing five children (under fourteen years) to every two families,

The number of children would be..............................	630,000
The number of parents, were they all living, would be..............	504,000

It is certain, that if the children are provided for, the parents are relieved of consequence, because it is from the expence of bringing up children that their poverty arises.

Having thus ascertained the greatest number that can be supposed to need support on account of young families, I proceed to the mode of relief or distribution, which is,

To pay as a remission of taxes to every poor family, out of the surplus taxes, and in room of poor-rates, four pounds a-year for every child under fourteen years of age; enjoining the parents of such children to send them to school, to learn reading, writing, and common arithmetic; the ministers of every parish, of every denomination to certify jointly to an office, for that purpose, that this duty is performed. The amount of this expence will be,

For six hundred and thirty thousand children at £4 per annum each	£2,520,000

By adopting this method, not only the poverty of the parents will be relieved, but ignorance will be banished from the rising generation, and the number of poor will hereafter become less, because their abilities, by the aid of education, will be greater. Many a youth, with good natural genius, who is apprenticed to a mechanical trade, such as a carpenter, joiner, millwright, shipwright, blacksmith, etc., is prevented getting forward the whole of his life from the want of a little common education when a boy.

I now proceed to the case of the aged.

I divide age into two classes. First, the approach of age, beginning at fifty. Secondly, old age commencing at sixty

At fifty, though the mental faculties of man are in full vigour, and his judgment better than at any preceding date, the bodily powers for laborious life are on the decline. He cannot bear the same quantity of fatigue as at an earlier period. He begins to earn less, and is less capable of enduring wind and weather; and in those retired employments where much sight is required, he fails apace, and sees himself, like an old horse, beginning to be turned adrift.

At sixty his labour ought to be over, at least from direct necessity. It is painful to see old age working itself to death, in what are called civilized countries for daily bread.

To form some judgment of the number of those above fifty years of age, I have several times counted the persons I met in the streets of London, men, women, and children, and have generally found that the average is about one in sixteen or seventeen. If it be said that aged persons do not come much in the streets, so neither do infants; and a great proportion of grown children are in schools and in workshops as apprentices. Taking, then, sixteen for a divisor, the whole number of persons in England of fifty years and upwards, both sexes, rich and poor, will be four hundred and twenty thousand.

The persons to be provided for out of this gross number will be husbandmen, common labourers, journeymen of every trade and their wives, sailors, and disbanded soldiers, worn out servants of both sexes, and poor widows.

There will be also a considerable number of middling tradesmen, who having lived decently in the former part of life, begin, as age approaches, to lose their business, and at last fall to decay.

Besides these there will be constantly thrown off from the revolutions of that wheel which no man can stop nor regulate, a number from every class of life connected with commerce and adventure.

To provide for all those accidents, and whatever else may befall, I take the number of persons who, at one time or other of their lives, after fifty years of age, may feel it necessary or comfortable to be better supported than they can support themselves, and that not as a matter of grace and favour, but of right, at one-third of the whole number, which is one hundred and forty thousand, and for whom a distinct provision was proposed to be made. If there be more, society, notwithstanding the show and pomposity of Government, is in a deplorable condition in England.

Of this one hundred and forty thousand, I take one half, seventy thousand, to be of the age of fifty and under sixty, and the other half to be sixty years and upwards. Having thus ascertained the probable proportion of the number of aged persons, I proceed to the mode of rendering their condition comfortable, which is,

To pay every such person of the age of fifty years, and until he shall arrive at the age of sixty, the sum of six pounds per annum out of the surplus taxes, and ten pounds per annum during life after the age of sixty. The expence of which will be,

Seventy thousand persons, at £6 per annum....................	£420,000
Seventy thousand ditto, at £10 per annum......................	700,000
	£1,120,000

This support, as already remarked, is not of the nature of a charity but of a right. Every person in England, male and female, pays on an average in taxes two pounds eight shillings and sixpence per annum from the day of his (or her) birth; and if the expence of collection be added, he pays two pounds eleven shillings and sixpence; consequently, at the end of fifty years he has paid one hundred and twenty-eight pounds fifteen shillings, and at sixty one hundred and fifty-four pounds ten shillings. Converting, therefore, his (or her) individual tax into a tontine, the money he shall receive after fifty years is but little more than the legal interest of the nett money he has paid; the rest is made up from those whose circumstances do not require them to draw such support, and the capital in both cases defrays the expences of Government. It is on this ground that I have extended the probable claims to one-third of the number of aged persons in the Nation. Is it, then, better that the lives of one hundred and forty thousand aged persons be rendered comfortable, or that a million a year of public money be expended on any one individual, and him often of the most worthless or insignificant character? Let reason and justice, let honour and humanity, let even hypocrisy, sycophancy and Mr. Burke, let George, let Louis, Leopold, Frederic, Catherine, Cornwallis, or Tippoo Saib, answer the question.

The sum thus remitted to the poor will be,

To two hundred and fifty-two thousand poor families, containing six hundred and thirty thousand children....................	£2,520,000
To one hundred and forty thousand aged persons...............	1,120,000
	£3,640,000

There will then remain three hundred and sixty thousand pounds out of the four millions, part of which may be applied as follows:—

After all the above cases are provided for there will still be a number of families who, though not properly of the class of poor, yet find it difficult to give education to their children; and such children, under such a case, would be in a worse condition than if their parents were actually poor. A Nation under a well-regulated Government should permit none to remain uninstructed. It is monarchical and aristocratical Government only that requires ignorance for its support.

Suppose, then, four hundred thousand children to be in this condition, which is a greater number than ought to be supposed after the provisions already made, the method will be:

To allow for each of those children ten shillings a year for the expence of schooling for six years each, which will give them six months' schooling each year, and half-a-crown a year for paper and spelling books.

The expence of this will be annually £250,000.

shillings per head, men, women, and children. The difference, therefore, between the two Governments is as under:—

	England			America		
	£	s.	d.	£	s.	d.
For a family of five persons	14	17	6	1	5	0
For a family of six persons	17	17	0	1	10	0
For a family of seven persons	20	16	6	1	15	0

There will then remain one hundred and ten thousand pounds.

Notwithstanding the great modes of-relief which the best instituted and best principled Government may devise, there will still be a number of smaller cases, which it is good policy as well as beneficence in a Nation to consider.

Were twenty shillings to be given immediately on the birth of a child, to every woman who should make the demand, and none will make it whose circumstances do not require it, it might relieve a great deal of instant distress.

There are about two hundred thousand births yearly in England, and if claimed, by one fourth,

The amount would be .... £50,000.

And twenty shillings to every new-married couple who should claim in like manner. This would not exceed the sum of £20,000.

Also twenty thousand pounds to be appropriated to defray the funeral expences of persons, who, travelling for work, may die at a distance from their friends. By relieving parishes from this charge, the sick stranger will be better treated.

I shall finish this part of the subject with a plan adapted to the particular condition of a metropolis, such as London.

Cases are continually occurring in a metropolis different to those which occur in the country, and for which a different, or rather an additional, mode of relief is necessary. In the country, even in large towns, people have a knowledge of each other, and distress never rises to that extreme height it sometimes does in a metropolis. There in no such thing in the country as persons, in the literal sense of the word, starved to death, or dying with cold from the want of a lodging. Yet such cases, and others equally as miserable, happen in London.

Many a youth comes up to London full of expectations, and with little or no money, and unless he get immediate employment he is already half-undone; and boys bred up in London without any means of a livelihood, and as it often happens of dissolute parents, are in a still worse condition; and servants long out of place are not much better off. In short, a world of little cases is continually arising, which busy or affluent life knows not of, to open the first door to distress. Hunger is not among the postponeable wants, and a day, even a few hours, in such a condition is often the crisis of a life of ruin.

These circumstances which are the general cause of the little thefts and pilferings that lead to greater, may be prevented. There yet remain twenty thousand pounds out of the four millions of surplus taxes, which with another fund hereafter to be mentioned, amounting to about twenty thousand pounds more, cannot be better applied than to this purpose. The plan then will be:

First,—To erect two or more buildings, or take some already erected, capable of containing at least six thousand persons, and to have in each of these places as many kinds of employment as can be contrived, so that every person who shall come may find something which he or she can do.

Secondly,—To receive all who shall come, without inquiring who or what they are. The only condition to be, that for so much, or so many hours' work, each person shall receive so many meals of wholesome food and a warm lodging, at least as good as a barrack. That a certain portion of what each person's work shall be worth shall be reserved, and given to him or her, on their going away; and that each person shall stay as long or as short a time, or come as often as he chuse, on these conditions.

If each person stayed three months, it would assist by rotation twenty-four thousand persons annually, though the real number, at all times. would be but six thousand. By establishing an asylum of this kind, persons to whom temporary distresses occur would have an opportunity to recruit themselves, and be enabled to look out for better employment.

Allowing that their labour paid but one half the expence of supporting them, after reserving a portion of their earnings for themselves, the sum of forty thousand pounds additional would defray all other charges for even a greater number than six thousand.

The fund very properly convertible to this purpose, in addition to the twenty thousand pounds remaining of the former fund, will be the produce of the tax upon coals, so iniquitously and wantonly applied to the support of the Duke of Richmond. It is horrid that any man, more especially at the price coals now are, should live on the distresses of a community; and any Government permitting such an abuse deserves to be dismissed. This fund is said to be about twenty thousand pounds per annum.

I shall now conclude this plan with enumerating the several particulars, and then proceed to other matters.

The enumeration is as follows:—

First—Abolition of two million poor-rates.

Secondly—Provision for two hundred and fifty-two thousand poor families.

Thirdly—Education for one million and thirty thousand children.

Fourthly—Comfortable provision for one hundred and forty thousand aged persons.

Fifthly—Donation of twenty shillings each for fifty thousand births.

Sixthly—Donation of twenty shillings each for twenty thousand marriages.

Seventhly—Allowance of twenty thousand pounds for the funeral expences of persons travelling for work, and dying at a distance from their friends.

Eighthly—Employment, at all times, for the casual poor in the cities of London and Westminster.

By the operation of this plan, the poor laws, those instruments of civil torture, will be superseded, and the wasteful expence of litigation prevented. The hearts of the humane will not be shocked by ragged and hungry children, and persons of seventy or eighty years of age, begging for bread. The dying poor will not be dragged from place to place to breathe their last, as a reprisal of parish upon parish. Widows will have a maintenance for their children, and not be carted away, on the death of their husbands, like culprits and criminals; and children will no longer be considered as increasing the distresses of their parents. The haunts of the wretched will be known, because it will be to their advantage, and the number of petty crimes, the offspring of distress and poverty, will be lessened. The poor, as well as the rich, will then be interested in the support of Government, and the cause and apprehension of riots and tumults will cease. Ye who sit in ease, and solace yourselves in plenty—and such there are in Turkey and Russia, as well as in England—and who say to yourselves, "Are we not well off?" have ye thought of these things? When ye do, ye will cease to speak and feel for yourselves alone.

The plan is easy in practice. It does not embarrass trade by a sudden interruption in the order of taxes, but effects the relief by changing the application of them; and the money necessary for the purpose can be drawn from the excise collections, which are made eight times a year in every market town in England.

Having now arranged and concluded this subject, I proceed to the next.

Taking the present current expences at seven millions and a half, which is the least amount they are now at, there will remain (after the sum of one million and a half be taken for the new current expences and four millions for the before-mentioned service) the sum of two millions; part of which to be applied as follows:

Though fleets and armies, by an alliance with France, will, in a great measure, become useless, yet the persons who have devoted themselves to those services, and have thereby unfitted themselves for other lines of life, are not to be sufferers by the means that make others happy. They are a different description of men to those who form or hang about a court.

A part of the army will remain, at least for some years, and also of the navy, for which a provision is already made in the former part of this plan of one million, which is almost half a million more than the peace establishment of the army and navy in the prodigal times of Charles the Second.

Suppose, then, fifteen thousand soldiers to be disbanded, and that an allowance be made to each of three shillings a-week during life, clear of all deductions, to be paid in the same manner as the Chelsea College pensioners are paid, and for them to return to their trades and their friends; and also that an addition of fifteen thousand sixpences per week be made to the pay of the soldiers who shall remain. The annual expence will be:—

To the pay of fifteen thousand disbanded soldiers, at 3s. per week	£117,000
Additional pay to the remaining soldiers	19,500
Suppose that the pay to the officers of the disbanded corps be of the same amount as the sum allowed to the men	117,000
	£253,500
To prevent bulky estimations, admit the same sum to the disbanded navy as to the army, and the same increase of pay	253,500
Total	£507,000

Every year some part of this sum of half a million (I omit the odd seven thousand pounds for the purpose of keeping the account unembarrassed) will fall in, and the whole of it in time, as it is on the ground of life annuities, except the encreased pay of twenty-nine thousand pounds. As it falls in, a part of the taxes may be taken off; for instance, when thirty thousand pounds fall in, the duty on hops may be wholly taken off; and as other parts fall in, the duties on candles and soap may be lessened, till at last they will totally cease. There now remains at least one million and a half of surplus taxes.

The tax on houses and windows is one of those direct taxes which, like the poor rates, is not confounded with trade, and when taken off, the relief will be instantly felt. This tax falls heavy on the middling class of people.

The amount of this tax by the returns of 1788 was—

	£	s.	d.
Houses and windows, by the Act of 1766	£385,459	11	7
Ditto, by the Act of 1779	130,739	14	5½
Total	£516,199	6	0½

If this tax be struck off, there will then remain about one million of surplus taxes; and as it is always proper to keep a sum in reserve for incidental matters, it may be best not to extend reductions further in the first instance, but to consider what may be accomplished by other modes of reform.

Among the taxes most heavily felt is the commutation tax. I shall therefore offer a plan for its abolition, by substituting another in its place, which will effect three objects at once.

First, That of removing the burthen to where it can best be borne.

Secondly, Restoring justice among families by a distribution of property.

Thirdly, Extirpating the overgrown influence arising from the unnatural law of primogeniture, and which is one of the principal sources of corruption at elections.

The amount of the commutation tax by the returns of 1788 was £771,657.

When taxes are proposed, the country is amused by the plausible language of taxing luxuries. One thing is called a luxury at one time, and something else at another; but the real luxury does not consist in the article, but in the means of procuring it, and this is always kept out of sight.

I know not why any plant or herb of the field should be a greater luxury in one country than another; but an overgrown estate in either is a luxury at all times, and, as such, is the proper object of taxation. It is, therefore, right to take those kind tax-making gentlemen upon their own word, and argue on the principle themselves have laid down, that of *taxing luxuries*. If they or their champion, Mr. Burke, who, I fear, is growing out of date, like the man in armour, can prove that an estate of twenty, thirty, or forty thousand pounds a year is not a luxury, I will give up the argument.

Admitting that any annual sum, say, for instance, a thousand pounds, is necessary for the support of a family, consequently the second thousand is of the nature of a luxury, the third still more so, and by proceeding on we shall at last arrive at a sum that may not improperly be called a prohibitable luxury. It would be impolitic to set bounds to property acquired by industry, and therefore it is right to place the prohibition beyond the probable acquisition to which industry can extend; but there ought to be a limit to property or the accumulation of it by bequest. It should pass in some other line. The richest in every Nation have poor relations, and those often very near in consanguinity.

The following table of progressive taxation is constructed on the above principles, and as a substitute for the commutation tax. It will reach the point of prohibition by a regular operation, and thereby supersede the aristocratical law of primogeniture.

TABLE I

A tax on all estates of the clear yearly value of £50, after deducting the land tax, and up

	s.	d.	
To £500	0	3	per pound
From £500 to £1,000	0	6	" "
On the second thousand	0	9	" "
On the third thousand	1	0	" "
On the fourth thousand	1	6	" "
On the fifth thousand	2	0	" "
On the sixth thousand	3	0	" "
On the seventh thousand	4	0	" "
On the eighth thousand	5	0	" "
On the ninth thousand	6	0	" "
On the tenth thousand	7	0	" "
On the eleventh thousand	8	0	" "
On the twelfth thousand	9	0	" "
On the thirteenth thousand	10	0	" "
On the fourteenth thousand	11	0	" "
On the fifteenth thousand	12	0	" "
On the sixteenth thousand	13	0	" "
On the seventeenth thousand	14	0	" "
On the eighteenth thousand	15	0	" "
On the nineteenth thousand	16	0	" "
On the twentieth thousand	17	0	" "
On the twenty-first thousand	18	0	" "
On the twenty-second thousand	19	0	" "
On the twenty-third thousand	20	0	" "

The foregoing table shows the progression per pound on every progressive thousand. The following table shows the amount of the tax on every thousand separately, and in the last column the total amount of all the separate sums collected.

TABLE II

								£	s.	d.
An estate	of	£50	per annum,	at 3d.	per pound,	pays		£0	12	6
"	"	100	"	"	"	"		1	5	0
"	"	200	"	"	"	"		2	10	0
"	"	300	"	"	"	"		3	15	0
"	"	400	"	"	"	"		5	0	0
"	"	500	"	"	"	"		7	5	0

After £500 the tax of 6d. per pound takes place on the second £500; consequently an estate of £1,000 per annum pays £21 15s., and so on.

	£		s.	d.			£	s.		Total amount £	s.
1st	£500	at	0	3	per	pound	7	5	}	21	15
2nd	"	"	0	6	"	"	14	10			
2nd	£1,000	"	0	9	"	"	37	10	....	59	5
3rd	"	"	1	0	"	"	50	0	....	109	5
4th	"	"	1	6	"	"	75	0	....	184	5
5th	"	"	2	0	"	"	100	0	....	284	5
6th	"	"	3	0	"	"	150	0	....	434	5
7th	"	"	4	0	"	"	200	0	....	634	5
8th	"	"	5	0	"	"	250	0	....	880	5
9th	"	"	6	0	"	"	300	0	....	1,180	5
10th	"	"	7	0	"	"	350	0	....	1,530	5
11th	"	"	8	0	"	"	400	0	....	1,930	5
12th	"	"	9	0	"	"	450	0	....	2,380	5
13th	"	"	10	0	"	"	500	0	....	2,880	5
14th	"	"	11	0	"	"	550	0	....	3,430	5
15th	"	"	12	0	"	"	600	0	....	4,030	5
16th	"	"	13	0	"	"	650	0	....	4,680	5
17th	"	"	14	0	"	"	700	0	....	5,380	5
18th	"	"	15	0	"	"	750	0	....	6,130	5
19th	"	"	16	0	"	"	800	0	....	6,930	5
20th	"	"	17	0	"	"	850	0	....	7,780	5
21st	"	"	18	0	"	"	900	0	....	8,680	5
22nd	"	"	19	0	"	"	950	0	....	9,630	5
23rd	"	"	20	0	"	"	1,000	0	....	10,630	5

At the twenty-third thousand the tax becomes 20s. in the pound, and consequently every thousand beyond that sum can produce no profit but by dividing the estate. Yet, formidable as this tax appears, it will not, I believe, produce so much as the commutation tax: should it produce more, it ought to be lowered to that amount upon estates under two or three thousand a year.

On small and middling estates it is lighter (as it is intended to be) than the commutation tax. It is not till after seven or eight thousand a year that it begins to be heavy. The object is not so much the produce of the tax as the justice of the measure. The Aristocracy has screened itself too much, and this serves to restore a part of the lost equilibrium.

As an instance of its screening itself, it is only necessary to look back to the first establishment of the excise laws, at what is called the Restoration, or the coming of Charles the Second. The aristocratical interest then in power commuted the feudal services itself was under, by laying a tax on beer brewed for *sale;* that is, they compounded with Charles for an exemption from those services for themselves and their heirs by a tax to be paid by other people. The Aristocracy do not purchase beer brewed for sale, but brew their own beer free of the duty; and if any commutation at that time were necessary, it ought to have been at the expence of those for whom the exemptions from those services were intended; instead of which, it was thrown on an entire different class of men.

But the chief object of this progressive tax (besides the justice of rendering taxes more equal than they are), is, as already stated, to extirpate the overgrown influence arising from the unnatural law of primogeniture, and which is one of the principal sources of corruption at elections.

It would be attended with no good consequences to inquire how such vast estates as thirty, forty, or fifty thousand a year could commence, and that at a time when commerce and manufactures were not in a state to admit of such acquisitions. Let it be sufficient to remedy the evil by putting them in a condition of descending again to the community, by the quiet means of apportioning them among all the heirs and heiresses of those families. This will be the more necessary, because hitherto the Aristocracy have quartered their younger children and connections upon the public, in useless posts, places and offices, which when abolished will leave them destitute, unless the law of primogeniture be also abolished or superseded.

A progressive tax will, in a great measure, effect this object, and that as a matter of interest to the parties most immediately concerned, as will be seen by the following table, which shows the nett produce upon every estate, after subtracting the tax. By this it will appear that after an estate exceeds thirteen or fourteen thousand a year the remainder produces but little profit to the holder, and consequently will pass either to the younger children or to other kindred.

TABLE III

Shewing the nett produce of every estate from one thousand to twenty-three thousand pounds a year:—

No. of Thousands per Ann.	*Total Tax Subtracted.*	*Nett Produce.*
£	£	£
1,000	21	979
2,000	59	1,941
3,000	109	2,891
4,000	184	3,816
5,000	284	4,716
6,000	434	5,566

No. of Thousands per Ann.	*Total Tax Subtracted.*	*Nett Produce.*
£	£	£
7,000	634	6,366
8,000	880	7,120
9,000	1,100	7,820
10,000	1,530	8,470
11,000	1,930	9,070
12,000	2,380	9,620
13,000	2,880	10,120
14,000	3,430	10,570
15,000	4,030	10,970
16,000	4,680	11,320
17,000	5,380	11,620
18,000	6,130	11,870
19,000	6,930	12,170
20,000	7,780	12,220
21,000	8,680	12,320
22,000	9,630	12,370
23,000	10,630	12,370

N.B.—The odd shillings are dropped in this table.

According to this table, an estate cannot produce more than £12,370 clear of the land tax and the progressive tax, and therefore the dividing such estates will follow as a matter of family interest. An estate of £23,000 a year, divided into five estates of four thousand each and one of three, will be charged only £1,129, which is but 5 per cent., but if held by one possessor will be charged £10,630.

Although an enquiry into the origin of those estates be unnecessary, the continuation of them in their present state is another subject. It is a matter of national concern. As hereditary estates, the law has created the evil, and it ought also to provide the remedy. Primogeniture ought to be abolished, not only because it is unnatural and unjust, but because the country suffers by its operation. By cutting off (as before observed) the younger children from their proper portion of inheritance the public is loaded with the expence of maintaining them; and the freedom of elections violated by the overbearing influence which this unjust monopoly of family property produces. Nor is this all. It occasions a waste of national property. A considerable part of the land of the country is rendered unproductive by the great extent of parks and chases which this law serves to keep up, and this at a time when the annual production of grain is not equal to the national consumption. In short, the evils of the aristocratical system are so great and numerous, so inconsistent with everything that is just, wise, natural, and beneficent, that when they are considered, there ought not to be a doubt that many, who are now classed under that description, will wish to see such a system abolished.

What pleasure can they derive from contemplating the exposed condition and almost certain beggary of their younger offspring? Every aristocratical family has an appendage of family beggars hanging round it, which in a few ages or a few generations are shook off, and console themselves with telling their tale in almshouses, workhouses, and prisons. This is the natural consequence of Aristocracy. The peer and the beggar are often of the same family. One extreme produces the other; to make one rich many must be made poor; neither can the system be supported by other means.

There are two classes of people to whom the laws of England are particularly hostile, and those the most helpless: younger children and the poor. Of the former I have just spoken; of the latter I shall mention one instance out of the many that might be produced, and with which I shall close this subject.

Several laws are in existence for regulating and limiting workmen's wages. Why not leave them as free to make their own bargains as the law-makers are to let their farms and houses? Personal labour is all the property they have. Why is that little, and the little freedom they enjoy, to be infringed? But the injustice will appear stronger if we consider the operation and effect of such laws. When wages are fixed by what is called a law, the legal wages remain stationary, while everything else is in progression; and as those who make that law still continue to lay on new taxes by other laws, they increase the expence of living by one law and take away the means by another

But if those gentlemen law-makers and tax-makers thought it right to limit the poor pittance which personal labour can produce, and on which a whole family is to be supported, they certainly must feel themselves happily indulged in a limitation on their own part of not less than twelve thousand a year, and that of property they never acquired (nor probably any of their ancestors), and of which they have made so ill a use.

Having now finished this subject, I shall bring the several particulars into one view, and then proceed to other matters.

The first Eight Articles are:

1. Abolition of two millions poor-rates.

2. Provision for two hundred and fifty-two thousand poor families at the rate of four pounds per head for each child under fourteen years of

age; which, with the addition of two hundred and fifty thousand pounds, provides also education for one million and thirty thousand children.

3. Annuity of six pounds per annum each for all poor persons, decayed tradesmen, or others (supposed seventy thousand) of the age of fifty years, and until sixty

4. Annuity of ten pounds each for life for all poor persons, decayed tradesmen, and others (supposed seventy thousand), of the age of sixty years.

5 Donations of 20s. each for fifty thousand births.

6. Donations of 20s. each for twenty thousand marriages.

7. Allowance of twenty thousand pounds for the funeral expences of persons travelling for work, and dying at a distance from their friends.

8. Employment at all times for the casual poor in the cities of London and Westminster.

Second Enumeration

9. Abolition of the tax on houses and windows.

10. Allowance of 3s. per week for life to fifteen thousand disbanded soldiers, and a proportionable allowance to the officers of the disbanded corps.

11 Encrease of pay to the remaining soldiers of £19,500 annually.

12 The same allowance to the disbanded navy, and the same increase of pay as to the army.

13. Abolition of the commutation tax.

14. Plan of a progressive tax, operating to extirpate the unjust and unnatural law of primogeniture, and the vicious influence of the aristocratical system.

There yet remains, as already stated, one million of surplus taxes. Some part of this will be required for circumstances that do not immediately present themselves, and such part as shall not be wanted will admit a further reduction of taxes equal to that amount.

Among the claims that justice requires to be made, the condition of the inferior revenue officers will merit attention. It is a reproach to any Government to waste such an immensity of revenue in sinecures and nominal and unnecessary places and offices, and not allow even a decent livelihood to those on whom the labour falls. The salary of the inferior officers of the revenue has stood at the petty pittance of less than fifty pounds a year for upwards of one hundred years. It ought to be seventy. About one hundred and twenty thousand pounds applied to this purpose will put all those salaries in a decent condition.

This was proposed to be done almost twenty years ago, but the treasury board then in being startled at it, as it might lead to similar expectations from the army and navy; and the event was that the King, or somebody for him, applied to Parliament to have his own salary raised a hundred thousand a year, which being done, everything else was laid aside.

With respect to another class of men, the inferior clergy, I forbear to enlarge on their condition; but all partialities and prejudices for or against different modes and forms of religion aside, common justice will determine whether there ought to be an income of twenty or thirty pounds a year to one man and of ten thousand to another. I speak on this subject with the more freedom because I am known not to be a Presbyterian; and therefore the cant cry of court sycophants about Church and meeting, kept up to amuse and bewilder the Nation, cannot be raised against me.

Ye simple men, on both sides of the question, do ye not see through this courtly craft? If ye can be kept disputing and wrangling about Church and meeting, ye just answer the purpose of every courtier, who lives the while on the spoil of the taxes, and laughs at your credulity Every religion is good that teaches man to be good; and I know of none that instructs him to be bad.

All the before-mentioned calculations, suppose only sixteen millions and a half of taxes paid into the exchequer, after the expence of collection and drawbacks at the custom house and excise office are deducted, whereas the sum paid into the exchequer, is very nearly, if not quite, seventeen millions. The taxes raised in Scotland and Ireland are expended in those countries, and therefore their savings will come out of their own taxes; but if any part be paid into the English exchequer it might be remitted. This will not make one hundred thousand pounds a year difference.

There now remains only the national debt to be considered. In the year 1789 the interest, exclusive of the tontine, was £9,150,138. How much the capital has been reduced since that time the minister best knows. But after paying the interest, abolishing the tax on houses and windows, the commutation tax, and the poor rates, and making all the provisions for the poor, for the education of children, the support of the aged, the disbanded part of the army and navy, and encreasing the pay of the remainder, there will be a surplus of one million.

The present scheme of paying off the national debt appears to me, speaking as an indifferent person, to be an ill-concerted, if not a fallacious job. The burden of the national debt consists not in its being so many millions, or so many hundred millions, but in the quantity of taxes collected every year to pay the interest. If this quantity continue the same, the burden of the national debt is the same to all intents and purposes, be the capital more or less. The only knowledge which the public can have of the reduction of the debt, must be through the reduction of taxes for paying the interest. The debt, therefore, is not reduced one farthing to the public by all the millions that have been paid; and it would require more money now to purchase up the capital than when the scheme began.

Digressing for a moment at this point, to which I shall return again, I look back to the appointment of Mr. Pitt as minister.

I was then in America. The war was over; and though resentment had ceased, memory was still alive.

When the news of the coalition arrived, though it was a matter of no concern to me as a citizen of America, I felt it as a man. It had something in it which shocked, by publicly sporting with decency, if not with principle. It was impudence in Lord North; it was want of firmness in Mr. Fox.

Mr. Pitt was, at that time, what may be called a maiden character in politics. So far from being hackneyed, he appeared not to be initiated into the first mysteries of Court intrigue. Everything was in his favour. Resentment against the coalition served as friendship to him, and his ignorance of vice was credited for virtue. With the return of peace, commerce and prosperity would rise of itself; yet even this encrease was thrown to his account.

When he came to the helm the storm was over, and he had nothing to interrupt his course. It required even ingenuity to be wrong, and he succeeded. A little time shewed him the same sort of man as his predecessors had been. Instead of profiting by those errors which had accumulated a burden of taxes unparalleled in the world, he sought, I might almost say he advertised, for enemies, and provoked means to encrease taxation. Aiming at something, he knew not what, he ransacked Europe and India for adventures, and abandoning the fair pretensions he began with, became the knight-errant of modern times.

It is unpleasant to see character throw itself away. It is more so to see one's self deceived. Mr. Pitt had merited nothing, but he promised much. He gave symptoms of a mind superior to the meanness and corruption of Courts. His apparent candour encouraged expectations; and the public confidence, stunned, wearied, and confounded by a chaos of parties, revived and attached itself to him. But mistaking, as he has done, the disgust of the Nation against the coalition, for merit in himself, he has rushed into measures which a man less supported would not have presumed to act.

All this seems to shew that change of ministers amounts to nothing. One goes out, another comes in, and still the same measures, vices, and extravagnce are pursued. It signifies not who is minister. The defect lies in the system. The foundation and the superstructure of the Government are bad. Prop it as you please, it continually sinks into Court Government, and ever will.

I return, as I promised, to the subject of the national debt—that offspring of the Dutch-Anglo Revolution, and its handmaid the Hanover succession.

But it is now too late to enquire how it began. Those to whom it is due have advanced the money; and whether it was well or ill spent, or pocketed, is not their crime. It is, however, easy to see, that as the Nation proceeds in contemplating the nature and principles of Government, and to understand taxes, and make comparisons between those of America, France, and England, it will be next to impossible to keep it in the same torpid state it has hitherto been. Some reform must, from the necessity of the case, soon begin. It is not whether these principles press with little or much force in the present moment. They are out. They are abroad in the world, and no force can stop them. Like a secret told, they are beyond recall; and he must be blind indeed that does not see that a change is already beginning.

Nine million of dead taxes is a serious thing; and this not only for bad, but in a great measure for foreign Government. By putting the power of making war into the hands of foreigners who came for what they could get, little else was to be expected than what has happened.

Reasons are already advanced in this work shewing that whatever the reforms in the taxes may be, they ought to be made in the current expences of Government, and not in the part applied to the interest of the national debt. By remitting the taxes of the poor, *they* will be totally relieved, and all discontent on their part will be taken away; and by striking off such of the taxes as are already mentioned the Nation will more than recover the whole expence of the mad American War.

There will then remain only the national debt as a subject of discontent; and in order to remove, or rather to prevent this, it would be good policy in the stockholders themselves to consider it as property, subject, like all other property, to bear some portion of the taxes. It would give to it both popularity and security, and as a great part of its present inconvenience is balanced by the capital which it keeps alive, a measure of this kind would so far add to that balance as to silence objections.

This may be done by such gradual means as to accomplish all that is necessary with the greatest ease and convenience.

Instead of taxing the capital the best method would be to tax the interest by some progressive ratio, and to lessen the public taxes in the same proportion as the interest diminished.

Suppose the interest was taxed one halfpenny in the pound the first year, a penny more the second, and to proceed by a certain ratio to be determined upon, always less than any other tax upon property. Such a tax would be subtracted from the interest at the time of payment without any expence of collection.

One halfpenny in the pound would lessen the interest, and consequently the taxes, twenty thousand pounds. The tax on waggons amounts to this sum, and this tax might be taken off the first year. The second year the tax on female servants, or some other of the like amount, might also be taken off, and by proceeding in this manner, always applying the tax raised from the property of the debt towards its extinction, and not carry it to the current services, it would liberate itself.

The stockholders, notwithstanding this tax, would pay less taxes than they do now. What they would save by the extinction of the poor-rates, and the tax on houses and windows, and the commutation tax, would be considerably greater than what this tax, slow but certain in its operation, amounts to.

It appears to me to be prudence to look out for measures that may apply under any circumstances that may approach. There is, at this moment, a crisis in the affairs of Europe that requires it. Preparation now is wisdom. If taxation be once let loose it will be difficult to reinstate it; neither would the relief be so effectual as to proceed by some certain and gradual reduction.

The fraud, hypocrisy, and imposition of Governments, are now beginning to be too well understood to promise them any long career. The farce of Monarchy and Aristocracy in all countries is following that of chivalry, and Mr. Burke is dressing for the funeral. Let it then pass quietly to the tomb of all other follies, and the mourners be comforted.

The time is not very distant when England will laugh at itself for sending to Holland, Hanover, Zell, or Brunswick, for men, at the expence of a million a year, who understood neither her laws, her language, nor her interest, and whose capacities would scarcely have fitted them for the office of a parish constable. If Government could be trusted to such hands, it must be some easy and simple thing indeed, and materials fit for all the purposes may be found in every town and village in England.

When it shall be said in any country in the world my poor are happy; neither ignorance nor distress is to be found among them; my jails are empty of prisoners, my streets of beggars; the aged are not in want; the taxes are not oppressive; the rational world is my friend, because I am the friend of its happiness: When these things can be said, then may that country boast its Constitution and its Government.

Within the space of a few years we have seen two Revolutions, those of America and France. In the former the contest was long, and the conflict severe; in the latter the Nation acted with such a consolidated impulse, that, having no foreign enemy to contend with, the Revolution was complete in power the moment it appeared. From both those instances it is evident that the greatest forces than can be brought into the field of Revolutions are reason and common interest. Where these can have the opportunity of acting opposition dies with fear, or crumbles away by conviction. It is a great standing which they have now universally obtained; and we may hereafter hope to see Revolutions, or changes in Governments, produced with the same quiet operation, by which any measure, determinable by reason and discussion, is accomplished.

When a Nation changes its opinion and habits of thinking it is no longer to be governed as before; but it would not only be wrong, but bad policy, to attempt by force what ought to be accomplished by reason. Rebellion consists in forcibly opposing the general will of a Nation, whether by a party or by a Government. There ought, therefore, to be in every Nation a method of occasionally ascertaining the state of public opinion with respect to Government. On this point the old Government of France was superior to the present Government of England, because, on extraordinary occasions, recourse could be had to what was then called the States-General. But in England there are no such occasional bodies; and as to those who are now called representatives, a great part of them are mere machines of the Court, placemen, and dependents.

I presume that though all the people of England pay taxes, not an hundredth part of them are electors, and the members of one of the Houses of Parliament represent nobody but themselves. There is, therefore, no power but the voluntary will of the people that has a right to act in any matter respecting a general reform; and by the same right that two persons can confer on such a subject, a thousand may. The object in all such preliminary proceedings, is to find out what the general sense of a Nation is and to be governed by it. If it prefer a bad or defective Government to a reform, or chuse to pay ten times more taxes than there is occasion for, it has a right so to do: and so long as the majority do not impose conditions on the minority, different from what they impose on themselves, though there may be much error, there is no injustice. Neither will the error continue long. Reason and discussion will soon bring things right, however wrong they may begin. By such a process no tumult is to be apprehended. The poor in all countries are naturally both peaceable and grateful in all reforms in which their interest and happiness is included. It is only by neglecting and rejecting them that they become tumultuous.

The objects that now press on the public attention are the French Revolution, and the prospect of a general Revolution in Governments. Of all Nations in Europe there is none so much interested in the French Revolution as England. Enemies for ages, and that at a vast expence, and without any rational object, the opportunity now presents itself of amicably closing the scene, and joining their efforts to reform the rest of Europe. By doing this they will not only prevent the further effusion of blood and encrease of taxes, but be in a condition of getting rid of a considerable part of their present burdens, as has been already stated. Long experience, however, has shown that reforms of this kind are not those which old Governments wish to promote; and therefore it is to Nations, and not to such Governments, that these matters present themselves.

In the preceding part of this work I have spoken of an alliance between England, France and America, for purposes that were to be afterwards mentioned. Though I have no direct authority on the part of America I have good reason to conclude that she is disposed to enter into a consideration of such a measure, provided that the Governments with which she might ally acted as national Governments, and not as Courts enveloped in intrigue and mystery. That France as a Nation, and a national Government, would prefer an alliance with England, is a matter of certainty. Nations, like individuals, who have long been enemies without knowing each other, or knowing why, become the better friends when they discover the errors and impositions under which they had acted.

Admitting, therefore, the probability of such a connection, I will state some matters by which such an alliance, together with that of Holland, might render service, not only to the parties immediately concerned, but to all Europe.

It is, I think, certain, that if the fleets of England, France and Holland were confederated they could propose, with effect, a limitation to, and a general dismantling of, all the navies in Europe, to a certain proportion to be agreed upon.

First, That no new ship of war shall be built by any power in Europe, themselves included.

Secondly, That all the navies now in existence shall be put back, suppose to one-tenth of their present force. This will save to France and England at least two millions sterling annually to each, and their relative force be in the same proportion as it is now. If men will permit themselves to think, as rational beings ought to think, nothing can appear more ridiculous and absurd, exclusive of all moral reflections, than to be at the expence of building navies, filling them with men, and then hauling them into the ocean, to try which can sink each other fastest. Peace, which costs nothing, is attended with infinitely more advantage than any victory with all its expence. But this, though it best answers the purpose of Nations, does not that of Court Governments, whose habited policy is pretence for taxation, places and offices.

It is, I think, also certain, that the above confederated powers, together with that of the United States of America, can propose with effect, to Spain, the independence of South America, and the opening those countries of immense extent and wealth to the general commerce of the world, as North America now is.

With how much more glory and advantage to itself does a Nation act when it exerts its powers to rescue the world from bondage and to create itself friends, than when it employs those powers to encrease ruin, desolation and misery. The horrid scene that is now acting by the English Government in the East Indies, is fit only to be told of Goths and Vandals, who, destitute of principle, robbed and tortured the world they were incapable of enjoying.

The opening of South America would produce an immense field of commerce, and a ready money market for manufactures, which the eastern world does not. The east is already a country full of manufactures, the importation of which is not only an injury to the manufactures of England, but a drain upon its specie. The balance against England by this trade is regularly upwards of half a million annually sent out in the East India ships in silver; and this is the reason, together with German intrigue and German subsidies, there is so little silver in England.

But any war is harvest to such Governments, however ruinous it may be to a nation. It serves to keep up deceitful expectations, which prevent a people looking into the defects and abuses of Government. It is the *lo here!* and the *lo there!* that amuses and cheats the multitude.

Never did so great an opportunity offer itself to England, and to all Europe, as is produced by the two Revolutions of America and France. By the former, freedom has a national champion in the western world; and by the latter, in Europe. When another Nation shall join France, despotism and bad Government will scarcely dare to appear. To use a trite expression, the iron is becoming hot all over Europe. The insulted German and the enslaved Spaniard, the Russ and the Pole, are beginning to think. The present age will hereafter merit to be called the Age of Reason, and the present generation will appear to the future as the Adam of a new world.

When all the Governments of Europe shall be established on the representative system, Nations will become acquainted, and the animosities and the prejudices fomented by the intrigue and artifice of Courts will cease. The oppressed soldier will become a freeman; and the tortured sailor, no longer dragged along the streets like a felon, will pursue his mercantile voyage in safety. It would be better that Nations should continue the pay of their soldiers during their lives, and give them their discharge, and restore them to freedom and their friends, and cease recruiting, than retain such multitudes at the same expence in a condition useless to society and themselves. As soldiers have hitherto been treated in most countries they might be said to be without a friend. Shunned by the citizens on an apprehension of being enemies to liberty, and too often insulted by those who commanded them, their condition was a double oppression. But where general principles of liberty pervade a people everything is restored to order; and the soldier, civilly treated, returns the civility

In contemplating Revolutions, it is easy to perceive that they may arise from two distinct causes; the one, to avoid or get rid of some great calamity; the other, to obtain some great and positive good; and the two may be distinguished by the names of active and passive Revolutions. In those which proceed from the former cause, the temper becomes incensed and soured; and the redress, obtained by danger, is too often sullied by revenge. But in those which proceed from the latter, the heart, rather animated than agitated, enters serenely upon the subject. Reason and discussion, persuasion and conviction, become the weapons in the contest, and it is only when those are attempted to be suppressed that recourse is had to violence. When men unite in agreeing that a *thing is good,* could it be obtained, such as relief from a burden of taxes and the extinction of corruption, the object is more than half accomplished. What they approve as the end they will promote in the means.

Will any man say, in the present excess of taxation, falling so heavily on the poor, that a remission of five pounds annually of taxes to one hundred and four thousand poor families is not a *good thing?* Will he say that a remission of seven pounds annually to one hundred thousand other poor families, of eight pounds annually to another hundred thousand poor families, and of ten pounds annually to fifty thousand poor and widowed families, are not *good things?* And to proceed a step farther in this climax, will he say that to provide against the misfortunes to which all human life is subject, by securing six pounds annually for all poor, distressed, and reduced persons of the age of fifty and until sixty, and of ten pounds annually after sixty, is not a *good thing?*

Will he say that an abolition of two million of poor-rates to the housekeepers, and of the whole of the house and window light tax, and of the commutation tax, is not a *good thing?* Or will he say that to abolish corruption is a *bad thing?*

If, therefore, the good to be obtained be worthy of a passive, rational, and costless Revolution, it would be bad policy to prefer waiting for a calamity that should force a violent one. I have no idea, considering the reforms which are now passing and spreading throughout Europe, that England will permit herself to be the last; and where the occasion and the opportunity quietly offer, it is better than to wait for a turbulent necessity. It may be considered as an honour to the animal faculties of man to obtain redress by courage and danger, but it is far greater honour to the rational faculties to accomplish the same object by reason, accommodation, and general consent.

As Reforms, or Revolutions, call them which you please, extend themselves among Nations, those Nations will form connections and conventions, and when a few are thus confederated, the progress will be rapid, till despotism and corrupt Government be totally expelled, at least out of two quarters of the world, Europe and America. The Algerine piracy may then be commanded to cease, for it is only by the malicious policy of old Governments, against each other, that it exists.

Throughout this work, various and numerous as the subjects are, which I have taken up and investigated, there is only a single paragraph upon religion, viz. "*that every religion is good, that teaches man to be good.*"

I have carefully avoided to enlarge upon the subject, because I am inclined to believe, that what is called the present Ministry wish to see contentions about religion kept up, to prevent the Nation turning its attention to subjects of Government. It is, as if they were to say, "*Look that way, or any way, but this.*"

But as religion is very improperly made a political machine, and the reality of it is thereby destroyed, I will conclude this work with stating in what light religion appears to me.

If we suppose a large family of children, who, on any particular day, or particular circumstance, made it a custom to present to their parent some token of their affection and gratitude, each of them would make a different offering, and most probably in a different manner. Some would pay their congratulations in themes of verse or prose; some by little devices, as their genius dictated, or according to what they thought would please; and, perhaps the least of all, not able to do any of those things, would ramble into the garden, or the field, and gather what it thought the prettiest flower it could find, though perhaps it might be but a simple weed. The parent would be more gratified by such variety than if the whole of them had acted on a concerted plan, and each had made exactly the same offering. This would have the cold appearance of contrivance, or the harsh one of controul. But of all unwelcome things nothing could more afflict the parent than to know that the whole of them had afterwards gotten together by the ears, boys and girls fighting, scratching, reviling, and abusing each other about which was the best or the worst present.

Why may we not suppose that the great Father of all is pleased with variety of devotion? and that the greatest offence we can act is that by which we seek to torment and render each other miserable? For my own part I am fully satisfied that what I am now doing, with an endeavour to conciliate mankind, to render their condition happy, to unite Nations that have hitherto been enemies, and to extirpate the horrid practice of war, and break the chains of slavery and oppression, is acceptable in his sight; and being the best service I can perform I act it cheerfully.

I do not believe that any two men, on what are called doctrinal points, think alike, who think at all. It is only those who have not thought that appear to agree. It is in this case as with what is called the British Constitution. It has been taken for granted to be good, and encomiums have supplied the place of proof. But when the Nation comes to examine into its principles and the abuses it admits, it will be found to have more defects than I have pointed out in this work and the former.

As to what are called national religions, we may with as much propriety talk of national Gods. It is either political craft or the remains of the Pagan system, when every Nation had its separate and particular deity. Among all the writers of the English Church clergy, who have treated on the general subject of religion, the present Bishop of Llandaff has not been excelled: and it is with much pleasure that I take the opportunity of expressing this token of respect.

I have now gone through the whole of the subject, at least as far as it appears to me at present. It has been my intention for the five years I have been in Europe to offer an address to the people of England on the subject of Government, if the opportunity presented itself, before I returned to America. Mr. Burke has thrown it in my way and I thank him. On a certain occasion, three years ago, I pressed him to propose a national convention, to be fairly elected, for the purpose of taking the state of the Nation into consideration; but I found that however strongly the parliamentary current was then setting against the party he acted with, their policy was to keep everything within that field of corruption, and trust to accidents. Long experience had shewn that Parliaments would follow any change of ministers, and on this they rested their hopes and expectations.

Formerly, when divisions arose respecting Governments, recourse was had to the sword, and a civil war ensued. That savage custom is exploded by the new system; and reference is had to national conventions. Discussion and the general will arbitrate the question, and to this private opinion yields with a good grace, and order is preserved uninterrupted.

Some gentlemen have affected to call the principles upon which this work and the former part of the *Rights of Man* are founded "a new fangled doctrine." The question is not whether those principles are new or old, but whether they are right or wrong. Suppose the former, I will shew their effect by a figure easily understood.

It is now towards the middle of February. Were I to take a turn into the country the trees would present a leafless winterly appearance. As people are apt to pluck twigs as they walk along, I perhaps might do the same, and by chance might observe that a *single bud* on that twig had begun to swell. I should reason very unnaturally, or rather not reason at all, to suppose *this* was the *only* bud in England which had this appearance. Instead of deciding thus, I should instantly conclude that the same appearance was beginning, or about to begin, everywhere; and though the vegetable sleep will continue longer on some trees and plants than on others, and though some of them may not *blossom* for two or three years, all will be in leaf in the summer, except those which are *rotten*. What pace the political summer may keep with the natural, no human foresight can determine. It is, however, not difficult to perceive that the spring is begun. Thus wishing, as I sincerely do, freedom and happiness to all Nations, I close the SECOND PART.

Appendix

As the publication of this work has been delayed beyond the time intended, I think it not improper, all circumstances considered, to state the causes that have occasioned the delay.

The reader will probably observe, that some parts in the plan contained in this work for reducing the taxes, and certain parts in Mr. Pitt's speech at the opening of the present session, Tuesday, January 31, are so much alike, as to induce a belief, that either the Author had taken the hint from Mr. Pitt, or Mr Pitt from the Author.—I will first point out the parts that are similar, and then state such circumstances as I am acquainted with, leaving the reader to make his own conclusion.

Considering it almost an unprecedented case, that taxes should be proposed to be taken off, it is equally as extraordinary that such a measure should occur to two persons at the same time; and still more so (considering the vast variety and multiplicity of taxes), that they should hit on the same specific taxes. Mr. Pitt has mentioned, in his speech, the tax on *Carts* and *Waggons*—that on *Female Servants*—the lowering the tax on *Candles,* and the taking off the tax of three shillings on *Houses* having under seven windows.

Every one of those specific taxes are a part of the plan contained in this work, and proposed also to be taken off. Mr. Pitt's plan, it is true, goes no farther than to a reduction of three hundred and twenty thousand pounds; and the reduction proposed in this work to nearly six millions. I have made my calculations on only sixteen millions and a half of revenue, still asserting that it was "very nearly, if not quite, seventeen millions." Mr. Pitt states it at 16,690,000. I know enough of the matter to say, that he has not *over*-stated it. Having thus given the particulars, which correspond in this work and his speech, I will state a chain of circumstances that may lead to some explanation.

The first hint for lessening the taxes, and that as a consequence flowing from the French Revolution, is to be found in the Address and Declaration of the Gentlemen who met at the Thatched-House Tavern, August 20, 1791. Among many other particulars stated in that Address, is the following, put as an interrogation to the Government opposers of the French Revolution. *"Are they sorry that the pretence, for new oppressive taxes, and the occasion for continuing many old taxes will be at an end?"*

It is well known, that the persons who chiefly frequent the Thatched-House Tavern, are men of Court connections, and so much did they take this Address and Declaration respecting the French Revolution and the reduction of taxes in disgust, that the Landlord was under the necessity of informing the Gentlemen, who composed the meeting of the twentieth of August, and who proposed holding another meeting, that he could not receive them.

What was only hinted at in the Address and Declaration, respecting taxes and principles of Government, will be found reduced to a regular system in this work. But as Mr. Pitt's speech contains some of the same things respecting taxes, I now come to give the circumstances before alluded to.

The case is: This work was intended to be published just before the meeting of Parliament, and for that purpose a considerable part of the copy was put into the printer's hands in September, and all the remaining copy, as far as page 273, which contains the parts to which Mr. Pitt's speech is similar, was given to him full six weeks before the meeting of Parliament, and he was informed of the time at which it was to appear. He had composed nearly the whole about a fortnight before the time of Parliament meeting, and had printed as far as page 241, and had given me a proof of the next sheet, up to page 251. It was then in sufficient forwardness to be out at the time proposed, as two other sheets were ready for striking off. I had before told him, that if he thought he should be straitened for time, I would get part of the work done at another press, which he desired me not to do. In this manner, the work stood on the Tuesday fortnight preceding the meeting of Parliament, when all at once, without any previous intimation, though I had been with him the evening before, he sent me, by one of his workmen, all the remaining copy, from page 241, declining to go on with the work *on any consideration*.

To account for this extraordinary conduct I was totally at a loss, as he stopped at the part where the arguments on systems and principles of Government closed, and where the plan for the reduction of taxes, the education of children, and the support of the poor and the aged begins; and still more especially, as he had, at the time of his beginning to print, and before he had seen the whole copy, offered a thousand pounds for the copy-right, together with the future copy-right of the former part of the Rights of Man. I told the person who brought me this offer that I should not accept it, and wished it not to be renewed, giving him as my reason, that though I believed the printer to be an honest man, I would never put it in the power of any printer or publisher to suppress or alter a work of mine, by making him master of the copy, or give to him the right of selling it to any minister, or to any other person, or to treat as a mere matter of traffic that which I intended should operate as a principle.

His refusal to complete the work (which he could not purchase) obliged me to seek for another printer, and this of consequence would throw the publication back till after the meeting of Parliament, otherways it would have appeared that Mr. Pitt had only taken up a part of the plan which I had more fully stated.

Whether that gentleman, or any other, had seen the work, or any part of it, is more than I have authority to say. But the manner in which the work was returned, and the particular time at which this was done, and that after the offers he had made, are suspicious circumstances. I know what the opinion of booksellers and publishers is upon such a case, but as to my own opinion, I chuse to make no declaration. There are many ways by which proof sheets may be procured by other persons before a work publicly appear; to which I shall add another circumstance, which is,

A ministerial bookseller in Piccadilly who had been employed, as common report says, by a clerk of one of the boards closely connected with the Ministry (the Board of Trade and Plantation of which Hawksbury is president) to publish what he calls my Life (I wish that his own life and the lives of all the Cabinet were as good), used to have his books printed at the same printing-office that I employed; but when the former part of *Rights of Man* came out, he took his work away in dudgeon; and about a week or ten days before the printer returned my copy, he came to make him an offer of his work again, which was accepted. This would consequently give him admission into the printing-office where the sheets of this work were then lying; and as booksellers and printers are free with each other, he would have the opportunity of seeing what was going on.—Be the case, however, as it may, Mr. Pitt's plan, little and diminutive as it is, would have had a very awkward appearance, had this work appeared at the time the printer had engaged to finish it.

I have now stated the particulars which occasioned the delay, from the proposal to purchase, to the refusal to print. If all the Gentlemen are innocent, it is very unfortunate for them that such a variety of suspicious circumstances should, without any design, arrange themselves together.

Having now finished this part, I will conclude with stating another circumstance.

About a fortnight or three weeks before the meeting of Parliament, a small addition, amounting to about twelve shillings and six pence a year, was made to the pay of the soldiers, or rather, their pay was docked so much less. Some Gentlemen who knew, in part, that this work would contain a plan of reforms respecting the oppressed condition of soldiers, wished me to add a note to the work, signifying, that the part upon that subject had been in the printer's hands some weeks before that addition of pay was proposed. I declined doing this, lest it should be interpreted into an air of vanity, or an endeavour to excite suspicion (for which, perhaps, there might be no grounds) that some of the Government gentlemen, had, by some means or other, made out what this work would contain: and had not the printing been interrupted so as to occasion a delay beyond the time fixed for publication, nothing contained in this appendix would have appeared.

THOMAS PAINE.

FOUR

The Age of Reason

IN ORDER to understand the circumstances that produced *The Age of Reason,* we must know something of the events that led up to the writing of it. When Paine fled from England, he did not, for the time at least, abandon hope in the situation he left behind him. The revolution in England had failed, but the French Revolution was then in the first sweep of its young glory; France was the strongest, the most populous of the western European nations. A democratic France, united and firm in its stand against tyranny, could rally every revolutionary element in Europe: so thought Paine, and Paine also was certain the young American Republic across the sea would join hands firmly with France.

He landed in France at the port of Calais, and the people of Calais made him a deputy to the National Convention. At the Convention, he was one of the committee who framed the new French Constitution. But his day of glory in France was short lived. He tried to superimpose on France the pattern of the American Revolution. He fell in with the party of Condorcet, and he mistook their reactionary stand for an enlightened program; his lack of knowledge of the French language abetted his misunderstanding. He was growing old: change—yes, he still believed in change, but orderly change. He was against the execution of the king; in such a situation, his American comrades would not have executed the king. He could not clearly see the difference between a united, comparatively isolated America and a disunited France surrounded by enemies.

At the same time, his hope in a real working alliance between France and America began to fade. It is one of history's great tragedies that the anti-democratic Federalist movement of Hamilton and John Adams should have gained control of America's first two administrations, and in so doing destroyed our solid friendship with France. Blow after blow was now falling upon Paine. He lost his influence in the Convention. Revolutionary France moved ahead of him. Unlike others in the Condorcet faction, he never betrayed any interest of France—indeed, he was incapable of ever betraying the people's interest—but he found himself left behind, alone, in a sense forsaken. Gouverneur Morris, the Federalist minister to France, plotted against the French Republic, and Paine, in efforts to expose him, earned his undying enmity

When Robespierre and his party came into power, Paine was almost ready to accept his exclusion from the revolutionary current. It came to him finally that he would not move Europe as he had moved America, that he could not rally the people of France behind him, as he had once rallied the American farmers and artisans. He retired to a farmhouse on the outskirts of Paris, and there he sat down to write the one book he considered might still have influence and importance.

In France, Paine had felt a trend toward atheism. So long had the established church been in league with the aristocracy, with all the forces of tyranny, that the reaction against it produced a reaction against every form of religion. To Paine, a deeply religious man, this was nothing less than a tragedy. Religion, he felt, could be as reasonable and as much a friend of society as any other social force.

So, in 1793, he wrote a book, setting down his religious beliefs, setting down a pattern of reasonable religion for all men. This book was called *The Age of Reason.* Hardly had Paine completed the manuscript, when Robespierre's agents came with orders for his arrest.

In this world, where reason is at such a premium, the unreasonable should not be hard to accept: that is the only premise upon which to understand how the author of so deeply religious a book as *The Age of Reason* was condemned as an atheist on the basis of that very book. Too many people accept without inquiring. Among the common people of Great Britain, there were a comparatively few thousand who had read *Rights of Man.* Those knew Paine for their friend, for the friend of all mankind, for a good man and a hero. But many thousand more were fed the foul lies circulated by the anti-democrats about Paine, and those, who should have adored him, vilified him, becoming so much more the tools of their masters. Those people were ripe and ready to believe anything of Paine's new book; none of them read it,—*The Age of Reason* had not nearly as large a reading audience as Paine's previous work—but all of them accepted the statement that Paine had denounced and attempted to dethrone God. So it came about that in England, this great, good Englishman, was depicted with horns, was the butt of smutty sayings and foul rhymes, so readily do certain self-styled pious advocates turn to filth to enshrine their deity.

And in America, the reaction was even more bitter. The book appeared more than a decade after the revolution. The rising Federalist power attacked any and all patriots who would not play into the hands of the anti-democrats.

Of course, hardly anyone read it in America either; but since when has knowledge been a criterion for slander? You may ask, did they forget in so short a time? Paine's comrades never forgot, but they were so few! The country had grown, and even during the revolution, civil war had divided the nation. Paine had his enemies; he was a bad politician and not a man for compromise. He was attacked from the pulpit, on the streets, at meetings, in the newspapers and magazines—and this while he was still in France.

How was it that a book could be so completely misinterpreted? Well, for one thing, it presented a degree of opposition to the organized church; it called for complete and unequivocal freedom of religion and demanded that there be no middleman between a person and his God. It also criticized the Bible and the method whereby the Bible was interpreted. It was a deistic work, and it took the not-so-strange attitude that one serves God best who serves his fellow man. But anti-religious it was not, and certainly not atheistic.

The crux of the matter was this; at that time, atheism was not nearly the menace to the established church that deism was. Atheism has very little appeal to a church-raised man; deism has a great deal more. *Reason* was the main overtone of all eighteenth century revolutionary movements, and the ideological appeal was to the natural rights of all men. If all men were created equal in the sight of the natural laws of man, then could it not be that they were also created equal in the sight of God? And could it not be that God would judge them solely by their social behavior and not by their churchly demeanor? That was like a knife-edge cutting at the church, and combined with the humanistic theories of the goodness of man, taking hold at the time, it presented no inconsiderable menace to organized religion. Remember that then the "fundamentalist" quality in the church was far more powerful than today

Undoubtedly, Paine's prime motive in writing *The Age of Reason* was to give the opponents of atheism firm ground on which to stand. From his point of view, love of one's fellow man and love of God were incontestably one. If the broad revolutionary movement, with which he had so closely identified himself, abandoned God, then would it not abandon man? Yet he could make out no case for the God of organized religion; he had to find a new conception of God, a broad and wise conception wherein there was only wisdom and love—and that God, as Paine saw it, was as broad as all things and all hope. That is the God he wrote about in his book; and whether he was right or wrong, the sincerity of his viewpoint must be recognized. The bugaboo that he was an atheist should be laid to rest, once and for all.

Paine finished *The Age of Reason* only in time to pass it on to a friend before he was marched off to jail by order of Robespierre. For long and weary months, Paine languished in prison, watching the long parade of victims go to their deaths under the Terror. Again and again, he suspected that he would be next—but the government fell and Paine still lived. Then, through the intercession of James Monroe, the new ambassador to France, Paine was released, a tired and sick old man.

The Age of Reason

Being an Investigation of True and Fabulous Theology

It has been my intention, for several years past, to publish my thoughts upon religion; I am well aware of the difficulties that attend the subject, and, from that consideration, had reserved it to a more advanced period of life. I intended it to be the last offering I should make to my fellow citizens of all nations, and that at a time when the purity of the motive that induced me to it, could not admit of a question, even by those who might disapprove the work.

The circumstance that has now taken place in France of the total abolition of the whole national order of priesthood, and of every thing appertaining to compulsive systems of religion, and compulsive articles of faith, has not only precipitated my intention, but rendered a work of this kind exceedingly necessary, lest, in the general wreck of superstition, of false systems of government, and false theology, we lose sight of morality, of humanity, and of the theology that is true.

As several of my colleagues, and others of my fellow-citizens of France, have given me the example of making their voluntary and individual profession of faith, I also will make mine; and I do this with all that sincerity and frankness with which the mind of man communicates with itself.

I believe in one God, and no more; and I hope for happiness beyond this life.

I believe the equality of man; and I believe that religious duties consist in doing justice, loving mercy, and endeavouring to make our fellow creatures happy.

But, lest it should be supposed that I believe many other things in addition to these, I shall, in the progress of this work, declare the things I do not believe, and my reasons for not believing them.

I do not believe in the creed professed by the Jewish church, by the Roman church, by the Greek church, by the Turkish church, by the Protestant church, nor by any church that I know of. My own mind is my own church.

All national institutions of churches, whether Jewish, Christian, or Turkish, appear to me no other than human inventions, set up to terrify and enslave mankind, and monopolize power and profit.

I do not mean by this declaration to condemn those who believe otherwise; they have the same right to their belief as I have to mine. But it is necessary to the happiness of man, that he be mentally faithful to himself. Infidelity does not consist in believing, or in disbelieving; it consists in professing to believe what he does not believe.

It is impossible to calculate the moral mischief, if I may so express it, that mental lying has produced in society. When a man has so far corrupted and prostituted the chastity of his mind, as to subscribe his professional belief to things he does not believe, he has prepared himself for the commission of every other crime. He takes up the trade of a priest for the sake of gain, and, in order to qualify himself for that trade, he begins with a perjury. Can we conceive any thing more destructive to morality than this?

Soon after I had published the pamphlet, "COMMON SENSE," in America, I saw the exceeding probability that a revolution in the system of government would be followed by a revolution in the system of religion. The adulterous connection of church and state, wherever it had taken place, whether Jewish, Christian, or Turkish, had so effectually prohibited, by pains and penalties, every discussion upon established creeds, and upon first principles of religion, that until the system of government should be changed, those subjects could not be brought fairly and openly before the world, but that whenever this should be done, a revolution in the system of religion would follow. Human inventions and priest-craft would be detected; and man would return to the pure, unmixed, and unadulterated belief of one God, and no more.

Every national church or religion has established itself by pretending some special mission from God, communicated to certain individuals. The Jews have their Moses; the Christians their Jesus Christ, their apostles, and saints; and the Turks their Mahomet, as if the way to God was not open to every man alike.

Each of those churches show certain books, which they call *revelation,* or the word of God. The Jews say, that their word of God was given by God to Moses, face to face; the Christians say, that their word of God came by divine inspiration; and the Turks say, that their word of God (the Koran) was brought by an angel from Heaven. Each of those churches accuse the other of unbelief; and, for my own part, I disbelieve them all

As it is necessary to affix right ideas to words, I will, before I proceed further into the subject, offer some other observations on the word *revelation.* Revelation when applied to religion, means something communicated *immediately* from God to man.

No one will deny or dispute the power of the Almighty to make such a communication, if he pleases. But admitting, for the sake of a case, that something has been revealed to a certain person, and not revealed to any other person, it is revelation to that person only. When he tells it to a second person, a second to a third, a third to a fourth, and so on, it ceases to be a revelation to all those persons. It is revelation to the first person only, and *hearsay* to every other, and, consequently, they are not obliged to believe it.

It is a contradiction in terms and ideas, to call any thing a revelation that comes to us at second-hand, either verbally or in writing. Revelation is necessarily limited to the first communication—after this, it is only an account of something which that person says was a revelation made to him; and though he may find himself obliged to believe it, it cannot be incumbent on me to believe it in the same manner; for it was not a revelation made to *me*, and I have only his word for it that it was made to him.

When Moses told the children of Israel that he received the two tables of the commandments from the hands of God, they were not obliged to believe him, because they had no other authority for it than his telling them so; and I have no other authority for it than some historian telling me so. The commandments carry no internal evidence of divinity with them; they contain some good moral precepts, such as any man qualified to be a lawgiver, or a legislator, could produce himself, without having recourse to supernatural intervention.

When I am told that the Koran was written in Heaven, and brought to Mahomet by an angel, the account comes too near the same kind of hearsay evidence and second-hand authority as the former. I did not see the angel myself, and, therefore, I have a right not to believe it.

When also I am told that a woman called the Virgin Mary, said, or gave out, that she was with child without any cohabitation with a man, and that her betrothed husband, Joseph, said that an angel told him so, I have a right to believe them or not; such a circumstance required a much stronger evidence than their bare word for it; but we have not even this—for neither Joseph nor Mary wrote any such matter themselves; it is only reported by others that *they said so*—it is hearsay upon hearsay, and I do not choose to rest my belief upon such evidence.

It is, however, not difficult to account for the credit that was given to the story of Jesus Christ being the son of God. He was born when the heathen mythology had still some fashion and repute in the world, and that mythology had prepared the people for the belief of such a story. Almost all the extraordinary men that lived under the heathen mythology were reputed to be the sons of some of their gods. It was not a new thing, at that time, to believe a man to have been celestially begotten; the intercourse of gods with women was then a matter of familiar opinion. Their Jupiter, according to their accounts, had cohabited with hundreds; the story therefore had nothing in it either new, wonderful or obscene; it was conformable to the opinions that then prevailed among the people called Gentiles, or Mythologists, and it was those people only that believed it. The Jews, who had kept strictly to the belief of one God, and no more, and who had always rejected the heathen mythology, never credited the story.

It is curious to observe how the theory of what is called the Christian Church, sprung out of the tail of heathen mythology. A direct incorporation took place in the first instance, by making the reputed founder to be celestially begotten. The trinity of gods that then followed was no other than a reduction of the former plurality, which was about twenty or thirty thousand; the statue of Mary succeeded the statue of Diana of Ephesus; the deification of heroes changed into the canonization of saints; the mythologists had gods for every thing; the Christian Mythologists had saints for every thing; the church became as crowded with the one, as the pantheon had been with the other; and Rome was the place of both. The Christian theory is little else than the idolatry of the ancient Mythologists, accommodated to the purposes of power and revenue; and it yet remains to reason and philosophy to abolish the amphibious fraud.

Nothing that is here said can apply, even with the most distant disrespect, to the *real* character of Jesus Christ. He was a virtuous and an amiable man. The morality that he preached and practised was of the most benevolent kind; and though similar systems of morality had been preached by Confucius, and by some of the Greek philosophers, many years before; by the Quakers since; and by many good men in all ages, it has not been exceeded by any.

Jesus Christ wrote no account of himself, of his birth, parentage, or anything else; not a line of what is called the New Testament is of his own writing. The history of him is altogether the work of other people; and as to the account given of his resurrection and ascension, it was the necessary counterpart to the story of his birth. His historians, having brought him into the world in a supernatural manner, were obliged to take him out again in the same manner, or the first part of the story must have fallen to the ground.

The wretched contrivance with which this latter part is told, exceeds every thing that went before it. The first part, that of the miraculous conception, was not a thing that admitted of publicity; and therefore the tellers of this part of the story had this advantage, that though they might not be credited, they could not be detected. They could not be expected to prove it, because it was not one of those things that admitted of proof, and it was impossible that the person of whom it was told could prove it himself.

But the resurrection of a dead person from the grave, and his ascension through the air, is a thing very different as to the evidence it admits of, to the invisible conception of a child in the womb. The resurrection and ascension, supposing them to have taken place, admitted of public and occular demonstration, like that of the ascension of a balloon, or the sun at noon day, to all Jerusalem at least. A thing which every body is required to believe, requires that the proof and evidence of it should be equal to all, and universal; and as the public visibility of this last related act, was the only evidence that could give sanction to the former part, the whole of it falls to the ground, because that evidence never was given. Instead of this, a small number of persons, not more than eight or nine, are introduced as proxies for the whole world, to say they saw it, and all the rest of the world are called upon to believe it. But it appears that Thomas did not believe the resurrection; and, as they say, would not believe without having occular and manual demonstration himself. *So neither will I,* and the reason is equally as good for me, and for every other person, as for Thomas.

It is in vain to attempt to palliate or disguise this matter. The story, so far as relates to the supernatural part, has every mark of fraud and imposition stamped upon the face of it. Who were the authors of it is as impossible for us now to know, as it is for us to be assured, that the books in which the account is related, were written by the persons whose names they bear; the best surviving evidence we now have respecting this affair is the Jews. They are regularly descended from the people who lived in the time this resurrection and ascension is said to have happened, and they say, *it is not true.* It has long appeared to me a strange inconsistency to cite the Jews as a proof of the truth of the story. It is just the same as if a man were to say, I will prove the truth of what I have told you, by producing the people who say it is false.

That such a person as Jesus Christ existed, and that he was crucified, which was the mode of execution at that day, are historical relations strictly within the limits of probability. He preached most excellent morality, and the equality of man; but he preached also against the corruptions and avarice of the Jewish priests, and this brought upon him the hatred and vengeance of the whole order of priesthood. The accusation which those priests brought against him was that of sedition and conspiracy against the Roman government, to which the Jews were then subject and tributary; and it is not improbable that the Roman government might have some secret apprehensions of the effects of his doctrine as well as the Jewish priests; neither is it improbable that Jesus Christ had in contemplation the delivery of the Jewish nation from the bondage of the Romans. Between the two, however, this virtuous reformer and revolutionist lost his life.

It is upon this plain narrative of facts, together with another case I am going to mention, that the Christian Mythologists, calling themselves the Christian Church, have erected their fable, which for absurdity and extravagance, is not exceeded by any thing that is to be found in the mythology of the ancients.

The ancient Mythologists tell us that the race of Giants made war against Jupiter, and that one of them threw a hundred rocks against him at one throw; that Jupiter defeated him with thunder, and confined him afterwards under Mount Etna, and that every time the Giant turns himself, Mount Etna belches fire.

It is here easy to see that the circumstance of the mountain, that of its being a volcano, suggested the idea of the fable; and that the fable is made to fit and wind itself up with that circumstance.

The Christian Mythologists tell us, that their Satan made war against the Almighty, who defeated him, and confined him afterwards, not under a mountain, but in a pit. It is here easy to see that the first fable suggested the idea of the second; for the fable of Jupiter and the Giants was told many hundred years before that of Satan.

Thus far the ancient and the christian Mythologists differ very little from each other. But the latter have contrived to carry the matter much farther. They have contrived to connect the fabulous part of the story of Jesus Christ with the fable originating from Mount Etna; and, in order to make all the parts of the story tie together, they have taken to their aid the traditions of the Jews; for the Christian mythology is made up partly from the ancient mythology, and partly from the Jewish traditions.

The Christian Mythologists, after having confined Satan in a pit, were obliged to let him out again to bring on the sequel of the fable. He is then introduced into the Garden of Eden in the shape of a snake or a serpent, and in that shape he enters into familiar conversation with Eve, who is no way surprised to hear a snake talk; and the issue of this tete-a-tete is, that he persuades her to eat an apple, and the eating of that apple damns all mankind.

After giving Satan this triumph over the whole creation, one would have supposed that the church Mythologists would have been kind enough to send him back to the pit: or, if they had not done this, that they would have put a mountain upon him, (for they say that their faith can remove a mountain) or have put him *under* a mountain, as the former Mythologists had done, to prevent his getting again among the women and doing more mischief. But instead of this, they leave him at large, without even obliging him to give his parole—the secret of which is, that they could not do without him; and after being at the trouble of making him, they bribed him to stay. They promised him ALL the Jews, ALL the Turks by anticipation, nine-tenths of the world beside, and Mahomet into the bargain. After this, who can doubt the bountifulness of the Christian mythology.

Having thus made an insurrection and a battle in Heaven, in which none of the combatants could be either killed or wounded—put Satan into the pit—let him out again—given him a triumph over the whole creation—damned all mankind by the eating of an apple, these Christian Mythologists bring the two ends of their fable together. They represent this virtuous and amiable man, Jesus Christ, to be at once both God and Man, and also the Son of God, celestially begotten, on purpose to be sacrificed, because they say that Eve in her longing had eaten an apple.

Putting aside every thing that might excite laughter by its absurdity, or detestation by its profaneness, and confining ourselves merely to an examination of the parts, it is impossible to conceive a story more derogatory to the Almighty, more inconsistent with his wisdom, more contradictory to his power, than this story is.

In order to make for it a foundation to rise upon, the inventors were under the necessity of giving to the being, whom they call Satan, a power equally as great, if not greater than they attribute to the Almighty. They have not only given him the power of liberating himself from the pit, after what they call his fall, but they have made that power increase afterwards to infinity. Before this fall they represent him only as an angel of limited existence, as they represent the rest. After his fall, he becomes, by their account, omnipresent. He exists everywhere, and at the same time. He occupies the whole immensity of space.

Not content with this deification of Satan, they represent him as defeating, by stratagem, in the shape of an animal of the creation, all the power and wisdom of the Almighty. They represent him as having compelled the Almighty to the *direct necessity* either of surrendering the whole of the creation to the government and sovereignty of this Satan, or of capitulating for its redemption by coming down upon earth, and exhibiting himself upon a cross in the shape of a man.

Had the inventors of this story told it the contrary way, that is, had they represented the Almighty as compelling Satan to exhibit *himself* on a cross, in the shape of a snake, as a punishment for his new transgression, the story would have been less absurd—less contradictory. But, instead of this, they make the transgressor triumph, and the Almighty fall.

That many good men have believed this strange fable, and lived very good lives under that belief (for credulity is not a crime) is what I have no doubt of. In the first place, they were educated to believe it, and they would have believed any thing else in the same manner. There are also many who have been so enthusiastically enraptured by what they conceived to be the infinite love of God to man, in making a sacrifice of himself, that the vehemence of the idea has forbidden and deterred them from examining into the absurdity and profaneness of the story. The more unnatural any thing is, the more is it capable of becoming the object of dismal admiration.

But if objects for gratitude and admiration are our desire, do they not present themselves every hour to our eyes? Do we not see a fair creation prepared to receive us the instant we are born—a world furnished to our hands, that cost us nothing? Is it we that light up the sun, that pour down the rain, and fill the earth with abundance? Whether we sleep or wake, the vast machinery of the universe still goes on. Are these things, and the blessings they indicate in future, nothing to us? Can our gross feelings be excited by no other subjects than tragedy and suicide? Or is the gloomy pride of man become so intolerable, that nothing can flatter it but a sacrifice of the Creator?

I know that this bold investigation will alarm many, but it would be paying too great a compliment to their credulity to forbear it upon that account; the times and the subject demand it to be done. The suspicion that the theory of what is called the Christian church is fabulous, is becoming very extensive in all countries; and it will be a consolation to men staggering under that suspicion, and doubting what to believe and what to disbelieve, to see the subject freely investigated. I therefore pass on to an examination of the books called the Old and New Testament.

These books, beginning with Genesis and ending with Revelation, (which, by the bye, is a book of riddles that requires a revelation to explain it) are, we are told, the word of God. It is, therefore, proper for us to know who told us so, that we may know what credit to give to the report. The answer to this question is, that nobody can tell, except that we tell one another so. The case, however, historically appears to be as follows:—

When the church Mythologists established their system, they collected all the writings they could find, and managed them as they pleased. It is a matter altogether of uncertainty to us whether such of the writings as now appear under the name of the Old and New Testament, are in the same state in which those collectors say they found them, or whether they added, altered, abridged, or dressed them up.

Be this as it may, they decided by *vote* which of the books out of the collection they had made, should be the WORD OF GOD, and which should not. They rejected several; they voted others to be doubtful, such as the books called the Apocrypha; and those books which had a majority of votes, were voted to be the word of God. Had they voted otherwise, all the people, since calling themselves Christians, had believed otherwise—for the belief of the one comes from the vote of the other. Who the people were that did all this, we know nothing of, they called themselves by the general name of the Church; and this is all we know of the matter.

As we have no other external evidence or authority for believing these books to be the word of God, than what I have mentioned, which is no evidence or authority at all, I come, in the next place, to examine the internal evidence contained in the books themselves.

In the former part of this Essay, I have spoken of revelation.—I now proceed further with that subject, for the purpose of applying it to the books in question.

Revelation is a communication of something, which the person, to whom that thing is revealed, did not know before. For if I have done a thing, or seen it done, it needs no revelation to tell me I have done it, or seen it, nor to enable me to tell it, or to write it.

Revelation, therefore, cannot be applied to any thing done upon earth, of which man is himself the actor or the witness; and consequently all the historical and anecdotal part of the Bible, which is almost the whole of it, is not within the meaning and compass of the word revelation, and, therefore, is not the word of God.

When Sampson ran off with the gate-posts of Gaza, if he ever did so, (and whether he did or not is nothing to us,) or when he visited his Delilah, or caught his foxes, or did any thing else, what has revelation to do with these things? If they were facts, he could tell them himself; or his secretary, if he kept one, could write them, if they were worth either telling or writing; and if they were fictious, revelation could not make them true; and whether true or not, we are neither the better nor the wiser for knowing them. When we contemplate the immensity of that Being, who directs and governs the incomprehensible WHOLE, of which the utmost ken of human sight can discover but a part, we ought to feel shame at calling such paltry stories the word of God.

As to the account of the Creation, with which the book of Genesis opens, it has all the appearance of being a tradition which the Israelites had among them before they came into Egypt; and after their departure from that country, they put it at the head of their history, without telling (as it is most probable) that they did not know how they came by it. The manner in which the account opens, shows it to be traditionary. It begins abruptly: it is nobody that speaks; it is nobody that hears; it is addressed to nobody; it has neither first, second, or third person; it has every criterion of being a tradition, it has no voucher. Moses does not take it upon himself by introducing it with the formality that he uses on other occasions, such as that of saying, *The Lord spake unto Moses, saying.*

Why it has been called the Mosaic account of the Creation, I am at a loss to conceive. Moses, I believe, was too good a judge of such subjects to put his name to that account. He had been educated among the Egyptians, who were a people as well skilled in science, and particularly in astronomy, as any people of their day; and the silence and caution that Moses observes in not authenticating the account, is a good negative evidence that he neither told it nor believed it.—The case is, that every nation of people has been world-makers, and the Israelites had as much right to set up the trade of world-making as any of the rest; and as Moses was not an Israelite, he might not choose to contradict the tradition. The account, however, is harmless; and this is more than can be said of many other parts of the Bible.

Whenever we read the obscene stories, the voluptuous debaucheries, the cruel and torturous executions, the unrelenting vindictiveness, with which more than half the Bible is filled, it would be more consistent that we called it the word of a demon, than the word of God. It is a history of wickedness, that has served to corrupt and brutalize mankind; and, for my own part, I sincerely detest it, as I detest every thing that is cruel.

We scarcely meet with any thing, a few phrases excepted, but what deserves either our abhorence or our contempt, till we come to the miscellaneous parts of the Bible. In the anonymous publications, the Psalms, and the Book of Job, more particularly in the latter, we find a great deal of elevated sentiment reverentially expressed of the power and benignity of the Almighty; but they stand on no higher rank than many other compositions on similar subjects, as well before that time as since.

The Proverbs which are said to be Solomon's, though most probably a collection, (because they discover a knowledge of life, which his situation excluded him from knowing) are an instructive table of ethics. They are inferior in keenness to the proverbs of the Spaniards, and not more wise and economical than those of the American Franklin.

All the remaining parts of the Bible, generally known by the name of the Prophets, are the works of the Jewish poets and itinerant preachers, who mixed poetry, anecdote, and devotion together—and those works still retain the air and style of poetry, though in translation.*

There is not, throughout the whole book called the Bible, any word that describes to us what we call a poet, nor any word that describes what we call poetry. The case is, that the word *prophet,* to which latter times have affixed a new idea, was the Bible word for poet, and the word *prophesying* meant the art of making poetry. It also meant the art of playing poetry to a tune upon any instrument of music.

We read of prophesying with pipes, tabrets, and horns—of prophesying with harps, with psalteries, with cymbals, and with every other instru-

* As there are many readers who do not see that a composition is poetry, unless it be in rhyme, it is for their information that I add this note.

Poetry consists principally in two things—imagery and composition. The composition of poetry differs from that of prose in the manner of mixing long and short syllables together. Take a long syllable out of a line of poetry, and put a short one in the room of it, or put a long syllable where a short one should be, and that line will lose its poetical harmony. It will have an effect upon the line like that of misplacing a note in a song.

The imagery in those books, called the prophets, appertains altogether to poetry. It is fictitious, and often extravagant, and not admissible in any other kind of writing than poetry.

To show that these writings are composed in poetical numbers, I will take ten syllables, as they stand in the book, and make a line of the same number of syllables (heroic measure) that shall rhyme with the last word. It will then be seen that the composition of those books is poetical measure. The instance I shall produce is from Isaiah:—

> *"Hear, O ye heavens, and give ear, O earth!"*
> 'Tis God himself that calls attention forth.

Another instance I shall quote is from the mournful Jeremiah, to which I shall add two other lines, for the purpose of carrying out the figure, and showing the intention of the poet.

> *"O! that mine head were waters and mine eyes"*
> Were fountains flowing like the liquid skies;
> Then would I give the mighty flood release,
> And weep a deluge for the human race.

ment of music then in fashion. Were we now to speak of prophesying with a fiddle, or with a pipe and tabor, the expression would have no meaning, or would appear ridiculous and to some people contemptuous, because we have changed the meaning of the word.

We are told of Saul being among the *prophets,* and also that he prophesied; but we are not told what *they prophesied,* nor what *he prophesied.* The case is, there was nothing to tell; for these prophets were a company of musicians and poets, and Saul joined in the concert, and this was called *prophesying.*

The account given of this affair in the book called Samuel, is, that Saul met a *company* of prophets; a whole company of them! coming down with a psaltery, a tabret, a pipe, and a harp, and that they prophesied, and that he prophesied with them. But it appears afterwards, that Saul prophesied badly; that is, performed his part badly; for it is said, that, an *"evil spirit from God"* * came upon Saul, and he prophesied.

Now, were there no other passage in the book called the Bible, than this, to demonstrate to us that we have lost the original meaning of the word *prophesy,* and substituted another meaning in its place, this alone would be sufficient; for it is impossible to use and apply the word *prophesy,* in the place it is here used and applied, if we give to it the sense which latter times have affixed to it. The manner in which it is here used strips it of all religious meaning, and shows that a man might then be a prophet, or he might *prophesy,* as he may now be a poet or musician, without any regard to the morality or immorality of his character. The word was originally a term of science, promiscuously applied to poetry and to music, and not restricted to any subject upon which poetry and music might be exercised.

Deborah and Barak are called prophets, not because they predicted any thing, but because they composed the poem or song that bears their name, in celebration of an act already done. David is ranked among the prophets, for he was a musician, and was also reputed to be (though perhaps very erroneously) the author of the Psalms. But Abraham, Isaac, and Jacob are not called prophets; it does not appear from any accounts we have, that they could either sing, play music, or make poetry.

We are told of the greater and the lesser prophets. They might as well tell us of the greater and the lesser God; for there cannot be degrees in

* As those men who call themselves divines and commentators, are very fond of puzzling one another, I leave them to contest the meaning of the first part of the phrase, that of *an evil spirit of God.* I keep to my text—I keep to the meaning of the word prophesy.

prophesying consistently with its modern sense.—But there are degrees in poetry, and therefore the phrase is reconcileable to the case, when we understand by it the greater and the lesser poets.

It is altogether unnecessary, after this, to offer any observations upon what those men, styled prophets, have written. The axe goes at once to the root, by showing that the original meaning of the word has been mistaken, and consequently all the inferences that have been drawn from those books, the devotional respect that has been paid to them, and the laboured commentaries that have been written upon them, under that mistaken meaning, are not worth disputing about. In many things, however, the writings of the Jewish poets deserve a better fate than that of being bound up, as they now are, with the trash that accompanies them, under the abused name of the word of God.

If we permit ourselves to conceive right ideas of things, we must necessarily affix the idea, not only of unchangeableness, but of the utter impossibility of any change taking place, by any means or accident whatever, in that which we would honour with the name of the word of God; and therefore the word of God cannot exist in any written or human language.

The continually progressive change to which the meaning of words is subject, the want of an universal language which renders translation necessary, the errors to which translations are again subject, the mistakes of copyists and printers, together with the possibility of wilful alteration, are of themselves evidences that the human language, whether in speech or in print, cannot be the vehicle of the word of God. The word of God exists in something else.

Did the book, called the Bible, excel in purity of ideas and expression all the books now extant in the world, I would not take it for my rule of faith, as being the word of God, because the possibility would nevertheless exist of my being imposed upon. But when I see throughout the greatest part of this book, scarcely any thing but a history of the grossest vices, and a collection of the most paltry and contemptible tales, I cannot dishonor my Creator by calling it by his name.

Thus much for the Bible; I now go on to the book called the New Testament. The *New* Testament! that is, the *new* will, as if there could be two wills of the Creator.

Had it been the object or the intention of Jesus Christ to establish a new religion, he would undoubtedly have written the system himself, or *procured it to be written* in his life time. But there is no publication extant authenticated with his name. All the books called the New Testament were written after his death. He was a Jew by birth and by profession; and he was the son of God in like manner that every other person is—for the Creator is the Father of All.

The first four books, called Matthew, Mark, Luke, and John, do not give a history of the life of Jesus Christ, but only detached anecdotes of him. It appears from these books, that the whole time of his being a preacher was not more than eighteen months; and it was only during this short time, that those men became acquainted with him. They make mention of him at the age of twelve years, sitting, they say, among the Jewish doctors, asking and answering them questions. As this was several years before their acquaintance with him began, it is most probable they had this anecdote from his parents. From this time there is no account of him for about sixteen years. Where he lived, or how he employed himself during this interval, is not known. Most probably he was working at his father's trade, which was that of a carpenter. It does not appear that he had any school education, and the probability is, that he could not write, for his parents were extremely poor, as appears from their not being able to pay for a bed when he was born.

It is somewhat curious that the three persons whose names are the most universally recorded, were of very obscure parentage. Moses was a foundling; Jesus Christ was born in a stable; and Mahomet was a mule driver. The first and the last of these men were founders of different systems of religion; but Jesus Christ founded no new system. He called men to the practice of moral virtues, and the belief of one God. The great trait in his character is philanthropy.

The manner in which he was apprehended, shows that he was not much known at that time; and it shows also, that the meetings he then held with his followers were in secret; and that he had given over or suspended preaching publicly. Judas could no otherwise betray him than by giving information where he was, and pointing him out to the officers that went to arrest him; and the reason for employing and paying Judas to do this could arise only from the cause already mentioned, that of his not being much known, and living concealed.

The idea of his concealment, not only agrees very ill with his reputed divinity, but associates with it something of pusillanimity; and his being betrayed, or in other words, his being apprehended, on the information of one of his followers, shows that he did not intend to be apprehended, and consequently that he did not intend to be crucified.

The Christian Mythologists tell us, that Christ died for the sins of the world, and that he came on *purpose to die*. Would it not then have been the same if he had died of a fever, or of the small pox, of old age, or of any thing else?

The declaratory sentence which, they say, was passed upon Adam, in case he eat of the apple, was not, that *thou shalt surely be crucified, but, thou shalt surely die*—the sentence of death, and not the manner of dying. Crucifixion, therefore, or any other particular manner of dying, made no part of the sentence that Adam was to suffer, and consequently, even upon their own tactics, it could make no part of the sentence that Christ was to suffer in the room of Adam. A fever would have done as well as a cross, if there was any occasion for either.

The sentence of death, which they tell us, was thus passed upon Adam, must either have meant dying naturally, that is, ceasing to live, or have meant what these Mythologists call damnation; and consequently, the act of dying on the part of Jesus Christ, must according to their system, apply as a prevention to one or other of these two *things* happening to Adam and to us.

That it does not prevent our dying is evident, because we all die; and if their accounts of longevity be true, men die faster since the crucifixion than before; and with respect to the second explanation, (including with it the *natural death* of Jesus Christ as a substitute for the *eternal death or damnation* of all mankind,) it is impertinently representing the Creator as coming off, or revoking the sentence, by a pun or a quibble upon the word *death*. That manufacturer of quibbles, St. Paul, if he wrote the books that bear his name, has helped this quibble on by making another quibble upon the word *Adam*. He makes there to be two Adams; the one who sins in fact, and suffers by proxy; the other who sins by proxy, and suffers in fact. A religion thus interlarded with quibble, subterfuge, and pun, has a tendency to instruct its professors in the practice of these arts. They acquire the habit without being aware of the cause.

If Jesus Christ was the being which those Mythologists tell us he was, and that he came into this world to *suffer,* which is a word they sometimes use instead of *to die,* the only real suffering he could have endured, would have been *to live*. His existence here was a state of exilement or transportation from Heaven, and the way back to his original country was to die.—In fine, every thing in this strange system is the reverse of what it pretends to be. It is the reverse of truth, and I become so tired of examining into its inconsistencies and absurdities, that I hasten to the conclusion of it, in order to proceed to something better.

How much, or what parts of the books called the New Testament, were written by the persons whose names they bear, is what we can know nothing of, neither are we certain in what language they were originally written. The matters they now contain may be classed under two heads—anecdote and epistolary correspondence.

The four books already mentioned, Matthew, Mark, Luke, and John, are altogether anecdotal. They relate events after they had taken place. They tell what Jesus Christ did and said, and what others did and said to him; and in several instances they relate the same event differently. Revelation is necessarily out of the question with respect to those books; not only because of the disagreement of the writers, but because revelation cannot be applied to the relating of facts by the persons who saw them done, nor to the relating or recording of any discourse or conversation by those who heard it. The book called the Acts of the Apostles (an anonymous work) belongs also to the anecdotal part.

All the other parts of the New Testament, except the book of enigmas, called the Revelations, are a collection of letters under the name of epistles; and the forgery of letters has been such a common practice in the world, that the probability is at least equal, whether they are genuine or forged. One thing, however, is much less equivocal, which is, that out of the matters contained in those books, together with the assistance of some old stories, the church has set up a system of religion very contradictory to the character of the person whose name it bears. It has set up a religion of pomp and of revenue, in pretended imitation of a person whose life was humility and poverty.

The invention of purgatory, and of the releasing of souls therefrom, by prayers, bought of the church with money; the selling of pardons, dispensations and indulgencies, are revenue laws, without bearing that name or carrying that appearance. But the case nevertheless is, that those things derive their origin from the paroxysm of the crucifixion and the theory deduced therefrom which was, that one person could stand in the place of another, and could perform meritorious services for him. The probability, therefore, is, that the whole theory or doctrine of what is called the redemption (which is said to have been accomplished by the act of one person in the room of another) was originally fabricated on purpose to bring forward and build all those secondary and pecuniary redemptions upon; and that the passages in the books upon which the idea of theory of redemption is built, have been manufactured and fabricated for that purpose. Why are we to give this church credit, when she tells us that those books are genuine in every part, any more than we give her credit for every thing else she has told us; or for the miracles she says she has performed? That she *could* fabricate writings is certain, because she could write; and the composition of the writings in question, is of that kind that any body might do it; and that she *did* fabricate them is not more inconsistent with probability, than that she should tell us, as she has done, that she could and did work miracles.

Since, then, no external evidence can, at this long distance of time, be produced to prove whether the church fabricated the doctrines called redemption or not, (for such evidence, whether for or against, would be subject to the same suspicion of being fabricated,) the case can only be referred to the internal evidence which the thing carries within itself; and this affords a very strong presumption of its being a fabrication. For the internal evidence is, that the theory or doctrine of redemption has for its basis an idea of pecuniary justice, and not that of moral justice.

If I owe a person money, and cannot pay him, and he threatens to put me in prison, another person can take the debt upon himself, and pay it for me; but if I have committed a crime, every circumstance of the case is changed; moral justice cannot take the innocent for the guilty, even if the innocent would offer itself. To suppose justice to do this, is to destroy the principle of its existence, which is the thing itself; it is then no longer justice; it is indiscriminate revenge.

This single reflection will show that the doctrine of redemption is founded on a mere pecuniary idea, corresponding to that of a debt, which another person might pay; and as this pecuniary idea corresponds again with the system of second redemptions, obtained through the means of money given to the church for pardons, the probability is, that the same persons fabricated both one and the other of those theories; and that, in truth, there is no such thing as redemption; that it is fabulous, and that man stands in the same relative condition with his Maker he ever did stand, since man existed, and that it is his greatest consolation to think so.

Let him believe this, and he will live more consistently and morally, than by any other system; it is by his being taught to contemplate himself as an out-law, as an out-cast, as a beggar, as a mumper, as one thrown, as it were, on a dunghill, at an immense distance from his Creator, and who must make his approaches by creeping and cringing to intermediate beings, that he conceives either a contemptuous disregard for every thing under the name of religion, or becomes indifferent, or turns, what he calls, devout. In the latter case, he consumes his life in grief, or the affectation of it; his prayers are reproaches; his humility is ingratitude; he calls himself a worm, and the fertile earth a dunghill; and all the blessings of life, by the thankless name of vanities; he despises the choicest gift of

God to man, the GIFT OF REASON; and having endeavoured to force upon himself the belief of a system against which reason revolts, he ungratefully calls it *human reason,* as if man could give reason to himself.

Yet, with all this strange appearance of humility, and this contempt for human reason, he ventures into the boldest presumptions; he finds fault with every thing; his selfishness is never satisfied; his ingratitude is never at an end. He takes on himself to direct the Almighty what to do, even in the government of the universe; he prays dictatorially; when it is sun-shine, he prays for rain, and when it is rain, he prays for sun-shine; he follows the same idea in every thing that he prays for; for what is the amount of all his prayers, but an attempt to make the Almighty change his mind, and act otherwise than he does? It is as if he were to say—thou knowest not so well as I.

But some perhaps will say—Are we to have no word of God—no revelation! I answer, Yes: there is a word of God; there is a revelation.

THE WORD OF GOD IS THE CREATION WE BEHOLD: And it is in *this word,* which no human invention can counterfeit or alter, that God speaketh universally to man.

Human language is local and changeable, and is therefore incapable of being used as the means of unchangeable and universal information. The idea that God sent Jesus Christ to publish, as they say, the glad tidings to all nations, from one end of the earth to the other, is consistent only with the ignorance of those who knew nothing of the extent of the world, and who believed, as those world-saviours believed, and continued to believe, for several centuries, (and that in contradiction to the discoveries of philosophers and the experience of navigators,) that the earth was flat like a trencher; and that a man might walk to the end of it.

But how was Jesus Christ to make any thing known to all nations? He could speak but one language, which was Hebrew; and there are in the world several hundred languages. Scarcely any two nations speak the same language, or understand each other; and as to translations, every man who knows any thing of languages, knows that it was impossible to translate from one language to another, not only without losing a great part of the original, but frequently of mistaking the sense; and besides all this, the art of printing was wholly unknown at the time Christ lived.

It is always necessary that the means that are to accomplish any end, be equal to the accomplishment of that end, or the end cannot be accomplished. It is in this, that the difference between finite and infinite power and wisdom discovers itself. Man frequently fails in accomplishing his ends, from a natural inability of the power to the purpose; and frequently from the want of wisdom to apply power properly. But it is impossible for infinite power and wisdom to fail as man faileth. The means it useth are always equal to the end; but human language, more especially as there is not an universal language, is incapable of being used as an universal means of unchangeable and uniform information, and therefore it is not the means that God useth in manifesting himself universally to man.

It is only in the CREATION that all our ideas and conceptions of a *word of God* can unite. The Creation speaketh an universal language, independently of human speech or human language, multiplied and various as they be. It is an ever-existing original, which every man can read. It cannot be forged; it cannot be counterfeited; it cannot be lost; it cannot be altered; it cannot be suppressed. It does not depend upon the will of man whether it shall be published or not; it publishes itself from one end of the earth to the other. It preaches to all nations and to all worlds, and this *word of God* reveals to man all that is necessary for man to know of God.

Do we want to contemplate his power? We see it in the immensity of the Creation. Do we want to contemplate his wisdom? We see it in the unchangeable order by which the incomprehensible whole is governed. Do we want to contemplate his munificence? We see it in the abundance with which he fills the earth. Do we want to contemplate his mercy? We see it in his not withholding that abundance even from the unthankful. In fine, do we want to know what God is? Search not the book called the Scripture, which any human hand might make, but the Scripture called the Creation.

The only idea man can affix to the name of God, is that of a *first cause,* the cause of all things. And, incomprehensible and difficult as it is for a man to conceive what a first cause is, he arrives at the belief of it, from the tenfold greater difficulty of disbelieving it. It is difficult beyond description to conceive that space can have no end; but it is more difficult to conceive an end. It is difficult beyond the power of man to conceive an eternal duration of what we call time; but it is more impossible to conceive a time when there shall be no time.

In like manner of reasoning, every thing we behold carries in itself the internal evidence that it did not make itself. Every man is an evidence to himself, that he did not make himself; neither could his father make himself, nor his grandfather, nor any of his race; neither could any tree, plant, or animal make itself; and it is the conviction arising from this evidence, that carries us on, as it were, by necessity, to the belief of a first cause eternally existing, of a nature totally different to any material existence we know of, and by the power of which all things exist; and this first cause man calls God.

It is only by the exercise of reason, that man can discover God. Take away that reason, and he would be incapable of understanding any thing; and, in this case it would be just as consistent to read even the book called the Bible to a horse as to a man. How then is it that those people pretend to reject reason?

Almost the only parts in the book called the Bible, that convey to us any idea of God, are some chapters in Job, and the 19th Psalm; I recollect no other. Those parts are true *deistical* compositions; for they treat of the *Deity* through his works. They take the book of Creation as the word of God, they refer to no other book, and all the inferences they make are drawn from that volume.

I insert, in this place, the 19th Psalm, as paraphrased into English verse by Addison. I recollect not the prose, and where I write this I have not the opportunity of seeing it.

The spacious firmament on high,
With all the blue etherial sky,
And spangled heavens, a shining frame,
Their great original proclaim.
The unwearied sun, from day to day,
Does his Creator's power display;
And publishes to every land,
The work of an Almighty hand.
Soon as the evening shades prevail
The moon takes up the wondrous tale,
And nightly to the listning earth,
Repeats the story of her birth;
Whilst all the stars that round her burn,
And all the planets, in their turn,
Confirm the tidings as they roll,
And spread the truth from pole to pole.
What though in solemn silence all
Move round this dark terrestrial ball;
What though no real voice, nor sound,
Amidst their radient orbs be found,
In reason's ear they all rejoice,
And utter forth a glorious voice,
For ever singing as they shine,
THE HAND THAT MADE US IS DIVINE.

What more does man want to know, than that the hand or power, that made these things is divine, is omnipotent? Let him believe this with the force it is impossible to repel, if he permits his reason to act, and his rule of moral life will follow of course.

The allusions in Job have all of them the same tendency with this Psalm; that of deducing or proving a truth that would be otherwise unknown, from truths already known.

I recollect not enough of the passages in Job, to insert them correctly: but there is one occurs to me that is applicable to the subject I am speaking upon. "Canst thou by searching find out God? Canst thou find out the Almighty to perfection?"

I know not how the printers have pointed this passage, for I keep no Bible; but it contains two distinct questions, that admit of distinct answers.

First—Canst thou by searching find out God? Yes; because in the first place, I know I did not make myself, and yet I have existence; and by *searching* into the nature of other things, I find that no other thing could make itself; and yet millions of other things exist; therefore it is, that I know, by positive conclusion resulting from this search, that there is a power superior to all those things, and that power is God.

Secondly—Canst thou find out the Almighty to *perfection?* No; not only because the power and wisdom He has manifested in the structure of the Creation that I behold is to me incomprehensible, but because even this manifestation, great as it is, is probably but a small display of that immensity of power and wisdom, by which millions of other worlds, to me invisible by their distance, were created and continue to exist.

It is evident that both of these questions are put to the reason of the person to whom they are supposed to have been addressed; and it is only by admitting the first question to be answered affirmatively, that the second could follow. It would have been unnecessary, and even absurd, to have put a second question more difficult than the first, if the first question had been answered negatively. The two questions have different objects; the first refers to the existence of God, the second to his attributes; reason can discover the one, but it falls infinitely short in discovering the whole of the other.

I recollect not a single passage in all the writings ascribed to the men called apostles, that convey any idea of what God is. Those writings are chiefly controversial; and the subject they dwell upon, that of a man dying in agony on a cross, is better suited to the gloomy genius of a monk in a cell, by whom it is not impossible they were written, than to any man breathing the open air of the Creation. The only passage that occurs to me, that has any reference to the works of God, by which only his power and wisdom can be known, is related to have been spoken by Jesus Christ, as a remedy against distrustful care. "Behold the lilies of the field, they toil not, neither do they spin." This, however, is far inferior to the allusions in Job and in the 19th Psalm; but it is similar in idea, and the modesty of the imagery is correspondent to the modesty of the man.

As to the Christian system of faith, it appears to me as a species of atheism—a sort of religious denial of God. It professes to believe in a man rather than in God. It is a compound made up chiefly of manism with but little deism, and is as near to atheism as twilight is to darkness. It introduces between man and his Maker an opaque body, which it calls a Redeemer, as the moon introduces her opaque self between the earth and the sun, and it produces by this means a religious or an irreligious eclipse of light. It has put the whole orbit of reason into shade.

The effect of this obscurity has been that of turning every thing upside down, and representing it in reverse; and among the revolutions it has thus magically produced, it has made a revolution in Theology.

That which is now called natural philosophy, embracing the whole circle of science, of which Astronomy occupies the chief place, is the study of the works of God, and of the power and wisdom of God in his works, and is the true theology.

As to the theology that is now studied in its place, it is the study of human opinions, and of human fancies *concerning* God. It is not the study of God himself in the works that he has made, but in the works or writings that man has made; and it is not among the least of the mischiefs that the Christian system has done to the world, that it has abandoned the original and beautiful system of theology, like a beautiful innocent, to distress and reproach, to make room for the hag of superstition.

The book of Job, and the 19th Psalm, which even the church admits to be more ancient than the chronological order in which they stand in the book called the Bible, are theological orations conformable to the original system of theology. The internal evidence of those orations proves to a demonstration that the study and contemplation of the works of Creation, and of the power and wisdom of God, revealed and manifested in those works, made a great part of the religious devotion of the times in which they were written; and it was this devotional study and contemplation that led to the discovery of the principles upon which, what are now called Sciences, are established; and it is to the discovery of these principles that almost all the Arts that contribute to the convenience of human life, owe their existence. Every principal art has some science for its parent, though the person who mechanically performs the work does not always, and but very seldom, perceive the connexion.

It is a fraud of the Christian system to call the sciences *human invention;* it is only the application of them that is human. Every science has for its basis a system of principles as fixed and unalterable as those by which the universe is regulated and governed. Man cannot make principles, he can only discover them.

For example—Every person who looks at an Almanack sees an account when an eclipse will take place, and he sees also that it never fails to take place according to the account there given. This shows that man is acquainted with the laws by which the heavenly bodies move. But it would be something worse than ignorance, were any church on earth to say, that those laws are a human invention. It would also be ignorance, or something worse, to say that the scientific principles, by the aid of which man is enabled to calculate and foreknow when an eclipse will take place, are a human invention. Man cannot invent any thing that is eternal and immutable; and the scientific principles he employs for this purpose must, and are, of necessity, as eternal and immutable as the laws by which the heavenly bodies move, or they could not be used as they are to ascertain the time when, and the manner how, an eclipse will take place.

The scientific principles that man employs to obtain the foreknowledge of an eclipse, or of any thing else, relating to the motion of the heavenly bodies, are contained chiefly in that part of science which is called Trigonometry, or the properties of a triangle, which when applied to the study of the heavenly bodies, is called Astronomy; when applied to direct the course of a ship on the ocean, it is called Navigation; when applied to the construction of figures drawn by rule and compass, it is called Geometry; when applied to the construction of plans of edifices, it is called Architecture; when applied to the measurement of any portion of the surface of the earth, it is called Land-surveying. In fine, it is the soul of science; it is an eternal truth; it contains the *mathematical demonstration* of which man speaks, and the extent of its uses is unknown.

It may be said, that man can make or draw a triangle, and therefore a triangle is an human invention.

But the triangle, when drawn, is no other than the image of the principle; it is a delineation to the eye, and from thence to the mind, of a principle that would otherwise be imperceptible. The triangle does not make the principle, any more than a candle taken into a room that was dark, makes the chairs and tables that before were invisible. All the properties of a triangle exist independently of the figure, and existed before any triangle was drawn or thought of by man. Man had no more to do in the formation of those properties or principles, than he had to do in making the laws by which the heavenly bodies move; and therefore the one must have the same divine origin as the other.

In the same manner as it may be said, that man can make a triangle, so also may it be said, he can make the mechanical instrument called a lever; but the principle, by which the lever acts is a thing distinct from the instrument, and would exist if the instrument did not: it attaches itself to the instrument after it is made; the instrument, therefore, can act no otherwise than it does act; neither can all the efforts of human invention make it act otherwise—that which, in all such cases, man calls the *effect,* is no other than the principle itself rendered perceptible to the senses.

Since then man cannot make principles, from whence did he gain a knowledge of them, so as to be able to apply them, not only to things on earth, but to ascertain the motion of bodies so immensely distant from him as all the heavenly bodies are? From whence, I ask, *could* he gain that knowledge, but from the study of the true theology?

It is the structure of the universe that has taught this knowledge to man. That structure is an ever-existing exhibition of every principle upon which every part of mathematical science is founded. The offspring of this science is mechanics; for mechanics is no other than the principles of science applied practically. The man who proportions the several parts of a mill, uses the same scientific principles, as if he had the power of constructing an universe; but as he cannot give to matter that invisible agency, by which all the component parts of the immense machine of the universe have influenced upon each other and act in motional unison together, without any apparent contact, and to which man has given the name of attraction, gravitation, and repulsion, he supplies the place of that agency by the humble imitation of teeth and cogs.—All the parts of man's microcosm must visibly touch: but could he gain a knowledge of that agency, so as to be able to apply it in practice, we might then say, that another *canonical book* of the word of God had been discovered.

If man could alter the properties of the lever, so also could he alter the properties of the triangle: for a lever (taking that sort of lever which is called a steel-yard, for the sake of explanation) forms, when in motion, a triangle. The line it descends from, (one point of that line being in the fulcrum,) the line it descends to, and the cord of the arc, which the end of the lever describes in the air, are the three sides of a triangle. The other arm of the lever describes also a triangle; and the corresponding sides of those two triangles, calculated scientifically, or measured geometrically:

and also the sines, tangents, and secants generated from the angles, and geometrically measured, have the same proportions to each other, as the different weights have that will balance each other on the lever, leaving the weight of the lever out of the case.

It may also be said, that man can make a wheel and axis, that he can put wheels of different magnitudes together, and produce a mill. Still the case comes back to the same point, which is, that he did not make the principle that gives the wheels those powers. That principle is as unalterable as in the former case, or rather it is the same principle under a different appearance to the eye.

The power that two wheels, of different magnitudes, have upon each other, is in the same proportion as if the semi-diameter of the two wheels were joined together and made into that kind of lever I have described, suspended at the part where the semi-diameters join; for the two wheels, scientifically considered, are no other than the two circles generated by the motion of the compound lever.

It is from the study of the true theology that all our knowledge of science is derived, and it is from that knowledge that all the arts have originated.

The Almighty lecturer, by displaying the principles of science in the structure of the universe, has invited man to study and to imitation. It is as if he had said to the inhabitants of this globe, that we call ours, "I have made an earth for man to dwell upon, and I have rendered the starry heavens visible, to teach him science and the arts. He can now provide for his own comfort AND LEARN FROM MY MUNIFICENCE TO ALL, TO BE KIND TO EACH OTHER."

Of what use is it, unless it be to teach man something, that his eye is endowed with the power of beholding, to an incomprehensible distance, an immensity of worlds revolving in the ocean of space? Or of what use is it that this immensity of worlds is visible to man? What has man to do with the Pleiades, with Orion, with Sirius, with the star he calls the north star, with the moving orbs he has named Saturn, Jupiter, Mars, Venus, and Mercury, if no uses are to follow from their being visible? A less power of vision would have been sufficient for man, if the immensity he now possesses were given only to waste itself, as it were, on an immense desert of space glittering with shows.

It is only by contemplating what he calls the starry heavens, as the book and school of science, that he discovers any use in their being visible to him, or any advantage resulting from his immensity of vision. But when he contemplates the subject in this light, he sees an additional motive for saying, that *nothing was made in vain;* for in vain would be this power of vision if it taught man nothing.

As the Christian system of faith has made a revolution in theology, so also has it made a revolution in the state of learning. That which is now called learning, was not learning, originally. Learning does not consist, as the schools now make it consist, in the knowledge of languages, but in the knowledge of things to which language gives names.

The Greeks were a learned people, but learning with them did not consist in speaking Greek, any more than in a Roman's speaking Latin, or a Frenchman's speaking French, or an Englishman's speaking English. From what we know of the Greeks, it does not appear that they knew or studied any language but their own, and this was one cause of their becoming so learned; it afforded them more time to apply themselves to better studies. The schools of the Greeks were schools of science and philosophy, and not of languages; and it is in the knowledge of the things that science and philosophy teach, that learning consists.

Almost all the scientific learning that now exists, came to us from the Greeks, or the people who spoke the Greek language.—It, therefore, became necessary for the people of other nations, who spoke a different language, that some among them should learn the Greek language, in order that the learning the Greeks had, might be made known in those nations, by translating the Greek books of science and philosophy into the mother tongue of each nation.

The study, therefore, of the Greek language (and in the same manner for the Latin) was no other than the drudgery business of a linguist; and the language thus obtained, was no other than the means, as it were the tools, employed to obtain the learning the Greeks had. It made no part of the learning itself; and was so distinct from it, as to make it exceedingly probable that the persons who had studied Greek sufficiently to translate those works, such, for instance, as Euclid's Elements, did not understand any of the learning the works contained.

As there is now nothing new to be learned from the dead languages, all the useful books being already translated, the languages are become useless, and the time expended in teaching and learning them is wasted. So far as the study of languages may contribute to the progress and communication of knowledge, (for it has nothing to do with the *creation* of knowledge,) it is only in the living languages that new knowledge is to be found; and certain it is, that, in general, a youth will learn more of a living language in one year, than of a dead language in seven; and it is but seldom that the teacher knows much of it himself. The difficulty of learning the dead languages does not arise from any superior abstruseness in the languages themselves, but in their *being dead,* and the pronunciation entirely lost. It would be the same thing with any other language when it becomes dead. The best Greek linguist that now exists, does not understand Greek so well as a Grecian ploughman did, or a Grecian milkmaid: and the same for the Latin, compared with a ploughman or milkmaid of the Romans; it would therefore be advantageous to the state of learning to abolish the study of the dead languages, and to make learning consist, as it originally did, in scientific knowledge.

The apology that is sometimes made for continuing to teach the dead languages is, that they are taught at a time, when a child is not capable of exerting any other mental faculty than that of memory; but that is altogether erroneous. The human mind has a natural disposition to scientific knowledge, and to the things connected with it. The first and favourite amusement of a child, even before it begins to play, is that of imitating the works of man. It builds houses with cards or sticks; it navigates the little ocean of a bowl of water with a paper boat, or dams the stream of a gutter, and contrives something which it calls a mill; and it interests itself in the fate of its works with a care that resembles affection. It afterwards goes to school, where its genius is killed by the barren study of a dead language, and the philosopher is lost in the linguist.

But the apology that is now made for continuing to teach the dead languages, could not be the cause, at first, of cutting down learning to the narrow and humble sphere of linguistry; the cause, therefore, must be sought for elsewhere. In all researches of this kind, the best evidence that can be produced, is the internal evidence the thing carries with itself, and the evidence of circumstances that unites with it; both of which, in this case, are not difficult to be discovered.

Putting then aside, as a matter of distinct consideration, the outrage offered to the moral justice of God, by supposing him to make the innocent suffer for the guilty, and also the loose morality and low contrivance of supposing him to change himself into the shape of a man, in order to make an excuse to himself for not executing his supposed sentence upon Adam; putting, I say, those things aside as a matter of distinct consideration, it is certain that what is called the Christian system of faith, including in it the whimsical account of the creation—the strange story of Eve—the snake and the apple—the ambiguous idea of a man-god—the corporeal idea of the death of a god—the mythological idea of a family of gods, and the Christian system of arithmetic, that three are one, and one is three, are all irreconcilable, not only to the divine gift of reason, that God hath given to Man, but to the knowledge that man gains of the power and wisdom of God, by the aid of the sciences, and by studying the structure of the universe that God has made.

The setters-up, therefore, and the advocates of the Christian system of faith, could not but foresee that the continually progressive knowledge that man would gain, by the aid of science, of the power and wisdom of God, manifested in the structure of the universe, and in all the works of Creation, would militate against, and call into question, the truth of their system of faith; and therefore it became necessary to their purpose to cut learning down to a size less dangerous to their project, and this they effected by restricting the idea of learning to the dead study of dead languages.

They not only rejected the study of science out of the Christian schools, but they persecuted it; and it is only within about the last two centuries that the study has been revived. So late as 1610, Galileo, a Florentine, discovered and introduced the use of telescopes, and by applying them to observe the motions and appearance of the heavenly bodies, afforded additional means for ascertaining the true structure of the universe. Instead of being esteemed for those discoveries, he was sentenced to renounce them, or the opinions resulting from them, as a damnable heresy. And, prior to that time, Vigilius was condemned to be burned for asserting the antipodes, or in other words, that the earth was a globe, and habitable in every part where there was land; yet the truth of this is now too well known even to be told.

If the belief of errors not morally bad did no mischief, it would make no part of the moral duty of man to oppose and remove them. There was no moral ill in believing the earth was flat like a trencher, any more than there was moral virtue in believing that it was round like a globe; neither was there any moral ill in believing that the Creator made no other world than this, any more than there was moral virtue in believing that he made millions, and that the infinity of space is filled with worlds. But when a system of religion is made to grow out of a supposed system of creation that is not true, and to unite itself therewith in a manner almost inseparable therefrom, the case assumes an entirely different ground. It is then that errors, not morally bad, become fraught with the same mischiefs as if they were. It is then that the truth, though otherwise indifferent itself, becomes an essential, by becoming the criterion, that either confirms by corresponding evidence, or denies by contradictory evidence, the reality of the religion itself. In this view of the case, it is the moral duty of man to obtain every possible evidence that the structure of the heavens, or any other part of creation affords, with respect to systems of religion. But this, the supporters or partizans of the Christian system, as if dreading the result, incessantly opposed, and not only rejected the sciences, but persecuted the professors. Had Newton or Descartes lived three or four hundred years ago, and pursued their studies as they did, it is most probable they would not have lived to finish them; and had Franklin drawn lightning from the clouds at the same time, it would have been at the hazard of expiring for it in flames.

Later times have laid all the blame upon the Goths and Vandals; but, however unwilling the partizans of the Christian system may be to believe or to acknowledge it, it is nevertheless true, that the age of ignorance commenced with the Christian system.—There was more knowledge in the world before that period, than for many centuries afterwards; and as to religious knowledge, the Christian system, as already said, was only another species of mythology; and the mythology to which it succeeded, was a corruption of an ancient system of theism.*

It is owing to this long interregnum of science, *and to no other cause,* that we have now to look through a vast chasm of many hundred years to the respectable characters we call the ancients.—Had the progression of knowledge gone on proportionably with the stock that before existed, that chasm would have been filled up with characters rising superior in knowledge to each other; and those ancients we now so much admire, would have appeared respectably in the back ground of the scene. But

* It is impossible for us now to know at what time the heathen mythology began; but it is certain, from the internal evidence that it carries, that it did not begin in the same state or condition in which it ended. All the gods of that mythology, except Saturn, were of modern invention. The supposed reign of Saturn was prior to that which is called the heathen mythology, and was so far a species of theism, that it admitted the belief of only one God. Saturn is supposed to have abdicated the government in favor of his three sons and one daughter, Jupiter, Pluto, Neptune, and Juno; after this, thousands of other gods and demi-gods were imaginarily created, and the calendar of gods increased as fast as the calendar of saints, and the calendars of courts have increased since.

All the corruptions that have taken place, in theology and in religion, have been produced by admitting of what man calls *revealed religion.* The Mythologists pretended to more revealed religion than the Christians do. They had their oracles and their priests, who were supposed to receive and deliver the word of God verbally, on almost all occasions.

Since then all corruptions down from Molock to modern predestinarianism, and the human sacrifices of the heathens to the Christian sacrifice of the Creator, have been produced by admitting of what is called *revealed religion,* the most effectual means to prevent all such evils and impositions is, not to admit of any other revelation than that which is manifested in the book of creation, and to contemplate the creation as the only true and real work of God that ever did, or ever will exist; and that every thing else, called the word of God, is fable and imposition.

the Christian system laid all waste; and if we take our stand about the beginning of the sixteenth century, we look back through that long chasm, to the times of the ancients, as over a vast sandy desart, in which not a shrub appears to intercept the vision to the fertile hills beyond.

It is an inconsistency scarcely possible to be credited, that any thing should exist, under the name of a religion, that held it to be *irreligious* to study and contemplate the structure of the universe that God had made. But the fact is too well established to be denied. The event that served more than any other to break the first link in this long chain of despotic ignorance, is that known by the name of the Reformation by Luther. From that time, though it does not appear to have made any part of the intention of Luther, or of those who are called reformers, the sciences began to revive, and liberality, their natural associate, began to appear. This was the only public good the Reformation did; for, with respect to religious good, it might as well not have taken place. The mythology still continued the same; and a multiplicity of National Popes grew out of the downfall of the Pope of Christendom.

Having thus shown from the internal evidence of things, the cause that produced a change in the state of learning, and the motive for substituting the study of dead languages, in the place of the sciences, I proceed, in addition to the several observations, already made in the former part of this work, to compare, or rather to confront the evidence that the structure of the universe affords, with the Christian system of religion; but, as I cannot begin this part better than by referring to the ideas that occurred to me at an early part of life, and which I doubt not have occurred in some degree to almost every other person at one time or other, I shall state what those ideas were, and add thereto such other matter as shall arise out of the subject, giving to the whole, by way of preface, a short introduction.

My father being of the Quaker profession, it was my good fortune to have an exceeding good moral education, and a tolerable stock of useful learning. Though I went to the grammar school,* I did not learn Latin, not only because I had no inclination to learn languages, but because of the objection the Quakers have against the books in which the language is taught. But this did not prevent me from being acquainted with the subjects of all the Latin books used in the school.

The natural bent of my mind was to science. I had some turn, and I believe some talent for poetry; but this I rather repressed than encour-

* The same school, Thetford in Norfolk, that the present Counsellor Mingay went to, and under the same master.

aged, as leading too much into the field of imagination. As soon as I was able, I purchased a pair of globes, and attended the philosophical lectures of Martin and Ferguson, and became afterwards acquainted with Dr. Bevis, of the society, called the Royal Society, then living in the Temple, and an excellent astronomer.

I had no disposition for what is called politics. It presented to my mind no other idea than is contained in the word Jockeyship. When, therefore, I turned my thoughts towards matters of government, I had to form a system for myself, that accorded with the moral and philosophic principles in which I had been educated. I saw or at least I thought I saw, a vast scene opening itself to the world in the affairs of America; and it appeared to me, that unless the Americans changed the plan they were then pursuing, with respect to the government of England, and declared themselves independent, they would not only involve themselves in a multiplicity of new difficulties, but shut out the prospect that was then offering itself to mankind through their means. It was from these motives that I published the work known by the name of *"Common Sense,"* which is the first work I ever did publish; and so far as I can judge of myself, I believe I should never have been known in the world as an author, on any subject whatever, had it not been for the affairs of America. I wrote *"Common Sense"* the latter end of the year 1775, and published it the first of January, 1776. Independence was declared the fourth of July following.

Any person, who has made observations on the state and progress of the human mind, by observing his own, cannot but have observed, that there are two distinct classes of what are called Thoughts; those that we produce in ourselves by reflection and the act of thinking, and those that bolt into the mind of their own accord. I have always made it a rule to treat those voluntary visitors with civility, taking care to examine, as well as I was able, if they were worth entertaining; and it is from them I have acquired almost all the knowledge that I have. As to the learning that any person gains from school education, it serves only, like a small capital, to put him in the way of beginning learning for himself afterwards.—Every person of learning is finally his own teacher, the reason of which is, that principles, being of a distinct quality to circumstances, cannot be impressed upon the memory; their place of mental residence is the understanding, and they are never so lasting as when they begin by conception. Thus much for the introductory part.

From the time I was capable of conceiving an idea, and acting upon it by reflection, I either doubted the truth of the Christian system, or thought it to be a strange affair; I scarcely knew which it was: but I well remember, when about seven or eight years of age, hearing a sermon read by a relation of mine, who was a great devotee of the church, upon the subject of what is called *redemption by the death of the Son of God*. After the sermon was ended, I went into the garden, and as I was going down the garden steps (for I perfectly recollect the spot) I revolted at the recollection of what I had heard, and thought to myself that it was making God Almighty act like a passionate man, that killed his son, when he could not revenge himself any other way; and as I was sure a man would be hanged that did such a thing, I could not see for what purpose they preached such sermons. This was not one of those kind of thoughts that had any thing in it of childish levity; it was to me a serious reflection, arising from the idea I had, that God was too good to do such an action, and also too almighty to be under any necessity of doing it. I believe in the same manner at this moment; and I moreover believe, that any system of religion that has any thing in it that shocks the mind of a child, cannot be a true system.

It seems as if parents of the Christian profession were ashamed to tell their children any thing about the principles of their religion. They sometimes instruct them in morals, and talk to them of the goodness of what they call Providence; for the Christian mythology has five deities—there is God the Father, God the Son, God the Holy Ghost, the God Providence, and the Goddess Nature. But the Christian story of God the Father putting his son to death, or employing people to do it, (for that is the plain language of the story,) cannot be told by a parent to a child; and to tell him that it was done to make mankind happier and better, is making the story still worse, as if mankind could be improved by the example of murder; and to tell him that all this is a mystery, is only making an excuse for the incredibility of it.

How different is this to the pure and simple profession of Deism! The true Deist has but one Deity; and his religion consists in contemplating the power, wisdom, and benignity of the Deity in his works, and in endeavoring to imitate him in every thing moral, scientifical, and mechanical.

The religion that approaches the nearest of all others to true Deism, in the moral and benign part thereof, is that professed by the Quakers: but they have contracted themselves too much, by leaving the works of God out of their system. Though I reverence their philanthropy, I cannot help smiling at the conceit, that if the taste of a Quaker could have been consulted at the creation, what a silent and drab-colored creation it would have been! Not a flower would have blossomed its gaieties, nor a bird been permitted to sing.

Quitting these reflections, I proceed to other matters. After I had made myself master of the use of the globes, and of the orrery,* and conceived an idea of the infinity of space, and the eternal divisibility of matter, and obtained, at least, a general knowledge of what is called natural philosophy, I began to compare, or, as I have before said, to confront the eternal evidence those things afford with the Christian system of faith.

Though it is not a direct article of the Christian system, that this world that we inhabit, is the whole of the habitable creation, yet it is so worked up therewith, from what is called the Mosaic account of the Creation, the story of Eve and the apple, and the counterpart of that story, the death of the Son of God, that to believe otherwise, that is, to believe that God created a plurality of worlds, at least as numerous as what we call stars, renders the Christian system of faith at once little and ridiculous, and scatters it in the mind like feathers in the air. The two beliefs cannot be held together in the same mind; and he who thinks that he believes both, has thought but little of either.

Though the belief of a plurality of worlds was familiar to the ancients, it is only within the last three centuries that the extent and dimensions of this globe that we inhabit have been ascertained. Several vessels, following the tract of the ocean, have sailed entirely round the world, as a man may march in a circle, and come round by the contrary side of the circle to the spot he set out from. The circular dimensions of our world, in the widest part, as a man would measure the widest round of an apple, or a ball, is only twenty-five thousand and twenty English miles, reckoning sixty-nine miles and an half to an equatorial degree, and may be sailed round in the space of about three years.*

A world of this extent may, at first thought, appear to us to be great;

* As this book may fall into the hands of persons who do not know what an orrery is, it is for their information I add this note, as the name gives no idea of the uses of the thing. The orrery has its name from the person who invented it. It is a machinery of clock-work, representing the universe in miniature, and in which the revolution of the earth round itself and round the sun, the revolution of the moon round the earth, the revolution of the planets round the sun, their relative distances from the sun, as the centre of the whole system, their relative distances from each other, and their different magnitudes, are represented as they really exist in what we call the heavens.

* Allowing a ship to sail, on an average, three miles in an hour, she would sail entirely round the world in less than one year, if she could sail in a direct circle; but she is obliged to follow the course of the ocean.

but if we compare it with the immensity of space in which it is suspended, like a bubble or balloon in the air, it is infinitely less, in proportion, than the smallest grain of sand is to the size of the world, or the finest particle of dew to the whole ocean, and is therefore but small; and, as will be hereafter shown, is only one of a system of worlds, of which the universal creation is composed.

It is not difficult to gain some faint idea of the immensity of space in which this and all the other worlds are suspended, if we follow a progression of ideas. When we think of the size or dimensions of a room, our ideas limit themselves to the walls, and there they stop; but when our eye, or our imagination darts into space, that is, when it looks upwards into what we call the open air, we cannot conceive any walls or boundaries it can have; and if for the sake of resting our ideas, we suppose a boundary, the question immediately renews itself, and asks, what is beyond that boundary? and in the same manner, what beyond the next boundary? and so on till the fatigued imagination returns and says, *there is no end.* Certainly, then, the Creator was not pent for room, when he made this world no larger than it is; and we have to seek the reason in something else.

If we take a survey of our own world, or rather of this, of which the Creator has given us the use, as our portion in the immense system of Creation, we find every part of it, the earth, the waters, and the air that surrounds it, filled, and, as it were, crowded with life, down from the largest animals that we know of to the smallest insects the naked eye can behold, and from thence to others still smaller, and totally invisible without the assistance of the microscope. Every tree, every plant, every leaf, serves not only as an habitation, but as a world to some numerous race, till animal existence becomes so exceedingly refined, that the effluvia of a blade of grass would be food for thousands.

Since then no part of our earth is left unoccupied, why is it to be supposed that the immensity of space is a naked void, lying in eternal waste? There is room for millions of worlds as large or larger than ours, and each of them millions of miles apart from each other.

Having now arrived at this point, if we carry our ideas only one thought further, we shall see, perhaps, the true reason, at least a very good reason, for our happiness, why the Creator, instead of making one immense world, extending over an immense quantity of space, has preferred dividing that quantity of matter into several distinct and separate worlds, which we call planets, of which our earth is one. But before I explain my ideas upon this subject, it is necessary (not for the sake of those that already know, but for those who do not) to show what the system of the universe is.

That part of the universe that is called the solar system (meaning the system of worlds to which our earth belongs, and of which Sol, or in English language, the Sun, is the centre) consists, besides the Sun, of six distinct orbs, or planets, or worlds, besides the secondary bodies, called the satellites or moons, of which our earth has one that attends her in her annual revolution round the Sun, in like manner as other satellites or moons, attend the planets or worlds to which they severally belong, as may be seen by the assistance of the telescope.

The Sun is the centre, round which those six worlds or planets revolve at different distances therefrom, and in circles concentrate to each other. Each world keeps constantly in nearly the same track round the Sun, and continues, at the same time, turning round itself, in nearly an upright position, as a top turns round itself when it is spinning on the ground, and leans a little sideways.

It is this leaning of the earth (23½ degrees) that occasions summer and winter, and the different length of days and nights. If the earth turned round itself in a position perpendicular to the plane or level of the circle it moves in around the Sun, as a top turns round when it stands erect on the ground, the days and nights would be always of the same length, twelve hours day and twelve hours night, and the seasons would be uniformly the same throughout the year.

Every time that a planet (our earth for example) turns round itself, it makes what we call day and night; and every time it goes entirely round the Sun, it makes what we call a year, consequently our world turns three hundred and sixty-five times round itself, in going once round the Sun.*

The names that the ancients gave to those six worlds, and which are still called by the same names, are Mercury, Venus, this world that we call ours, Mars, Jupiter, and Saturn. They appear larger to the eye than the stars, being many million miles nearer to our earth than any of the stars are. The planet Venus is that which is called the evening star, and sometimes the morning star, as she happens to set after, or rise before the Sun, which in either case, is never more than three hours.

The Sun, as before said, being the centre, the planet, or world, nearest the Sun, is Mercury; his distance from the Sun is thirty-four million miles, and he moves round in a circle always at that distance from the

* Those who supposed that the Sun went round the earth every 24 hours, made the same mistake in idea that a cook would do in fact, that should make the fire go round the meat, instead of the meat turning round itself towards the fire.

Sun, as a top may be supposed to spin round in the track in which a horse goes in a mill. The second world is Venus, she is fifty-seven million miles distant from the Sun, and consequently moves round in a circle much greater than that of Mercury. The third world is that we inhabit, and which is eighty-eight million miles distant from the Sun, and consequently moves round in a circle greater than that of Venus. The fourth world is Mars, he is distant from the Sun one hundred and thirty-four million miles, and consequently moves round in a circle greater than that of our earth. The fifth is Jupiter, he is distant from the Sun five hundred and fifty-seven million miles, and consequently moves round in a circle greater than that of Mars. The sixth world is Saturn, he is distant from the Sun seven hundred and sixty-three million miles, and consequently moves round in a circle that surrounds the circles, or orbits, of all the other worlds or planets.

The space, therefore, in the air, or in the immensity of space, that our solar system takes up for the several worlds to perform their revolutions in round the Sun, is of the extent in a straight line of the whole diameter of the orbit or circle, in which Saturn moves round the Sun, which being double his distance from the Sun, is fifteen hundred and twenty-six million miles: and its circular extent is nearly five thousand million; and its globical content is almost three thousand five hundred million times three thousand five hundred million square miles.*

But this, immense as it is, is only one system of worlds. Beyond this, at a vast distance into space, far beyond all power of calculation, are the stars called the fixed stars. They are called fixed, because they have no revolutionary motion, as the six worlds or planets have that I have been describing. Those fixed stars continue always at the same distance from each other, and always in the same place, as the Sun does in the centre of our system. The probability, therefore, is, that each of those fixed stars

* If it should be asked, how can man know these things I have one plain answer to give, which is, that man knows how to calculate an eclipse, and also how to calculate to a minute of time when the planet Venus, in making her revolutions round the Sun, will come in a straight line between our earth and the Sun, and will appear to us about the size of a large pea passing across the face of the Sun. This happens but twice in about an hundred years, at the distance of about eight years from each other, and has happened twice in our time, both of which were foreknown by calculation. It can also be known when they will happen again for a thousand years to come, or to any other portion of time. As, therefore, man could not be able to do these things if he did not understand the solar system, and the manner in which the revolutions of the several planets or worlds are performed, the fact of calculating an eclipse, or a transit of Venus, is a proof in point that the knowledge exists; and as to a few thousand, or even a few million miles, more or less, it makes scarcely any sensible difference in such immense distances.

is also a Sun, round which another system of worlds or planets, though too remote for us to discover, performs its revolutions, as our system of worlds does round our central Sun.

By this easy progression of ideas, the immensity of space will appear to us to be filled with systems of worlds; and that no part of space lies at waste, any more than any part of the globe or earth and water is left unoccupied.

Having thus endeavoured to convey, in a familiar and easy manner, some idea of the structure of the universe, I return to explain what I before alluded to, namely, the great benefits arising to man in consequence of the Creator having made a *plurality* of worlds, such as our system is, consisting of a central Sun and six worlds besides satellites, in preference to that of creating one world only of a vast extent.

It is an idea I have never lost sight of, that all our knowledge of science is derived from the revolutions (exhibited to our eye and from thence to our understanding) which those several planets or worlds, of which our system is composed, make in their circuit round the Sun.

Had then the quantity of matter which these six worlds contain been blended into one solitary globe, the consequence to us would have been, that either no revolutionary motion would have existed, or not a sufficiency of it to give us the idea and the knowledge of science we now have; and it is from the sciences that all the mechanical arts that contribute so much to our earthly felicity and comfort, are derived.

As, therefore, the Creator made nothing in vain, so also must it be believed that He organized the structure of the universe in the most advantageous manner for the benefit of man; and as we see, and from experience feel, the benefits we derive from the structure of the universe, formed as it is, which benefits we should not have had the opportunity of enjoying, if the structure, so far as relates to our system, had been a solitary globe—we can discover at least one reason why a *plurality* of worlds has been made, and that reason calls forth the devotional gratitude of man, as well as his admiration.

But it is not to us, the inhabitants of this globe, only, that the benefits arising from a plurality of worlds are limited. The inhabitants of each of the worlds of which our system is composed, enjoy the same opportunities of knowledge as we do. They behold the revolutionary motions of our earth, as we behold theirs. All the planets revolve in sight of each other; and, therefore, the same universal school of science presents itself to all.

Neither does the knowledge stop here. The system of worlds next to us exhibits, in its revolutions, the same principles and school of science, to the inhabitants of their system, as our system does to us, and in like manner throughout the immensity of space.

Our ideas, not only of the almightiness of the Creator, but of his wisdom and his beneficence, become enlarged in proportion as we contemplate the extent and the structure of the universe. The solitary idea of a solitary world, rolling or at rest in the immense ocean of space, gives place to the cheerful idea of a society of worlds, so happily contrived as to administer, even by their motion, instruction to man. We see our own earth filled with abundance; but we forget to consider how much of that abundance is owing to the scientific knowledge the vast machinery of the universe has unfolded.

But, in the midst of those reflections, what are we to think of the Christian system of faith, that forms itself upon the idea of only one world, and that of no greater extent, as is before shown, than twenty-five thousand miles? An extent which a man, walking at the rate of three miles an hour, for twelve hours in the day, could he keep on in a circular direction, would walk entirely round in less than two years. Alas! what is this to the mighty ocean of space, and the almighty power of the Creator!

From whence then could arise the solitary and strange conceit, that the Almighty, who had millions of worlds equally dependent on his protection, should quit the care of all the rest, and come to die in our world, because, they say, one man and one woman had eaten an apple! And, on the other hand, are we to suppose that every world in the boundless creation, had an Eve, an apple, a serpent and a redeemer? In this case, the person who is irreverently called the Son of God, and sometimes God himself, would have nothing else to do than to travel from world to world, in an endless succession of death, with scarcely a momentary interval of life.

It has been by rejecting the evidence, that the word or works of God in the creation affords to our senses, and the action of our reason upon that evidence, that so many wild and whimsical systems of faith, and of religion, have been fabricated and set up. There may be many systems of religion, that so far from being morally bad, are in many respects morally good: but there can be but ONE that is true; and that one necessarily must, as it ever will, be in all things consistent with the ever existing word of God that we behold in his works. But such is the strange construction of the Christian system of faith, that every evidence the Heavens afford to man, either directly contradicts it, or renders it absurd.

It is possible to believe, and I always feel pleasure in encouraging myself to believe it, that there have been men in the world, who persuade themselves that, what is called a *pious fraud,* might at least under particular circumstances, be productive of some good. But the fraud being once established, could not afterwards be explained; for it is with a pious fraud as with a bad action, it begets a calamitous necessity of going on.

The persons who first preached the Christian system of faith, and in some measure combined it with the morality preached by Jesus Christ, might persuade themselves that it was better than the heathen mythology that then prevailed. From the first preachers the fraud went on to the second, and to the third, till the idea of its being a pious fraud became lost in the belief of its being true; and that belief became again encouraged by the interests of those who made a livelihood by preaching it.

But though such a belief might, by such means, be rendered almost general among the laity, it is next to impossible to account for the continual persecution carried on by the church, for several hundred years, against the sciences, and against the professors of sciences, if the church had not some record or tradition, that it was originally no other than a pious fraud, or did not foresee, that it could not be maintained against the evidence that the structure of the universe afforded.

Having thus shown the irreconcileable inconsistencies between the real word of God existing in the universe and that which is called *the word of God,* as shown to us in a printed book that any man might make, I proceed to speak of the three principal means that have been employed in all ages, and perhaps in all countries, to impose upon mankind.

Those three means are Mystery, Miracle, and Prophesy. The two first are incompatible with true religion, and the third ought always to be suspected.

With respect to mystery, every thing we behold is, in one sense, a mystery to us. Our own existence is a mystery; the whole vegetable world is a mystery. We cannot account how it is that an acorn, when put into the ground, is made to develope itself, and become an oak. We know not how it is that the seed we sow unfolds and multiplies itself, and returns to us such an abundant interest for so small a capital.

The fact, however, as distinct from the operating cause, is not a mystery, because we see it; and we know also the means we are to use, which is no other than putting seed in the ground.—We know, therefore, as much as is necessary for us to know; and that part of the operation that we do not know, and which if we did we could not perform, the Creator takes upon himself and performs it for us. We are, therefore, better off than if we had been let into the secret, and left to do it for ourselves.

But though every created thing is, in this sense, a mystery, the word mystery cannot be applied to *moral truth,* any more than obscurity can be applied to light. The God in whom we believe is a God of moral truth, and not a God of mystery or obscurity. Mystery is the antagonist of truth. It is a fog of human invention, that obscures truth, and represents it in distortion. Truth never envelopes *itself* in mystery; and the mystery in which it is at any time enveloped, is the work of its antagonist, and never of itself.

Religion, therefore, being the belief of a God, and the practice of moral truth, cannot have connection with mystery. The belief of a God, so far from having any thing of mystery in it, is of all beliefs the most easy, because it arises to us, as is before observed, out of necessity. And the practice of moral truth, or, in other words, a practical imitation of the moral goodness of God, is no other than our acting towards each other as he acts benignly towards all. We cannot *serve* God in the manner we serve those who cannot do without such service; and, therefore, the only idea we can have of serving God, is that of contributing to the happiness of the living creation that God has made. This cannot be done by retiring ourselves from the society of the world, and spending a recluse life in selfish devotion.

The very nature and design of religion, if I may so express it, prove, even to demonstration, that it must be free from every thing of mystery, and unincumbered with every thing that is mysterious. Religion, considered as a duty, is incumbent upon every living soul alike, and, therefore, must be on a level to the understanding and comprehension of all. Man does not learn religion as he learns the secrets and mysteries of a trade. He learns the theory of religion by reflection. It arises out of the action of his own mind upon the things which he sees, or upon what he may happen to hear or to read, and the practice joins itself thereto.

When men, whether from policy or pious fraud, set up systems of religion incompatible with the word or works of God in the creation, and not only above, but repugnant to human comprehension, they were under the necessity of inventing or adopting a word that should serve as a bar to all questions, inquiries and speculations. The word *mystery* answered this purpose; and thus it has happened that religion, which is in itself without mystery, has been corrupted into a fog of mysteries.

As *mystery* answered all general purposes, *miracle* followed as an occasional auxiliary. The former served to bewilder the mind; the latter to puzzle the senses. The one was the lingo, the other the legerdemain.

But before going further into this subject, it will be proper to inquire what is to be understood by a miracle.

In the same sense that every thing may be said to be a mystery, so also may it be said that every thing is a miracle, and that no one thing is a greater miracle than another. The elephant, though larger, is not a greater miracle than a mite; nor a mountain a greater miracle than an atom. To an almighty power, it is no more difficult to make the one than the other; and no more difficult to make a million of worlds than to make one. Every thing, therefore, is a miracle, in one sense, whilst in the other sense, there is no such thing as a miracle. It is a miracle when compared to our power, and to our comprehension; it is not a miracle compared to the power that performs it; but as nothing in this description conveys the idea that is affixed to the word miracle, it is necessary to carry the inquiry further.

Mankind have conceived to themselves certain laws, by which what they call nature is supposed to act; and that a miracle is something contrary to the operation and effect of those laws, but unless we know the whole extent of those laws, and of what are commonly called the powers of nature, we are not able to judge whether any thing that may appear to us wonderful or miraculous, be within, or be beyond, or be contrary to, her natural power of acting.

The ascension of a man several miles high into the air, would have every thing in it that constitutes the idea of a miracle, if it were not known that a species of air can be generated several times lighter than the common atmospheric air, and yet possess elasticity enough to prevent the balloon, in which that light air is enclosed, from being compressed into as many times less bulk, by the common air that surrounds it. In like manner, extracting flames or sparks of fire from the human body, as visible as from a steel struck with a flint, and causing iron or steel to move without any visible agent, would also give the idea of a miracle, if we were not acquainted with electricity and magnetism; so also would many other experiments in natural philosophy, to those who are not acquainted with the subject. The restoring persons to life, who are to appearance dead, as is practised upon drowned persons, would also be a miracle, if it were not known that animation is capable of being suspended without being extinct.

Besides these, there are performances by slight of hand, and by persons acting in concert, that have a miraculous appearance, which, when known, are thought nothing of. And, besides these, there are mechanical and optical deceptions. There is now an exhibition in Paris of ghosts or spectres, which, though it is not imposed upon the spectators as a fact, has an astonishing appearance. As, therefore, we know not the extent to which either nature or art can go, there is no criterion to determine what a miracle is; and mankind, in giving credit to appearances, under the idea of their being miracles, are subject to be continually imposed upon.

Since then appearances are so capable of deceiving, and things not real have a strong resemblance to things that are, nothing can be more inconsistent than to suppose that the Almighty would make use of means, such as are called miracles, that would subject the person who performed them to the suspicion of being an impostor, and the person who related them to be suspected of lying, and the doctrine intended to be supported thereby to be suspected as a fabulous invention.

Of all the modes of evidence that ever were intended to obtain belief to any system or opinion to which the name of religion has been given, that of miracle, however successful the imposition may have been, is the most inconsistent. For, in the first place, whenever recourse is had to show, for the purpose of procuring that belief, (for a miracle, under any idea of the word, is a show,) it implies a lameness or weakness in the doctrine that is preached. And, in the second place, it is degrading the Almighty into the character of a show-man, playing tricks to amuse and make the people stare and wonder. It is also the most equivocal sort of evidence that can be set up; for the belief is not to depend upon the thing called a miracle, but upon the credit of the reporter, who says that he saw it; and, therefore, the thing, were it true, would have no better chance of being believed than if it were a lie.

Suppose I were to say, that when I sat down to write this book, a hand presented itself in the air, took up the pen and wrote every word that is herein written; would any body believe me? Certainly they would not. Would they believe me a whit the more if the thing had been a fact; certainly they would not. Since then a real miracle, were it to happen, would be subject to the same fate as the falsehood, the inconsistency becomes the greater, of supposing the Almighty would make use of means that would not answer the purpose for which they were intended, even if they were real.

If we are to suppose a miracle to be something so entirely out of the course of what is called nature, that she must go out of that course to accomplish it, and we see an account given of such miracle by the person who said he saw it, it raises a question in the mind very easily decided, which is, is it more probable that nature should go out of her course, or that a man should tell a lie? We have never seen, in our time, nature go out of her course; but we have good reason to believe that millions of lies have been told in the same time; it is, therefore, at least millions to one, that the reporter of a miracle tells a lie.

The story of the whale swallowing Jonah, though a whale is large enough to do it, borders greatly on the marvellous; but it would have approached nearer to the idea of miracle, if Jonah had swallowed the whale. In this, which may serve for all cases of miracles, the matter would decide itself, as before stated, namely, is it more probable that a man should have swallowed a whale or told a lie.

But supposing that Jonah had really swallowed the whale, and gone with it in his belly to Ninevah, and to convince the people that it was true, have cast it up in their sight, of the full length and size of a whale, would they not have believed him to have been the devil, instead of a prophet? or, if the whale had carried Jonah to Ninevah, and cast him up in the same public manner, would they not have believed the whale to have been the devil, and Jonah one of his imps.

The most extraordinary of all the things called miracles, related in the New Testament, is that of the devil flying away with Jesus Christ, and carrying him to the top of a high mountain; and to the top of the highest pinnacle of the temple, and showing him and promising to him *all the kingdoms of the world*. How happened it that he did not discover America; or is it only with *kingdoms* that his sooty highness has any interest?

I have too much respect for the moral character of Christ, to believe that he told this whale of a miracle himself: neither is it easy to account for what purpose it could have been fabricated, unless it were to impose upon the connoisseurs of miracles, as is sometimes practised upon the connoisseurs of Queen Anne's far things, and collectors of relics and antiquities; or to render the belief of miracles, ridiculous, by outdoing miracles, as Don Quixotte outdid chivalry; or to embarrass the belief of miracles, by making it doubtful by what power, whether of God or the Devil, any thing called a miracle was performed. It requires, however, a great deal of faith in the devil to believe this miracle.

In every point of view in which those things called miracles can be placed and considered, the reality of them is improbable, and their existence unnecessary. They would not, as before observed, answer any useful purpose, even if they were true; for it is more difficult to obtain belief to a miracle, than to a principle evidently moral, without any miracle. Moral principle speaks universally for itself. Miracle could be but a thing of the moment, and seen but by a few; after this it requires a transfer of faith from God to man to believe a miracle upon man's report. Instead, therefore, of admitting the recitals of miracles as evidence of any system of religion being true, they ought to be considered as symptoms of its being fabulous. It is necessary to the full and upright character of truth that it rejects the crutch; and it is consistent with the character of fable, to seek the aid that truth rejects. Thus much for mystery and miracle.

As mystery and miracle took charge of the past and the present, prophesy took charge of the future, and rounded the tenses of faith. It was not sufficient to know what had been done, but what would be done. The supposed prophet was the supposed historian of times to come; and if he happened, in shooting with a long bow of a thousand years, to strike within a thousand miles of a mark, the ingenuity of posterity could make it point-blank; and if he happened to be directly wrong, it was only to suppose, as in the case of Jonah and Ninevah, that God had repented himself and changed his mind. What a fool do fabulous systems make of man!

It has been shown, in a former part of this work, that the original meaning of the words *prophet* and *prophesying* has been changed, and that a prophet, in the sense of the word as now used, is a creature of modern invention; and it is owing to this change in the meaning of the words, that the flights and metaphors of the Jewish poets, and phrases and expressions now rendered obscure, by our not being acquainted with the local circumstances to which they applied at the time they were used, have been erected into prophecies, and made to bend to explanations, at the will and whimsical conceits of sectaries, expounders and commentators. Every thing unintelligible was prophetical, and every thing insignificant was typical. A blunder would have served as a prophecy; and a dish-clout for a type.

If by a prophet we are to suppose a man, to whom the Almighty communicated some event that would take place in future, either there were such men, or there were not. If there were, it is consistent to believe that the event so communicated, would be told in terms that could be understood; and not related in such a loose and obscure manner as to be out of the comprehensions of those that heard it, and so equivocal as to fit almost any circumstance that might happen afterwards. It is conceiving very irreverently of the Almighty, to suppose he would deal in this jesting manner with mankind; yet all the things called prophesies in the book called the Bible, come under this description.

But it is with prophecy as it is with miracle; it could not answer the purpose even if it were real. Those to whom a prophecy should be told, could not tell whether the man prophesied or lied, or whether it had been revealed to him, or whether he conceited it; and if the thing that he prophesied, or intended to prophecy, should happen, or something like it, among the multitude of things that are daily happening, nobody could again know whether he foreknew it, or guessed at it, or whether it was accidental. A prophet, therefore, is a character useless and unnecessary; and the safe side of the case is, to guard against being imposed upon by not giving credit to such relations.

Upon the whole, mystery, miracle, and prophecy, are appendages that belong to fabulous and not to true religion. They are the means by which so many *Lo heres!* and *Lo theres!* have been spread about the world, and religion been made into a trade. The success of one imposter gave encouragement to another, and the quieting salvo of doing *some good* by keeping up a *pious fraud* protected them from remorse.

Having now extended the subject to a greater length than I first intended, I shall bring it to a close by abstracting a summary from the whole.

First—That the idea or belief of a word of God existing in print, or in writing, or in speech, is inconsistent in itself for reasons already assigned. These reasons, among many others, are the want of an universal language; the mutability of language; the errors to which translations are subject; the possibility of totally suppressing such a word; the probability of altering it, or of fabricating the whole, and imposing it upon the world.

Secondly—That the Creation we behold is the real and ever existing word of God, in which we cannot be deceived. It proclaims his power, it demonstrates his wisdom, it manifests his goodness and beneficence.

Thirdly—That the moral duty of man consists in imitating the moral goodness and beneficence of God manifested in the creation towards all his creatures. That seeing as we daily do the goodness of God to all men, it is an example calling upon all men to practise the same towards each other; and, consequently, that every thing of persecution and revenge between man and man, and every thing of cruelty to animals, is a violation of moral duty.

I trouble not myself about the manner of future existence. I content myself with believing, even to positive conviction, that the power that gave me existence is able to continue it, in any form and manner he pleases, either with or without this body; and it appears more probable to me that I shall continue to exist hereafter, than that I should have had existence, as I now have, before that existence began.

It is certain that, in one point, all nations of the earth and all religions agree; all believe in a God; the things in which they disagree, are the redundancies annexed to that belief; and, therefore, if ever an universal religion should prevail, it will not be believing any thing new, but in getting rid of redundancies, and believing as man believed at first. Adam, if ever there was such a man, was created a Deist; but in the mean time, let every man follow, as he has a right to do, the religion and the worship he prefers.

☆ ☆ ☆

Paine, shortly after his release from prison, wrote a second part to *The Age of Reason.* In this, he adds little to the searching moral inquiry of the first part, and his dissection of the Bible has only an antique interest today. Only the first part is included here, and it should be noted that it is the first part which is usually referred to when one speaks of *The Age of Reason.*

FIVE

Letter to Washington

IN presenting Paine's *Letter to Washington,* it pays to speculate once more on how different his career would have been had he remained in America and played his part in the great struggle for democracy and against the Hamiltonians that Jefferson led. Had he done so, he would have understood, as Jefferson so well did, how innocent Washington was of any complicity in the Federalist plot to destroy the republic; he would have recognized, along with Jefferson, the lonely and rather forlorn devotion of the President to the United States. And he would have known, as Jefferson knew so well, how the Federalist plotters, led by Alexander Hamilton and Aaron Burr and John Adams, traduced and falsified, for America, the nature of the revolution in France.

But Paine was not in America, and only distance, ill-fortune, and his sufferings in prison can explain his headlong attack upon George Washington. Remember that Paine adored Washington; that during the revolution they were comrades in arms; that again and again Paine proclaimed his immense esteem of the commander-in-chief. Remember that Paine dedicated *Rights of Man* to Washington. But remember this, too, that after the American Constitutional Convention, the Federalists, a thoroughly unprincipled and reactionary group of men, gained control of the country, swindling the old soldiers, attacking the patriots, using the Supreme Court as the first step to set up a dictatorship, dealing illegally with foreign governments, plotting, buying, selling, working so fervently to wreck the American Republic that a second revolution was needed to drive them to their holes.

And remember that Paine saw this from France. When America could have supported France whole-heartedly and perhaps changed the future bloody history of Europe, Paine saw America, under the Federalists, betray France and abandon her. It would have taken a Paine as objective as the man he had been a decade before to separate Washington from the men around him; and Paine was not the same man he had been once. Moreover when, during his long imprisonment, Paine appealed again and again for help to the country he had once served, he was as often refused, and allowed to languish, fall sick, and join the list of victims for whom the guillotine waited. This was actually the doing of Gouverneur Morris, an old personal enemy of Paine. Washington was in no way involved, nor is it likely that he knew the truth of Paine's imprisonment; but Paine, after all his suffering, could not believe that Washington had not deliberately deserted him.

Keep all of that in mind as you read Paine's letter to Washington. Accept the clear and damning indictment of the Federalists, for that was the old Paine, mourning the rise of reaction in a country he had once fought for; but understand that when he speaks of Washington, Tom Paine is an old and sickly man, who, abandoned by all, turned on a great good man who was once his comrade.

TO GEORGE WASHINGTON,

PRESIDENT OF THE UNITED STATES.

Paris, September 20, 1795.

Sir,

I had written you a letter by Mr. Letombe, French consul, but, at the request of Mr. Monroe, I withdrew it, and the letter is still by me. I was the more easily prevailed upon to do this, as it was then my intention to have returned to America the latter end of the present year (1795;) but the illness I now suffer prevents me. In case I had come, I should have applied to you for such parts of your official letters (and your private ones, if you had chosen to give them) as contained any instructions or directions either to Mr. Monroe, to Mr. Morris, or to any other person, respecting me; for after you were informed of my imprisonment in France, it was incumbent on you to have made some enquiry into the cause, as you might very well conclude that I had not the opportunity of informing you of it. I cannot understand your silence upon this subject upon any other ground, than as connivance at my imprisonment; and this is the manner it is understood here, and will be understood in America, unless you will give me authority for contradicting it. I therefore write you this letter, to propose to you to send me copies of any letters you have written, that I may remove this suspicion. In the preface to the Second Part of the *Age of Reason,* I have given a memorandum from the hand-writing of Robespierre, in which he proposed a degree of accusation against me, "*for the interest of America as well as of France.*" He could have no cause for putting America in the case, but by interpreting the silence of the American government into connivance and consent. I was imprisoned on the ground of being born in England; and your silence in not enquiring the cause of that imprisonment, and reclaiming me against it, was tacitly giving me up. I ought not to have suspected you of treachery; but whether I recover from the illness I now suffer, or not, I shall continue to think you treacherous, till you give me cause to think otherwise. I am sure you would have found yourself more at your ease, had you acted by me as you ought; for whether your desertion of me was intended to gratify the English government, or to let me fall into destruction in France, that you might exclaim the louder against the French revolution; or whether you hoped by my extinction to meet with less opposition in mounting up the American government; either of these will involve you in reproach you will not easily shake off.

THOMAS PAINE.

Here follows the letter above alluded to, which had been withdrawn:

TO GEORGE WASHINGTON,

PRESIDENT OF THE UNITED STATES.

Paris, February 22, 1795.

SIR,

As it is always painful to reproach those one would wish to respect, it is not without some difficulty that I have taken the resolution to write to you. The danger to which I have been exposed cannot have been unknown to you, and the guarded silence you have observed upon that circumstance, is what I ought not to have expected from you, either as a friend or as President of the United States.

"You knew enough of my character, to be assured that I could not have deserved imprisonment in France; and, without knowing any thing more than this, you had sufficient ground to have taken some interest for my safety. Every motive arising from recollection ought to have suggested to you the consistency of such a measure. But I cannot find that you have so much as directed an enquiry to be made whether I was in prison or at liberty, dead or alive; what the cause of that imprisonment was, or whether there was any service or assistance you could render. Is this what I ought to have expected from America, after the part I have acted towards her? Or will it redound to her honor or to your's that I tell the story? I do not hesitate to say, that you have not served America with more fidelity, or greater zeal, or more disinterestedness, than myself, and perhaps not with better effect. After the revolution of America had been established, you rested at home to partake its advantages, and I ventured into new scenes of difficulty to extend the principles which that revolution had produced. In the progress of events, you beheld yourself a president in America, and me a prisoner in France; you folded your arms, forgot your friend, and became silent.

"As every thing I have been doing in Europe was connected with my wishes for the prosperity of America, I ought to be the more surprised at this conduct on the part of her government. It leaves me but one mode of explanation, which is, *that every thing is not as it ought to be amongst you,* and that the presence of a man who might disapprove, and who had credit enough with the country to be heard and believed, was not wished for. This was the operating motive with the despotic faction that imprisoned me in France, (though the pretence was, that I was a foreigner,) and those that have been silent and inactive towards me in America, appear to me to have acted from the same motive. It is impossible for me to discover any other.

"After the part I have taken in the revolution of America, it is natural that I feel interested in whatever relates to her character and prosperity. Though I am not on the spot to see what is immediately acting there, I see some part of what she is acting in Europe. For your own sake, as well as for that of America, I was both surprised and concerned at the appointment of Governeur Morris, to be Minister to France. His conduct has proved, that the opinion I had formed of that appointment was well founded. I wrote that opinion to Mr. Jefferson at the time, and I was frank enough to say the same thing to Morris, that *it was an unfortunate appointment*. His prating, insignificant pomposity rendered him at once offensive, suspected, and ridiculous; and his total neglect of all business, had so disgusted the Americans, that they proposed drawing up a protest against him. He carried this neglect to such an extreme, that it was necessary to inform him of it; and I asked him one day, *if he did not feel himself ashamed to take the money of the country, and do nothing for it?* But Morris is so fond of profit and voluptuousness, that he cares nothing about character. Had he not been removed at the time he was, I think his conduct would have precipitated the two countries into a rupture; and in this case, hated *systematically* as America is, and ever will be, by the British government, and at the same time suspected by France, the commerce of America would have fallen a prey to both.

If the inconsistent conduct of Morris exposed the interest of America to some hazard in France, the pusillanimous conduct of Mr. Jay in England has rendered the American government contemptible in Europe. Is it possible that any man, who has contributed to the independence of America, and to free her from the tyranny and injustice of the British government, can read without shame and indignation the note of Jay to Grenville? It is a satire upon the Declaration of Independence, and an encouragement to the British government to treat America with contempt. At the time this minister of petitions was acting this miserable part, he had every means in his hands to enable him to have done his business as he ought. The success or failure of his mission depended upon the success or failure of the French arms. Had France failed, Mr. Jay might have put his humble petition in his pocket, and gone home. The case happened to be otherwise, and he has sacrificed the honor, and perhaps the advantage of it, by turning petitioner. I take it for granted, that he was sent over to demand indemnification for the captured property; and, in this case, if he thought he wanted a preamble to his demand, he might have said, "That, though the government of England might suppose it-"self under the necessity of seizing American property bound to France, "yet that supposed necessity could not preclude indemnification to the "proprietors, who, acting under the authority of their own government, "were not accountable to any other." But Mr. Jay sets out with an implied recognition of the right of the British government to seize and condemn: for he enters his complaint against the *irregularity* of the seizures, and the condemnation, as if they were reprehensible only by not being conformable to the terms of the proclamation under which they were seized. Instead of being the envoy of a government, he goes over like a lawyer to demand a new trial. I can hardly help thinking that Grenville wrote that note himself, and Jay signed it; for the style of it is domestic and not diplomatic. The term, *his Majesty,* used without any descriptive epithet, always signifies the King whom the minister represents. If this sinking of the demand into a petition was a juggle between Grenville and

Jay to cover the indemnification, I think it will end in another juggle, that of never paying the money; and be made use of afterwards to preclude the right of demanding it: for Mr. Jay has virtually disowned the right by appealing to the *magnanimity of his Majesty against the capturers.* He has made this magnanimous Majesty the umpire in the case, and the government of the United States must abide by the decision. If, Sir, I turn some part of this business into ridicule, it is to avoid the unpleasant sensation of serious indignation.

"Among other things which I confess I do not understand, is your proclamation of neutrality. This has always appeared to me as an assumption on the part of the executive. But passing this over, as a disputable case, and considering it only as political, the consequence has been that of sustaining the losses of war, without the balance of reprisals. When the profession of neutrality, on the part of America, was answered by hostilities on the part of Britain, the object and intention of that neutrality existed no longer; and to maintain it after this, was not only to encourage farther insults and depredations, but was an informal breach of neutrality towards France, by passively contributing to the aid of her enemy. That the government of England considered the American government as pusillanimous, is evident from the increasing insolence of the conduct of the former towards the latter, till the affair of General Wayne. She then saw that it might be possible to kick a government into some degree of spirit. So far as the proclamation of neutrality was intended to prevent a dissolute spirit of privateering in America under foreign colors, it was undoubtedly laudable; but to continue it as a government neutrality, after the commerce of America was made war upon, was submission and not neutrality. I have heard so much about this thing called neutrality, that I know not if the ungenerous and dishonorable silence (for I must call it such,) that has been observed by your part of the government towards me, during my imprisonment, has not in some measure arisen from that policy.

"Though I have written you this letter, you ought not to suppose it has been an agreeable undertaking to me. On the contrary, I assure you, it has caused me some disquietude. I am sorry you have given me cause to do it; for, as I have always remembered your former friendship with pleasure, I suffer a loss by your depriving me of that sentiment.

THOMAS PAINE.

SIX

Tom Paine: an Estimate

WHEN all is said and done, how are we to assess Thomas Paine? As a writer, for clarity, for forceful prose, and for the straight-forward and reasonable statement of an idea, he had few if any contemporary equals. Not even Jefferson could phrase an abstraction so well in words the average person would understand.

Paine broke with the writing traditions of his day and struck out in a bold and homely style; yet in conjunction with the content, from which it cannot be separated, he bears comparison with any writer of his times. He wrote for the people, deliberately, and thereby created works that have long outlived those of writers who scorned a broad audience. What he lacked in grace, he made up for with his tremendous sincerity. He was a writer who loved people, and that love comes through his words.

As a political thinker, Paine worked with the ideas of his time, activating theories which existed rather than setting out to discover new ones. His greatest personal contribution was the plan for social security which he proposed in *Rights of Man.* But he was more interested in taking the democratic method out of the vault and airing it in full view than in discovering new philosophies. The tremendous circulation of his political writing indicates that he influenced more people than any of those writers upon whom he drew.

As a pamphleteer, he has had no equal. There is no other case in history of a great people's movement finding its voice in one man, and finding it so clearly and decisively. There is no other case where one man created so large a proportion of the fighting slogans of a revolution. There is no other case where a whole nation rallied to a single book, and united on the basis of its plea.

Paine has that rare historical distinction of being unique; there are no comparisons, because there has been no one, before him or since, quite like him. He had the fortune to arrive in the right place at the right time, and once there, he accepted history instead of attempting to avoid it.

As a man, Paine was more than most men, less than some. Tall, powerful, a pair of wide, sloping shoulders, a hooked nose, slanting brown eyes—he was the very opposite of the "dirty little atheist" Theodore Roosevelt once called him without ever having read *The Age of Reason*. Paine was driven by a flame inside him; on issues he believed in, he was absolutely unequivocal, and perhaps his greatest failing was his inability to compromise. He was more than generous; money meant nothing to him. He never refused an appeal for help, and he neither admired nor envied the ability to create a fortune.

In later life, seeing that his much-dreamed-of utopia and brotherhood of man would not be realized for perhaps many, many generations, he fell back upon a somewhat mystical conception of the omnipresence and goodness of God, but until then his materialistic objectivity was amazing for his time. Even at the very end, tortured upon his deathbed by bigots who begged him to recant—though God knows what he had to recant—he held firm. Death had no terrors for him.

To the very end, he clung to his conception of a world that changes constantly, an evolution of society—not a haphazard evolution, but an evolution proposed and forwarded by working individuals.

He had that wonderful grasp of history in perspective that is granted to so few men. He summed up historic situations in terms of their dynamic factors, not in terms of silly platitudes—as so many so-called statesmen do today. And always, in all he wrote, was the concept of forces aligned against each other, of movement and change.

He was a good man and a great man—one who will be remembered long after those who attacked and slandered him are dead and forgotten.

CITIZEN TOM PAINE

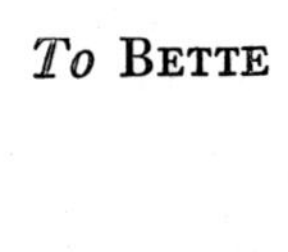

To BETTE

There is nothing more common than to confound the terms of *American Revolution* with those of the *late American War*. The American war is over, but this is far from being the case with the American revolution. On the contrary, nothing but the first act of the great drama is closed.

1787 BENJAMIN RUSH

Author's Foreword

It is no accident that the name of Tom Paine, so long forgotten and almost unmentioned in this country, came to the fore constantly during this war; nor is it an accident that I chose this time to write the story of Citizen Tom Paine. It is the nature of democratic nations, in times of crisis, to seek out of their past men who fought tyranny bravely and forthrightly. It gives us a sense of continuing tradition, a link not only with the past but with the still unborn future, and thereby we take our places in the timeless march of men of good will.

In the two years since *Citizen Tom Paine* was first published, there have been literally thousands of mentions of his name, thousands of quotations from his writings. Some of this may have been due to the book; most of it was evidence of a sincere desire for a certain type of national hero: and Paine comes closest to being that type. Most significant are the number of requests from men overseas for both the *Crisis* and the *Rights of Man*—a real hunger to know something more of the forgotten and much-maligned pamphleteer who fought so well and with such deep understanding in our first war of national liberation. Add to that the many radio programs of Paine's life, the quotation from his *Crisis* by President Roosevelt, and the numberless quotations from him that have appeared in political speeches, and you have a very real reawakening of the American memory.

This is a good thing, a healthy thing. Paine was not the first people's hero to be submerged by the tide of American reaction. At one time or another, all of the following were wiped from our national slate of honor: Abraham Lincoln, Woodrow Wilson,

Thomas Jefferson, Andrew Jackson, John Brown, Samuel Adams, Samuel Houston, John P. Altgeld, Charles Sumner, Thaddeus Stevens—and many more. Yet in most cases, the people found their heroes again—and in time they will find all.

The Tom Paine in the pages which follow represents my best efforts to know a man through his writings and through the scattered references of his contemporaries. As I saw him, he was a very human person, compounded of good and bad, of strength and weakness, and of a devout belief in the goodness of his fellow men. Some have complained of his failings, others of his strength; I can only say that I wrote about him with admiration and sincere respect.

Contents

PART ONE: AMERICA

PART ONE
America

ONE

My Name Is Paine

On a cool, pleasant early fall morning, in the year 1774, Dr. Benjamin Franklin was told that Thomas Paine had been waiting to see him for almost an hour. Dr. Franklin, who had lived in England for many years, who was known through all the civilized world as a great scholar, a witty philosopher, a scientist of no mean parts, and altogether a good deal of a man, was acquainted with everyone in England who mattered, and a good many who did not matter, but whose names did. Yet he could not recall ever having heard of Thomas Paine.

The old man who announced visitors said that Mr. Paine was not a gentleman.

It was no novelty for Dr. Franklin to have visitors who were not gentlemen, yet the curl of the old servant's lips defined an extreme. Franklin wrinkled his nose to set his glasses a trifle closer to his eyes, moved his big, shaggy head, and said without looking up from the letter he was writing, "Well, show him in, why don't you?" and then added somewhat testily, "Why didn't you tell me he was waiting? Why didn't you show him in before?"

"He be dirty," the old man said sourly, and went out, and then came back a moment later leading the other, who set himself just inside the door, almost defiantly, and said,

"My name is Paine, sir!"

Dr. Franklin put away his pen, studied his visitor for a moment or two, and then smiled and said, "Mine is Franklin, sir. I'm sorry I kept you waiting," nodding for the servant to leave the room.

"I'm sorry I waited," Paine said belligerently. "You had no other visitors. You can tell me to go to the devil now, and I'll be off. I didn't want to see the King, only Dr. Franklin. And I didn't have anything to do but to sit there."

Dr. Franklin continued to smile and look at his visitor. Paine wasn't handsome; he wasn't prepossessing; somewhere between thirty and forty, the doctor thought, his sharp hooked nose adding years if anything. His chin was sharp, his mouth full, his oddly twisted eyes tight with bitterness and resentment; virtue or evil in that face, but no joy for a long time and no hope either. His whiskers were a week on his face, and he needed washing. He was not tall nor short, but of medium height, with the powerful, sloping shoulders of a workman who has put in long hours at a bench, and his hands were from the bench, meaty and broad. His cheap coat had split under both arms and his breeches were paper thin at the knees; his stockings were a shambles and his toes breathed freely in what were never good shoes.

"How long is it since you've eaten?" Franklin asked.

"That's none of your damn business! I didn't come for charity."

"Sit down, please," Franklin said quietly, and then went out and came back in a few minutes with a loaf of bread, a piece of meat, and a crock of beer. He set it all down on the table, and then went back to his letter writing, nor did he look up again until Paine had finished and was standing up, uncomfortable and somewhat abashed.

"Feel better?" Franklin asked.

Paine nodded; inside of him, something was burning uneasily; his toes tried to draw into the battered shoes, and with a hand in either pocket, he attempted to stare Franklin down. Drawing out of one pocket a handful of dirty bills and silver, he said, "There's thirty guineas. I didn't come for charity."

"I didn't think you did," Franklin answered. "Why don't you sit down? Why don't you let the world roll by, Mr. Paine, instead of trying to hold it on your shoulders? I approve of thrift, and if a man wants thirty guineas in his pocket and not a shilling's worth on his back, it's reasonable enough for me. But a man's bread isn't to be refused, and there's no charity in breaking some of it. Who are you, Mr. Paine, and what do you want of me?"

"I want to go to America," Paine blurted out. "You're an American. I heard you were an easy man, even with nobody, and not to begrudge something that won't cost you a penny. I thought maybe you'd write me a letter for a position."

"I will."

Still holding the money in his hand, Paine nodded slowly, put the money away, tried to say something, and succeeded only in muttering a few words that meant practically nothing. Then he sat down and spread his broad hands to cover his threadbare knees. Then he fingered his week's growth of beard. Franklin didn't watch him; sealing a letter, glancing up only for a moment, he asked Paine's trade.

"Staymaker," Paine answered, and then added, "Yes—for ladies' corsets and men's vests. I was an excise man," he said, "a gauger for fifty pounds a year. I'm a bad carpenter; I cobbled shoes for sixpence a day because I wanted to live, although God knows why. I swept a weaver's booth for half of that and sold ribbons for maybe twice. I write sometimes," he finished.

"What do you write?" Franklin asked quietly.

"What a man can't say because he's got no guts in him to say it!"

They had talked for an hour. Paine had put down a quart of the beer. His twisted eyes glittered and his broad hands clenched and unclenched with almost rhythmical nervousness. He had forgotten his clothes, his beard, his unwashed skin, his memories; and lost himself in the fascination of an old man who was strangely young and vibrant, and wise as men said he was.

"What is America like?" he asked Franklin.

"Like a promise, or like Scotland or Wales or Sussex, or like none of them, or like a yoke around a man's neck, depending on the man, or like a bonnet to set on his head."

"Big?"

"It goes on," Franklin said. "It's not been explored or surveyed—" There was a note of regret in his voice, as if here was one thing he would have liked to do, but had let slip by.

"I thought of it that way."

"Good wages," Franklin said. "Nobody starves if he wants to work."

"Nobody starves," Paine repeated.

"You can burn there." Franklin smiled. "The fire won't singe anybody."

"I've had enough of burning," Paine said stolidly. "I want a coat on my back and a pair of good shoes. I want to be able to walk into a tavern and put down a guinea like I knew what a guinea was instead of just the smell of it, and I don't have to worry about the change."

"Have you any Latin?"

"A little."

"You're Quaker born and bred, aren't you?"

"I was, I don't know what I am now. I tried to bang out, and I hit my head against the wall. I'm a little drunk, Dr. Franklin, and there's no bridle on my tongue, but this isn't a good country; it stinks, it rots like a pile of dung, and I want to go away and get out of it and not see it again, and aside from that I don't want so much, only some food and a place to sleep and some work to do."

"You can have that," Franklin said thoughtfully. "I'll write you a letter, if it will help you. Don't bang against the wall, but put a penny by here and there and find a piece of land in Pennsylvania, where land's cheap, and get your hands into it."

Paine nodded.

"I'll write to my son-in-law, who will do something for you."

Paine kept nodding, trying to say somehow that Franklin was being good to him, very good. Paine was a little drunk and tired, his sharp head rocking forward, his twisted eyes closing, the whole of him, wretched clothes and dirty skin and beard, and curious pointed features making a disturbing enigma that Franklin remembered for long years afterward whenever he thought of Tom

Paine. Franklin had a taste for enigmas, yet this was one he would never solve.

"Get thee to America, if thee will not work," Paine's father told him when the boy was thirteen years old, and had had more than enough of schooling and dreaming and wandering in the lush fields of old Thetford and climbing in the ruins of the old castle and building castles of his own and thinking that childhood goes on forever.

"Not stays," he said stubbornly.

"And thee are one to say stays or not stays!"

"Not stays."

"And thee know another trade, thee stubborn, ill-mannered, ill-weaned whelp."

He was apprenticed to the art and shown how an artist works. Mrs. Hardy, who was some sort of quality, on the borderline in those days when quality was not nearly so rigidly defined as twenty-five years later, had come to have her corset fitted. Mrs. Hardy weighed two hundred pounds, and most of it was in midriff and above, a bosom like the heathered hills of Scotland and a belly that had given passage to more ale than the Dog's Head Inn. She hadn't bathed in the fourteen months since she had been to the watering place at Bath, and in his first day as a staymaker he had to ram his head against her belly. He had to go into the mysteries and tug and tug, while she squealed like a pig.

"Get thee onto it, Thomas!" his father commanded.

He hung on the laces, while Mrs. Hardy roared, "Paine, you rascal, you're twelve inches short."

"You're twelve inches long," the thirteen-year-old thought miserably. He braced a hand, and it sank deep into a monstrous huge breast.

"Get thee onto it, Thomas," his father repeated, stony and secure in his shell, then stepping out of the room for a moment. Thomas was lost; he sank deeper and deeper into the ocean of flesh; caught in terror and hot misery, he forgot the laces and the corset snapped open and the flesh rolled out at him. Snickering,

"You little rascal, you little rascal," she caught him in her arms. He struggled, sank deeper, fought for his life, then broke loose and ran from the shop, across the fields, panting like a dog until he threw himself down in the shadow of the old ruins.

Twelve of the best laid his behind open and bleeding; he was going to be a staymaker; his father had been a staymaker. Otherwise, get thee to America. Old Paine wasn't a hard man, but there was a way of things, and what you were your son was; the world was a bitter, angry place, and if you earned your honest shilling, that was all God gave you reason to expect. Now Tom Paine was going to America, leaving more broken things behind him than a set of stays, and no man really remembers what was here and what was there at the age of thirteen. He had dozed off, and he looked up now to hear Benjamin Franklin reading the letter he had written so kindly to his son-in-law, Richard Bache, a person of influence in a far-off place called Philadelphia:

"—the bearer, Mr. Thomas Paine (and that was America for you, titled Mr. Paine, this dirty raggle-taggle, and not by nobody or anybody, but by Dr. Benjamin Franklin, the wisest man in the world) is very well recommended to me as an ingenious worthy young man—(and hear that, worthy young man). He goes to Pennsylvania with a view of settling there. I request you to give him your best advice and countenance, as he is quite a stranger there. If you can put him in the way of obtaining employment as a clerk, or assistant tutor in a school, or assistant surveyor, of all of which I think him very capable, so that he may procure a subsistence at least, till he can make acquaintance and obtain a knowledge of the country, you will do well and much oblige your affectionate father—"

"I want to do something," Paine said. "No one was so good to me; I have no friends. If I thought to give you some money, you would laugh at me."

"Give it to someone else," Franklin said evenly. "Stop pitying yourself. Wash and shave off your beard, and don't think the world has knocked you harder than anyone else."

TWO

America Is the Promised Land

THIS was the great crossing, east to west for nine weeks, and then off the edge of the world, as the old folks back in Thetford believed, having never gotten more than a mile or two from their native heath. But he was Tom Paine the traveler and adventurer, not the staymaker and weaver's assistant, and he had sailed for nine weeks on a fever-ridden ship. Now he was dying; no one knew and no one cared, and the captain was too sick himself to be bothered. The ship gently rocked in the placid sunshine that flooded the Delaware River, with the red roofs of Philadelphia only a stone's throw off, while in the blackness of the sick-hold Tom Paine groaned away his life.

He didn't care, he told himself. Franklin had said, "Stop pitying yourself." He cursed Franklin; well enough for Franklin, who lived like a fat old toad in England; the world was good for some, but you could count them on the fingers of a hand, and for the others it was a pen and a jail and a desolation. Like a pinned-down fly on a board, a man struggled for a time and then died, and then there was nothing, as in the beginning there had been nothing. Why should Tom Paine fight it? Why should he fight disease and hunger and loneliness and misery?

He wouldn't fight it, now he would die, and his pity was such an enormous thing that he was thrilled and amazed by the spectacle of himself. He wept for himself, and then wiped away the tears and allowed sunny memories of long ago to creep in. A child in Thetford walked on a flower-decked hillside. May Adams, who had long braids, ran before him into the vine-grown ruins and fell and hurt her knee, and he licked out the dirt and then kissed her. Wrong, she said, and when he asked why, only repeated, wrong, wrong; yet for all that they became lovers and no one knew. She died of the pox when he was not much older and he held the sorrow inside of him, sitting at his bench and making a corset for Jenny Literton, not eating, not stopping, his father saying, "There's a boy with industry, and a change from the rascal he was."

Everything died; now he was dying because Franklin had sent him off to America.

The fever ship held the spotlight at the waterfront, and in the twenty-four hours after she docked almost half the people in Philadelphia came down to have a look at her. It was told how five bodies were dropped overboard during the nine weeks, though you wouldn't know it just to look at her; as the sickly passengers, the convalescing passengers, the tottering passengers came ashore, each told a different version of the lurid story. One of them mentioned a man in the hold who had a letter written by Franklin, and Dr. Kearsley who was trying to set up in the great city of America and having a rather hard time of it, smelled a fee.

"What's his name?"

"Paine, I think."

"Did you see the letter?" Kearsley asked cautiously.

"No, I heard about it."

"You?" the doctor asked someone else.

"No."

A fee was a fee, but to go onto the fever ship for nothing at all was not part of a doctor's duty. "Did he come in the bilge?"

"Cabin passenger."

The bilge had been full of indentured servants, among whom the sickness had first started, and already the still tottering captain was discussing their sale with a pair of prosperous Philadelphia merchants.

"Duty's duty," the doctor said, and went on board. He went down into the stinking hold, and stumbling over bodies, cursing and regretting that duty bulked so large, yelled above the groaning for Mr. Paine.

Mr. Paine answered. The doctor had a candle which wavered and flickered in the foul air, but candle and all it was a task to pick out Tom Paine, and the search over, a thankless task it seemed to the doctor. The clothes were the same, the beard worse, the dirt thicker, the whole a disgusting bundle of rags and misery that whispered for the doctor to go away and allow it to die in peace.

"Ah, and die you shall," the doctor said to himself.

"Go away," Paine groaned.

"You have a letter from Franklin?" Kearsley inquired, clutching at one last straw.

"Yes, damn him!"

"Ah—and what money, my good lad?"

"Three pounds seven," Paine whispered.

"Ah! And tomorrow you'll be up and walking! Got the money with you? Got any luggage?"

"Can't you see I'm dying?"

The doctor left and then returned with the boatman, who demanded three shillings before he would step onto the ship. Hand and foot, they took Tom Paine, dragged him out into the air, and then dumped him like a pile of rags into the bottom of the boat.

There was a last spark of defiance and consciousness in Paine, only enough for him to call the doctor and boatman a pair of bastards and ask why he hadn't been left to die. The doctor was equally frank, and as the boatman pulled for shore he leaned over his sweating, suffering patient and explained, "Because three pounds seven are not come by every day, not by a man who's starting in practice. I'm not a thief; I'll earn the money; you'll live, though God only knows why."

"The Lord giveth; the Lord taketh away; blessed be the Lord," said a Quaker lady who brought him a box of cookies and a scent bag to hang under his nose. She had heard that there was a homeless one living with Kearsley, and that he was profane and dirty, and that Kearsley had wagered the great Dr. Japes twenty pounds that the patient wouldn't die. That was blasphemous. Now Paine admitted to her that he had been born and raised a Quaker, while Kearsley snickered at the foot of the bed—which made matters worse.

"Pray," she told Paine. "Beg the Lord's forgiveness and his everlasting mercy."

"He's cured now." Kearsley smiled.

"Pray, pray!" she called back as she fled from the room, and Kearsley leaned over the footboard, shaking with laughter.

"What a filthy devil you are," Paine said.

"Call the kettle black! Didn't I give you your first bath?"

"Get out of here."

"I came to remind you that you owe me ten pounds," the doctor said. "You've been here six weeks, so that's reasonable. I've saved your life, for what that's worth, and altogether it's a small piece of gratitude you've shown. What is a man's life worth?"

"I'm grateful," Paine muttered, "and mine's worth little enough. I'll pay you when I find work."

"Doing what?"

Paine shrugged.

"I could throw you into jail for the debt," the doctor speculated.

"You could," Paine admitted. He was thin and worn with his sickness, white skin into which the twisted brown eyes were sunk like heavy question marks, bones stretching him like old clothes on a dryer. Kearsley said he was well, but he felt too tired to talk or plead.

"I'll give you a month," Kearsley said suddenly. "You can leave here tomorrow." And Paine nodded gratefully and closed his eyes.

He must have slept for a while, and now the doctor had gone, and the little room was mellow with twilight. There was a single dormer window that showed him, from where he lay, a half a dozen of the red-tiled Philadelphia rooftops. Beyond, a church steeple poked up against the gray sky, and as Tom Paine watched, the snow began to fall, clean, white, lazy flakes that drifted down faster and faster until a white curtain closed in the little window. The coals of a fire lay in the grate; Kearsley wasn't a brute, but a man tired of poverty and ignorance, all of which Paine could understand and even sympathize with now; Kearsley had cured him and given him back his life, and ten pounds wasn't such a stone around a man's neck. Less tired now, somewhat uncertain but finding his feet strong enough to hold him, Paine left his bed and went to the window. This was the America he had come to, and he was looking at it for the first time, a church steeple in the distance, some roofs flaked with white, some people walking on the cobbled street, the city of brotherly love, America, the land, the dream, the empire, that and much more that he had thought of once, the sum of it coming back to him as his will to live and be Tom Paine returned to him. There was a sweet quality in this winter evening, almost a nostalgia; the church bells began to toll faintly, and it seemed to Paine that the people in the streets were moving more quickly now.

Now life was a sweet thing, like an old song. He began to tremble with eagerness, and then he went back to his bed, but he couldn't sleep that night.

If the place had a prophet, it was Benjamin Franklin; the letter he had given Paine was mildewed, creased and worn, but Bache, Franklin's son-in-law, spread it out, read it carefully, and said, yes, he would do something for Paine. Nothing big or special, but this America was a good place, Pennsylvania a good country, and Philadelphia a good city, God bless King George. Nobody had to starve, not if a man had any guts in him. He wasn't one to say anything about the old country, but in some ways this place was better than the old country.

"I think so," Paine nodded.

Could Paine do anything? Was he a journeyman?

"In stays," Paine admitted. But rather than make corsets, he could cobble a little, weave a little, good work even if it wasn't journeyman work. But he had been sick, and—his face reddening

—if he could use his brain instead of his hands for a time it might be a good thing. Not presumptuously, because he hadn't anything in the way of scholarship. But he could spell and sum and he had a little Greek and a little Latin. Bache's face remained noncommittal, and desperately, Paine quoted,

"Faber est quisque suae fortunae."

Bache, fat, prosperous, Paine's age, but a world above him in assurance, nodded, patted Paine's shoulder, and said, "Good enough, I'll find you some sort of place."

With his first few shillings, after two days of near starvation, he went to a coffee house and had rolls and butter and a whole pot of viscous black fluid. Successful men, men like Bache, sat around him, and whereas in London the state of his clothes alone would have prevented him from going into any respectable eating place, here hardly a second glance was thrown at him. Hardly a glance—why, in the corner was a buckskin wildman from the backlands, with leather leggings and a fur cap, and his rifle between his knees as he ate with his hands, just as if he hadn't seen a fork or knife before. So what if his work was teaching the two Dolan children that one and one made two, that c-a-t spelled cat, and Mrs. Dolan came in midday and said, "Won't you have a cup of tea, mister?" and that tomorrow it would be the Smith children, two little girls and a boy.

Two months ago, he would have raged and burned, but this was America and he had been given back his life, and teaching was better than to be a journeyman staymaker. Or maybe inside of himself something had burned out, that he was content not even to look for tomorrow, but only to drift along, satisfying himself with the knowledge that he was Tom Paine, and no more.

A man changes; he wasn't old and he wasn't young, but even Kearsley, who was blunt and hard and could be neatly cruel, had a streak of pity for Paine, not the man, but the wreck. As shown so well when Paine came back to renew his promise on the debt, and Kearsley said, "Forget about it. I won twenty pounds on you."

"I heard about that," Paine admitted, without anger.

"I don't say you're not worth more," the doctor temporized. "I don't know what a man's worth. I hear you are teaching."

"That's right."

"I hope you do well at it," the doctor said, sincere this time.

Paine shrugged; a shilling a day was enough, and two shillings more than enough, and when Mrs. Cradle gave him her husband's third best pair of breeches, he took it. He didn't work hard, and there were whole days when he did nothing at all but wander around Philadelphia, almost childishly intrigued by the colorful, un-European pageant that passed along the streets. There were red Indians out of the wooded mountains, wrapped in their bright and dirty blankets, clay pipes clenched in their teeth; there were wooden-shoed Dutchmen down on their flatboats from the Jerseys, sharp-nosed Yankees from Boston, tall Swedes from the Delaware country, dirty leather-coated hunters from the back counties, carrying their six-foot-long rifles wherever they went, silk-and-satin Tidewater gentlemen up from the south with their slaves, black and white and red and brown, and gray-clad Quakers of the inner circle, Penns and Darleys and Rodmonts. Up First Street, down Spruce, round about the Square, along Broad, he could walk slowly and lazily, divorced from the world in a murky way, his past severed, his future non-existent, a shilling teacher, the butt of smutty stories, his home sometimes a room in one tavern and sometimes in another if the weather was bad, if it snowed and rained and the wind lashed; but if the day was good enough he wasn't averse to bedding into a pile of hay in some Quaker's stable, thereby saving sixpence, which was about the price of the cheapest room a tavern sold.

If he thought of himself at all, it was with pity; when he could afford a bottle of wine it went down in such self-sympathy that he would usually wind up a mass of maudlin tears. And he didn't have to drink alone, since there was usually a tavern drunk to keep him company. Look at his own life, he would point out. Had he a chance? Staymaker when he was still a boy, finding a woman he loved and then losing her, grinding through what lower-middle-class England called life, drunk two weeks, a month on bad gin, the whole world like a fluttering pinwheel, groping in a haze for a little beauty, himself ugly and raw and unkempt.

He wasn't a fool; often he told himself, passively, that the mere fact he had wanted so many things proved it; and never acceptance, since he had hated with such ferocity kings, noblemen, ladies and gentlemen of quality, beggars and thieves and fat, prosperous merchants, sluts and whores and decent women too—and whom had he loved?

There was once a woman he loved, he knew.

Now he didn't love and he didn't hate; he had accomplished one great thing, his passage to the thin fringe of colonies on the American mainland; thereupon he rested. No one gave him shoes, and his shoes wore out; his stockings were a blunt deception; he had been given an old coat that flapped threadbare about his shoulders, and he meandered through the streets with his head down against the cold blasts of wind, his appearance unusual enough for people to begin to know him in such a small city as Philadelphia was then.

"There goes Tom Paine," they said.

A committee of Quaker ladies called on him. They brought him a new coat and a vest. "Thee are a shame to us," they pointed out. "Thee will go on this way until God will turn away his face."

He had been drinking, and he said, smiling foolishly, "I lick God's belly."

That got around the city, and he lost half his tutoring jobs.

That month, January, in the year 1775, was the beginning of a year that would change the destiny of mankind, yet it was such a January as we often have in the midlands, rain sometimes, snow sometimes, sleet sometimes, and sometimes a clear warm day that might very well be June. It was the beginning of a year that was the beginning of an era, and Christ himself might have walked on earth to raise so fierce yet so gentle a voice from long speechless mankind. Yet men for the most part didn't know and didn't care, what with one and a hundred things to be done, buying and selling and providing, loving and hating, profiting and losing.

In Philadelphia, it promised to be a good year. The town was rapidly becoming a city, and situated as a keystone among the nations of America, Virginia, Maryland, Pennsylvania, New York, Massachusetts and the rest, the city gave promise of being one of the great urban centers of the earth. Through its streets, its centers of commerce, which were the coffee houses, its warehouses and its wharves, teemed the trade of all the English colonies in America and of several European nations. It is true that already in the past year a somewhat incoherent body called the First Continental Congress had met in Philadelphia, but they had accomplished nothing, and solid citizens did not believe that the Congress was any menace to the security and prosperity of the colonies. There were disturbances and mutterings, in Boston for the most part and in other Yankee towns to the north; but when was there a time without disturbances? There was unrest in the back counties of the South, but what more could you expect of wild woodsmen who tramped around free as Huns with their six-foot-long rifles?

On the other hand, there was more than adequate compensation. In the highlands, the beavers were thick as rabbits, and shepherded by lean Scotsmen and black-bearded Jews a steady stream of glossy pelts poured into the city. The Tidewater tobacco crop was better than good; the Jerseys were bursting with food; and raft after raft of good white pine floated down the Delaware. Never had the pigs in the German counties been so fat and never had the sheep, grazing in the rolling pastures north of the city, been so heavy with wool. In the wild woods, the Allegheny reaches, the lake country and the Fincastle Highlands, the deer ran thick as flies; venison in Philadelphia sold for fourpence a pound and bear meat could hardly be given away. The deer hides by the thousands piled up in stinking bales on the wharves, ready to change men's fashions in all of Europe. Master carpenters were fighting the fad for Chippendale and Sheraton and other English cabinet makers; with a loop, a claw, and a turn, a slim back, a graceful leg, they were not merely imitating but creating a truly American furniture. The working men of the city were strong and their hands itched to make. Houses were going up, and sometimes the bricks were native as well as the cement.

There were stirrings and murmurings, but there was also an abundance of good things. There was discontent, yet there was enough content. War was in the air, albeit vaguely, but people did not want war; freedom was in the air, too, but most people didn't give two damns about freedom.

The city was a good one, carefully laid out, bought by Penn, not plundered from the red men, full of rich Quakers and poor Quakers, and rich and poor who were not Quakers; but altogether with such a determined air of middle-class prosperity as you would not find in any European city. The houses were solid structures, mostly brick, some half-timber, some frame. Many of the streets were cobbled, named not for men in an ungodly fashion, but for trees, or descriptively, or numbered. There was a good fire department, a good guard, a good library. There was a philosopher, Ben Franklin, come out of the city. There was more good glass, linen, silver, and furniture than anywhere else in America; and after a fashion there was more freedom of religion and thought. Here in the promised land, Philadelphia was the promised city.

Paine went to a slave sale, not because he wanted to buy or had the money to buy, but because it was on an afternoon when he had nothing else to do, and because he was curious to know what it was like to see human beings bought and sold. The auction was held in a big old barn, with the doors locked, and there were a dozen merchants present. It was a sale of breeding wenches, which meant that only women would be put on the auction block, that they would be either virgin or pregnant, and that the bidding would be very brisk. Not only that, but from what Paine had heard it would partake of other aspects than mere buying and selling.

He was hardly drunk today, only rosy, only enough to say to himself, "Why shouldn't they buy them and sell them? White, too, why only black?" Yet he was neither angry nor offended, but rather pleased with himself that he had persuaded the good merchants to let him in. They were good enough to call him a scrivener instead of a shilling-tutor, and he had a half-formed thought that he might write something about this and try to sell it to a magazine.

In the half hour before the bidding started, the merchants sat around, perched comfortably on bales of hay, smoking, taking snuff, talking a commercial brand of filth, yet at the same time nervous and shy as adolescents in a bawdy house. For a while, Paine couldn't understand, and then it came to him that they would show the Negroes naked. His throat constricted; he was hot and cold and ashamed and eager, and for the first time in months he despised himself.

He saw that he was unshaven, unkempt and ragged; his fingernails were black crescents and his stockings like ladders; his pity for himself was a wet sop, a lie and a delusion, and if no one could offer proof of any kind for man's nobility, they could at least exhibit Tom Paine as satisfactory evidence of man's debasement.

The auction started. Miles Hennisy, one of the greatest slave callers of his day, came out of the little pen behind the barn where the Negroes were herded, prodding a sixteen-year-old girl in front of him with his silver-headed stick. Hennisy, from his powdered, beautifully curled wig to his polished pumps, was a glorious vision of sartorial splendor; the stockings were silk, the knee breeches black satin, the vest a brocade of silver and gold thread; at his neck and at his throat was bunched lace, five pounds' worth, perhaps; he wore a coat of black Portuguese broadcloth and a three-cornered hat of soft and lovely felt. Such was Hennisy, who was a legend, who sailed to Africa with his own slave ships, who had sold a black emperor, four black kings, and at least a hundred royal fledglings, who prided himself on the fact that when he sold a pregnant Negress, she was pregnant by him. He was a devil and a murderer—and the darling of Tidewater society; he had a long, handsome brown face and tiny blue eyes, and he spoke seven west-coast dialects.

He smiled now, and poked the girl up onto the wooden platform. She was wrapped in a blanket, with only her woolly, frightened head protruding; sweat and terror gave her strange round face a sheen like black marble. Hennisy said, "This, gentlemen, my good friends, is sixteen years old, soft as a lamb, strong as an ox, virgin and beautiful to look on, and old Solomon himself would have given a jewel of his crown to possess her. Her blood is royal, and as for her mind, already she speaks enough of the King's tongue to make herself understood. Her breasts are like two Concord grapes, her behind like the succulent hams of a suckling pig. I start the bidding at fifty pounds to give her away; and, gentlemen, make it a hundred and call out stout and strong; gentlemen, take her home, or to bed, or into the hayloft; make it sixty, gentlemen, make it seventy-five, make it eighty. The blanket goes off at eighty!"

"Eighty pounds!" someone called.

Hennisy ripped off the blanket; she was a little girl, frightened and shivering. She cowered back as Hennisy called, "Virgin, gentlemen, virgin, come up and see for yourselves!"

Paine stumbled through the snow. He had wanted to kill a man, and he had been afraid; he had roamed the streets of Philadelphia for three hours; his feet were soaking wet and cold. As darkness approached, he went into a tavern and sat down in front of the fire, and for half the night he sat there without speaking or moving.

Robert Aitken was one of those lonely, unsmiling Scotsmen who had been drifting into America by ones and twos ever since it had been opened for colonization. They were curious people, utterly beyond stamp or index, likely to settle down and become rich and satisfied, or just as likely to go off and trade for a lifetime with the Indians, never seeing a white face. Perversely, out of their Calvinism came as much broad tolerance as close stubbornness, and it was a common thing for a Scotsman and a Jew to become lifelong partners in the fur trade. Considered a foreigner by the bulk of Americans, who were of English descent, the Scotsman nevertheless put his finger on the soul of the little nation and kept it there.

Aitken was long and narrow, with a tight face that told people who never talked to him that he was dull and without imagination. He had a store where he bought and sold books; he had a box of upper-case type, a box of lower-case, and a straight up-and-down press. Now and then he published a small book or a pamphlet. He had in his mind bigger things, but he was obstinate in going about them and perverse in approaching Paine. It was the day after the slave sale, and Paine had come into his store.

"What can I do for ye?" Aitken asked.

Paine explained, stammeringly, that he was a writer of sorts, that in England he had written a pamphlet or two, and that here he had been a shilling teacher.

"And a mighty drinker," Aitken said sourly.

Paine nodded.

"I hold toward temperance," Aitken said. "Look at the image of yerself, dirty, filthy, wretched—and a mighty nerve you got to come in here and ask me for an honest living!"

"Give me a chance," Paine said.

"And why should I do that? The talk is that you came off the boat with a letter from Franklin, and sure you did the good man false. You're walking around the city like a man daft and wanting his own soul. Sure as God, you're a bad penny!"

Paine turned toward the door, but with his hand on the knob, heard the Scotsman's sharp voice calling him back.

"Would you work for a pound a week?" Aitken demanded.

Paine's big, ugly head nodded; his twisted brown eyes fixed themselves upon Aitken as if the skinny bookseller were the sole arbiter of his fate.

"Seen it hard and lonely," Aitken said more softly. "I don't look at a man, but underneath him. You're in no way a fool, and neither am I, although a lot of fat bellies in the town here would think us both so. I put a shilling by, but I spend a shilling when I have to, and I mark a good investment." He went to his till and took out a handful of silver. "Here's a pound, and if you drink it down, don't let me see your dirty face again. Go to a barber, and then buy some decent clothes and put a coat on your back, and then come back here."

Paine nodded, took the money, and went out; he couldn't trust himself to speak, not to think even; as if he had been released from jail, starving, he felt a sudden sickening hunger—he wanted the whole world; he could have it—he wanted the Negro maid, trembling on the auction block; he wanted to take her in his arms and tell her that it would be all right; his sense of power was only the result of the simple fact that he still lived, that he still wanted and hungered and hoped.

He came back in brown homespun, with his face shaven and his hair powdered and his nails clean. Aitken gave him dinner, and then they sat down and talked. The bookseller was an extraordinary man, not brilliant, but filled with a detailed material knowledge about the colonies. He told Paine, frankly, "I have faith in ye because you come cheap. That's the Scotsman in me, and maybe the fool."

They talked all evening, and by midnight, the Pennsylvania Magazine was born. That night, Paine stayed over at Aitken's house, not sleeping, but lying on his back and staring into the darkness.

THREE

The Rat Trap

PAINE was a bad one; a boy or a man should know his place, but Paine beat his head against the wall. At fourteen he was mute, but his silence was dark and sullen, and that revealed to people clearly enough that there was a devil inside of him. Once the Squire whipped him half to death for trespass, and Paine screamed out through his agony, "God help you and your kind! God help you! God damn you! God damn you!"

"A bad one, and take the rod to him before he does murder," the Squire told Paine's father.

Tom said, "He's a fat swine." There was truth in that; two hundred and thirty-five pounds, the Squire was a prime and ruddy English gentleman, hounds in the morning, roast beef and port for dinner, hounds in the afternoon, roast beef and port for supper, hunting talk and whisky until midnight—"By Gawd, he's a fair fine gentleman, God bless him," his tenants said. He was all that, and it was a wonder he put up with the devilishness of the staymaker's son.

The Squire had his own son in Eton, a tall, strong, handsome young man of fifteen, a pleasure to look at, and so well set out that there wasn't a villager but was delighted to pull a forelock and give young master Harry Good Morning. Young Harry, during his last term at school, had lost eight hundred pounds at cards, and the Squire, hearing about it, slapped his knee and roared with laughter: "Damned young devil! Damned young devil!"

Home from school with three other young bloods, Harry found

country life boring. Necessity spurred him to a certain degree of inventiveness, and he and his friends decided to do a bit of lessoning on Tom Paine. However, they preserved an air of legitimacy, waiting for him to trespass, a circumstance not at all rare considering the amount of land the Squire owned. They caught the boy, beat him insensible with birch rods, and then hanged him by his foot from an oak tree. They cut him down only when it seemed that he was dead, and then, slightly disappointed to find him still breathing, they stripped him naked and rolled him in a bog. They gave him some whisky to revive him, and then whipped him home naked. Altogether, it was such a game go as they hadn't even dared to hope for that summer, and it would provide them with an endless stream of conversation at school the following year. The Squire himself told and retold the tale, and whenever he related it went into such paroxysms that his wife feared he would have a stroke.

At his bench, fastening stays under his father's eye, Tom said quietly, "Thee were a staymaker, and I—and if thee were a beggar, that way I, and if thee were a thief, that way I, kneel down to the Squire, live in poverty and dirt, jump from the path when the hounds come running, pull a forelock when the lady comes, go to church and pray to God—"

"Shut thee!" his father roared.

"I'm a man!" the boy cried hoarsely. "I tell thee, I'm a man, a man, a man!"

"Shut thee!" his father yelled. "Shut thee, or I'll break thee sinful head!"

"You are a staymaker, and I am a staymaker," the boy sobbed.

"Thee! Thee, thee sinful devil! With the brain of Gentiles and the speech of Gentiles, God help thee!"

The devil was in him, roaring, buzzing in his ears, prodding him on. A month later, he ran off to sea, shipping aboard a privateer as a cabin boy. The captain, grinning, said to him, "What do I want with a Quaker?"

"Take me, try me."

"Will you fight?"

"I'll fight," Tom said eagerly. "I'll fight, I swear I'll fight." Here was a vision of freedom broad and dazzling; on the sea, a man was his own master; riches meant freedom, and there were no heights to which a man might not rise. The captain caught him across the ear and flung him full length on the deck.

"Come along, little one, come along," he smiled.

The captain was drunk constantly and a beast about it; the mate was drunk only half the time and only half a beast about it; but both of them took it out on the cabin boy, and by the time they had coasted around and into the Thames, Tom Paine was a livid mass of bruises. There was only one relief, and that was to get at the captain's rum and swill it down. And for that, the beatings were doubled. Anchored outside of London, the boy slipped over the side and swam to shore. For the next two weeks he lived in the hut of a half-witted garbage collector, and in that time he ate what he could pick out of the buckets.

They had warned him in Thetford that London was a sinful city, but as he wandered wide-eyed among the sewer-like streets, he began to understand the difference between those who sin and those whose life is a sin. The lower-class Londoner of that time, the beast whose forest was a maze of alleyways, lived on cheap gin, cheap sin, and cheap robbery. For the first, the punishment was slow death, for the second horrible death, and for the last death by hanging or stoning or quartering. For a tupenny piece a man could get roaring, crazy drunk, and since drunkenness was the only way for the poor to forget that hell was now and not in the hereafter, gin had during the course of years come to replace almost every other food. Three-year-olds drank gin by the glassful, nursing mothers lived on gin and quieted their babies with it, working men took for their supper a can of gin, old folks hastened death with it, and adolescents made themselves insane with it. In some streets, at certain times of the day, the whole population would be screaming drunk with gin. Prostitutes lost their livelihood when any female from a child to a mother would sell herself for a penny to grind in the gin mill.

In this, Tom Paine lived and drank and ran like a rat, and stole and cursed and fought, and slept in alleys and sheds and slimy basements. Until one day he took hold of himself, left Gin Row, and apprenticed himself to a staymaker.

There was no hope, he knew, no escape, no salvation.

Sixteen, a staymaker's assistant, he hadn't touched gin in over a year. His clothes were clean, if not good, and he read books. Night after night, he read books, all the books he could lay hands on—Swift and Addison and Pope and Defoe and Congreve and Fielding and Richardson, even Spenser, and sometimes Shakespeare; most of what he read he did not understand; Defoe and Fielding were somewhat plain to him, yet he rather resented that they should write of what he knew so well, instead of the dream world he fancied in print. He was a man, making his own way; it took him only a little while to completely expunge the Quaker "thee" from his speech. He swaggered through London, and with a rosy haze before his eyes, he would stand for hours before White's, the great Tory gambling house, or Brooks's, the Whig equivalent, and watch the bloods come to lay their thousands and their tens of thousands on the turn of a card. "That for me," he would say to himself, "that for me, by God!"

He made two friends, Alec Stivvens, a draper's assistant, a thin, tubercular boy of fifteen, and Johnny Coot, apprentice chimney sweep, twenty-two, but with the body of a twelve-year-old. The three of them would go to a tavern and drink bitters until their heads felt like mighty lumps of lead, and then hanging onto each other, they would go reeling home, singing at the top of their lungs. These drinking bouts meant beatings for two of the apprentices, but for Tom there was always the intercession of Mistress Morris, his master's wife.

It had started the time Master Morris, a wasted little man of sixty, went off to Nottingham on a matter of business. His wife, twenty years younger, plump, pretty, considering that smallpox had marked her whole face, called Tom in to fix a split corset.

She said to Tom afterwards, "You're a sly devil, the way of you Quakers. But don't you go to talk on me or I'll put a knife in your back." Still she couldn't harm a flea, and it made him feel like a man afterwards, boasting to Stivvens and Coot. She was good to him, and she brought him cakes and cookies and kept impressing Morris with what a fine boy Tom was. But Stivvens, inflamed by Paine's stories, tried the same thing on his mistress; a rolling pin put an inch-high lump on his head.

Stivvens wanted to be a highwayman; he talked of almost nothing else, and he said a hundred times if he said it once that as soon as he was sixteen he would go off and join Red Gallant's band on the Dover Road. That was in the time when highwaymen still wielded great power, when bands of forty and fifty cutthroats roamed over the King's Roads and fought pitched battles with the redcoat troops.

" 'E's a prince, that Red Gallant is," Stivvens would say.

"Fair enough, but it's a short life. Me to live to ninety," Coot remarked cautiously.

Tom said there was only one way of life, and that among the bloods. If you weren't blood in England, you were dirt. He was minding the bloods and watching their ways.

"Be one yerself, eh?"

"Maybe," Tom said.

"And 'ow?"

"There are ways. I ain't saying it comes easy, but there are ways."

Stivvens was impressed. "You got a way, Tom?" he inquired.

"Ah—"

"Lum!" Coot snorted. "Out a dirt ye come; dirt breeds dirt! Don't I know? Down it's easy, but no goin' up."

"I ain't saying," Tom nodded.

"Lum!"

But Stivvens afterwards told Tom that he had faith; a man didn't have a head on his shoulders for nothing, and he himself was making for a take, a small take, nothing impressive, but as Stivvens put it, "Enough shillings for an evening full a noxies. Pretty ones too. Four shillings a poke, I intends to pay."

Tom saw the intent and warned the boy, "They can hang you for stealing."

"If they catch me."

Tom dreamed that night, slept fitfully, had nightmares, woke and slept, and the next day begged Stivvens, "Don't do it, Alec, don't."

They caught Stivvens; he had broken into the till of a weaver next door to his master's shop and made off with two pounds eight. Like a fool, he put the money into his shoes, and while he overslept in the morning, his master took the shoes to cobble, thinking he would take the cost out of the boy's pay. The weaver came in to tell his tale, and the sum of the money fitted in too nicely. They beat the boy, and it took only thirty of the best to make him confess.

For the next few weeks, Coot talked of nothing else but Stivvens in Old Bailey. "Fancy," he would say to Tom, "little Stivvens."

"It don't seem possible," Tom agreed.

"They'll try him with the great ones," Coot decided.

"Hanging?"

"Don't see what else."

"They can't hang him, he's a baby, a little fool. He never had sense. His wits were addled."

"Lum, open and shut. 'E broke in, now it's a rope around 'is neck. Open and shut."

Open and shut it was. Tom and Coot managed to see him once after the judge had done the sentencing. It was the first time Tom had been in jail, but Coot was an old hand at such things, having been in debtors' prison twice, and it was he who suggested that they bring along a loaf of bread and a bottle of gin. They each brought a quart. and Coot assured Tom it was a handy thing to make the rope stretch easy. At the jail, Stivvens couldn't say a word, but just sat and stared and stared, the tears making little designs on his dirty cheeks.

"A tight lip," Coot said. "You're in with the great ones now—on the same scaffold as Johnny Hasbrook of Watling Street was stretched, all the time laughing. By God, 'e was a great un, murderous mean an' having twice the men as Red Gallant ever did."

But there wasn't a sparkle from Stivvens, only the tears running down his emaciated cheeks.

"Save the gin and drink it tomorrow," Tom forced himself to say.

"Save it, save it," Coot agreed. "Lum, get heated, and you won't feel the rope, but by God you'll spit in the hangman's eye."

They both went to the procession the following day, their masters giving them the afternoon off; and they would have gone, even if they hadn't known Stivvens, for when there was a great hanging procession, starting out at Newgate, and proceeding in such a magnificent manner two miles to Tyburn, all of London took a holiday. All along the two-mile line of the march, the mob made a sea of human faces, a raggle taggle that swayed and shifted and screamed and cursed and hooted and shouted and whistled and shrieked, men, women and children, old gaffers, babies, almost everyone with bread and cheese and pickles, wine for the sturdy tradesman or journeyman, gin and bitters for the working folk, pickpockets, ruffians, sluts, noblemen, scholars, and in carriages and chairs the great gentlemen and ladies of the land. For when a human being went to die, it was drama, high and glorious, such as the stage or the bedroom could never provide; and what did it matter so near to the gates of heaven or hell whether the condemned person was high-born or low-born?

Coot groaned and whimpered at his lack of size; he charged the crowd, worming his way through like an eel; he was indefatigable, and he wore Tom out. And once he got through and caught a glimpse of Stivvens, swaying in the cart, his peaked little face hardly able to comprehend that he himself was the author of this glorious fete, the cart would pass on, and the plunging and squirming would have to start over again.

"It ain't no way to treat his friends," Coot complained. "It ain't no way."

For an hour the chimney sweep and the staymaker's apprentice battled their way along the line to the gallows, and during that hour Tom Paine noticed a change come over Stivvens. Either the gin was taking effect, or else the glory of the occasion had driven the fear from his heart. Stivvens was posturing and bowing and posing; he even did a little dance in the cart; he waved his hands; he grimaced like a little ape.

" 'Igh and mighty, 'e is," Coot crowed. " 'Igh and mighty."

And the crowd cheered him. Not even Johnny Hasbrook of Watling Street had gone to his death in that fashion.

And even on the scaffold Stivvens stood and smiled foolishly.

That night, Paine left Morris; he ran away; he beat his head blindly against the walls of the cage; he wandered for two days in the streets of London, and then he fed himself into the gin mill. He holed up in a haunt of beggars and thieves and heard things that are not good for human ears; but he was not human, and the beggars and thieves were not human.

For two months he dragged himself through hell, and then, because part of his stubbornness was a will to live, he apprenticed himself to a cobbler. He was able to hold onto the simple belief that it was better to make shoes than stays.

FOUR

The Nineteenth of April and 'Seventy-Five

LONG afterward, he would remember the day; for while it meant nothing to some, and something to a few, to him it was the beginning and always would be the beginning, the break between two periods in his life and two periods in the life of mankind, the time when he discovered that Tom Paine was made of stuff strange and terrible—and he didn't cry for himself again.

He had been many things, and now he was an editor, a man with a job, a little money in his pocket, shaven, a good suit of clothes on his back, a good pair of shoes, stockings without holes, a person of some standing in the community, respected by some, liked by some, disliked by some, but truly and actually a person of standing. Walking down Front Street and having them say, "Good morning to you, Mr. Paine," or "Have you heard the latest from Europe, Mr. Paine?" or "I've read your latest issue and it's brisk, Mr. Paine, brisk, I repeat," he had to shake his head and concentrate on his identity, nor could he pass a beggar nor a loafer nor some poor wretched devil without thinking, "There, but by the grace of God, goes Thomas Paine."

Yet with his position, with the value Aitken placed upon him, with issue after issue of the Pennsylvania Magazine emerging under his hand, he still could not shake off his terror of life. Life was a beast, and when this holiday was over, the beast would tear at him again. A man was a fool to struggle or fight back, since in the end a man was grooved in his place, and in the world there was neither pity nor justice.

That was until something happened on the nineteenth of April, in seventeen seventy-five. Then, for Paine, there was a beginning; a crack showed in the wall against which he had been battering his head, and sunlight came through. The devil reared up on his hind legs and bared his teeth, and twenty angels blew a mighty chorus upon their trumpets. But otherwise the world was mighty little disturbed; in places the sun shone, and in other places it rained, and the sound of musketry was heard no farther than a man may hear those things. No shot fired was heard round the world, and up and down the American coast line, where a motley arrangement of three million people were settled, life went on in the placid, bucolic way it had gone on before.

But not in Lexington. On the evening of the eighteenth, a whooping, shouting, over-excited horseman drove into this pretty little New England village, and roaring at the top of his lungs woke everyone who was not already awake. From the white clapboard houses, the tavern, the manse, and even from a farm or two not properly in the village, the good Massachusetts householders came pouring, clad in their long white nightshirts and their tasseled white night caps, their clumsy firelocks in hand, their wives chattering behind them, their children poking heads out of upstairs windows.

"What's to pay?" they demanded of the rider, whose name was Paul Revere.

"Hell's to pay!" he shouted.

From the house of the Reverend Jonah Clark came two gentlemen for whom his statement had deadly pertinence. They rubbed their necks feelingly and drew their nightshirts closer about them. Their names were Adams and Hancock; the first was a politician, the second a smuggler, and together they shared a stubborn resentment of foreign rule of the little seaboard colony wherein they lived. Their resentment had taken the form of meetings, congresses, incitements to riot, and wholesale parading of every grievance their compatriots might have; they were dealing with good material for their purpose, stubborn, stiff-necked farmers who had come from a fertile, pleasant land to scratch at this rocky coast simply because they had odd notions about religious and personal freedom. Now, albeit gingerly, the British king, the British prime minister, and the British government were hacking at these liberties of theirs, nibbling the edges, clipping away a right here, a privilege there, adding a tax here, a duty there; nothing really to make a man's life less pleasant, less easy, but enough to set him to thinking if he was of this stiff-necked, stubborn breed.

The hot-headed rider was brought down to earth by Pastor Clark, who wheedled detail after detail out of him, while the nightshirted farmers, angry to be thus routed from their sleep, crowded closer.

"The British are coming," he kept insisting.

"From where? On foot?"

He nodded and said from Boston. Then there was time. Pastor Clark assured everyone that there was time enough to think out things, and that there never was a Christian soul saved by hot-headedness, and that they might as well go back and get their sleep.

"There's time for sleep and time for other things," someone snorted.

"And time for sleep now," the reverend said quietly. "God's in his heaven by night as well as by day. But night was made for slumber."

"Now, pastor," said a tall, hook-nosed husbandman, "will you be telling that to the redcoats?"

"I will if I can herd them into my church," Clark pronounced, and this sally fetched a laugh all around, easing the tension considerably. Someone dragged out a huge, turnip-shaped silver watch, stared at the face, and pronounced solemnly, "Two hours past midnight."

"Lord a mercy!" a woman squealed, and began to shout at her children to get their faces inside the window and go to bed, or she'd take a stick to them right this minute. A group of giggling girls managed to attract the attention of three nightshirted boys, weighted down by the immense firelocks they carried. Abner Green told his little sister to scat, and then he himself was dragged away by his mother, who had taken a firm grip on his ear. "Fine state of things," she said. "Men acting like children and children acting like men."

The night was cool, the pastor's words cooler, and the men, under the influence of both, drifted away, a few back to their beds, but most to the Buckman Tavern, where already a great fire was roaring in the hearth. The husbandmen leaned their guns against the kitchen wall, sent children and wives for their breeches, so loath were they to leave the excitement and warm comradeship of the group for even a moment, and then brewed pitcher after pitcher of hot flip, a concoction of rum, molasses, and beer—which they drank with a heady instinct that sometime before dawn destiny would come seeking them.

But back at Clark's house, Hancock and Adams still felt gingerly at their necks and wondered what was this strange devil of revolt they had raised. The pastor nodded, and agreed sagely that if the British caught them, they would no doubt hang them.

"I hate to run away," Hancock muttered.

"This is only the beginning," Clark said seriously. "Do you know what you've raised up? Men will fight and die, and there will be more than one running away."

"Don't condemn me," Hancock said. "I did what was right."

"We all do what is right," the pastor nodded, "and I condemn no one. For me, tomorrow, I will take the Book under one arm and the gun under the other, and God forgive me. I never killed a man; I never thought I would, but there are times when a man puts God behind him and turns away his face. I'll have horses brought for you, gentlemen."

It was curious how quickly the memories of the other world, England, Thetford, London, Dover, faded after Paine, with the dour blessing of Aitken, undertook the publication of the Pennsylvania Magazine. For the first time in his life, he had work he loved, work that did not demean him, work that allowed him the simple dignity of hope and intelligence. In the attic which the Scotsman had given him for an office, he sat and labored, in the beginning from dawn through to midnight. He had never been an editor; he had to learn typography, spelling, punctuation; he read the colonial magazines until his eyes ached to get the style, the taste, and, most of all, the political and economic feel of the colonies.

He shed his Britishness as a duck sheds water. He had no time to travel now, but in the taverns and coffee houses, he buttonholed everyone who had been to the far-off countries, or who lived there and was passing through Philadelphia: New Yorkers, Vermont men, Virginians, men from the Deep South, Carolina, Georgia, drawling backwoodsmen, boatmen from the Ohio, soft-voiced Creoles from New Orleans, rangers who had crossed over the mountains into the wild canebrake of Kentucky, leathery-skinned fishermen from Maine.

Philadelphia was the place for that, and if you waited long enough the whole of America passed along Broad Street. Paine pumped them, and for the first time in his life he found many men, men from every walk of life, who treated him with respect.

Out of this, out of the town itself, out of Aitken, out of the things he read, he was beginning to form a picture of America—a picture detailed by the fringe of tidewater colonization. Here was a land of no one people, of no one prejudice, of no one thought, a country so big that all England could be tucked away in a corner and forgotten, a country so youthful that half the people one met were foreigners or the first generation of foreigners, a country so inevitable that it was calmly, even lazily, stirring itself to revolt against the greatest power on earth.

It was the inevitability of America that stirred him most; here was a new breed of men, not out of blood nor class nor birth, but out of a promise pure and simple; and the promise when summed up, when whittled down, when made positive and negative, shorn of all the great frame of mountains, rivers, and valleys, was freedom, and no more and no less than that.

He was not blind; he had been in the rat cage too long to ever be blinded, and he saw the bad with the good. It was flung in his face, for directly across the street from the print shop in which he worked was the chief public slave market of Philadelphia. There was brought the run of Pennsylvania, Maryland, and Jersey human merchandise, the black to be sold body and soul and forever, the white to be auctioned off for bond, for debt, for punishment. Morning and afternoon, the auctioneer would be singing out: "Here's a buck, here's a buck, here's a choice fat black buck, strong as iron, ripe as an apple, as full of juice as a rip-snorting stallion, feel him, come in back, gentlemen, come in back and see his virility, he's been whipped fine, he's been broken and trained—" Oh, it was the city of brotherly love, all right, but who ever went through it without stopping for an hour at the slave mart?

The open shed where the selling took place fronted on the swank London Coffee House where the young fops, gotten out in laces and ribbons and silks and satins, a credible imitation of the bloods and macaronis in the old country, sipped their drinks and enjoyed the show.

And there was not only the slave market; there were the stocks, the whipping posts, the gallows, the incredibly foul jails where debtors and murderers, men, women, and children were thrown together in a tight pen of death and disease.

There was the bad with the good in Philadelphia, but there was no rat cage. If a man had guts or brains—or a little of each, he made his own way. Look at Franklin!

But Aitken would say, when Paine paused at his work to stare at the shed across the road, "Keep a tight lip, Thomas, that be no part a yer business."

Sometimes Paine wondered what was his business.

"Ye'll no' be writing slavery in the magazine," the Scotsman said. "There's slaver and non-slaver pay their shilling. Ye'll no' be writing rift and rebellion and incite to riot. I hold no brief for the fat king in London, but his way is a way of peace and prosperity, and I dinna hold with them that scream so loud for liberty."

Aitken was never quite sure what lay behind Paine's rough, hook-nosed face, his twisted eyes that seemed to be turned inward more than outward. The magazine which had started off as a venture was rapidly becoming a success, six hundred for the first issue, fifteen hundred for the second—and, at a shilling a copy, Aitken could see a fortune just over the horizon.

"I have a debt to you," Paine murmured. "But the magazine is my making. Remember that."

"And yer my making, remember that," Aitken said. "Ye were a dirty wretch when I picked you up. Show yer ingratitude to others, not to me."

A few months before Tom Paine arrived in America, a number of men on horseback had converged toward this same town of Philadelphia. They came from a good many of the countries that made up the fringe of settlements, and some were rich and some were poor; some were brilliant and some not so brilliant, and some were known in their day and others long afterward. There were the two cousins from Massachusetts, Sam and John Adams, Cushing from the same state, strange and burning those Yankee men were, Randolph from Virginia, Patrick Henry also from Virginia—and a big, quiet planter from the Potomac country—his name was Washington—Middleton from the Deep South, and many more, dandies, tradesmen, farmers, hunters, and philosophers.

In Philadelphia they roamed all over the streets, mainly because many of them had never seen a good-sized city before; they ate too much, drank too much, talked too much. They called themselves the Continental Congress. They had a long list of grievances against the British way of government, taxes in which they had no say, repression of trade, heavy duties, import monopolies held by Britain, restrictions on manufacture, redcoat troops quartered on colonists, encouragement for the Indians on the frontier to kill and loot—but with all those grievances, they didn't know what to do and hadn't thought too deeply about what they could do.

Not only that, but among themselves, they were strangers. The

Yankees didn't like slavery and made no bones about it, and the Tidewater and Deep South people didn't like Yankees and made no bones about that either. Sam Adams, the rabble rouser from Boston, whom many of them thought just a wee bit mad, ventured to talk of complete independence; he was shut up and marked down for a fool and a dangerous fanatic. But he captured the imagination of a rawboned, bespectacled Virginian, Patrick Henry by name, who roared out, "By God, I am not a Virginian; I'm American!" Then, while the Congress was in session, Massachusetts reared up back at home and declared her independence from British authority. Paul Revere rode down from Boston to Philadelphia with the news, and the Congress wrote a Declaration of Rights. Then the bleak, terrible prospect of what they had done broke on them.

"If it means war—" they said softly to one another.

But, of course, it wouldn't mean war; it simply couldn't; they talked down any suggestion of danger; they talked and talked and talked, and all the words made them certain that everything would come out in the best way possible. They drank that peculiar, vile American concoction, flip, by the hundreds of gallons, and on October 27, 1774, they disbanded, saddled their horses, and started on the long ride home.

Some months afterwards, the London, Dover, and Thetford staymaker, Tom Paine, devoured the record of all they had said and didn't think it too wordy. "Words pile up," he said, "and afterwards men do things. First the words." He was holding out at the Ridgeway Coffee Shop with Clare Benton, the printer, Judah Perez, the Jewish fur trader, Anthony Bent, a smith, and Captain Isaac Lee of the Philadelphia militia.

"This is a new thing here," Paine said. "That's why no one knows what to do."

"When the time comes to fight, we'll know what to do," Captain Lee insisted, giving stubborn emphasis to a theme he had repeated over and over.

"No, we have to know what to do first. It's no use to fight if you don't know what you're fighting for. Even if you win, it's no good."

"And I think," Perez put in, "that if you know what you're fighting for, it doesn't make too much difference if you win or lose."

"You don't lose," Paine said heatedly. "This is like no other thing the world has seen; it's new; it's a beginning, and it has to be explained. We have something here, and yet we haven't got it, and suppose we lose it and it slips through our fingers?"

"Then we're as well off," Bent grinned.

"Are we? You don't know; you're American! I came from back there!"

"What does that mean?" Benton demanded. "You shook the king's hand?"

"I didn't even spit in his face," Paine said sourly.

"That kind of talk is still treason."

"Is it? Treason's a word for a lot of things."

"Easy, easy," the smith said.

"I go easy," Paine said. "Believe me, I hate no man for what he is, not even that fat German bastard, George the Third. But I've seen man nailed to a cross, nailed there for God knows how many thousands of years, nailed with lies, oppression, gunpowder, swords. Now someone puts an ax in my hand, and I have a chance to help cut down that cross. I don't pass that chance by." Paine's voice was loud; his words rang out, and by the time he had finished speaking, half the men in the coffee house were gathered about the table. Someone put in, "Is it Independence you're talking?"

"Independence is a word."

"You seem almighty fond of words."

"And not afraid of them!" Paine roared. "I come into a land of free men and find them afraid of the one word that would bind their freedom! This is a land of promise, and there is no other on earth!"

He was quieter on paper than vocally. All his life he had wanted to write, and now he had a whole magazine at his disposal. The more writing he did on his pound a week, the better pleased Aitken was, and Paine could see a good deal of reason in his desire to keep the magazine on the fence. His writing wasn't good, but he poured it onto paper—essays, bad poems, scientific research, even a letter or two to the great Benjamin Franklin. Fortunately for him, the literary taste of the Pennsylvania people was sufficiently untutored for them to accept Paine and the magazine and the dozen pen names he used—and even to be somewhat enthralled by the breathless pace of his energy. All at once Paine was a theologian, a historian, and a scientist, and he brought into the magazine the wide knowledge of a staymaker, a cobbler, a weaver, and an exciseman. The combination was good, and the circulation went up steadily.

But Paine couldn't stay quiet; he had too many memories, too many sleepless nights, too many dreams. Looking out of his windows, he would see the white chattel slaves being sold in the market. And there were other things he would see as, pen poised, he remembered all the years before now.

"I'll be raising yer wages," Aitken said to him one day.

He had respectability, position, a job—and yet he had nothing. His torments drove him to the brothels where were kept the limp-eyed, half-foolish bondwomen, brought over from England and Scotland by regular firms of dealers, selling their poor peasant graces to all comers for three shillings, sixpence of which was supposed to go for their freedom. Yet somehow none of them got their freedom, but became hard, painted, vile-tongued tarts. For Paine, there was no relief in those places, and even when he bought freedom for two of the girls, his conscience was not eased.

Rum was a way out. He went back to the bottle, and was drunk more and more frequently. Deep in his cups, he had a run-in with Ben Frady, the Tory mouthpiece, and they were both dragged off before the magistrate.

Aitken said, "Yer dirt, and back to the dirt ye go."

"God damn you, shut up!"

"Be none too certain with yer damn Whiggish way. That pound more will no' go on yer salary."

"Go to hell!" Paine yelled.

Then, one night, he sat in front of his candles and wrote and wrote. It came from the heart and now he had no trouble with words. All his hatred for slavery poured onto the paper, all his pent-up fury. And not able to print it himself, he went out in the morning and posted it to a rival magazine. A week later it was printed, and that same day Aitken rushed in holding it in his hand.

"Be this yours?" he cried.

"That it is," Paine nodded.

"Then out ye go and back to the dirt!"

"Do you have another editor for a pound a week?" Paine smiled.

"I give ye a month's notice!"

"Make it two months," Paine said, "or by God, I'll make it two weeks."

And that night, for the first time in a long while, Tom Paine slept quietly and easily without the benefit of drink.

It was the twenty-fourth of April, seventeen seventy-five, the slow end of a cool, bright spring afternoon. Long, rich shadows lay over the cobbled streets, and on the air, blowing from the inland hills, was the tangy smell of growing things, new leaves, turned dirt. On that quiet afternoon, the streets of Philadelphia rang with hard-driven hoofbeats, and a lathered rider on a lathered horse drove to a halt in front of the City Tavern. He yelled that he had news, big news, mighty news, and from every side people came running. Then the rider refused to talk until he had finished off a mug of beer, and as a good horseman should, seen his horse wiped and watered. While he drank, the word spread like wildfire, and the crowd became larger and larger. Paine, who was at his shop, heard men shouting, and ran along with the rest.

"It's war," the rider said, wiping his lips. "It's bloody damn war!"

Someone gave him a pinch of snuff; others kept back the crowd.

"Of course, they knew that Hancock and Adams were at Lexington," he said.

Coherency was asked for: dates, details, background.

"That was April eighteenth," he said.

There was a sudden hush; news went slowly, but events moved fast, and with startled, pale faces the men and women in the crowd looked at each other.

"They were at Pastor Clark's house," the messenger went on. "That was all right. Men went out of Boston to warn them, and there was time enough, since the redcoats went on foot and our boys rode like hell. And Pastor Clark kept a cool head; he sent them away."

"They weren't captured, Hancock and Adams?"

"They got away."

Again the hush; the journalists scribbled furiously, but the rest waited, and the only sound was the shrieking of children who scurried like hares on the outside of the crowd. The rider called for another mug of beer, and it was rushed through the crowd.

"He couldn't send the whole town away," the messenger said. "They were all awake, and most of them stayed awake—" There was more talk, more beer, more questions. Bit by bit the whole story came out, haltingly some of it, some with a rush, sometimes a long break when the rider just stared and attempted to comprehend the events he was narrating.

That night of the eighteenth, few of the Lexington villagers slept. Most of those who were dragged home by their wives dressed themselves and slipped away, taking gun, powderhorn, and bullet pouch with them, to join the group at the tavern. The devil walked tonight, but angels were behind him; there was never such a night before, and there wouldn't be one again. The men at the tavern talked in whispers, although they could have shouted and not found a sleeping body to be wakened, and they fingered their guns nervously, counted their bullets, and wondered whether to shoot a man was any different from shooting squirrels and rabbits. Captain Parker, their commander, who had seen guns go off during the French War, was none too easy himself, and found it difficult to answer all the questions flung at him.

A while before dawn, out of a need to do something, Parker sent Zeke Sudberry over to the church to set the bells ringing. Zeke rang until everyone in the village was thoroughly awake, the women with their heads out the windows crying, "Shame, shame that a lot of grown men don't know any better!"

Parker told his men to fall in, which they did rather self-consciously, grinning at each other, whispering back and forth:

"Fine soldier you are, Isaac."

"Click your heels, Jed. Act like you got a real fancy waistcoat on."

And to fourteen-year-old Jerry Hicks, "Now, Jerry, why don't you go home and study your lessons."

"Forward march!" Parker shouted, and they stamped over to the lawn in front of the Congregational Church. Once there, Parker scratched his head, seemingly unable to think of a further movement. The pastor, a light fowling piece in his hand, came out and said, "Bless my soul, and it isn't Sunday."

It was nice having him there, and everyone became easier and began to talk a great deal. The gray of the dawn was now changing to pastel pink and peach and taupe, and across the fields the crows screamed angrily, "Caw, caw, caw!" Joshua Lang's dog, who was a fool for any sort of bird noise, ran toward the crows, barking at the top of his lungs.

Then the talk stopped; they stiffened; they looked at one another. There was another sound in the world. Faintly, thinly at first, and then more clearly, and then sharp and hard came the beating of drums, the shrilling of pipes, a mocking swinging cadence, an invitation to glory, death—and God only knows what else.

No one had to say who it was; they knew, and no one spoke. Leaning on their guns in that cheerful April morning, tense, frightened most of them, knowing for the first time in their lives an overpowering desire to run away, men, boys, old gaffers, children, the simple folk of a simple New England farming community, they kept their appointment with destiny.

At the City Tavern in Philadelphia, the rider had his fourth glass of beer and said, "They stood, by God!"

"A fight?" someone asked.

"Hell, man! I said they stood. Boy and man, they faced up and goddamned the redcoats all to hell."

"And then?"

"You never saw a bloody lobster turn his back on a gun," the messenger snorted.

The redcoat troops marched to within a dozen yards of the villagers before their officer commanded them to halt, and then they stood in their precise files, in their precise and colorful uniforms, in their great shakos, in their white wigs and white belting, men of London, of Suffolk and Norfolk, of Devon and Wales and Scotland and Ireland, staring so curiously at the gawky farmers, who, having come from the same places that bred them, were now outlanders, incredible rustics. For long moments the two groups faced one another; it was a moment the redcoats were trained for, but the farmers' hands were wet on their guns.

Then Major Pitcairn, commanding the British, made up his mind, spurred to the front and roared, "Disperse!"

The farmers growled.

"God damn you bloody rebels, lay down your guns!"

It was there, hot and terrible; they were rebels. This idea that they had conceived, that they should be free men with the right to live their lives in their own way, this tenuous, dream-like idea of liberty that men of good will had played with for thousands of years had suddenly come to its brutish head on a village green in Lexington. The farmers growled and didn't lay down their arms; instead one of them fired, and in the moment of stillness after the roar of the big musket had echoed and re-echoed, a redcoat clutched at his tunic, knelt, and then rolled over on the ground.

After that, there was no order, no memory even. The redcoat files fired a volley; the farmers fired their guns singly, by twos and threes. The women screamed and came running from their houses. Children began to cry and dogs barked madly. Then the firing died away and there was no sound except the moans of the wounded and the shrill pleading of the women.

A fifth glass of beer in front of the City Tavern in Philadelphia, and the rider told how the redcoats had marched away. "They were not after Lexington, but after Concord," he explained. "That's where the stores were."

"They took the farmers?" someone asked.

"No, they did not take them! Do you take a mad dog? They left well enough alone and went to Concord and walked into the town and stayed there maybe four, five hours. Then they set out back with never a thing done, like their wits were addled. And when they came to the bridge, the folk was waiting for them, not a few now, but over four hundred.

" 'You dirty bastards!' the major yells, 'you dirty peasant bastards! Clear out and back to home!'

"They didn't move," the rider said.

"God damn you bastards, clear the bridge!" the major roared.

They were solemn and they didn't move; their jaws worked evenly; their guns crept to level and their lips tightened, yet they didn't move. And then the British attacked and hell broke loose. Cannon roared, and there was crash after crash of musketry. With bayonets fixed, the British charged the bridge, and with clubbed muskets the farmers drove them back. Yelling, screaming, cursing, praying, the Yankees forced the redcoats off the bridge back on the Concord side of the stream. But the effort couldn't be sustained; they were farmers, not soldiers, and after the first heat of rage had passed, they gave back and allowed the redcoats to re-form, cross the bridge, and resume their march toward Lexington.

It was only then, after they had laid out their dead and tended their wounded, that the farmers realized a victory had slipped through their fingers. A cold New England bitterness took the place of their hot-headed fury. They picked up their guns and began to run—down the road to Lexington.

It was six miles to Lexington, six miles of perdition for the redcoats. The whole countryside blazed, and that April afternoon every stone wall, every fence, every house, every bush, every tree roared defiance. Sick men crawled to their windows to fire at the invaders, boys crept through the grass and picked their targets, women behind barn doors loaded guns for their husbands, farmers ran the length of New England stone walls, firing again and again. A boy climbed into a tree with a brace of horse pistols, killed a redcoat subaltern passing underneath, and himself was shot. But on the whole, the redcoat volleys were useless against this stabbing, hacking, hidden warfare.

There was no leadership, no direction, no command; the farmers fought instinctively, desperately, more brilliantly than they were ever to fight again, as if they knew that here, today, the poor, suffering simple folk had finally felt their power.

Six miles to Lexington before the British had any surcease. The town was a place of homes, and in the town were women and children, and therefore the men waited out in the fields and the woods. At Lexington, reinforcements met the redcoats, but at the same time hundreds and hundreds of farmers, drawn by the noise of the firing, by the swiftly spread news, were converging on the village.

Reinforced, the British set out once more on their retreat to Boston—and this time the hell was worse. Stabbed, hacked, bleeding, they staggered along—

"They got to Charlestown," the rider said, "what was left of them."

FIVE

The Making of a Revolutionist

Out of it, the noise, the tumult, the strange story that the rider brought down from New England, was coming something new, something colossal and beyond understanding, something that could be translated into movement and action, but not into plan and reason. So Tom Paine thought the next day, standing as one of the surging mob in front of the State House, the biggest mob in all the history of Philadelphia, almost eight thousand people. The mob was a mob and no more; it yelled, shouted, flurried, eddied, and quieted partially now and again to listen to various speakers who climbed up to denounce tyrants and oppression, both very general and very safe terms. Predominantly, the mob was pro-Boston in sentiment, but here and there a Tory stood, smiling the way Tories were prone to smile these past several months.

For all that speakers were addressing the whole mob, smaller fry competed in their own particular circle, and Jackson Earle, a journeyman wheelwright, who was delivering a furious indictment of kings and tyrants in general, and one king in particular, called upon Paine to be his witness.

"Tom," he demanded, "do we have over us a German or an Englishman?"

Paine shrugged. Yesterday had excited and terrified him, but today he was cold, and the old lassitude was returning. He had dreamed one brief, bright vision, and he didn't know now why this crowd was helping it to dissipate. Yet he knew one thing, that he was outside of it; he was Paine, the editor, he had been Paine, the beggar, but in both stages, he had nothing. He could hate and squirm and protest, but how could he dream?

"George, I mean," Earle persisted.

"German, I suppose."

"German! And what manner of a German?" Earle asked the crowd. "A slaving Hanoverian, a fat, guzzling swine—and his is the divine right! From God? Now listen, my good friends, and I'll tell you! Put me in God's place—"

The speaker, Quincy Lee, perched on an impromptu platform of boxes, was begging for quiet. Arnold, who was a Quaker, had just proposed a militia, armed. "And what of it?" Lee yelled at the top of his lungs, a tall, gangling, cross-eyed man, hopping with excitement. "What have the people to say?"

The crowd roared.

"Who will be the first to step up and offer, as I offer, my life, my arms, my sword for this sacred thing called freedom—"

How the crowd roared!

"As they died at Lexington and Concord—"

As Paine pushed out of the crowd, Arnold was crying, "As Englishmen have always fought for the rights of Englishmen—"

"Drinking?" Aitken said to him as he came in out of the cool, starlit night.

"Drinking," Paine nodded.

"Yer liver will be so rotten ye'll no' have it in you long."

Paine grinned and nodded again.

"Were ye at the square today?"

"I was there," Paine said, dropping into a chair and staring at his feet.

"And were ye happy now that ye got yer blood and thunder?"

"I was not happy," Paine said. "I was afraid."

"Then ye're drunk. My little man, ye're good on paper, but bad with a clenched fist."

"I wasn't afraid of that."

"Ye should no' be." The Scotsman had settled his long form

back against the counter, and now was taking a savage delight in prodding his editor. "Ye should no' be, I tell ye, for what is yer life worth?"

"Nothing."

"Ah, then—and ye admit it?"

"I know it," Paine said savagely.

"But ye're afraid."

Someone knocked at the door, and Aitken broke off his attack to answer. It was an old man whom Paine knew by sight, Isaac de Heroz, the beadle of the Jewish congregation. Under his arm he carried a tattered prayer book, which, after bowing in slow greeting to both Paine and the Scotsman, he spread on the counter, handling the loose pages gently and lovingly.

"Can you print one like it?" he asked Aitken.

Both Paine and Aitken bent over the book, Paine looking curiously at the first Hebrew writing he had ever seen, Aitken squinting at the old type.

"I have no' the letters nor the skill."

"I have some type, not all. The rest you can cast. You set as they are set."

"And what is the meaning? I will no' set a devil's concoction."

"They are prayers," the old man smiled.

"I would no' set a Papish prayer," Aitken said doggedly. "I would no' set a heathen prayer. Yet ye ask me to break my neck contriving the letters."

"They are simple prayers that anyone could understand," the old man said softly.

"Read that in English," Aitken said, turning the pages and pointing at random.

The old man read,

> *"These things I do remember: O I pour*
> *my soul out for them. All the ages long*
> *hatred pursueth us; through all the years*
> *ignorance like a monster hath devoured*
> *our martyrs as in one long day of blood.*

Rulers have risen through the endless years,
oppressive, savage in their witless power,
filled with a futile thought: to make an end
of that which God hath cherished. There was once
a tyrant searching in the Book of God
for some word there to serve him as a sword
to slay us; and he found the line which spake:
'He that doth steal a man and selleth him,
he shall be surely put to death—' "

Paine stopped him, putting a hand on the old man's arm. "That's enough, father, we'll print it."

Aitken, who was going to say something, looked at Paine and stayed quiet, and Paine asked the old man, "Were you at the State House today?"

"I was there."

"And what did you think?"

"I thought that this is the beginning of something long and hard."

That night, past midnight, hours after the old man had gone, Paine sat and watched Aitken wrestle with the Hebrew characters and curse under his breath.

"Go to bed," Aitken told him for the fifth time.

"I'm in no mood for sleep."

"I ought to give ye notice, getting me into this hell's broth."

Paine wanted desperately to talk; he wanted a human being to sound to his thoughts; he wanted to hear laughter and tears, song and music.

"Have you ever loved a woman?" he asked Aitken.

"Are ye daft?"

He wanted to find a part of his past he could take something from, and then give it to another before it vanished like smoke.

Paine had been a staymaker in Thetford, in London, in Dover, in Sandwich, in Portsmouth and Brighton in the south, at Bath, at

Winchester, at Bristol—no place could hold him. Always when he tried another trade, it was back to stays, from weaving, cobbling, carving, sewing, digging, plowing, planting, it was back to stays, which was his place. And it was at Sandwich that he saw Mary Lambert.

She was plump, saucy, pretty in a way; she had a dimple in either cheek, brown eyes, round arms, and she was a few years younger than he. At that time, he was twenty-one.

She was in service, and the first time he saw her, she was out buying chops. She wasn't the kind to be content with looking at her meat; she felt it, pinched it, and then spoke up to the shopkeeper, "Now, mind you, not all fat. I won't be cheated."

"They're as pretty chops as you ever seen," the butcher said.

"Coo! I should have a shilling for all I seen better!"

"One dozen."

"And cut the fat, mind you."

All this time Paine was staring at her, and she knew it, staring and forgetting why he had come into the shop, whether to buy a piece of meat for his supper, or a bone for the dog he had at that time, or because he had known that she would be there and then nothing on earth could keep him away.

As she left, he followed her, not hearkening to the butcher's, " 'Ere you, what do you want?" walking after her some twenty feet before she turned and faced him and told him,

"Be on your way."

Paine stood foolishly and dumbly.

"Now get on! I want nothing of your sort."

"I meant no harm," Paine said.

"Coo!" she snapped, and turned on her heels and strode along, Paine after her, Paine catching up and begging, "Please, tell me your name."

"Tell you my name! And what else should I tell you?"

"Let me carry your bundles, please."

"I'm well enough able. And get along and keep a clean nose, or I'll have a word to my master about you."

He saw her again; it was impossible not to in a little place like Sandwich. He asked about her, and discovered that her name was Mary Lambert. Of course, she knew; he couldn't keep away from her, but followed her, stalked her, even managed to say a word to her now and again. When she smiled at him, as she sometimes did, he would be in an ecstasy of delight. His master at that time, John Greeg, took to winking at him, poking him in the ribs, and putting a tongue in his cheek.

"Eh, Tom, you be a sly un, but I know."

He was hopelessly, madly in love, and at something like that would only smile foolishly.

"Eee—un got an arm around 'er yet? I'll be putting ye up a shilling."

Sometimes she let him walk with her. He had taken to buying her things because he found she was more tractable toward him when he gave her a gift. He had asked her to walk down toward the stream with him one quiet evening, to which she said, "Coo, it's softy, dirty marsh!"

"It's pretty there. And you're so beautiful—"

"You're a funny un, you are, Master Paine. Ain't you not had a girl before?"

He screwed up his courage and said, "Not one I loved."

She shrugged her shoulders and tossed her head.

"Mary—"

"I like to walk in town," she said. "A maid shouldn't be off alone."

"Mary, don't you care for me, a little?"

"Maybe."

"Mary!"

She began to ramble on about the house, her mistress, the second housemaid, the cook, the footman who was quite crazy about her. "Bussed me yesterday, 'e did," she said.

"Mary, I love you!"

"Coo!" she smiled.

He asked her once about being in service.

"I always been with quality," she said.

"But did you like it, being a servant?"

She bristled. "It's better than some I knows ain't got the graces to go in service."

"I didn't mean any wrong," he apologized. "Only I don't like to think of you as a servant."

"Think what you please."

"I love you."

She tossed her head.

"Doesn't that mean anything? I tell you I love you, I tell you I'd be willing to die for you—I'm not just a staymaker. I want to do things and be things; I want the whole world and I want to give it to you!"

"Coo!"

"I can give it to you," he said fiercely.

She placed her hands on her hips and dropped a curtsey. "Master Duke!"

He tried to kiss her, and she slapped his face with all her might. He stood there and stared at her and rubbed his cheek and thought of the footman.

"High and mighty," she snapped. "Just a corsetmaker, but them in service ain't fit to be with you."

"You hate me, don't you?"

"Maybe."

Then he made up his mind that he would never look at her again, and for two weeks he managed not to see her, muttering at his work, black and hopeless.

"Get an arm around un," Master Greeg advised him.

"Shut up and go to the devil."

"I'll dock ye that shilling."

The black mood passed, and he had a fit of tremendous resolve. He would set up for himself. Carefully, he had laid by nineteen pounds, and now he left Greeg, took an old shop, and moved his tools and bench in. Morning until night he worked, putting by every penny he could save, denying himself food, denying himself every little bit of comfort a man could have, drink, things to read, dreaming only of the day when he could afford to marry the woman he loved. And then he sought her out and asked her.

"I knew ye'd come back," she said smugly.

"Yes, I had to."

"Then mind you behave."

"I want to marry you," he said desperately.

"Coo!"

"I love you, I'll do anything for you, I'll make you happy—"

"Go on." But she was weakening; this was better than the footman, who had never proposed marriage, better than the butcher's way, better than her master who would catch her in the pantry; for a moment the twisted, burning eyes of the staymaker captured and held her, and in her small, fluttering mind she formed one glimpse of half-born dreams. She smiled and dropped a curtsey, and Tom Paine's soul reeled with gorgeous triumph.

"Kiss me, go on," she said.

He held her in his arms and the world was his.

"And mind, no nonsense about being in service."

"No, no, you're the whole world for me! Do I care what you've been. You'll be Tom Paine's wife now and I'll put you high as a duchess—higher!"

"Go on."

"I'll be rich. I won't always be a staymaker!"

"High and mighty for you— Eee, you're a strange one."

"You care a little," he begged her.

"Mind you, marriage."

"Yes, yes, my love, my darling."

"You are a chap for words," she said admiringly.

"They don't mean much; they're cheap. We'll have more, we'll have children."

"Mouths to feed. Things come high," she pointed out, making a face.

"If only you love me—"

"Maybe," she pouted.

He thought afterward that if certain things had not been, if certain things had gone otherwise, it might have been different. What she was, she couldn't help, and knowing that only made it worse for him. Long after, he would think of how he had tried to teach her to read and write, and how after ten or fifteen minutes of struggling with an idea, she would turn on him with childish fury. Sometimes he was sure she hated him, and sometimes, holding her in his arms, he would have a brief moment in which he knew she loved him. She was what she was, beaten into shape by her tiny world, a tribal creature laid over and over with a thousand taboos. Sometimes, probing as gently as he could, uncovering layer after layer, he would be at the point of finding her frightened little soul, and she would burst out at him, "Coo! High and mighty and fine you are, making fun of me again, you with your fine airs!"

"I have no airs, Mary darling."

"Acting like a duke, and you a corsetmaker."

He would shrug and nod and tell her that he was sorry.

"Scornful of service you are, and I was that comfortable there, with gentlefolk too, not your dirty pigpen quality!" Or if she really became enraged, she would tell him details concerning the footman, her master, others, pouring it on to see him squirm and twist.

Nothing went right with his business. Staymaking was a long-term trade, and unless you had quality on your list you could just as well give up. There was not enough business in Sandwich to support two staymakers, and when Paine could no longer pay his rent, when he was down to his last crown piece, he went back to Greeg.

"You be na a steady un," Greeg said stolidly, and that was the end of it.

They were given their eviction notice, and Paine said, "We'll try another town."

"And I was to be higher than a duchess," she mimicked him.

"Things go up and down," Paine said quietly. "I'm not beaten." But for the first time in his life he felt old, he at twenty-two, longing for a childhood he had never known, caught in the cage and racing round and round, like a squirrel on a treadmill. This time he expected her to go back into service, but she stuck with him, berating herself for it, giving him worse, yet caught by the glimpse of a dream she once had known, hating him for his ugliness, for his gangling insufficiency, for his hopelessness as a man of any practical affairs, but at the same time in awe of him.

The other town was no better, and then it was a third, the two of them trudging along the dusty highroad, Paine with his tools on his back, Mary with everything else they owned tied together in a kerchief. For Paine there was only a deep and abiding sense of guilt, and if Mary screamed at him, "It's your fault, your fault, I was that comfortable and that well," he could only nod his head. "Not even able to keep a roof over my head!" Yes, that was true. "Fine ideas, fine ideas, fine ideas! Looking down your big nose at me in service! Going to change the world, you are, coo, Master Tom Paine—ye dirty, lazy lout!"

They would lie behind a hedge at night, with the cool mist of evening settling on them, with all the sweet, late smells of the English countryside riding the dark winds, and if it was quite cool she would move close to him, and for a brief time there would be peace. He could hold her and say to himself, I am in my castle, my home, and she would be sleepy enough to give in and hold her tongue. His love was so fierce and desperate, challenging God—you gave me this, she's mine and beautiful and lovely, and I can make her into what I desire, that every movement of hers, every whimper, every twitch of fright struck a deep chord of pain in him. He didn't blame her, but only himself; something deep and terrible inside of him gave him the power to look at the world and know, to see justice and injustice, and feel in his own soul the whip laid on the backs of millions. He was twenty-two and he was old, and what wasn't broken inside of him was being forged into a hard core of steel; but she was just a child, and at night when she was asleep, he would croon softly over her, "My baby, my little one, my darling."

He stole that they might eat, and that gave her a stronger club to hold over his head, so that in her fury she would scream, "I'll give you to the sheriff, ye dirty poacher!" The penalty was death.

He crept into a barn and took a sack of turnips. The penalty was to be drawn apart by two teams of horses. He killed a rabbit, and for that the penalty was to have his ears and nose removed. But he would have murdered, killed in cold blood, his bitterness was such a growing, grinding thing; only toward her did he display any sweetness and mercy.

In Margate, where they finally arrived, footsore and weary, he talked his way into the lease of a shop. Mary was pregnant, and Paine's desperation became almost a form of madness. All day he toiled over his bench, and at night hired himself out for whatever work there was. She was ailing so that the bitterness went out of her, and she whimpered and fretted like a hurt child. He didn't eat, and one by one sold his precious tools to give her cream and fowl and now and then a piece of beefsteak with pudding; half starved, he could think of only one thing, to keep a roof over her head, a fire in the grate, and a little food in the pot. His trade, what there was of it, barely paid the rent, and his efforts to obtain other necessities became a sort of frenzy. He remembered Gin Row, put a patch over one eye, bound and twisted a limb, and begged through the streets. He was sure a leech could help his wife, and finally, with many threats and coaxings, got one to come to the shop for a shilling.

"Festering fever," the leech said, while Mary looked at him, wide-eyed and frightened.

"What can you do?" Paine asked him, afterward and away from the bed.

"One performs and expects a certain amount of blood-letting," the doctor remarked. "Docendo discimus of the evil vapors, the spirits that distend her veins. Haud longis intervallis the blood must flow—"

Paine shook his head wearily. "I don't have Latin."

"Ah, but medical terms, medical trade, medical mystery. Keep doors and windows close locked. When sickness comes, the devils dance like noxies. . . ."

That night she said, "Tommy, Tommy, I'm going for to die—"

"No, no, the doctor said you would be all right."

All her spleen was gone, and she held onto his hand as if it was the last real thing on earth. And that night, white and wax-like from all the bleeding, she closed her eyes and turned her face away from Paine.

He sat all the next day, wide-eyed, silent, while the curious thronged the house, while the neighbors who had never taken any notice of them, poured in and out. He had no grief now, only a blazing anger that would burn within him forever.

West of the town of Philadelphia lay a green and rolling meadow called the Commons, and there Tom Paine made his way to watch the militia drill. He had thought of a mob before coming to the meadow on this placid, sunny spring afternoon, but this he saw was no mob. Neither was it an army, even in promise; neither was it anything the world had ever seen before, this group of men and boys, apprentices, journeymen, masters, clerks and students, smiths and millers, carpenters, weavers, barbers, printers, potters, men in aprons with the stain of their trade on their hands. These were the citizens of Philadelphia, yet not all the citizenry. The distinction eluded him, though it was there. Not that they were workingmen all, for there were masters and rich men as well as those who worked for hire; there was one banker, two mercers, a journalist, Tom Jaffers, who was rich enough to do nothing at all, three pastors, a grain speculator, and a fur buyer, to add to those who worked with their hands. There were Quakers, who were pacifists, Methodists, Puritans, Baptists, Roman Catholics, Presbyterians, Jews, Congregationalists, Dissenters, Diests, Agnostics, and Atheists. There were free blacks along with the whites, Negro slaves along with their masters.

What moved them? Paine wondered. What distinguished them? What had brought them together?

Slowly, he walked around the field, his heart racing with excitement, apprehension, fear too, withal a hopefulness he had never known before. He watched them drill with their own weapons, this awkward, stumbling, self-conscious first citizen army the world had ever known; firelocks they bore, great old muskets, bell-mouthed matchlocks that had come into the country more than a century ago, a few long, graceful rifles from the back counties, halberds, axes, pikes, cutlasses, rapiers, two-handed museum-piece swords, and those who had no weapon, not even a horse pistol, just sticks which they carried with dead seriousness. Some of them, those who had a shilling to spend strutting, already had uniforms, fantastically colored outfits with mighty cartridge boxes upon which was painted either "Liberty," or "Freedom," or "Death to Tyrants," or some other slogan calculated to impress the world with their state of mind. Officers they had too, fat old Fritz van Goort for a colonel, little Jimmy Gainsway a captain, Captain Jacob Rust, the miller, and that only the beginning, for the officers' list was near a mile long, with all of them shouting orders at once with no attempt at synchronization, left face, about face, forward march, halt, forward march, men poking into each other, being bowled over, stumbling, tripping, whole lines of men going over like tenpins, shouting, a musket firing by accident—of course, they all had them loaded, with shot, too.

Paine continued on his rounds, and there he was not alone, for a good half of the city had turned out to watch the militia in its first drill. The women stood in colorful clusters, umbrellas open to keep off the sun, the children ran back and forth screaming, and the old gaffers smoked their pipes and asked what the world was coming to. And the militiamen who saw their wives, sweethearts, or sisters, stopped their drill to wave or whistle. Sir Arnold Fitzhugh was the center of the Tory crowd, polite sneers and many silver snuff-boxes, and now and then a guffaw when the citizen soldiers did a particularly stupid thing. And when Paine approached them, Fitzhugh called merrily, "Well, scrivener, what do you think of our rebels?"

"I haven't been able to think yet."

"Blast me, hear that, he hasn't been able to think yet."

Pastor Blane, the Quaker, said, "I see thee are not with them, Tom."

"No—"

"Scruples."

"Doubts, I think," Paine answered slowly, thinking that if he went ahead now, there would be no turning back, ever.

"Thee see what has happened to their scruples," the pastor said, half sadly, half bitterly. "Eighteen of my flock in there. The Lord said, thou shalt not kill, but a Roman holiday is not to be turned aside from that easily, and now they are marching with sticks, as if the one worthy possession for a man were a gun."

"The strangest part of America," Paine said softly, 'is that men have guns. When they shoot them off—"

"I don't follow thee?"

"I don't follow myself," Paine shrugged.

Jacob Rust came to the print shop and said, "I want you in my company, Thomas, my boy." He was a little fat man with a great booming voice.

"Yes?"

"A damned fine little force we're going to have."

"I'll think about it," Paine nodded.

"Is it something to think about?"

"Yes. There's a devil of a lot to think about these days."

"Now look, Master Thomas, you're over from England these few months. People are going to ask, is he England or is he Pennsylvania? Does he smell sweet or does he stink?"

"I don't mind my smell," Paine grinned.

"But we do!"

"I don't go the way the wind blows," Paine said evenly. "I know what I have to do, or I am beginning to. I wonder whether you do, Rust? I wonder whether you know what all this is?"

"It's standing up for our rights as free Englishmen, by God!"

"Is it?"

"And we mean to fight for them!"

Paine shrugged and turned away.

And for some, nothing at all had changed. Paine went to a ball given by the Fairviews, wealthy importers of Tory leanings. They had him because he represented the Pennsylvania Magazine;

Paine went because he had to have answers, many answers and coming from all sides, answers to his doubts, his longings, his prayers, his hatreds. Four pounds bought a coat of fine, brown broadcloth, a better garment than any he had ever put on his back. He wore a ruffle at his throat, a new white wig, and good leather breeches, a gentleman right enough with a stick and a three-cornered hat, invited to the best, stepping into quality on his own, into a hall lit by four hundred candles, where a Negro slave called melodiously, "Mister Thomas Paine!"

Four hundred candles, and heaven was never lighted brighter. Black servants walking with silver trays and silver punch bowls, mounds of dainty cookies and cakes, cold meat from twelve different kinds of game and enough Claret, Madeira and Port to float the British Navy. The women were in heavy, brocaded gowns, gilded, silvered, the men in lace and satin and velvet, and he was Mr. Thomas Paine, his opinion asked on everything.

"This Lexington business—of course, a rustic rabble, but here in town, did you see the beggars trying to drill?" They had all been to Europe at one time and another.

"And for one who's seen the King Guards!"

"But, Mr. Paine, what line does an editor take, I mean, a man with a head on his shoulders?"

"I don't fancy a rebellion—I don't fancy anything more than a lot of noise and shouting."

Mr. Paine said practically nothing.

"It doesn't help trade."

"On the other hand it does. People get frightened, and then they buy like mad."

"Really, a straw in the wind. I fancy Lord North will take his sails in after he gives them a sound drubbing."

"I read your magazine faithfully, Mr. Paine," said a young woman, well-gowned, lovely, looking at him with admiration, he, Paine, the staymaker. "I read your poems," she said. "I think they're beautiful and that a man who writes poetry cannot help but have a soul, don't you think?"

"I think many people have souls."

"Do you? Now isn't that frightfully clever. I can't say clever things, but that's frightfully clever."

They had punch, cakes, and they walked in the gardens. There was a moon and stars, and finally she said how strange it was that he had never married.

"I was married." After a moment or so, he said his wife had died.

"What a terrible tragedy!"

"Yes."

"But don't you think it made you a better, a broader man, Mr. Paine?"

"What?"

"You're not listening to me at all, Mr. Paine."

"I am sorry," he said. "What were you saying?"

He wrote a piece for the magazine called *Reflections on Titles.* He was restrained. Again and again, he told himself, what happened to me does not matter. I must write as I think and know and reason and believe, so people will listen. They must listen.

He had it out with Aitken. *Reflections on Titles* struck at the privileged class and struck at them hard. He was not one of the mob, not one of the militia drilling on the Commons, not even one of the Congress party. Instead, alone, he groped in the dark and sought for direction, desperately and sometimes wildly. All the times before he had failed; now he must not fail.

"You will not print that," Aitken said.

"But I will!"

"Then ye part from me!"

"If you want to let me go, let me go. No halfway measures," Paine said.

He became persuasive. "Thomas, have we not always got together on one thing an' another, notwithstanding the arguments?"

"Yes?"

"An' why will ye be stirring in that devil's broth of rebellion?"

"Do I print it?"

"Print it an' be damned, an' have yer notice!"

Paine shrugged. He had been given his notice before, and he no longer cared. He still worked with the Pennsylvania Magazine, and finally he had kicked it off the fence and bent it to his own purposes; but as a part of his life, it was over. What the next part of his life would be, he didn't know, any more than he knew what would be here in America. It was not that he was animated by resolve so much as tension, and all that he could hope for was both nameless and formless.

On May the fifth, Benjamin Franklin returned to America, his mission in Europe over, all the long years there, considered politically, coming to nothing, an old man come home to a boiling country. He took up his residence at Market Street with the Baches, and there, after a few days, Paine managed to see him. Franklin had a half hour for Paine, no more; there were too many threads he had to pick up in America, too much to be done in too short a space of time. But he remembered Paine and shook his hand and said that he had been looking through the Pennsylvania Magazine; it was good; it was clever and it made bright reading.

"Do you like America?" Franklin asked.

Paine nodded; there was much he wanted to say, yet he didn't know how to say it. Having thought to himself for so long that of all the men he had known, Franklin was the wisest, the deepest, and the best, he was now strangely dissatisfied, almost antagonistic.

"You've found yourself," Franklin said.

That was trite, Paine thought, foolish almost. He had found nothing. "What is going to happen?" he asked Franklin. "Will there be war?"

"War? If fighting is war, yes. There has been fighting; there will be more."

"But what does it come to?" Paine demanded, almost fiercely. His next thought was that it was cruel to badger this old man, this very tired old man. "Where are we going—?" For the first time,

Paine felt and realized in himself a hard, driving cruelty. He didn't have to ask where they were going; for himself, he was going only one way, and each day it shaped itself more clearly.

Franklin said, "We have to be strong, that's the main thing, isn't it? Once we are strong enough, the ministry will see reason. There's no need for war, never any need for it. War is bad."

"As one would say salt is salty," Paine thought.

"We want our rights," Franklin went on. "We want our freedoms, we want our decencies, our privilege to live a full and good life—that makes good men, the chance to work and put a shilling by, to have a piece of land and a roof overhead. We are not owned part and parcel by England; they must realize that partnership and conciliation—"

"And what of independence?" Paine asked.

"Do we want that?"

"I don't know," Paine said tiredly. "When I was a little boy, even then, I felt that certain things should not be. And when everyone else accepted those things, I thought I was mad, that the devil rode on my shoulders. Can you build anything good on a rotten foundation?"

"Old men don't make revolutions."

"My God, sir," Paine said, "you're not old! You gave me back my youth!"

The next week, a second Continental Congress convened at Philadelphia.

Once more men from all the colonies converged toward Philadelphia. The militia put on a show, and welcomed and welcomed, as if to prove that all their drilling was not for nothing. Back and forth they marched, until their feet ached, and those of them who could afford horses made a cavalry troop to ride out and meet the delegates. "God and Jesus," men said to one another, "that we should live to see this, the port of Boston under siege by the British, the Congress back here in town, and old Ben Franklin still alive and here again." They were back again, the Adams cousins, Hancock, Randolph of Virginia, Jefferson, this time with another

Virginian, a big man who like a stage performer wore a magnificent uniform of buff and blue—he was a colonel of the Virginia militia and his face wasn't familiar in Philadelphia; Washington was his name; he walked with long, gangling steps and hardly ever opened his mouth, shy, stupid perhaps. Paine was introduced to him by young Tom Jefferson, "Colonel George Washington of Virginia," and Paine squinted at him.

"I'm glad to meet you, sir. Delegate?"

"I'm a writer," Paine said, as if to justify himself. "I edit the Pennsylvania Magazine."

"Yes, of course." But obviously, he had never heard of the Pennsylvania Magazine. He stood silently, looking at Paine, as if he could think of nothing to say, and afterwards Jefferson explained, apologetically, "He's very wealthy."

"Yes?"

"Perhaps the wealthiest man in America, but land poor, like many of us Virginians. Not clever, but he has guts."

"He wants to fight, and he doesn't have to talk about it. People talk so damned much."

"What makes you think he wants to fight?"

"The uniform. He's not a clown."

"I didn't think of it that way," Jefferson said. "He's an enigma to me."

Paine spent two days in his room, struggling to put down on paper what he thought. Then he went to listen to the Congress proclaim to the world that Americans had taken up arms for protection of their lives and property. Then he had beer with Sam Adams and Michael Closky, the expatriate Pole. Adams was violently furious, fanatically against compromise. Knowing he was despised by both the intellectuals and the gentlemen of the Congress, even by his cousin, John, he turned to these two whose violence, if not obvious, at least took strange directions.

"You know what you don't want," Paine said quietly, after listening to a half hour of Adams' denunciation. "That's only anarchy. What's positive? There is fire burning in a dozen parts of this country, but what does the fire mean?"

It meant nothing, the Pole said. In his country it had been the same. Was this the first time the common man lifted up his head to revolt? Yet always it came to nothing.

"The halfway measures," Paine said. "The fence sitters. I'll go so far and no further—"

"How far will you go?" Adams asked him, peering curiously at this British staymaker, this broad, hulking, hook-nosed man with his slab-like peasant hands.

"All the way," Paine said softly.

A little drunk, his stubble-covered face wavering in the light of the candle between them, Adams grinned like an imp and asked how far was all the way.

"I want a new world!"

"Utopia?" Adams said.

"God damn it, no! What we have here, a way of life, a way for children to smile, some freedom, some liberty, and hope for the future, men with rights, decent courts, decent laws. Men not afraid of poverty and women not afraid of childbirth—"

The Pole roared with laughter, but Adams' face was suddenly serious. "Independence," he said.

"For a beginning," Paine agreed, sleepy suddenly, tired before and not after the act, seeing his whole life arranged and frightening in its clarity. Now doubt was almost gone. Doubt, built up so slowly and painfully, had resolved itself. He knew some of the answers, and in a little while, he would know the rest.

SIX

How Tom Paine Wrote a Small Book

HIS PARTING from Aitken was curiously mild, and for the first time Paine realized that the Scotsman held him in some esteem and regarded him with a certain affection. Aitken, whom Paine had considered as far removed from emotion as a human being can be, shook his head stubbornly, and at first, when he gave Paine his hand, was able to say nothing at all. Paine knew it was not entirely the impending doom of the Pennsylvania Magazine that moved him; the publication was doomed, not only through its loss of its editor, but because the rising upheaval in the colonies made it already an antique of some vaguely remembered epoch. This whole peaceful land, which went on without much appearance of change—as lands do even when the world begins to burn—was inwardly bubbling and boiling and preparing to explode. Paine thought that Aitken knew it, not as a Tory, nor even as a rebel, but as one who losing security would lose all reason to live. Paine pitied him.

"Ye will no' change yer mind?" he asked.

That was not the question, as Paine knew. A pound a week was good pay and more than enough to keep him comfortably, and what with things he had written for other publications he had some twenty pounds to fall back on. Perhaps he was a fool to give it up, the more so since the course he planned was very vague.

"It is bread and butter," Aitken pressed him.

"No, I'm sorry."

"Think it over, Thomas. Ye'll be sucked in with the madmen, an' it's no' Christian, Thomas. Let well enough alone." But when Aitken saw he couldn't persuade him, the Scotsman said gruffly, "Ye'll no' hold a grudge, Thomas?"

"Why should I?"

"There are mean men an' there are sweet men, but ye no go in a category, Thomas."

"I never held a grudge," Paine said, "except against myself."

Tall, slim, fair as a girl and as comely as Paine was ugly, Tom Jefferson won him heart and soul. Jefferson was a gentleman in Paine's memory of the sharp division of things in England, and the Thetford staymaker's first reaction was one of sullen hostility. Jefferson was graceful and handsome and accomplished and clever, all that Paine was not, and in his first advances Paine saw only some petty need for the favor of the magazine. The gall in his soul poured acid on Jefferson, and admiring the man, thrilling with pleasure if Jefferson so much as nodded at him, Paine's outward reaction was only to try and turn the Virginian into an enemy. Jefferson wouldn't become an enemy; God only knows what he saw in the graceless staymaker, whose hands always had dirt under their nails; but whatever it was made him want to find the man beneath the crust. He pretended not to see the point in Paine's caustic remarks, and met the editor on such a basis of easy equality that bit by bit Paine's reserve disappeared. Being one of the inner circle of the Congress, Jefferson knew everything, met everyone, and was able to smooth things considerably for Paine. A few years younger than Paine, he combined fresh youthfulness and maturity in a manner that was, for Paine at least, completely charming.

To share a pot of coffee with him was something that Paine looked forward to; dinner with him was sheer delight, and after an evening spent with him in front of a fire, Paine glowed with a warm happiness he had never known before. Slowly and deliberately, Jefferson drew from him as much as any man could of the story of his life; he had a wonderful knack of taking the confused memory and assembling it with meaning. He once said to Paine, "All in all, as it was, with the dirt, the privation, the misery, the gin and the utter hopelessness in the way you and those around you lived, that alone, terrible as it was, could have been endured—" The sentence hung in the air, and Paine tried to see what he was driving at.

"Poverty is a degree of things," Jefferson said. "I have seen people here in America whose poverty was complete and absolute, yet they retained—"

"Dignity," Paine said.

"Dignity."

"Then that's all we live for," Paine reflected. "If there's any meaning in human life, then it's there, in the dignity of a human being."

"I think so."

"I never realized that before; I began to feel it here, but I didn't know until I spoke of it tonight. It's true though; all through ten thousand years men have been corrupted by having their dignity taken from them. When my wife died and the neighbors poured in to look at her poor, tired body, the little, evil thrill of it the only excitement in their lives, each bringing a scrap of food for admission, I could think, God help me, only of how comical it was. If we were made in the image of God, how rotten that image has become!"

Another time, Jefferson was giving a small dinner for George Washington and he asked Paine to come. Randolph was to be there, too, and at first Paine refused; he was frightened; he valued his relationship with Jefferson too much, and he was afraid he would make a fool of himself in front of the three Virginians whose culture, quality, and wealth were almost beyond his imagination. He had heard of Mount Vernon, Washington living there like a great feudal baron, with packs of hunting dogs, strings of horses, countless black slaves, rivers of wine, the "quality" coming and going endlessly, a coach that had cost two thousand pounds; he had heard of the Randolphs; certain Quakers of Philadelphia never tired telling tales of these three godless agnostics, and Paine had little basis upon which to separate the true from the false. What meaning for him or for any common man could a rebellion have if their kind were at the bottom of it? Wasn't it all a clever cover for their desire to be freed from the dictatorship of the British tobacco agents, and weren't they, as all their class, ruthless enough to spill a hundred thousand quarts of blood to see their great plantations thrive?

But at last he gave in to Jefferson's urging, forswore himself to sullen silence, put on his best suit, his best wig, and came to the dinner. He was surprised at how eagerly they shook hands with him; they knew of him; they read the Pennsylvania Magazine, even Washington who, Paine had presumed, read nothing at all. Peyton Randolph, the eldest of the three, had an eager, inquiring air, as if he had looked forward to nothing so much as meeting Paine. Washington said little; he sat and listened with his chin on his hand when he wasn't eating, his long face intent upon what was being said, his brow furrowed with a shade of annoyance now and again, perhaps most of it an impatience with his own lack of understanding. Jefferson took up the conversation and did most of the talking. Paine noticed that of the four, Washington drank the most and seemed least affected by what he drank.

Jefferson toyed with the idea of independence; as an intellectual concept it appealed to him, for it was filled with limitless and entrancing possibilities, but his manner of treating it was entirely objective, and Paine saw that he never considered it as any more than a dream. When he made a simile of a child being forced out of a house by his father, the child in this case being the colonies and the father England, Washington smiled, showing his bad teeth and said, "But he remains in the family."

"Only by name."

"Yet we are Englishmen, Virginians true enough, but Englishmen nevertheless," nodding generously at Paine, their provincialism polite as it was narrow.

"Oh, damn it, we're at war," Randolph said impatiently. "Why don't people realize that?"

"For our rights."

"Rights! Rights! What are rights? Where do they begin and end?"

Jefferson laughed and said, "What do you think of rights, Mr. Paine?"

"I think there are no such things. I think that by right of birth all things belong to all men. You can take away rights, but you can't give what belongs to all."

"You make no exceptions, Mr. Paine?" Randolph asked.

"None!"

"Then you would reform England as well as America?"

"It's not reform for men to claim what is theirs."

"But it's dangerous. You sound bloodthirsty, Mr. Paine."

"I hate war," Paine said slowly. "Of all ways to hold man in contempt and make a beast of him, war is the worst. There is nothing on earth I hate more than war."

Paine wasn't surprised when the Congress made Washington commander in chief of the rabble of Yankee farmers who lay like hungry wolves around Boston. There was something about the tall, dry-faced Virginian that made people trust him. "As they always trust stupidity," the Philadelphia wits said. But Paine wasn't certain of that, and on the day when Washington rode through the streets, cheered wildly, Paine stood in the crowd and tried to understand what dull, curious force in the man could draw out the admiration of these shouting fools.

Although a state of actual war was beginning to exist that summer of 1775, the people of Philadelphia could not take it quite seriously. For one thing, Massachusetts was so far away; for another, business was good. Even when news came to town that there had been a terrible, bloody battle fought in Boston, at a place called Breed's Hill, and that the redcoat dead lay like pigs in a slaughtering pen, it did not seem quite real to Philadelphia. After their first rush of enthusiasm, the militia enlistments fell off sharply; the wags did caricatures of the citizen soldiers. The drills became sloppy affairs; the men came to resent their officers, and the whole scheme of a citizen army showed signs of going to pieces.

For Paine, those early summer days were leisurely and almost carefree. He had money enough for the first time in his life; his lodgings cost little, and a few shillings a day more than provided for him. His reputation with the magazine gave him enough of a name for him to sell an article here and there, and his reaction from the restrictions laid down on him by Aitken was to write quickly, purposefully, and better than ever before. He read a good deal, talked a good deal, and took to long, rambling walks along the river front. The Pennsylvania countryside, so like yet so different from England, fascinated him, and he would wander out into the hills, put up for the night at the stone house of some Dutch farmer, smoke a pipe, drink good homemade beer, and argue about everything from crops to government. With workingmen he was able to drop the chip from his shoulder, and he, to whom good speech came with such difficulty, lapsed with ease into the broad Pennsylvania country drawl.

One day, hot and tired, he climbed over a stile into a farmyard where a buxom, fair-haired girl of twenty or twenty-one was drawing the buttermilk off her churn. "Could I have some?" Paine asked, and she poured some into a wooden mug and laughed at the way it ran from the corners of his mouth.

"Ah, you're a dry one," she said.

"Can I pay you?"

She laughed again and asked him whether he had come up out of Philadelphia.

"All the way," he said proudly. It was a good twelve miles, and only here in America had he learned the deep pleasure of walking.

"You don't look like a walker."

"No—"

"What do you do?"

He told her he was a writer, and she smiled at him quizzically, as if a writer were the strangest thing that had ever come her way. Then, as easily and inoffensively as she had made his acquaintance, she dropped it and went back to her butter-making as if he had never existed, running off the milk and lifting the rich white butter out of the churn, molding it like clay in her strong freckled hands. Paine, comfortable, quite rested now, sprawled in the shade of a tree, entranced by the wonderful pattern the sun and the leaves made on his dusty clothes, stretched out his legs, drank his milk, and watched her beat the butter on the board. The farm was evidently a prosperous one, the fieldstone house square and solid as a fortress, the barn half stone, half timber, strong hand-hewn beams jutting from under the eaves. They had had their first haying, and the sweet-smelling stuff was piled in great heaps out on the fields and, beyond, the corn and oats were coming up as if they could not hasten from the earth soon enough. There was a pen full of rooting black and whites, and the chickens ran loose and aimless. Out in the fields, a half mile or so away, two men were working a team, and a fat pile of smoke ran from the chimney to show that things were doing inside.

When the girl had finished her butter, she lifted the board in her arms and said to Paine over her shoulder, "You may come in if you wish." Her recollection of his presence was so casual and good-natured that he couldn't help but follow her, and they went into a long, low-ceilinged kitchen where another woman, evidently the girl's mother, was mixing a batter of dough.

At one side of the kitchen, there was a great hearth, full eight feet long, with a Dutch oven on either end. The floor of the kitchen was red brick, swept so clean you could eat off it, and down the center was a long sawbuck table. Two handmade benches flanked the fireplace; there was a wide sideboard, loaded to the shaking point with pewter and crockery. Those and several straight chairs made up the furnishings of the room, but from the ceiling hung smokings of ham and bacon and jerked venison and beef. And from one of the benches four tow-headed children, three boys and a girl, regarded Paine with a wide-eyed but reticent curiosity.

The girl said, "Mother, this here's a writing man, walked up out of Philadelphia."

Paine bowed and said, "My name is Thomas Paine, madam. I was hot and thirsty, and your daughter was good enough to give me a glass of buttermilk."

"We have plenty of that," the woman smiled, not leaving her work. She was past middle age, but broad-shouldered and strong, her sleeves rolled up, her large arms white with powder past the elbows. Her face, lined with work, was pleasant in its big, regular features. "Our name's Rumpel," she said. "That's Sarah." She pointed to the boys and called off, "Ephraim, Gideon, Samuel." The little girl was Rachel. Then she went on with her work, and Paine sat down in a cool corner.

At noon, the long table was set. The farmer, Jacob Rumpel, clumped in with his hired man, shook hands with Paine, and sat down at the table. Without words, they had made it evident that he would stay and eat, and he had no desire to leave. Sarah set a place for him next to her father; when she looked at him there was a twinkle in her eyes, and now and again Paine had a feeling she was laughing at him. The children raced to the board, never taking their eyes off Paine, and the farmer, who had been turning the name over in his mind, said finally, "You be with that Pennsylvania Magazine."

Paine nodded, somewhat pleased that they should know him here.

"I don't hold with it!" Jacob snapped.

"Neither do I."

"Then why are you not man enough to throw down your pen?"

"Father," Sarah said, "your food will be cold."

"I did."

"Ah—"

"That's why I can walk in the country," Paine smiled.

Turning to him suddenly, the farmer demanded, "Were you thrown out or did you quit them?"

"Some of each."

"I know Aitken, a tight man with a rope around his soul. He waves this way and that but lacks the guts to fall. Paine, there's good men in writing and bad. I read Ben Franklin and Jim Hall. I read MacCullough and Tom Jefferson. I like a man with gall. I like a man—"

"Pay no attention to father," Sarah said quietly.

"—who can look at a thing and say right or wrong. Right is right and wrong is wrong. I don't hold with in-between. I reckon I side with the Boston men, what's mine is mine so long as I got powder for my gun—" He was a tall, lean, brown-faced man, with a bobbing apple in his throat and tiny blue eyes.

"Go an' eat, Jacob," his wife said.

For Paine, the Rumpels were a new and wonderful experience. There was nothing like them in England, and he was sure there was nothing quite like them anywhere else in the world. In wealth and possessions they were richer than many a squire at home, yet Jacob Rumpel worked with his hands and Hester Rumpel, his wife, did the cooking for the whole huge family. They were not peasants, yet they could not be put in the class of the English yeomen farmers. Their hired man sat down with them at the table as an equal, not as a servant, and the children shared in the chores as if they took pleasure in the mere act of labor.

Jacob Rumpel plowed his own fields, yet at night he read not only the Pennsylvania Magazine but Voltaire and Defoe. His wit was the wit of Poor Richard; Ben Franklin was his god and the greatest intellectual influence upon his life; and he could only philosophize in terms of action. He made his own candles, his own soap, his own cloth for which he raised his own flax and wool. The farm was his, but a younger brother had packed his possessions in a wagon and gone west into the lonely hills of Fincastle, and Rumpel took it for granted that some of his sons would do the same. His wife came of Puritan stock, but he himself was comfortably agnostic, not out of reason, but rather out of unbounded confidence in things that are. He and God walked the earth on even terms; he did what was right, and he was content with his doubts. He hated slave-holders, and he drank no tea out of principle, but his admiration for the Boston men, whom he considered in other ways a bloodless and intolerant breed, would not be translated into action until the redcoats marched on Pennsylvania soil. When Paine asked him what he would do then, he said, matter of factly, "Take my gun."

"And the farm?"

"I reckon the farm'll limp along."

But after he had gone back to the farm half a dozen times, welcomed by Rumpel who was just naive enough to consider Paine a great figure in the intellectual life of Philadelphia, a favorite with the children to whom he told endless stories of highwaymen and privateers, Paine no longer denied to himself what brought him there so constantly. He was not in love with Sarah, not as love goes; inside he was dry and empty, and the memory of the serving girl who died in the shack in Margate hung like a stone around his neck.

But being with Sarah was compounded of peace and restfulness, and a content such as he had not known before. Indolence was something very new to him; unemployment he knew and starvation he knew, just as he knew poverty and drunkenness and squalor and all the shambling wrecks who did nothing because there was nothing for them to do. But the pleasure of sheer laziness, the sweet satisfaction of dawdling in a Pennsylvania summertime was as strange for him as was this curious family in their stone house with its foot-thick walls.

He would sit in the barnyard and watch the girl, or else in the kitchen where he told endless stories both to the children and Hester Rumpel. He found in himself a gift for a mild sort of funmaking; he found he could say things that would make them laugh. And as often as he could, he would help Sarah. That was difficult, for her own strength was a very matter-of-fact thing, while few people realized the layers of broad peasant muscle in Tom Paine's sloping shoulders. But in carrying buckets of water or sacks of feed, he was permitted to have his own way now and again, and it gave him a strange pleasure when his strength dragged from her a grudging smile of admiration.

She spoke little, as if taking it for granted that he knew how much she could convey with a smile and a word, or simply with a movement of her fair head. When Paine confided to her the work he was doing, he half doubted whether she understood more than a part of it.

"I'm writing a small book to make things clear," he said once.

"You mean the Boston men?"

"That and yourself."

She smiled and nodded and didn't ask him what he meant by that.

"It's like having lived for one thing," he tried to explain. "This book is the one thing. I want it to sweep everything out of the way, so men and women can start fresh."

"Father will enjoy reading it," she said.

There were never any words of love, he never kissed her. If he stayed of an evening after the children were put to bed, they might walk down the lane while Jacob smoked his pipe on the porch. There was a moon, waxing and waning through the nights; there were the birds courting in the darkness and competing with the crickets; there was the far-off barking of dogs. Yet it was no surprise to him when she said, on one of those evenings, "Will you be asking for my hand, Tom?" And then added, as if he had asked a question, "Mother says there's a mighty difference of age, but I don't hold with that. I've a great favor for you, Tom, and I think I love you with all my heart."

She was simple, he decided, simple and no more, but the rush of pain in his heart, searing, hopeless pain told him that never in his life had he wanted anything more than this fair-haired girl. Whether he loved her or not was suddenly unimportant; she was his first and last good hope; she was all that makes a man human, and after this he would not be human; after this he would walk silently and alone.

They went on a while further and then sat down on a stone fence, and he told her, "I was married twice before."

She looked at him without reproach, and he told her who his first wife was and how she had died.

"That was a sorrowful thing," she said, still without reproach, but he knew it was over and done with, that Sarah was alive again, freed from this strange, hook-nosed wanderer. He should have gone then, but he wanted to tell her; he wanted to justify himself where no justification was needed. He tried to make her understand how a man might be broken and go to shelter as an animal goes to ground; but in her way of life and thinking there was a dignity that could not be broken but only destroyed. The story came out haltingly; it was nine years after his first wife had died, and he was at the bottom; but what did she know of the bottom with her health and her bountiful vitality? He tried to tell her of the things he had done in those nine years, of the hell that was London for the poor, of his pent-up savage desire to be free, of the trades he had followed, the degradation, the misery, the brief surges of hope when he preached in the meadows with the Methodists—"Cast off sin and come ye into the arms of the Lord"—and then the hope gone, the bottom rungs of the ladder, and then finally the very bottom, the deepest bottom, the complete hopelessness where there was nothing but death.

"And then this man took me in," he said. "He was a good man. He kept a little tobacco shop and he had almost nothing at all, but he took me in. Like Christ, he knew not the evil from the good, but only the weak from the strong. God help me, I was weak, I was dying."

"But what was his life worth?" she might have thought from that brief picture of inferno.

"I had a debt to him?" he asked her.

"Yes."

"Then he died. He had a wife and daughter. I wanted to care for them, I stayed with them. And then there was talk, and for the mother's sake I married the girl whom I didn't love—"

She could see that.

He tried to tell how the business had broken up, it was such a poor little trade, the way his wife began to hate, how he tried to help others, to work some good. His words were no use any more. He couldn't tell how his wife despised him, how she left him, his dread of the debtors' prison, how he fled. He didn't want to make himself out to be anything, but the more he tore off in abasement, the less Sarah comprehended. This half-world, this dreadful twilight land of hopelessness, was as far away and as unreal to her as the sandy wastes of Egypt. For her, human beings were compounded flesh and blood, not pain and terror and wretchedness.

When he said goodnight, he knew he would never come back, and as he walked away she looked after him, neither happy nor sorrowful, but thinking of how he wanted to write a small book to make things clear.

Things were quieter in Philadelphia. Members of the Second Continental Congress, after they had said all they possibly could say and accomplished practically nothing at all, remembered their farms and estates, their mills, shops, and distilleries, and by ones and twos they trickled away from Philadelphia. The new commander in chief, General George Washington of Virginia, started his leisurely ride northward to Boston to take command of the several thousand Yankees who now sprawled around that city in a sort of siege. The bloody battle which afterwards came to be known as Bunker Hill but was then called Breed's Hill, was still fresh enough in the minds of the British to make them move very cautiously, and as things were now both sides waited for the other to make the next move.

In Philadelphia, a hot, slow summer set in. Prudent shopkeepers, feeling that this was another storm blown on its way, took down the shutters from their shop windows; and as a whole, the citizens of the town were quite satisfied things had not come to a head.

Meanwhile, Paine stayed close to the city, lived with it, and felt its pulse. He never went back to the Rumpels after that last evening there, yet he took a certain grim pride in the fact that the incident had not set him back on his heels. Slowly and painfully, out of all the broken, dirty pieces of his life, he was building a plan, a course, and a method. Now he was content to walk alone; he quite knew what he wanted to do, and he felt an ominous certainty that as time passed it would become even more clear. In the life on the peaceful, prosperous farm he saw something good and peaceful and sweet, yet he was half grateful that it was denied to him.

He had a little room, a bed, a bolster, chest, coat-rack, and table, two fairly good suits of clothes, ink and paper. That was enough, a man should want no more. He needed a few pennies for candles, something for food, something for drink. During this time he no longer allowed himself to be drunk, yet he saw no reason to do without liquor. Rum helped him; caring little for himself or for what became of him, he was ready to use anything that might make his pen move more easily on the paper. He was writing stuff out of thought and making something out of nothing, and after he had worked steadily for five, six, or seven hours, the little room closed in on him. Rum helped; as he drank, his movements would become slow and painful, but the quill would continue to scratch, which was all that mattered. He had no delusions; what he wrote might never be read by more than a dozen persons, but it was all he could do and what he had to do. Men don't make new worlds in an afternoon; brick has to be placed on brick, and the process is long and incredibly painful.

Without realizing it, he neglected his appearance, sometimes spending twenty-four hours in his room, shaving less often, hoarding his small store of money, allowing his stockings to wear out and his clothes to become shabby. Those citizens of Philadelphia who noticed the change remarked that Aitken was wise to fire him. "Good riddance to bad rubbish," they said. His money low, Paine spent a night writing a poem and took it to Aitken, who gave him a pound, certainly more than it was worth. But somewhere in his flint-like, Scotch shell, Aitken nursed a fondness for this plodding, almost bullish man, who childishly believed that the world wanted to hear his solution to its woes.

"How goes the masterpiece?" Aitken asked him.

"It's no masterpiece. It's an attempt at common sense, of which I have little enough, God knows."

"I will no' print it, so don't come asking me."

Paine grinned.

"Will ye have supper?"

"I will at that," Paine nodded. He hadn't eaten a good cooked meal in God knows how long, and he felt a sudden longing to be with people he knew. At Aitken's table was Joshua Craige, a linen merchant recently come over from England, full of news of how London was taking the revolt. "There's more for the colonies than against them," Craige said. "You would think the revolt is coming there, not here."

"And perhaps it is," Paine said thoughtfully.

"And how do you make that out, mister?"

Paine shrugged and avoided the question. Only vaguely defined in his mind was a picture of the whole world renewing itself, dreams of a brotherhood so vast, so complete that the half-drawn conception was overpowering and beyond words.

Jefferson would not call attention to Paine's poverty, his failings in matters of dress; Jefferson was in the process of adoring the common man, and being only thirty-two he was still young enough to attach reality to his conception. Himself the immaculate aristocrat, it astonished him—though it shouldn't have—to find that Paine arrived at much the same conclusions out of experience that he, Jefferson, had gathered out of philosophy and reading. But whereas Jefferson had dreamed enough democracy to make it real, he could never quite grasp the concept of revolution. For Paine it was the other way around, and his thoughts and ideas were closer to those of the average working man than Jefferson's ever could be. Listening to Paine read something of what he had written, Jefferson wondered whether Paine knew what devils he was loosing upon the quiet eighteenth-century world wherein they lived.

Paine read hoarsely and self-consciously, ashamed before Jefferson:

"The sun never shined on a cause of greater worth. 'Tis not the affair of a City, a County, a Province or a Kingdom; but of a continent—at least one-eighth part of the habitable globe. 'Tis not the concern of a day, a year, or an age; posterity are virtually involved in the contest, and will be more or less affected even to the end of time, by the proceedings now. Now is the seed-time of Continental union, faith and honor. The least fracture now will be like a name engraved with the point of a pin on the tender rind of a young oak; the wound would enlarge with the tree, and posterity read it in full grown characters. . . ."

There was no style; it came forth as raucously as the preaching of a Methodist minister, and it struck with frantic hammer blows. A man could memorize words like those and drive his plow or hammer to the rhythm—

"O! Ye that love mankind! Ye that dare oppose not only the tyranny but the tyrant, stand forth! Every spot of the old world is overrun with oppression. Freedom hath been hunted round the Globe. Asia and Africa have long expelled her. Europe regards her like a stranger, and England hath given her warning to depart. O! receive the fugitive, and prepare in time an asylum for mankind."

Jefferson didn't smile; a working man who cribbed from the Bible all he knew of style, who in the terms of a backwoods preacher roared a new creed for mankind, nevertheless said something no one else dared to say outright.

"What are you going to call it?" Jefferson asked.

"I think, common sense. That's all it is."

Word of Paine's project got around, and people would say, "That's common sense." They would say, "He is preaching dissolution and hatred and revolt. Separation from the mother country." Or, "Another common sense," when someone spoke a word for the independence of the thirteen colonies.

A little book to show men what to think.

"Of course, separation in time," old Ben Franklin said to him one day. "But be careful, Paine, be careful."

He carried the manuscript around with him, crumpled, ink-stained paper, and sitting in a tavern with a mug of rum, he would write, correct, write again, smudge and blot and scrape together the future of America.

"Is it still common sense?" he'd be asked.

He wove the Bible into what he was writing. To the devil with the sophisticates of the city, he told himself. The man with the plow is the man with the gun, and the man with the plow reads and believes only one book. So he took from the Bible whatever he could whenever he could, and wove it into the rest. One night in a coffee house, having had a little too much, he read aloud. Of course, it was common sense, and he could draw a crowd, and it was very well put that the devil can quote scripture.

"To hell with all of you and all of you be damned!" he roared at the well-dressed, well-paunched Philadelphia merchants. And then, going home that night, he was set upon by half a dozen young toughs, his manuscript torn to shreds, himself rolled in the mud and beaten, his pants removed and a lash laid twenty or thirty times over his behind.

He kept his lips tight about it, and when Aitken came to him and said he might have a hint as to who the assailants were, Paine simply shook his head.

"It doesn't matter. The few pages they tore up I know by heart."

"But you, man, you!"

"I'll live," Paine said briefly.

The Reverend Jared Heath of the Society of Friends put it to Paine in a different fashion.

Heath, a small, moist-eyed man, said to Paine with utter sincerity, "Thomas, thee know not what thee do."

"And exactly what am I doing that I don't know?" Paine demanded.

"Thee are setting brother against brother and father against son and workman against employer with this writing of independence. Who, Thomas, speaks for independence? Thee should know that not the good people, not the considerate, not the gentle, but the discontented, those who make mock of God, the foreigners among us. Thee are one of us, yet thee write to plunge us into bloodshed."

"I am one of many things," Paine said wearily, not wanting to hurt this little man who evoked memories of his father, his uncles, of the old meeting house at Thetford.

"Come to us and pray and thee will see light."

The summer past, the leaves turning red and brown and yellow as they rustled over the cobbled streets of Philadelphia, the cold clean winds blowing from the northwest, Paine still scraped at his paper. The thing was done or never done; he didn't know. He had written a little book to make men see the thing clearly, and it asked for independence. With deliberate hatred, he had torn apart the whole conception of monarchy. He had pointed out how long man had been nailed to the cross, and in words a farmer could understand begged for a good new world in this good new land. He had even tried his hand at a form of government. But always he harped on a single fact, that regardless of the pain, the torment, and the bloodshed, here must be a new and independent country.

He wrote on the first page, as if purging himself, "Common Sense, written by an Englishman."

And then it was done, a heap of scribbled-over paper. No one would read it and probably no one would print it, but it was for the doing that Paine worked.

He was tired and listless, not left even with a desire to be drunk. Fascinated by the cool change of season, he wandered lazily through the narrow streets of Old Philadelphia, sniffing the winds that blew from the wide and grave and mysterious west. Never in England came such a change of season, sharp and clean, the air washing over a whole continent to thunder at the tide-water wanderers fled from the old world.

He discovered, so short was the memory of men, even for a ribald jest, that few now remembered he was Common Sense, and fewer poked fun at him. He was left alone, and often he said to himself that was just as well.

He let Aitken read his finished manuscript; no animosity was left between them, and Aitken, glasses perched on his nose, followed the scrawl carefully and considerately. Finally he said, "It's no' a bad thing, Thomas, but, my lad, it's muckle dangerous."

"If anyone reads it," Paine said.

"I will no' publish it, but why na' take it to Bobby Bell, who's a fool for such matters."

"If you think so," Paine nodded.

Bell was a Scotsman too, hatchet-faced, with ink-grimed hands. He said a good morning to Paine, and then took the manuscript, leaned against his counter and began to read. Paine dropped to a chair, closed his eyes, dozed a little, opened his eyes to see that the Scotsman had started over at the front page. His face never moved, never changed expression as he went through the manuscript again. Then he folded it carefully, laid it down on the counter, and placed a paperweight on it to hold it in place.

"You don't want it," Paine said.

"No-o—"

Paine began to rise but the Scotsman said, "Be in no hurry. I canna guarantee a profit, but I will set type and make a book of it. A man canna say will sell or will no' sell, but I lean to standing up to what's mine. They're good, clear sentiments."

"I don't want any money," Paine said. "I wrote this because I had to, that's all. If you make money, you can have it; I don't want it."

"I have no argument with a man who desires to throw a penny in my lap."

"Then you'll print it."

"That I will," Bell said somberly.

And then Paine rose and left the shop as casually as he had entered.

SEVEN

Common Sense

DR. BENJAMIN RUSH, a young Philadelphia physician who had some time since decided that more than physical ills ailed mankind, told Ben Franklin how Bell had cooled toward the idea of Paine's book. "I think he was afraid," Rush said. "I don't blame him. Like a hundred thousand others, he doesn't know on what side his bread is buttered; he has other things to think about, all men have, I suppose.

"But, God, the more I think of it, the more I wonder how those farmers at Lexington had the guts to stand up to it."

"Did you read the book?" Franklin asked.

"Yes."

"And did you like it?"

"It's not something a man likes or dislikes. Neither is gunpowder, nor bleeding."

"Of course, you got Bell to go ahead?" Franklin said quietly.

"Was that wrong? He owes me, and I suppose I put my finger on him where it hurt a little."

"Things are not right and wrong any more," Franklin reflected, almost sadly. "We go ahead, and that's all."

"Of course, they're right and wrong!"

"Of course," Franklin shrugged. "It was right for kings to rule the world for a thousand years. It was right for little people to suffer and die. It was so right for men to be slaves that there was never a need for chains." He added, after a moment's hesitation, "I'm sorry I am an old man. I would like to see—"

"If you want to read the book," Rush said, "it will be off the presses in a few days. You've probably seen parts of it in manuscript. That man Paine certainly isn't reticent."

"Bring me a copy," Franklin nodded, reflecting that he had had a hand in opening Pandora's box, almost boyishly eager to see what Paine, who would shake the world apart, had to say.

From the press and just sewn together, it still smelled of ink and smudged as Paine held it in his hands, a thin book called "Common Sense, written by an Englishman," with big block letters on the cover, sticky as Paine opened it.

"Done," Bell said.

Paine told him, "I don't want you to suffer for this," and Bell shrugged. "I'll want to buy a few copies," said Paine.

Bell nodded.

"To show them to my friends."

"Ye may."

"You'll give it to me a little cheaper than the regular price?" Paine remarked, not able to keep a note of anxiety out of his voice, his hand in his pocket holding all the money he had in the world.

"I may."

"It makes a pretty book," said Paine.

Consigned to Baltimore by stage, the package had neither the sender's name nor the contents marked on it, only the destination, the shop of Marcus Leed, a small bookseller. But Bell, to purchase the driver's silence, had given him a dozen copies to sell himself at two shillings to whoever would buy. In the coach, the passengers took one to share among them and while away the hours with —fat, bespectacled Parson Amos Culwoodie, Methodist free preacher, reading sonorously:

"There is something exceedingly ridiculous in the composition of Monarchy."—The parson had always felt as much.—"It first excludes a man from the means of information, yet empowers him to act in cases where the highest judgment is required—" Jacob

Stutz, the miller, sitting alongside the parson, knew that if man doesn't live by bread alone, bread at least is as necessary as anything else, and now wondered what king on earth could do a simple grading of flour.

A long journey and a noisy one. The parson reaffirmed his position as God's right hand man when he read, "How came the king by a power the people are afraid to trust, and always obliged to check?"

"How indeed?" Mrs. Roderick Clewes asked.

The parson took off his hat in deference to a lady. "There is no divine right in man," he stated decisively.

"None?"

"None, I tell you, madam. For a minister, a call perhaps, an inspiration, an unfolding of the darkness, a nearness to God. But divine right—that, madam, I assure you, is dispensed by Satan."

In the old Brackmeyer Coffee House by Dr. Rush's arrangement were met David Rittenhouse, James Cannon, Christopher Marshall, Ludwig Rees, and Amberton St. Allen, a strange company of the high and the low, united by a desperate feeling that now there was no turning back. It gave them a feeling of romance, a feeling of living high and swiftly and gloriously, to know that when the redcoats came to Philadelphia they would be among the first hanged. Withal, theirs was an intellectual approach, and their god was Ben Franklin, not the Adams cousins. When Rush told them he had called them together to read a pamphlet, they nodded, called for drinks, and set themselves to listen.

"Never mind who wrote this," Rush said, and then he read slowly and meticulously for almost three hours, stopping now and then to answer a brief question, but toward the latter part of his reading holding his listeners in a rapt silence.

"It's called *Common Sense*," he said when he had finished.

"Of course, it's Paine's thing," Rittenhouse nodded.

"That's right."

"If this be treason—" someone paraphrased.

"You don't realize—it's so damned insidious."

"How much?"

"Two shillings."

"Well, it ought to be less."

"You think people will buy it?"

"Is there anyone who won't? The man's a devil and a genius."

"No, he's a peasant. Have you ever seen his hands, like slabs of beef. He's a peasant, and that's why he understands us, because we're a nation of peasants and shopkeepers and mechanics. He comes here a year ago and he knows what's in our guts. He's not writing for you and me, but for the man at the plow and the bench, and, God, how he flatters them, crawls inside of them, tickles them, seduces them, talks their own language, says to them: Isn't this reasonable? Isn't this common sense? Why haven't you done this long ago? Bathe the world in the blood of tyrants! You and I and all the rest, why are we slaves when we can be free? Is he Christ or the devil? I don't know. I know, after hearing that thing read, there will be no peace for a long time."

"For how long?"

"Not ten years—maybe a hundred, two hundred. Maybe never—I don't know if men were made to be slaves or free."

Abraham Marah was a trader with the Indians, a lonely man, a strong man but black-eyed and black-visaged. His name when he came to the country as a little boy had been Abraham ben Asher, but they called him Marah because he was bitter, and as he came of age and lived more and more in the dark forests he called himself Abraham Marah, after the new fashion. He was a Jew, but at the synagogue he was known as a rebel. "I'm a free man," he would say, "and God has done nothing for me."

But he wasn't slow with money when they asked for contributions. As they said, What use had he for money? With no home, no wife, no possessions but the pack on his back and his long Pennsylvania squirrel gun, he would roam on for months at a time. He knew the Indians—the Shawnee, the Miami, the Wyandot, and the Huron—and they knew him. Fur hunters they all were, and he could come back from six months in the dark forest with a fortune in pelts on his donkeys. Now, starting out again, he came to Bell and bought twenty copies of Paine's book.

"Why, Abraham?" Bell asked him.

"Because I read it, because where I go, others think twice, and then in the end stay home."

He brought the first copy to Fort Pitt. John Neville and his Virginia militia had already taken the post, and now they were sitting around, drinking more than was good for them, wondering whether to go home, wondering why they had taken up guns when there was neither purpose nor reason nor goal. They were long, hard men in dirty hunting shirts, and many of them had not deciphered a written word these ten years past. But, as Lieutenant Cap Heady said, when a Jew gives away something, there's a reason. Heady read out loud in the light of a campfire:

"In England a king hath little more to do than to make war and give away places; which, in plain terms, is to impoverish the nation and set it together by the ears. A pretty business indeed for a man to be allowed eight hundred thousand sterling a year for, and worshiped into the bargain! Of more worth is one honest man to society, and in the sight of God, than all the crowned ruffians that ever lived."

It was the sort of thing the Virginians enjoyed hearing. "Go on," they told Heady.

Marah's way was long and rambling. A copy stayed in a Kentucky stockade, another in an Ohio stockade, one in a lake cabin with the promise to pass it on and on. Three copies were saved for the French Canadians, the voyageurs whom Marah loved better than all other Americans, and one copy was unfolded, page by page, in an Iroquois longhouse as Marah painfully translated *Common Sense* into the Indian tongue.

General George Washington of Virginia was a troubled man; come up from his Mount Vernon, from his beloved Virginia, his broad and stately Potomac, from all the good, earthy things of his life, the lush fields, the fruit trees, the many bottles of good wine, he was now bogged down outside of Boston, in command of several thousand sprawling, lazy, totally undisciplined New England Yankees. The war, for all apparent purposes, had come to a halt; but the doubts of intelligent men, who had little idea of what it all meant or where it was taking them, went on. For Washington, who had come into this without any clear idea of means or end, but simply with a fierce love of the land he tilled, a decent respect for the dignity of himself and his friends, and a hatred of the English method of conducting the tobacco business, doubt mounted steadily and surely. The word "independence" was too frequently spoken; it had a quality of terror, burn, pillage, and kill—remake the world! Washington loved the world he lived in; the earth was good, and better were the fruits of the earth. But to remake this good-enough world into some uncertain horror of the future—

It was in such a mood that he sat down and read a book brought from Philadelphia by express messenger. It was called *Common Sense*. Jefferson wrote him, ". . . you will want to know that this is Paine's work; you remember him, I think. He has sound ideas for building a strong and united nation, and considers that already we are a people at war for our freedom. . . ."

They were a strange people in Vermont. "A mortal, sinful people," a pastor from Virginia said. "A presumptuous people. They build their fence posts of carved stone, as to say a man's days on earth are not numbered." A silent people too, and a cold people who covered their bridges and never spent a penny until after they had earned it. The saying went that Maine men were hard, but Vermont men harder, Maine men mean, but Vermont men meaner. People not so delicate in their speech said, Court a Vermont lass with gloves.

They liked figures, they liked to know that two and two made four, and they had little patience for ideals. Independence was all very well for Vermont, but they were not going to be hasty and pick up their guns for foreigners in New York and New

Jersey. And in the green hills it was bruited about that the middle countries were more or less Dutch provinces where a man could walk for weeks and never hear a word of English spoken.

They took *Common Sense* at arm's length. A few weeks after publication Hiram Jackson, the leather dealer, brought a dozen copies over the New Hampshire border into Vermont and handed them out to the farmers who sold him hides.

"Boston stuff," he said, which was his term for anything even mildly incendiary.

They were read carefully; where Paine pointed out that less than a third of the inhabitants of Pennsylvania were of English descent, they felt confirmed in something they had always suspected; when Paine said that it would be good business sense to break from the Empire, they read on. A copy came into the hands of Jeremiah Cornish, the Bennington printer. He approved of it after three days' discussion with his neighbors, and considering that Pennsylvania was a good distance off, certainly too far for an apology or a royalty payment, set it up himself. The first run was a thousand copies that went like fire for a shilling-fourpence, and Jeremiah seeing a small but respectable profit in the offing, did another run of five hundred which he sent across into New Hampshire. Ichabod Lewes, a New Hampshire printer, knew enough of Vermont people to suspect Cornish had wildcatted the edition, and accordingly set it himself, ran three thousand, of which he sent twelve hundred to Maine. The Maine men were frugal, but they liked the pamphlet; it made sense; somehow, it echoed what they had been thinking, just as it curiously echoed what men had been thinking in Vermont, New Hampshire, Massachusetts, New York, and other colonies down into the Deep South. It was the kind of thing that was good for an evening of raging debate; it was the kind of thing a man could chew on while he did his work.

They didn't reprint in Maine, but passed the things from hand to hand until they were falling to pieces.

Allen Johnson had a farm seven miles outside of Trenton, a

wife and three children, and eleven Bibles. He didn't need eleven; in fact, four or five of them had never been opened, and now and then in a moment of heresy he would say to himself, "What on God's earth does a man want with more than one Bible?" But the Bible man came through every November, regular as the frost, his cart bulging with Scriptures and almanacs.

Johnson didn't have the almanac habit, but it was a mortal sin to refuse a Bible offered for sale, like denying the word of God, and that being the case the row of Bibles became longer by one each year. Nor did Johnson blame the Bible man, who called himself Pastor Ames; one man's living was another man's backache, and that was the way things were. This year, Pastor Ames was almost a month late, and when he did show up, the almanacs were missing from his cart; instead he had about a hundred and fifty copies of a little book called *Common Sense.*

"Come with the word of God," he said to Johnson.

Doing his best not to hear, Johnson made a point of inspecting the stock. "No almanacs?" he questioned, as if this year he had just come around to buying one.

"Politics," the pastor said. "Lord bless us, it's a mighty year for politics."

Johnson picked up a copy of *Common Sense* and turned over the pages.

"Two shillings," Pastor Ames said.

The Bibles were four.

"I'll take one," Johnson said.

It was only afterwards that Johnson recalled that a purchase of the Bible relieved him from the arduous duty of reading it, a task that was taken from his shoulders every Sunday morning at church. On this little book, he had an investment of two shillings, and determined not to throw his money away, he sat down that same evening to read it. When his wife asked him what on earth he was reading, he said:

"For the Lord's sake, Mandy, leave a body alone!" He knit his brows and read on, and slowly what was a task turned into a most amazing discovery.

The printer, Bell, was astonished, almost frightened; this had never happened to him before; indeed it had never happened to anyone in the country of Pennsylvania before. After he had set type on Paine's book, he had started the printing with a moderate run in the hundreds, and that was as it should be according to all his experience. Almanacs, which were in great favor with the country folk, sold well, and sometimes, as was the case with Franklin's almanacs, in the tens of thousands; but in the country political pamphlets had never been in great favor, and even in town, unless they were throwaways, they had only a limited demand. Even with popular English novels, a run of fifteen hundred was considered most successful, while two thousand was distinctly out of the ordinary. Paine's book was overpriced; he had known that; two shillings put it out of the class of apprentices, most workmen and small farmers; but Bell had laid on the heavy price to protect himself in what he was quite certain would be a complete publishing failure. Paine had friends in Philadelphia, and what with the friends, the curious, and the opposition, Bell had felt confident of a sale of at least five hundred copies.

He had already, a week after publication, sold more than two thousand.

He ran a full thousand for New York, then another thousand; he took on a journeyman printer and two apprentices. They labored all one night getting out an edition of three thousand in demand here in Philadelphia. Franklin Grey, a local bookseller, asked for a thousand at a shilling-twopence, wholesale, and Bell agreed to supply him. Then, by post from Charleston, came an order for two thousand. Hartford wanted seven hundred; the little village of Concord in Massachusetts a hundred; a place he had never heard of, Brackton, fifty.

Angus MacGrae, a roving book jobber whose wide territory included Maryland, Virginia, and Carolina, and who sold as many books straight from his lumbering, canvas-covered wagon as he did to various small shopkeepers, was a regular customer of Bell's, as he was of the many other Philadelphia printers, publishers, and book dealers. He had picked up a copy of *Common Sense* in

Maryland, and for the hundred lazy miles between Baltimore and Philadelphia, he had let the reins hang and had read it and re-read it as his two old drays ambled along. If ever a man knew the pulse, the fever, the beating tempo of America, that man was MacGrae; he loved the written word only less than the spoken one, and if he had not given a good deal more effort to talking about books than selling them, he might have been a very rich man.

When he left a copy of Defoe in a backwoods log cabin, he glowed with pride, and it was he who talked several hundred good Presbyterians into believing that lush hours spent with Fielding would not destroy their immortal souls. He had sold Swift and Pope to buckskin-clad hill men as well as cultured plantation owners, and he had arranged for his own translation of *Candide*. His love for America was compounded of its literacy; European-born, he never ceased to wonder at this strange, hard-muscled motley conglomeration of people who had so tender and shy a love for the written word.

When he finished Paine's book, parts of it read over three and four times and committed to memory, he made up his mind to meet the writer, and when he did, said quietly,

"Mon, mon, but it is glorious."

Paine, still tired, still unable to comprehend what was happening with the small thing he had written, was able to say nothing, only nod foolishly.

"It must be read widely," MacGrae stated.

"I hope so."

"Be no' afraid of that. I have made other writers, such as the Frenchman Voltaire and the Englishman Swift, a reputation a mon need no' be ashamed of."

To Bell, MacGrae said, "I want five thousand copies."

"And are you entirely out of your head?"

"Almighty sane. I pay one shilling, and I will no' bargain with ye, Bell."

"I canna do it. I have no' the presses nor the paper nor the labor."

"Mon, I give ye two hundred pounds—what are ye afraid of?"

And Bell, all this beyond his understanding, sighed and agreed.

When old Ben Franklin came to Bell's shop for fifty copies to add to the fifty Franklin had already mailed here and there, Bell tried incoherently to explain what had happened. The Scotsman looked haggard, red-eyed from lack of sleep, grimed all over with printer's ink.

"It's no miracle," Franklin said. "A book sells because people want to read it, or because it answers things they've been asking."

Bell showed Franklin two wildcat editions, one from New England and another from Rhode Island.

"I wouldn't be angry at that," Franklin said.

"And I am not. I am a small man, and night and day my presses are not idle. God knows how many I've printed, not I. Over a hundred thousand, sir, I assure you. I weep for paper, I sob for ink, and I have moved out my family to make room for the apprentices. I dream nightmares, and it's *Common Sense*."

"Others will dream nightmares," Franklin smiled.

Outside of Boston, the sprawling, bickering, discontented Yankee army that had been besieging the British for so long now, fell avidly on *Common Sense*. The long, dreary hours in winter quarters had set them to wondering why they were fighting. In a fashion, Paine's book told them; they dreamed out the new world. At first, it was a copy read monotonously to a brigade, then argument, then a few more copies to set a man in his reasoning, then a hundred, then a thousand copies, then a dog-eared, dirty copy of *Common Sense* in every haversack, good to wipe a razor on, good to start fires with, good for a man's soul and his body, good to copy into apologetic letters sent home:

"My dear and Affectionate kept wife,

"Always in my memory, I think of you night and day, but do not entirely berate me for selfishness, as things are to be done and there is not a way to live Quietly and Happily without doing them. A man who is an Englishman not an American writes

Sundry and Sound reasons in a book called as COMMON SENSE. He says and I agree with him, O ye that love mankind! Ye that dare oppose not only the tyranny but the tyrant, stand forth! Every spot of the old world is overrun with oppression. Freedom hath been hunted round the Globe. I agree with him and you will when you read the Book I send you. Have Jamie stay with Jenny night and Day when she comes to Calf. . . ."

Out of a prisoner's rucksack, a copy came into the hands of Colonel Bently, who read it and brought it to General Howe of His Majesty's Army. Howe read it, too, and decided:

"My word, but the beggar's devilishly clever." He told Bently, "I want a point made of taking this *Common Sense*. I want him hanged, do you understand?"

EIGHT

The Times That Tried Men's Souls

"IN ONE way you are a fool," Franklin told him. "Not a brave man, but a fool."

"How is that, sir?"

"Have you ever shot a musket?"

"No."

"Or loaded one?"

"No."

"And wouldn't any farmer boy from the backwoods make a better soldier than you?"

"I suppose so," Paine admitted.

"What do you believe in? Did this war come out of the mouth of a gun or the mind of a man?"

"That's done," Paine said. "I wrote a little book because I wanted men to see what they were shooting at. I didn't know what would happen. Now would you want me to stay here and let others die for what I said?"

"So you could keep saying it," Franklin pointed out.

"No—"

Franklin shrugged.

"I'm happy," Paine said. "I've never been happy before. I suppose I could have a better musket, but suddenly they've become so scarce that I ought to be satisfied with what I've got. I know what I'm made for; I am not a fool nor a martyr, but just a man who has discovered what work he can do."

"When will you be leaving?" Franklin asked.

"Tomorrow."

"Good luck then," Franklin said.

"Thank you, sir—"

"And don't try to die. Don't doubt your own courage. Remember that this is only the beginning."

He was no longer Tom Paine; suddenly and curiously, he had become Common Sense. He had written a little book, a hope or a suggestion; he was a stranger in a tidewater colony that had defied the world. He was nobody, yet out of that he became everybody, for he had seen, with the candid eyes of a peasant, the hope of mankind.

Yet they never knew what to do. The farmers stood at Concord and Lexington. The militia roved through the forest to the backwoods posts and ripped them from their small British garrisons. New York and Philadelphia belonged to the radicals, although they had been driven, cursing, fighting, bleeding from Boston. It was much as if a wave of sudden, furious fire had burned through America, brightly at first, then with less intensity, then just a simmer of revolt that promised to die.

Now he was Common Sense.

One night, walking alone in the cool evening, trying one street of Philadelphia and then another, wanting nothing at the moment, not the warmth and companionship of a coffee house, not the hot sustenance of drink, not a woman or a man, but only himself in a proper perspective, Tom Paine turned over in his mind what he had done.

Not abruptly can a small man reach for the stars. Christ was a carpenter, and he, Paine, was only a staymaker, an exciseman, a cobbler, a weaver. "Paine, Paine, be humble," he told himself, and in his thoughts going back to the speech of his childhood:

"Thee are nothing, dirt thee are, dirt, dirt, and both cheeks have been slapped. Thee have been humbled, thee face in the filth—" And he found himself laughing and praying, "God, O my God, how thou hast exalted me." Love inside of him was without measure, and his strength too without measure. Again and again, he clenched and unclenched his hands. Men were brothers. "Oh, my brothers, my brothers," he whispered.

He said, "No, I'm not going mad—"

Benjamin Rush had pointed out to him, "Revolution, Paine, is a technique which we must learn with no history. We are the first, and that's why we blunder so. We have no precedent, but only a theory, and that theory is that strength lies in the hands of the armed masses. I am not speaking of ideals, of right and wrong, of good and bad, not even of a morality, for in the last analysis all those things are catchwords and the only implement is strength."

Paine nodded. Slowly and painfully, he had been coming around to the same point of view. "The strength was always with the people," he said.

"Of course—firearms don't change that. But there was never, in this world, a technique for revolution. There was a technique for tyranny and strength implemented it, but always the strength of a few. The strength of many is revolution, but curiously enough mankind has gone through several thousand years of slavery without realizing that fact. The little men have pleaded, but when before have they stood up with arms in their hands and said, This is mine!"

"There were never the circumstances before."

"Perhaps. It's true that we have here a nation of armed men who know how to use their arms; we have a Protestant tradition of discussion as opposed to autocracy; we have some notion of the dignity of man; and above all we have land, land enough for everyone. Those are fortunate circumstances, but now we must learn technique. The man with the iron glove has held this world for God knows how many thousands of years, and in how short a time do you suppose we can take it back from him—not to mention holding it?"

"I don't like to think about that."

"You must. We are learning a bloody, dreadful business, this technique of revolution, but we must learn it well. You wrote a little book, and because of that men will know why they fight. You wanted independence, and we're going to have it, mark my word. Six months ago you were rolled in the dirt because people knew what you were writing; two weeks ago a man in New York was almost tarred and feathered because he planned to publish an answer to *Common Sense*. That's not morality; that's strength, the same kind of strength the tyrants used, only a thousand times more powerful. Now we must learn how to use that strength, how to control it. We need leaders, a program, a purpose, but above all we need revolutionists."

Paine nodded.

"What are you going to do?"

"Join Washington," Paine said.

"I think you're right. Keep your eyes open, and don't be discouraged. We are a free people, but we are only a few generations away from the slaves. We will whimper and cry and groan, and we will want to give up. We are not an orderly people, Paine, and I don't think we will make good soldiers. In a little while we may forget what we are fighting for and throw away our muskets. Remember that—always remember that."

Fame sat uneasily on his shoulders, and suddenly Philadelphia was repugnant to him, a fat, satisfied town that talked eternally, criticized vehemently, and did almost nothing at all. On the streets and in the coffee houses, where Paine's book was fast becoming another Bible, talk of independence was free and easy, but in the Assembly the eastern delegates still held out against it. The frontier delegates stalked the streets with black faces, but there was nothing they could do.

A banquet was given for Paine; he did not have the money for a new coat, for lace cuffs, and he would neither beg nor borrow. He came as he was, shabby, without even a wig, sitting glumly at the table, thinking, "I told Franklin I was going, I told Rush—why don't I go?" But it didn't matter so much; the armies were sitting idle. Of course, give a thing a chance and it will blow over.

On the table, as a centerpiece, was a monster pasteboard replica of *Common Sense.*

"Oh, the glory that this stranger has given our cause!" said Thaddeus Green, the toastmaster. "Oh, words of his that are fire, live forever!" Green had come in his militia uniform, blue and yellow. "Will not freemen lay down their lives gladly?" he cried.

Paine was getting drunk. He drank thirty-two toasts, and lay with his head in his plate, his mouth drooling. Almost everyone else was drunk, snoring, telling dirty stories, pawing the waitresses, dirtying their fine and fanciful uniforms, their lace and silk, shouting suddenly:

"God damn King George!"

"Liberty forever."

"Like this," Paine muttered. "Here the glory of free men."

Jefferson had asked him to come. He sat there in a corner of the room, feeling like a fool, his hands on his knees, while Jefferson explained how Washington had reacted toward reading the book.

"You've done a great thing for your country—" Jefferson said.

Paine could not help thinking how empty and stupid words were. What was his country? What was he to these suave, aristocratic, lace-draped intellectual democrats? Why did he always feel like a fool?

"Naturally, you said what we've all been thinking," Jefferson went on. "What we've been saying too. Yet you have to say a thing so men will understand it and comprehend it, even a man like Washington, and he's no fool, you understand. Your book says it—and to everyone. Now we're committed to independence."

"I was waiting," Paine said. "I was never really certain."

"And what will you do now that you are satisfied—and I trust you are?"

"Join the army."

"Is that wise?"

Paine shrugged; to have his decision weighed so, back and forth, with the supercilious attitude that no man could serve this movement by taking a gun in his hand, but only by sitting here in

Philadelphia and mouthing words, was breaking down both his nerve and his determination. Slowly, he was becoming aware that these great and important men of the colonies, even Jefferson, whose reason was a creed and a religion, looked upon him as a sort of performing animal, a peasant to represent the numberless peasants who would make up the army of rebellion, a clever rabble rouser to be used for their purposes.

When in the newspapers someone attacked the revolutionary movement, the conception of an independent America, and Paine answered hoarsely and vehemently, there was a chorus of polite handclapping.

"We're in committee now," Jefferson said, "Franklin, Adams, Sherman, Livingston—I am making the draft of the declaration, purely and simply for Independence. I want you to know that I am using *Common Sense,* that I am proud to."

"But not proud enough to include me in committee," Paine thought, yet with a sort of satisfaction that he was out of that, that he could use himself according to his own desires. And he said, "When do you expect to have a vote on it?"

"In July, perhaps."

"And then it will be the United States of America?"

This time Jefferson smiled and shrugged. "We owe a great deal to you," he nodded.

"Nothing."

Handling the future with assurance, Jefferson said easily, "Remember, Paine, if out of this comes something real and concrete, a republican state, you will not find it ungrateful."

Then it was done, and the bright new world was made, and in the teeming, excited city of Philadelphia there were few who doubted that the people would rise to support this grandiloquent, rhetorical, generalized declaration of independence. Glory is born in July, 1776, they told each other. They paraded, singing that fantastic bit of doggerel that had attached itself to the army of the revolution, Yankee Doodle went to London Town—and who knew but that they would all be there? Invade Canada? Why not? And why not England? And why not the world, to make this the new Christianity? Of course, when Jefferson's first draft of the declaration had been submitted to the Continental Congress, Benjamin Harrison leaped up and roared, "There is but one word in this paper which I approve, and that is the word Congress." But on the other hand, hadn't Caesar Rodney ridden eighty miles in twelve hours, killing horses, just to be on the floor of the house on July fourth and sign the document?

Paine was honored; hurt and honored, when a few days before the presentation of the document Jefferson had come to him with a sudden tenderness and said:

"Let me read you this."

"Read it if you want to," Paine said.

"It's at the end, the summing up, and you did it. My God, Thomas, we don't know our debt to you. History is like bad housekeeping entered into an account book."

"Why don't you get on with it?" Paine thought.

"We, therefore," Jefferson read, "the representatives of the United States of America—" He glanced up at the slope-shouldered, unkempt man who had given him that phrase. "How does it sound?"

"Read it!"

"—in general Congress assembled, appealing to the Supreme Judge of the world for the rectitude of our intentions, do, in the name and by the authority of the good people of these colonies, solemnly publish and declare that these united colonies are, and of good right ought to be, free and independent States; that they are absolved from all allegiance to the British crown, and that all political connection between them and the states of Great Britain is, and ought to be, totally dissolved; and that, as free and independent States, they have full power to levy war, conclude peace, contract alliances, establish commerce, and to do all other acts and things which independent states may of right do. And for the support of this declaration, with a firm reliance on the protection of Divine Providence, we mutually pledge to each other our lives, our fortunes, and our sacred honor. . . ."

"Well, it's done," Paine said.

"Yes—"

Paine was thinking that now there was nothing left to keep him here, he could go away.

Roberdeau, general of Pennsylvania militia, was a portly man with a face as red as a beet, a huge pair of haunches, and a glorious uniform of blue and yellow. A successful merchant, he was quite sure he would be an even more successful soldier, and once he had decided to lead a detachment to Amboy, south and west of Staten Island, he was satisfied that General Washington's troubles were over. He offered Paine the post as his personal secretary. The Associators, as the militia called themselves, had drilled for a good many months now, and Roberdeau pointed out to Paine that to be with this brigade was something of a signal honor.

"I'll come," Paine said. "I don't want any commission. If I can serve you as a secretary, well enough."

"Such things as commissions can be arranged. I would, personally, prefer to see you as a major. More dignity in such a post than as a captain or a lieutenant. Aside from that, have you a uniform?"

Paine confessed that he hadn't.

"Important, my boy, important. Only with uniformity can we inject into the ranks a certain military tradition, such as gleamed like a halo around the great Marlborough and Frederick of Prussia."

"I'll do without one," Paine said, thinking of how those who had seen Washington's army reported that there was not a uniform to a brigade.

"If it's a matter of money . . ."

"It's not a matter of money," Paine said.

Bell had given him fifty copies of *Common Sense*; that, with his rusty old musket, powder, shot, a water bottle, and a bag of cornmeal, made up Paine's luggage. He trudged with the rest, partly out of desire, partly because he could not afford a horse. Roberdeau, who took Paine's abasement as a personal affront, did not talk to him for hours at a time; Paine hardly noticed that. Nothing else mattered but that now, after long last, he was marching shoulder to shoulder with his own kind, the shopkeepers, the clerks and mechanics, the weavers, carpenters, craftsmen. For the time, it was entirely emotional; they had met no enemy, seen nothing of war. And they knew nothing of it except what they had heard from New England. And in Massachusetts, hadn't American losses been fantastically small?

The night of the first bivouac, Paine sat at the fire, heating his corn gruel, tensely aware of himself, unable to speak, tears of joy in his eyes. The voices of the militiamen were loud, somewhat self-conscious, bright. It was:

"Comrade, a light!"

"Share my gruel—porridge for bacon?"

"The devil with that, comrade, I have enough for both of us."

"Citizen, how about a toast?"

There was a wagon full of rum in iron-bound casks. Roberdeau, patting his huge paunch, had one broken open. They toasted the Congress, Washington, Lee, Jefferson, who had written it all down so prettily, old Ben Franklin. A clear, youthful tenor began to sing:

"Oh, the pretty skies of Pennsylvania,
Oh, the meadows sylvan green,
Oh, the bluebird and the nightingale,
Oh, the countries, 'mong the countries,
Our sylvania is the Queen."

Paine could hardly carry a tune, but he sang with the rest. The artillery men sat on their brace of cannon, swaying back and forth, keeping time with their ramrods. The fires trailed a curtain of sparks toward the sky, and a sweet, cool wind blew from the west. This was all Paine had ever thought of or dreamed of, the common men of the world marching together, shoulder to shoulder, guns in their hands, love in their hearts.

For Paine, it was an almost mystical fulfillment, and he said to himself, "Who can measure the forces started here? Men of good will march together and know their own strength. With the power we have, what can stop us, or even slow us? What can't we achieve, what new worlds, what glories, what promises!"

But on the next day, their sublimity began to be more commonplace. A comrade is a comrade, but a blister on one's heel is not to be sneezed at. The glorious cause of independence remained a cause glorious, but the muskets grew no lighter. Most of the firelocks they carried were brand-new, the product of Anson Schmidt, a Front Street gunsmith whose theories were violently opposed to those of the back-country craftsmen. In the Pennsylvania hinterland, a slim, light, long-barreled rifle had been developed. It threw a lead slug the size of a large green pea with amazing accuracy and outranged by at least a hundred yards any other weapon known at the time. But Schmidt reasoned, and rightly, what was the use of such a rifle to a man who was not a marksman? He developed his own gun, the Patriot Lady, he called it, wide of bore, bound with iron, and heavy as a small cannon. It could be loaded with anything, shot, nails, glass, wire, stones, and at thirty yards it was brutally effective. Its great drawback was that it required a strong man to carry it.

The militia were not strong. For several hours they carried their muskets, and then someone got the idea of heaving his weapon into a supply wagon. Soon the supply wagons were groaning with the weight of a hundred muskets, and Roberdeau, blue with rage, screamed what kind of an army was this marching without arms?

"Well enough for you on your horse, fatty," a private told the general.

"God damn you, you'll have a hundred lashes for that!"

"And who'll lay them on?"

Roberdeau backed down, but assured the man that he would write a charge to the Continental Congress. The men were tired, begrimed with sweat, surly; and it was too early in the campaign to look for trouble. Since Paine was the secretary, Roberdeau put it to him, instructing him to write the following to the military committee:

"Whereas one, Alexander Hartson, indulged in treasonable talk—"

"I wouldn't say that," Paine interrupted.

"No?"

"His talk wasn't treasonable. It would be better to have him whipped."

"I think I know how to order my brigade," Roberdeau said. "Write what I tell you to; that's why you're here. I don't need instructions in military ethics from any twopence scrivener."

"Very well," Paine nodded.

There was a tall, loose-limbed man who took to walking alongside Paine. His name was Jacob Morrison, and he came from the wild and beautiful Wyoming Valley. His wife and child had died of smallpox, and he, sick of living alone in the dark woods, had come to Philadelphia, taken work as a hand in a flour mill, and there joined the Associators. Armed with a long rifle, clad in buckskin leggings and a hunting shirt, he almost alone in that motley group of militia appeared fitted for the business on which they were embarked. He took a liking to Paine, if for no other reason than that Paine continued to carry his own musket. He said to him once, in his slow, back-country drawl:

"Citizen, what do you think of our little war?"

"Things start slowly," Paine said.

"Yes, but I reckon I seldom seen a seedier lot of fighting men."

"Well, give them time—you don't make soldiers over night. And you don't make a new world in one day."

"You're English, aren't you?" Morrison said. "What got you into this?"

Paine shrugged.

"For me, I don't give a damn," the backwoodsman drawled. "I got nothing to lose. But, Lord, there's troubled times coming—"

That night Roberdeau took a new tack, changing from bullying to cajoling. He broke open an extra cask of rum, and announced to the men:

"We have with us here, citizens, a most illustrious patriot, the man who with words of fire wrote *Common Sense*. He has consented to say a few words to us concerning the cause for which we are determined to give our lives. Citizen Thomas Paine!"

Paine wasn't prepared. He stood up sheepishly, stumbled into the light of a fire, and began to talk, very haltingly at first—"We are embarked on a deed of small men, and that's what we are, small men, citizens, common people. We are going to find it hard, and grumble and complain, and some of us will go home. I think that's how a revolution starts—"

Their permanent bivouac was at Amboy, close to where the Raritan River flows into lower New York Bay. Across the river were the hills of Staten Island, and beyond, on Manhattan, a terrible drama was being enacted. Washington's orders were to hold New York with the rabble of militia he had under his command, twenty thousand in number, but none of them trained soldiers—New England Yankee farmers for the most part, some Pennsylvanians, some Jersey troops, a good many Virginians, and several brigades of Maryland troops, the latter the best of the lot. But to hold New York with that raggle-taggle mob was as absurd as it was impossible. Each day, more British transports and ships of the line sailed into the harbor, disgorging thousands and thousands of trained regulars and Hessians onto Staten Island. Meanwhile, Washington had split his army, placing half his men in Brooklyn to stave off a flank attack that might isolate him on the slim ridge of Manhattan. To counter this move, the British shifted part of their army to Long Island, and on the night of August 27, General Howe launched his attack. They found a weak spot in the American lines, captured a few sleeping sentries, flanked half of Washington's army, and then, holding it in pincer jaws, proceeded methodically to destroy it.

Only through his own cool courage and the aid of a brigade of Marblehead fishermen was Washington able to evacuate what was left of his shattered army to New York. And there, almost before he had time to reorganize, the British attacked again, this time determined to destroy what was left of the colonial army.

They came near to accomplishing that purpose. Landing on

Manhattan both from the East River and the Upper Bay, they again attempted to close the pincers, driving the routed, panic-stricken colonials before them. It became a wild foot-race, in which an utterly demoralized mob of militia threw away their weapons and ran like rabbits for the fortified line which the Americans still held where One Hundred and Twenty-fifth Street is today. Whole brigades were cut off by the Hessians, ripped to pieces with cold steel, made prisoner; men cowered in barns, hay-lofts, thickets; others drowned themselves trying to swim across the Hudson and reach the Jersey shore. Only through a miracle did a good part of the troops which had held lower New York escape. In a few weeks the twenty thousand had been reduced to less than fifteen thousand.

And during this time, the Philadelphia Associators made themselves very small at Amboy. More than enough news of what was happening in New York filtered into their lines, and the only concrete result was desertion. It was a thing of the past to call one's neighbor comrade, and as for citizen—

Paine had pleaded with General Roberdeau, with Colonel Plaxton, "What are we doing here? Over there in New York, the whole good hope of mankind is being smashed, and what are we doing here?"

"Our duty, which is to garrison Amboy."

"Christ, no! We could march up through Jersey and cross over at Fort Lee and join Washington. Better yet, we could cross the Raritan and attack the British where they're weakest, in Staten Island. Or we could raid over into Bayonne—"

Roberdeau smiled condescendingly. "You're a writer, Paine, a dreamer, shall we say. The hard military facts—"

"God damn it, sir, what do you know about military facts?"

Plaxton blew up with rage, but Roberdeau only pouted and spread his arms helplessly. "First the others, now you, turning against me, talking treason."

"Treason! My God, sir, is everything treason? Isn't it treason to sit here on our behinds?"

"Orders—"

"From whom? Did the orders take into account that Washington's army would be shattered, that we should lose New York? Has any man in your command fired a gun yet or faced an enemy?"

Fat, his face jelly-like in its impotence, Roberdeau blubbered his appeal to Plaxton, the slim, dandified gentleman, one of the Penn family, sneering and bored at the two of them:

"Is my duty my duty? Tell me? Am I to blame that Washington's army is driven from New York? Am I to blame that instead of soldiers they give me shop clerks?"

Then there were the desertions; Philadelphia was not far enough away, and each night a few of the militia slipped out of camp. Almost no discipline was left, and for the most part the officers were drunk; if the general objected, they laughed in his face. Paine stormed, pleaded, exhorted; and strangely, the militia did not take offense at him; rather, they became like schoolboys being scolded. When he sat by a fire and read to them from *Common Sense,* they listened, fascinated, intrigued, and then for a moment he could fill them with passion:

"Do you understand, this is for us, for you and me, for our children! We are the beginning, and we are making a new world!"

But it didn't take; they were homesick, frightened, bewildered by the reports from New York. If the British had cut to pieces Washington's great army, which had already been under fire at Boston, what would happen with raw, untried militia?

"Listen to me, comrades!"

Now they hated the word. What did words mean when words led only to death. The revolution was a farce; and it was doubtless true that the British hanged all rebels—or gave them to the mercy of the Hessians.

As Jacob Morrison said, there should be at least twenty who could be counted on; he had been sounding them out, and he told Paine, "In this cursed Jersey, there must be at least a few hundred others we could pick up, enough to make a raiding party. I seen too many like Roberdeau, who is no good, and in a little while he'll go home—mark my word."

"I suppose he'll go home," Paine shrugged.

"Then what's to hold us back? The Continental Congress?" asked Morrison derisively. Paine sat down and put his face in his hands; his head ached. He told Morrison:

"It's mutiny, you know."

Morrison asked him if he wanted to get drunk.

"All right."

There was no longer a pretense made of guarding the rum. They had a quart each, and staggered around the camp, roaring obscene songs at the top of their lungs. Like a helpless schoolmarm, Roberdeau called them names until Morrison ran at him with a bayonet. Paine stood on a supply cart, swaying, exhorting the militia, who were not entirely sober themselves, moving them and himself to maudlin tears, watching out of the corner of his eyes how Morrison staggered around, brandishing the bayonet, finally falling off the cart.

But when it came down to facts, the next day, they could not find twenty in the camp who would join them, not ten and not even one. Roberdeau, Plaxton, and a few other militia officers held a council of war, the outcome of which was a decision to march back to Philadelphia; and when the Associators heard the decision read, they cheered for a full fifteen minutes. Paine and Morrison sat on a fallen tree trunk, their firelocks on their knees, and watched the camp break up. It didn't take long, nor did Roberdeau speak to them; only when the Associators began to march did a few militiamen glance back and wave. Morrison began to hum softly, and Paine sighed and studied his rusty musket as if he had never seen it before.

"Not that I give a damn," Morrison said, "and I suppose they have something to go back for. The little man, Tom, is a timid rabbit—don't let it stick in your throat."

"No—"

"Do you want a drink?"

Paine nodded, and silently Morrison passed him a leathern flask of rum. They rocked it back and forth for a little while, and then when it was empty, they threw it away. "Ye that love mankind," Paine quoted, and Morrison said, "Shut up!"

"Ye that dare oppose not only the tyranny but the tyrant, stand forth!"

"God damn you, shut up!"

"All right," Paine nodded. "Only let's get out of here—let's get out of this damned place and not see it again."

They crossed the Raritan and set out to walk to Fort Lee on the west bank of the Hudson River, some thirty miles to the north. There was a garrison and there was a place in Washington's army for two men who held onto their guns. They took the old pike to Elizabethtown, trudging along through the cool September days, their guns over their shoulders, two left from all the Philadelphia militia, a tall backwoodsman and a slope-shouldered, broad-necked Englishman, profession: revolutionist, but just two of all the raggle-taggle that drifted along the road—deserters, farmers, cowboys, milkmaids, and even a British patrol now and then to send them diving into the underbrush. They had no money, but the weather was good, and they could sleep in a field and roast sweet corn over a fire.

For Tom Paine, there was a quality of relief in the disbanding of the Philadelphians; the weak went and a few of the strong were left, and he had never had a comrade before like this tall, slow-spoken Pennsylvanian. He read to him from *Common Sense*, and respect became a bond between them. Morrison told how his wife and child had died, leaving him alone in the dark forest, and trudging along they shared their loneliness and knew each other's thoughts. In those times, the flatlands of Jersey were not covered with smoking factories and an endless maze of railroads, but between the pine barrens, the sulphur swampland stretched for miles and miles, inhabited only by flocks of whirring birds, by snakes and frogs, desolate by daytime, but shining with an unearthly beauty at dawn and twilight.

Once they passed Elizabethtown, they walked for hours through this silent, stretching plain, for Paine so reminiscent of the British fens. He spoke to Morrison of the things he had seen as a boy in the gin hell of London; hope which had been so low in them rose higher, and the calm spaces of the swamps gave them new courage. Now they laughed at Roberdeau.

And then Morrison was shot through the head by a British sentry they stumbled over in the dark; the sentry, more frightened than Paine, ran away, and Paine, who had heard his first shot of war, took his friend's rifle and went on.

His way lost, his clothes soaked and dirty, he came into the light of a campfire where two deserters sat, boys of seventeen who snatched up their muskets and faced him like animals at bay:

"Who in hell are you?"

"Paine—Tom Paine."

"And what do you want, god damn you?"

"The way to Fort Lee, that's all," he said calmly, observing with speculative inward curiosity that he was not afraid of these two terrified children, not afraid but only deeply saddened and coming awake to the stuff his dreams were made of.

"That way," they said, grinning, easier once they had him covered and saw that he was alone.

"Do we still hold it?"

They shook with laughter that was partly hysterical. "We hold it," one of them said.

"Why did you run away?"

"You go to hell, you bastard, that's none of your business!"

"Why?"

And then the other lifted his shirt to show the fresh, raw marks of a lashing.

Like a low-crowned hat, Fort Lee sat on top of the Palisades, opposite Fort Washington on the Manhattan shore. The one was named after Charles Lee, the Englishman who had sold his services to the colonies for a substantial sum, who had been a professional soldier all his life, who lived on his own lush visions of glory; the other was named for a Virginia farmer who had blundered into the command of all the continental armies, and had, since August, been lashed by defeat after defeat. That farmer had already lost all of Manhattan to the enemy except Fort Washington and a few hundred acres of land surrounding it. He had been driven out of Manhattan and almost extinguished as a military factor at White Plains. He was now trying to regroup his shattered army and plan a campaign, and most of all make up his mind whether or not to abandon Fort Washington.

General Nathanael Greene, the handsome young Quaker in command of Fort Lee, believed that both points, facing each other across the Hudson River, could be held as long as was necessary. Rightly enough, he considered them a gate to the Hudson, and the Hudson a gate to the colonies. Now, at Fort Lee, he was informed that a man had arrived in camp who called himself Tom Paine.

"Paine?" Greene asked. He had a book, a small Bible called *Common Sense*, worn to pieces with two dozen readings. "Well, bring him here. Paine, you say? Of course, bring him here."

"I know you and I don't know you," Greene said to Paine, when they stood face to face, the one tall, sunburned, handsome and dapper in his buff and blue which he had had made in the style of his commander's Virginia militia uniform, the other broad and stocky, hook-nosed, hair in a knot and cheeks with three days' beard, his old clothes stained with dirt and blood. "You're Common Sense, aren't you?"

Paine nodded, and they shook hands. Greene, excited as a boy, called over his aides, introduced them, ran into his tent and brought out his own battered copy of Paine's book, ruffled the pages, smiling and trying to believe his eyes that Paine was here in front of him.

"You don't understand, of course—you don't know what this has meant to us. Everything, do you believe me?"

"I want to."

"Good. You know we've been beaten, no use trying to hide that. We were driven out of Brooklyn and we were driven out of New

York. All we hold in Manhattan is the fort, yet we have hopes of getting it all back, not military hopes entirely, but here, what you've given us, something to chew on and bite into, something solid and substantial that they can't take away from us. I've bought seventy-five copies myself and forced men to read them who have never opened a book in their lives—"

Paine shook his head dazedly.

"And now you're here. That's the wonder of it, your being here. I swear, sir, I'd rather have you than a regiment, and the general will say the same thing when he meets you."

For a day, Paine was left alone. He told Greene that was what he wanted, to be left alone, to walk around the camp, to clean himself up, to think. There were a good many things he had to think about, he told Greene. Well, naturally, you'd expect that. "Do whatever you want to," Greene said. "When you're ready, we'll talk."

Paine wandered through the fort leisurely, always coming back to the high bluff where he could lean on the parapet of tree trunks and look across the dancing little waves of the Hudson to the green, wooded hills of Manhattan. Actually, Lee was more a bivouac than a fortification, poorly protected, but amazingly picturesque in its high setting over the river. Paine found talking to the men easier than he had expected; they were Yankees, many of them, from the little villages of middle New England, but it had been noised about the camp that he was the author of *Common Sense*, and they were pleased to find him as simple as they were. Working men themselves, they recognized in him all the signs of a man who has used his hands unsparingly, the sloping shoulders, the heavy palms and short fingers, the thick, muscular forearms. They talked to him about his book, and he was amazed to find how keenly they could analyze material facts, the trade of the colonies, the potential for ship building, for weaving, for manufacture. Ten minutes after meeting him, they would be relating tales that Greene could not have dragged out of them with torture; they told him about their parents, their wives, children, farms. So many of them were boys under twenty, red-cheeked children who knew whole pages of his book by heart.

"You remember, sir?" they would say.

And he wouldn't remember. Here was none of the comrade, the citizen, the self-conscious dramatization of the Associators, but rather a subdued realization of what it meant to face the best troops in the world and be defeated constantly.

"Yes, sir, you'll find it mighty pertinent," and they would go on to quote him. "Now that matter of delegates to Congress, as you put it, I wouldn't take exception to it, Mr. Paine, but I might offer a mite of a suggestion. You speculate that Congress could choose a president—"

They were argumentative and keen and alive, but their education didn't include niceties. They were likely to pick their noses in a ruminative fashion, to chew tobacco and spit where it pleased them; they weren't clean. They were an abomination to the Virginians and Marylanders, with whom they bickered and fought constantly, and they couldn't get along with the Dutch.

Paine gave away Morrison's rifle. For himself, his old musket was good enough, and he was very doubtful of his ability to hit anything with it, even if he loaded with buckshot. He gave the long rifle to a Virginian who could use it.

When Greene had heard from Paine the full story of the Associators, he nodded and said, without passion, "Of course, it isn't the first time. That's happened in half a dozen places. It's happened with us, too, I suppose."

"They weren't cowards," Paine said.

"Men aren't cowards. It's a balance; either it's better to stay and fight, or it's better to run away."

"They didn't have any direction," Paine said. "They were molded by certain things for God knows how many hundreds of years, and how could you unmold them overnight? And they didn't have any leadership. Back in Philadelphia, Rush told me that revolution is a technique. What do we know about that technique?"

"Nothing—"

"And yet I can't get used to the idea that the cause is doomed. Do you think it's doomed?"

Greene said no, but not with assurance.

"No, of course, it's not doomed." Paine shook his head and rubbed his heavy fingers into his brow. "Revolution is something new, we don't know how new it is. I sometimes think that April last year a new era for the world began." He asked Greene how long it would be, how many years, and Greene said he didn't know, it might be twenty or a hundred years. They smiled at each other, Greene showing his large strong teeth, his blue eyes wrinkled in appreciation of the parts they both played in this curious comic opera. Paine was relieved to find someone saying what he had been thinking. Greene said he was glad that Paine was there.

"It means very little," Paine protested.

"No, I'm trying to learn how to make a campaign, but what's the good if they don't know why they're fighting?"

"Do you think I can tell them?"

"I think so," Greene nodded.

"All right."

"Do you want an officership?" Greene inquired. "It can be arranged, you know. A captaincy, easily; you could be a colonel or a major if you wish to—we have so many of them, God knows."

"No, I don't think so."

"In a way, it's a matter of respect," Greene said uncertainly.

"If I can't have their respect as Tom Paine, it's no good to me."

"Yes—"

"You see, all I can give them are reasons. I don't know anything about fighting."

He was in Hackensack when Fort Washington fell, dropping the ripe plum of three thousand men into the hands of the British. At Hackensack, five miles inland from Fort Lee, there was a larger encampment of the ragged continental troops, Jersey and Pennsylvania men, undisciplined, a swaggering, dirty, wretched camp that gave Paine a desolate reminder of the Philadelphia militia.

The bivouac was overrun by camp-followers, women of all ages in all the stages of decay. The men kept chickens and pigs and spent their time earning the undying hatred of the local farmers. Greene had said to him, "Go there and see whether you can make those swine understand why they're fighting."

The "swine" grinned at him when he spoke of the revolutionary army. They pelted him with mud when he tried to tell them why a man should want to die for this little civilization on the fringe of the forest, and for the first time in many years he used his fists. He was deceptively powerful, and his big shoulders hid layers of leathery muscle. They respected him when he had laid a few of them on their backs.

Henry Knox, the fat colonel of artillery who was in command of the camp, grinned appreciatively. "They understand that," he said. He had been a bookseller once, had even done a little publishing on his own, and he considered Paine his own private gift from God, something to lessen the boredom. Talking about the fantastic success of *Common Sense*, he would keep Paine in his tent for hours, and having a good, solemn liking for the bottle, they were quietly and warmly drunk on many an evening. Knox was the last person in the world to be in command of this dirty, disorderly, mutinous camp, a fat, smiling young man of twenty-six, florid in complexion, talking constantly about his wife, and again and again pressing Paine for the story of the book's sale. Did it sell more than two hundred thousand? That was the story.

Paine didn't know; he wasn't sure and they had lost all track of printings. And then it had been printed everywhere without permission.

"But, man, man, there was a fortune in it," Knox said.

"I suppose so."

"And you didn't touch it. By God, that was magnificent!"

Paine shrugged, and then Knox began to speculate upon the number of readers there must have been. Possibly everyone in the colonies who was literate. Possibly a million readers, one of three persons—but that was hardly possible. Yet it was enough to stagger the imagination.

"And here?" Paine asked. "What do we do and where do we go?"

Knox said he didn't know; they were here and the British were across the river, and it seemed like it might be that way forever. It had been terrible at first, being beaten in every engagement, but now they were learning how to fight. Perhaps it didn't look that way, the camp being what it was, but they were learning—

That was only a few weeks before Fort Washington fell. The fort, standing on a bluff on the east bank of the Hudson, was supposedly impregnable. Greene thought so, and so did Knox; if Washington had his doubts, he kept them to himself, and it was only Charles Lee, commanding about five thousand men in Westchester, who said out and out that the fort could not be held. It couldn't; the hills around it were taken, the defenders rolled back, flanked, cut off from retreat, the fort filled so full of fleeing continentals that it could not even fire a shot in its defense. Some three thousand men were taken, and Washington, watching the whole thing from a boat in the Hudson, saw what little hope he had left crumble and disappear.

Paine met him again only a few days before the fort was taken, and the Virginian had said, almost desperately:

"It's good to have you with us here. They don't know in Philadelphia—they think it's a very simple matter to make a war and a revolution."

Paine thanked him.

"Talk to the men," Washington said. "Only talk to them and make them understand this thing."

Then the fort was lost and the end was in sight. Paine sat stolidly and watched young Knox weep out his rage and disappointment, but when he turned to the Englishman for sympathy, Paine, in one of his rare bitter moods, snapped:

"You poor damn fool, did you expect nothing to happen? Did you expect them to give us America?"

"No, but the whole garrison—"

"And it will be more than three thousand men before we're

finished. Don't be an idiot," Paine said brutally. "Stop crying—is that all you're good for, tears?"

At Hackensack, the camp was dissolving; daily, there were more and more desertions. Paine went from man to man, pleaded, threatened, used his big fists; and they listened to him, because he wasn't an officer, because he was as unkempt and as ragged as any of them, because he could say a few words that would set a man's heart on fire. It was hard, and it was going to be harder; he admitted that, but they hadn't looked for a picnic, or had they? They weren't paid, well, neither was he, and he turned his pockets inside out to show them. Their shoes had holes in them, well, so had his. Then why? "I know what I'm doing," he grinned. "I'm feathering my own nest." How? Well, for one thing, he told them, the United States of America would be a good place to live in, comfortable, good for a working man. He knew; he had been a staymaker, cobbler, weaver, exciseman, down the whole line; for another, the enemy wasn't going to forget what had been until now. "Give up, and you'll pay the rest of your lives," he told them. And once he wangled a keg of rum from the dwindling commissary and got drunk with them, the way they could understand, roaring, yelling drunk.

"All right, all right, citizens," he told them. "A little of this and a little of that. We're just beginning."

Then the enemy crossed the Hudson, flanked them, and Greene had to take his garrison out of Fort Lee, double-time, a panic-stricken crowd running down the road to Hackensack, Washington leading them, Greene and old Israel Putnam whipping them along, more panic at Hackensack when they tried to reorganize with the mob, and then the whole rabble plodding out of Hackensack on the road to Newark, less than three thousand of them now; and they, with the five thousand stationed in Westchester under Lee, were all that was left of the twenty thousand continentals who had held New York. It rained and they dragged through the mud, whipped and miserable; they were starting a retreat that had no end in sight, and this was all that remained of the glorious revolution and the glorious army. In Newark they were jeered at by the Jersey citizens who were so sure they were seeing the last act of a miserable drama. They ran, fell, crawled, panted through the town, and scarcely were they out of one end than the British patrols entered the other.

Rain changed to the winter's first snow on the road to New Brunswick, and marching through the slow-drifting flakes, they were a column of sorry and forlorn ghosts, muskets and rusty bayonets, here and there a cocked hat, a bandage, a cannon or two trundling clumsily, no sound and no song and no cheering, the officers walking their horses with faces bent against the cold. The road was bordered with stone walls, mantled in white now; the fields were dead and flat and the houses wore masks of shutters.

Paine walked beside a boy whose name was Clyde Matton, and who came from Maine. Carrying his own gun and the boy's, Paine had an arm around his thin shoulder. "The march is short," Paine said, "when one minds the road and not the steps."

"I reckon it's too long either way."

"There'll be a warm fire tonight."

"Little comfort in that. I'm thinking of going home."

"Home's a far way off. There're few men here, but good men."

He walked by the carts of the wounded and told them stories. They found him a good story-teller; he could make things sound funny, and he was a fine mimic of accents. Already, he had picked up the vernacular of the various colonies, and he had a deadpan method of delivery, his heavy beaked nose inquiring for effect after each sentence. In spite of what he had gone through, he had never been healthier physically; his large, freckled face inspired confidence, and whether it was a cart mired in the muck or a man fainted from weariness, Paine's big shoulders and slab-like hands were ready and willing. Before this, strength had meant nothing, the power of mules and work-horses and slaves, but now it was something that gave him a heady sort of happiness—as once, when remaining behind with Knox and Alexander Hamilton and a dozen others to hold a rear guard crossing with a gun, he had alone driven off a flanking attack of dragoons, wading among the horses and sabers and flailing his big musket around his head like a light cane, taking nothing in return but a slight cut over the eye and a powder burn on the cheek. Telling about it admiringly, young Hamilton said:

"He's filthy and slovenly enough when you come to that, but he's the bravest man I ever saw, and he has the strength of a madman."

The bloodstains they left on the road where their bare feet dragged made him refuse Greene's offer of boots; he wasn't acting, but he was living the one life that was undeniably his own, this thing called revolution, learning a technique among this defeated, fleeing army, learning the one life he might live.

At night, they made their fires when they could not march a step more, and it was Paine to do the cooking for a hundred men, Paine to calm a boy's fear, Paine to read a man a letter from his wife and write one in return. Paine to sit with his strong hands clasped about his bent knees and slowly, simply explain what they were suffering for, the politics of an empire and a world, the struggles of mankind from the Romans to now, the new day of small men, not only in America but the world over.

The officers left him alone. He had hardly anything to do with them now, and they, in turn, realized that a dirty, unshaven English staymaker was one of the few things that kept what was left of the American cause from dissolving into thin air.

Washington was not the man Paine had met in Philadelphia, not the long, carefully groomed Virginia aristocrat, not the richest man in America and lord of Mt. Vernon, but haggard and skinny, the face drawn, the light gray eyes bloodshot, the buff and blue uniform, for all its launderings, spotted with dirt-stains and bloodstains. Washington was a man who said to Paine:

"Whatever you can do—"

"It's little that I can do," Paine nodded. "If you mean write something, it's hard to tell a man who is suffering and giving that he must suffer more and give more."

"I don't know you," the Virginian said. "But there are so many things I don't know now I thought I knew once. I don't know how to put my faith in a staymaker, but I am doing it. I am glad to call you my friend, Paine, and I would be proud if you'd take my hand, not as the writer of *Common Sense*, but as one man to another."

They shook hands, Paine with tears in his eyes.

"If you can write something," Washington said, "not only for the army but for the whole country. We're so near to the end—"

Paine was thinking he would die gladly for this man, die or kneel on the ground he walked.

Well, writing was what a writing man should do. With the drum held between his knees, with the top tilted to catch the wavering light of the fire, he scratched and scratched away, all the night through. The men gathered around him, men who knew Paine and loved him, men who had felt the strength of his arms, men who had slogged side by side with him. They read as he wrote, sometimes aloud in their stiff, nasal back-country accents:

"These are the times that try men's souls. The summer soldier and the sunshine patriot will, in this crisis, shrink from the service of their country; but he that stands it now, deserves the love and thanks of man and woman. Tyranny, like hell, is not easily conquered. . . ."

They read:

"If there be trouble, let it be in my day, that my child may have peace . . ."

With bloodshot eyes, they read and spoke softly:

"I call not upon a few, but upon all: not on this state or that state, but on every state: up and help us; lay your shoulders to the wheel; better have too much force than too little, when so great an object is at stake. Let it be told to the future world, that in the depth of winter, when nothing but hope and virtue could survive, that the city and the country, alarmed at one common danger, came forth to meet and repulse it. . . ."

"I thank God that I fear not," they read, and others on the edge of the crowd begged him, "Read it, Tom."

"Not all the treasures of the world, so far as I believe, could have induced me to support an offensive war, for I think it murder; but if a thief breaks into my house, burns and destroys my property, and kills or threatens to kill me, or those that are in it, and to *bind me in all cases whatsoever* to his absolute will, am I to suffer it? What signifies it to me, whether he who does it is a king or a common man; my countryman or not my countryman; whether it be done by an individual villain or by an army of them? If we reason to the root of things we shall find no difference; neither can any just cause be assigned why we should punish in one case and pardon in the other. Let them call me rebel, and welcome, I feel no concern from it; but I should suffer the misery of devils, were I to make a whore of my soul by swearing allegiance to one whose character is that of a sottish, stupid, stubborn, worthless, brutish man. . . ."

Hard, cruel, vulgar words they understood, and like a harsh and angry roar, their voices came:

"Read it!"

NINE

The Long War

THE ARMY was across the Delaware, safe for the moment on the south bank, when Paine decided to go to Philadelphia with old Israel Putnam and publish the paper he had written. Come out of the worst crisis they had known yet, he called it that, *Crisis,* and both Washington and Greene agreed that it might help. Putnam, a tired, aging man was going to try to find volunteers, to quiet the city and keep order, but he didn't put much faith in his mission. Jogging into the city with Paine, the two of them on moth-eaten nags, he muttered to the effect of its being over.

"Well, it's not over, if that's what you mean," Paine said.

"Almost—" Putnam pointed out that he, Paine, was young; he, Putnam, was an old man; he had rheumatism; and he hated Philadelphia; he was a Yankee himself, and he hated the midlanders.

"They're like other folk. You won't find much difference anywhere, plain people are plain people."

"Are they, the damn, dirty bastards?"

Paine had had a letter from Roberdeau, a pleading, apologetic letter. Understanding took time, Roberdeau said. All before the campaign had been like a storm coming up, and no one believed it, and now the storm was here.

Paine spoke more forthrightly than he should have; lashing into old Putnam, he said:

"All of you officers are the same; nothing matters but a military victory, and as far as you are concerned the men you lead might as well be tin soldiers!"

"Less than that."

"You old fool, haven't we done enough in just being! Did you expect it to be over in a week?"

Putnam glowered and closed up, and after that they rode on in silence. The snow-covered pike was bare and cold and lonely; everywhere in the Jersey and Pennsylvania counties now, houses were shuttered. It was a suspicious, surly land, and both men felt it. They were relieved to see the church spires of Philadelphia in the distance.

This was a frightened city. He saw a house burning, and nobody moved to fight the flames, and as ominous as the devil a pall of smoke rolled eastward on the wind. Frightened and not the city of brotherly love—a shop window smashed, a printing press wrecked in the street, a cart of household goods overturned. People ran, slowed to a walk, and ran again, and on a street corner an itinerant Quaker preacher called out, "He who takes up the sword must perish by the sword!"

And there were deserters everywhere spreading the news of what had happened on the long, sad march from New York to Trenton, how it was that the army had dissolved into nothing, and Washington, the blundering foxhunter, had hanged himself, surely, and Charles Lee was a prisoner of the British, taken in a bawdy house, and the soldiers were eating the leather of their shoes, and Greene had turned traitor and murdered George Washington, and Howe had Washington prisoner and the Virginian was going to lead a Tory army against his own people.

There were sad people going away with all they owned piled high on rickety wagons: *The enemy is here, don't you know?*

And hard people with set faces who walked to their work with muskets in their hands: *Let them come!*

And people who understood nothing of what was happening, when only yesterday it was peace.

It was not the city Tom Paine had left. The world goes on, and then suddenly something happens, and then never again is there peace and quiet. The thieves and cutthroats become bold, for they are the first to sense that an era has come to an end, and that never again will things be the same.

Bell would not print what Paine had written. "Mon, mon, do ye think me mad?" He was dismantling his presses. "When Congress goes, I go," he said.

"You're afraid."

"Aye, mon, and no' ashamed of it."

Paine was patient, a different man, Bell realized, a bulking, ragged man with a musket slung over his shoulder, but patient and explaining:

"You are wrong, Bell, the British will not take the city, and there are some things that have to be done, whether they take it or not. You see, this has to be printed; I call it *The Crisis*. We're in the first crisis, and we're going through it." Wheedling, "You and I can set it in one night."

"No!"

"God damn you, Bell, you made a fortune out of *Common Sense*. You're going to print this if I have to hold a bayonet at your throat!"

"No!"

For a moment they looked into each other's eyes, and then Paine whispered, "God damn you," and turned away.

Paine sold it to the *Pennsylvania Journal*, to an editor who told him, grimly smiling, that Congress had already left for Baltimore.

"Courage," the editor smiled, "is a nebulous conception. Of course, we must preserve the government."

Paine apologized for asking for money. He hadn't written this thing for money, just as he hadn't written *Common Sense* for money; but when a man's stomach is empty a few shillings become as necessary as breathing.

"Philadelphia is worse than the army," Paine explained. "The army is freezing and starving, but there's always a crust of bread.

But you don't last long in the city without a shilling in your pocket."

The editor nodded, and wondered whether the army could use him. He was fed up with the city.

"Don't go away," Paine said somberly. "There are few enough left who dare to print what has to be printed."

They worked together, setting and printing, and then they began to smile as they pulled copy after copy of the black, sticky manifesto that Paine had written on a drumhead.

"It's fire," the editor said. "I've seen a lot of writing, but nothing that was hot as this."

"I hope so," Paine agreed. "By God, I hope so!"

He met Roberdeau in the street, and Roberdeau shook his hand and asked where was he staying.

"Nowhere."

"Then come home with me." It was strange how calm the general was in this panic-stricken city. "Come along."

"You have worries enough."

"No, come along." Roberdeau was older and leaner, a shadow in back of his eyes that Paine had not noticed before. When asked about the Associators, he shook his head. He told Paine that then it had been a game.

"Of course, I didn't know. No one knew, I think. Is it all through with Washington?"

Paine was able to smile now. "You don't know him."

"No—I don't." He told Paine that he had read *The Crisis*. "Do you know what it made me feel? That I was rotten—all through rotten."

Paine nodded; he had felt much the same, writing it.

"It must be printed, you know, as a pamphlet."

"Nobody has guts enough for that now. I asked Bell, and Bell ran from the city with the Congress. The printers who stay are going to climb a fence and stay there." Paine fingered his neck and said ruefully, "You know, I begin to think of a rope myself. It doesn't matter so much with me, I have nothing to lose and nobody would care a lot—but to be hanged by the neck—"

"I know," Roberdeau shrugged. "Let's see about having it printed."

"Let's have a drink."

A few drinks loosened them up. Paine told Roberdeau what he had thought of him at Amboy, and Roberdeau, smiling grimly, suggested that Paine have a bath. They shook hands, Paine thinking of how a soft man past middle age can change and stay in a city that was dead, and not worry too much about being hanged by the neck. They went off to find a press, bought a small one, and lugged it in a cart to Roberdeau's house. Paine was dead tired and wanted to sleep, dead tired and dozing in the tub that Roberdeau and his son filled with hot water, and then sleeping restlessly while the general went off to find paper. When he woke, he had forgotten where he was, a feather bed that gave under his hands, quilts, and a bright room with good furniture.

When Roberdeau returned, Paine was sitting in the parlor, drinking black coffee and talking to a handsome girl of twenty-four, Roberdeau's niece. He had told her of the flight from New York, and she was leaning back, seeing it with her eyes half closed, her face and hands tense.

"But we begin again," Paine said. "It isn't over."

"I can see that," she nodded. "The way you tell about them, it wouldn't be over, ever. But how long—will it be years?"

Paine shook his head.

"But doesn't it matter to you?" she persisted.

"Not to me, no. You see, that's my life, nothing else. When it ends here, it starts somewhere else, and I go there."

"As if to say, where freedom is not, there is my place?"

Paine nodded.

"I pity you," she said.

"Why? I'm happy enough."

"Are you?" She felt like weeping; she rose and somehow left the room.

Roberdeau had been successful, in that he had been able to buy several hundred pounds of varying stocks and a few gallons of ink. He had also found a printer with guts enough to set on his own, a small man called Maggin who could print only a few hundred a day in his old-fashioned vise-type press. That night Paine set type, and all the following three days they printed, hardly sleeping, dirty with ink and working like madmen to turn out copies of the pamphlet before the city fell. Their courage was contagious, and other printers climbed off the fence. Within a week, *Crisis I* was circulating by the thousands, injecting new life into the Philadelphia bloodstream, bundles going to the army where they were read aloud, bundles smuggled into New York, which the British held, a sticky manifesto that screamed with rage, hope, and glory.

On Christmas Day, at night, Washington did the impossible. His army dissolving as quickly as wet sand, he found it beyond his power to do as once he had planned, retreat westward and further westward, beyond the mountains if necessary, but never risk an engagement with the British. After being battered and defeated time after time, he was coming to the realization that his course was not to fight a war of battles but a war of spaces, a war which might last for many, many years, but so long as his army was intact, one that he could not lose.

But his army was no longer intact. Unless some victory were achieved, some deed to spur the imagination of the people, it would cease to exist entirely. And at Christmas Day, at night, he recrossed the Delaware and attacked an encampment of drunken, sodden German mercenaries.

He took over a thousand prisoners; it was the first victory, sorely needed, and things that were almost at an end began again.

For the time, the city was saved; people who had fled came back to Philadelphia, even the Congress, and to half a dozen of them, in a coffee house, Paine said things that were not easily forgotten. He was a little drunk. To Roberdeau he made poor apologies, "Yes, I was drunk. How else can a man watch them?" They were planning campaigns on a tablecloth, and they had it figured up and down, forward and backward, how Washington could win the war in a month. "To hell with the lot of you!" Paine said.

They asked him what he meant, and he said he meant that some had stayed in the city and some had run away.

"Without the Congress, the revolution ceases to exist," they parried.

"Without the Congress!" Paine roared. "God save us—but tell me, what has the Congress done? A city like this with a thousand men to hold the houses and barricade the streets could last forever—forever, I tell you, and the whole British Empire could not force its way through it. But the Congress went, and the city lost its head, and I tell you, not you but Washington, not you but a few hundred poor ragged devils saved this cause! Not you!"

He was drunk, but they didn't quickly forget what he said. And between themselves, they decided that Paine might very well be dispensed with, that Paine was more a nuisance than an asset. They pointed to the clothes he wore, clothes not fit for a beggar, to his old, battered wig, to the fact that he carried a musket in the streets.

The armies had settled into the torpor of a cold winter, and Paine found a room where he could write. Another crisis was over, and the devil sat on his pen; he no longer had to seek for words; they came to him easily now, and every word was a bitter memory. ". . . Never did men grow old in so short a time," he wrote. "We have crowded the business of an age into the compass of a few months—" He would sit back and think of those months, and though he wrote easily enough, what he sought for did not come to him; he sought a rationalization, a scheme, and a progress for revolution; he wanted the whole and this was only a part. When through the murk a half-formed vision of a world remade appeared, his own impotence and futility drove him half mad. Then he would drink, and the righteous souls could point to him and be sustained.

There were few pastors in Philadelphia that winter who did not preach a sermon on Tom Paine. One roared, "Look you upon the unrepentant! What cause is served or benefited by a foul mouth

"I look like a beggar," Paine said. "I smell like a drunkard—but I pay my debts."

"This isn't a debt."

"I swear—"

"Don't swear!"

Paine stood a moment, stiff, trembling a little, then took the money and left, hardly able to keep from running, clutching the gold in both his hands, hiring a cart on the way to take the paper to Bell's.

All that night, he worked with Bell, all the next day, his hands wet with ink, the good, pungent smell filling the air about him.

Roberdeau came back and saw him on a street corner, looked as he would at a ghost, and then grasped one arm and cried sharply, "Paine!"

"Yes?"

He wasn't drunk, Roberdeau saw. "Come home with me," he said.

"Yes—"

He led Paine home, but he had to walk slowly, so that the stumbling figure could keep up with him. Roberdeau's niece was there as they came in, Paine edging shabbily forward clutching his hat.

"Irene, Mr. Paine is staying to dinner," Roberdeau told her.

Paine nodded and smiled and said nothing, nothing at dinner in the way of conversation; he ate slowly with control, but he ate and ate, smiling apologetically now and then. Bluntly, Roberdeau asked, "When did you eat last, Tom?"

"Two days, I think, or three."

The girl turned her head; Roberdeau, staring down at his plate, said brutally, "You can change the world, but you can't keep body and soul together. My God, Paine, are you mad?"

A shrug in reply, no words.

"What are you going to do now?"

"I don't know. I'm writing a crisis—we need one."

"You're writing a crisis—Paine, don't you realize that life goes on, even in wartime, that you're doing no one any good, not you, not Washington, not our cause by being a beggar and a drunkard on the streets of Philadelphia—"

"Shut up!"

"No, I'll talk, because you're worth something more than a damned filthy drunkard. I heard you at Amboy, and now you'll hear me!"

"I'm leaving," Paine said, rising.

"The devil you are. Irene, get out of here!" The girl left, but paused at the door a moment, giving Paine such a look of sympathy, of warm human kindness, that between that and the pressure of Roberdeau's heavy hand Paine sank back into his chair. Roberdeau sat facing him; he took some snuff, offered the box to Paine, and then filled two glasses with brandy. They drank and sat in silence for about five minutes.

"Say your piece," Paine nodded, and in that moment Roberdeau reflected upon a man who had sucked in the whole soul and being of America, even to the speech. In the unshaven, hook-nosed, wigless head, there was something both fierce and magnificent, a grinding savagery that might be sculpted as the whole meaning of revolution, unrest and cruelty combined with a deep-etched pattern of human suffering and understanding.

"Suppose you made this uprising," Roberdeau said carefully. "Let us say that without *Common Sense* there could have been no United States of America. Let us say that without the first *Crisis* we couldn't have pulled through the January of this year. What then: is it the beginning or the end? How many times have you said that we don't know yet what we've raised? At the rate you're going, you'll be dead in six months."

"I'm tougher than that."

"Are you? I don't think so. There are those who love you, Paine, but how many hate you?"

"Enough, I suppose."

"All right. You have to fight, and you're in no condition to fight. You have to live, and you haven't a penny to your name. Now listen to me, the Committee of Secret Correspondence is going to be reorganized as a permanent Office of Foreign Affairs. There's a post open for an official secretary, and I'm going to have Adams put you up for it."

"Through Congress?" Paine smiled.

"Through Congress."

"To hell with them," Paine muttered. "I'm a revolutionist, not a dirty, sneaking politician."

But Roberdeau said quietly, "Stay here with Irene. I'm going to see Adams."

He was gone a long while. Paine sat in a deep wingchair and listened to the girl play on the clavichord. He must have dozed a bit, because when he opened his eyes, she had stopped playing and was watching him.

"Tired?"

He said, no, he wasn't tired, and asked her what she had been playing.

"A fugue."

"Please play again," he asked her.

The little instrument rustled like a harp; Paine watched the girl's back, the motion of her head, the strong muscles that played her fingers.

She was less beautiful than strong and handsome; there was a tawny color in her hair that spoke of a Norman strain somewhere in the family, yet in every motion and gesture she was French. Through playing, she turned to Paine and she was startled by something in his eyes. For some reason Paine thought she would go. He asked her to stay.

"Yes, of course." She sat down near him and said, "Tell me about yourself."

He began to tell her, speaking in a soft voice, his eyes half closed. In a little while Roberdeau would return, and there might be a good chance that he had succeeded. Politics was a career, and Paine was very tired.

"I think you're the strangest man I have ever known," she said. "I think—"

"What?"

She walked over and kissed him, and then Paine was smiling strangely. "Of course, it's no good," she admitted. "You're damned, aren't you?"

Paine said nothing, and then they just sat and waited for Roberdeau.

To his amazement, Paine got the office, in spite of a fervent objection by a small clique, headed by Witherspoon, a Scotch pastor and one-time supporter of the bonnie Prince Charlie. Witherspoon hated Paine, not only because he was a fearless writer, but because he was both a Quaker and English. The clique accused him of everything from murdering children and being a secret agent for the British, to being an apostate and a devil without horns. But Adams and Jefferson and others stood up for him, and at the time there were reasons for the two parties to make a deal. Tom Paine became secretary to the committee of the new Department of Foreign Affairs, with a salary of seventy dollars a month.

It was a new feeling, respectability. Seventy dollars a month was not a fortune; indeed in the recently issued continental currency, it threatened to become nothing at all very soon; yet it was more than enough for Paine's simple needs, enough to pay the few debts he had, to buy him a decent suit of clothes, clean if not spacious quarters, pen and paper to write with, and no danger of starving.

And the respectability, of course; Paine the revolutionary was nothing; Paine the writer, whose book had been read and reread by almost every literate person in the thirteen colonies, and spoken aloud to most of those who were not literate, whose book had caused the British ministry to curse the day when the written word had been made available to commoners, was a mere scribbler; Paine the pamphleteer, who had done as much as any man in America to hold the army together in its worst hour, was a rabble rouser and no more: but Paine the secretary to the Committee of Foreign Affairs was a person of some consequence, on the inside among the circle of the gods that be, able to do a person a favor and say the right word in the right place. Or so they thought, and more hats were tipped to him, more hellos said more waists bent than ever before.

And Paine came to live in the world within, where the ivory tower protected even the most sensitive. Soon enough he discovered that where the quaint inner circle of colonial politics began, reality stopped. That war was being fought by a haggard, desperate little army led by a quiet and stubborn man called Washington, mattered so little to the Continental Congress of the United Thirteen Colonies that it was only by deliberate resolution that they could recall the nature of the situation.

On their side, it might be said that they were as impotent as any governing body could conceivably be; able to make treaties, they could not force observation of them; they had the right to coin money, but no power to buy gold or silver, and with the power to wage war, they could not raise a single soldier. In the one worst moment of crisis, when Washington's shivering and defeated troops had finally crossed to the southwest bank of the Delaware, they had abdicated voluntarily, fled in panic from Philadelphia to Baltimore, and given to Washington the full power of a dictator.

Their knowledge of warfare was confined to the continental military tracts they read so feverishly; each had his own personal military theory and fought for it, and the only military fact they agreed in was that it would be ridiculous to fight the war in the one style Americans knew, the silent, terrible bushwacking tactics that had torn a British army to ribbons between Concord and Lexington.

They were split into parties, the pro- and anti-confederation, the northern party, the southern, the pro-reconciliation and anti-reconciliation, the pro-Washington and anti-Washington. There were the isolationists who believed revolution was a property peculiar to Americans of pure British descent and of the eastern coast of North America and that all other persons and places should be excluded; and there were the internationalists, those who would rally the insular Dutch, Irish, Scotch, Swedes, Jews, Poles, French, and Germans, and add to them whatever liberal and anti-British feeling existed on the continent of Europe. Not the Sons of the American Revolution but the non-fighting ancestors were already working feverishly to make the roster exclusive.

And to add on the coals, they had discovered the good American device of lobbying.

They lobbied for everything: to have their local towns, counties, cities protected by troops; the Southerners to have tobacco adopted as a necessity for the troops; the downeasters to convince all that no one could fight without a liberal ration of rum; the wool-runners to sell woolen blankets at four times the price they had ever sold them; the midlanders to sell their grain; the New Englanders to have the troops fight on curds; the New Yorkers to have them fight on beef.

And they could agree on nothing, not on the style of the confederation, not on post-war aims, not on a constitution. The honest, sincere men among them fought and broke their hearts, and somehow things were done and somehow the war blundered along.

And into this Paine came, a revolutionist whom all regarded with suspicion. He did his work, he wrote another *Crisis*; he sat in a cubicle and pushed his pen as a clerk, and sometimes, when he closed his eyes, he would see men in rags with a rattlesnake banner. And he saw Irene Roberdeau and said, "Look at me. Do you like it?"

"I think you look better than you ever looked."

"Do I? And I tell you, something is dying inside of me." She noticed then what a flair he had for the dramatic.

"I can't stand much more of this," he decided.

"I hear you're greatly appreciated."

"You do? They're waiting for a chance to be rid of me, and the sooner it comes, the better. This is a people's war, and some day the people may awake to that."

"And can't you forget the war even for a while?"

"You told me I was damned," Paine smiled.

"But not beyond redemption," she said.

The carts came into Philadelphia with half a hundred badly wounded men, and Paine worked with others, feeding them, making them comfortable in the old Quaker meeting house to which they were taken. Some he knew; he was Common Sense to them. He found his *Crisis* papers among their belongings; a paper read a dozen times would end as dressing for wounds or wadding for a gun.

"A stout heart," he would say.

He sat all one night holding the hand of a boy who was dying, and the next day he washed the body and laid it out himself. It was before the time when women would go near a dying or a wounded man; the male nurses were tobacco-stained, filthy old devils. Paine told Irene Roberdeau soon after, "I'm going away, I must."

"Where?"

"To the army—I'm no good for this sort of thing."

She pleaded with him, asked him whether it was not enough to throw herself at his feet.

"I'm no good for you," he said. "I'm no good for anything except this stew I've brewed." Yet he lingered on in Philadelphia.

It was spring again, and the armies were moving in the field. Plowing over, farmers picked up their muskets, cleaned off the rust, and drifted down the country lanes toward Washington's encampment. Last summer was forgotten; the shop clerks forgot and left their shelves, and the mechanics laid away their tools. A lark and a campaign, and the war would be over. Spring does that, coming suddenly with the sky bluer than ever it was during the winter. The few thousand regulars, lean and hard, mocked the way Yankees mock at the summer soldiers, the militia who took their fighting as they would bird shooting, in between the planting and the harvest. "Where were you at Christmas Day?" became the taunt, harking back to the time they turned like wolves at bay and crossed the Delaware. This was the year for ending the war; they could prove that by the almanacs, by the stars, by gypsy fortune tellers. Ho and away; there were rations in plenty, and up from New Orleans by the bosom of broad mother Mississippi had come a thousand fat hogsheads of gunpowder, lead weight to cast a million of shot and three thousand shining Spanish bayonets. There was no treaty with Spain yet, but rustic farmers, suddenly turned astute politicians, winked and nodded their long heads as they ran a hard forefinger over the Toledo steel; one knew about those things.

It was in Washington's mind to make a campaign in the north against Burgoyne, but the middle country was screaming to be protected. Howe had packed his British and Hessians into their great ships and sailed away with them, and who knew where they would land? They were sighted off Delaware, and then word came that they were sailing into Chesapeake Bay. The American army, swelled to a considerable size now by the influx of militia, began to march south.

Paine watched them strut through Philadelphia. It was summer and hot, and stripped to the waist, their muskets slung over their backs, barefooted most of them, they appeared fine and ready and trim.

Paine was neither seen nor minded; he stood in the packed crowd that cheered and hooted and waved at the sunburned marchers, bright and gay with sprigs of green tucked under their caps and behind their ears. Washington rode by in his buff and blue, looking healthier and younger than he had this midwinter past; alongside of him was the boy Paine had heard of but not seen before, young Lafayette in white twill and satin, beribboned all over with gold braid. Hamilton was there and fat Harry Knox, nursing along their lumbering guns, and Nathanael Greene to whom Paine waved—but a man is not to be seen in a crowd.

Paine went to Roberdeau's home, but Irene was not there. She left a note for him that she had gone to watch the parade.

And then they were defeated at Brandywine Creek, slashed to pieces, cut and routed, the old story of men who were willing to die but didn't know how: the old story of mistakes, a listing of blunders, each one worse than the last.

With a dead, white face, Paine heard the news, walked to the office of the Committee with dragging steps. "Of course, Congress must leave the city again," everyone said. No one had the truth of what had happened; they were running around like chickens freshly slaughtered; they were frightened.

The whole city was catching the virus of panic, the Tories with fear that the rebels would take their revenge before they left, the rebels with fear that the Tories would not allow them to leave. Neither party quite knew the strength of the other. But the British would march on Philadelphia; that, at least, was obvious.

Paine found Irene, and she said to him what she hadn't dared to say before,

"Come with me—out of all this. Haven't you done enough and suffered enough? It's over now, and if they go on, how long will it be, ten years? or twenty? Paine, I've never loved anyone else—and if you leave me now—"

"And if I stay with you? What kind of happiness would you have with me! I have nothing, Irene, except an old shirt and a pen to write with. I'm a camp-follower of revolution, a scribbler, and a pamphleteer."

"I won't ask you again, Tom."

He nodded and went without kissing her, without saying anything else, and the next day he heard that she and her uncle had left the city. They were not alone in leaving. The Tories made a show of strength, brawls and gunshots and now and then a woman's scream—the city was dying and not gently. As during that last time when the city had been threatened, Paine tried to plead with the leaders of the Associators. Congress had gone, but there were one or two left, friends of his, with a little influence, and between them they managed to call a meeting in Carpenter's Hall. Less than two hundred persons appeared, and when Paine addressed them, they listened in silent apathy.

"A city," he cried, "is the best fortress in the world, the forest of the citizen soldier! Every street can become a fortress, every house a death trap! The army lost a battle, but this is a people's war, and the British army can break its back on the stout heart of Philadelphia—"

There was no stout heart in the city. Paine sat in his room and wrote a *Crisis* paper, and below him the streets were deserted. One by one, the pro-continental citizens went. At night, a pistol bullet whistled past his ear. There was a parade of Tories, with a great banner reading, "Death to every damned traitor!"

Paine carried his musket now; he saw them tar and feather a harmless old man, whose only sin was that he swept the hearths in Carpenter's Hall; he died after Paine and a few others had taken him from the stake to which he was bound. A round dozen had the nerve to remain—sullen, desperate men with guns in their hands, and they buried the old man openly. Paine said softly, "God help them when the day of reckoning comes."

Houses were burning; the volunteer fireman's association had gone to pieces completely; the houses burned and left their trail of smoke across the blue sky.

Paine reflected curiously upon what such a situation does to men, for among the few rebels who stayed was Aitken, a somber, aging man who nodded when Paine told him about the new *Crisis* paper.

"I'll print it," he said.

"And when the British come?"

Aitken shrugged; he didn't seem to care. Paine begged him to make some provision for leaving the city and getting his presses out, but he shook his head stolidly.

"A man does what a man can," he said. "I have no other place to go." And he stayed behind. When Paine came to say good-by, the Scotsman handed him five hundred freshly printed leaflets.

"Go on," he told Paine. "Get out before it's too late."

Paine found an old, swaybacked nag, bought a saddle for a few dollars, and rode out of one end of Philadelphia as the Hessians marched into the other. And on the Baltimore Pike, he drew up his horse and sat for a while, listening to the beating of the British drums.

He asked himself, "What am I now, propagandist without presses? Rabble rouser lingering at the scene of death after the mob has fled? Revolutionist surveying the dead corpse?" He rode slowly on the old nag, and often he looked over his shoulder at the city that had nursed a thing called America. He lay down to sleep in a copse, hobbling the nag first and keeping his musket by his side, but his dreams were not good. And the next day he stopped at a farm and called:

"Halloo!"

It was shuttered; a musket poked through a slit in the wood told him to be off. "Where is the army?" he called. "God damn you and the army," the slit said.

And wasn't it always that way when they suffered defeat, the countryside growing black and sullen, the houses shuttered, the cattle locked away, the whole face of the land becoming black and fearful? It had been so in New York, in Jersey, and now in Pennsylvania, and Paine began to wonder who it was that made and fought the revolution, when the fat, staid prosperity of the land was so awfully against it. He rode on and in circles, and once when he faced a farm, a bullet ripped the cloth of his jacket. In a cornfield, his horse tethered beside him, he lay and watched the blood-red sun setting; and never before had he been so lonely a stranger in so lonely a land. He saw once, far off and down a road, three men of the continentals, unmistakable, gaunt and barefoot and ragged as they were, but as he whipped his nag down on them they raced into the woods. And a milkmaid, whom he would have asked for a drink, parched and hungry as he was, fled into a barn when he made toward her. A frightened land. Paine rode in broad, slow circles. He rode out of dawning and into sunset, a lonely Englishman, a renegade Quaker who pursued a will-o'-the-wisp called revolution; he lay alone and hungry, and remembered Irene Roberdeau's eyes and voice, her throat and her swelling breasts, and he cursed himself, his fate, all his destiny and all that was Tom Paine.

And then one evening, he was stopped by a fierce, half-naked sentry, who wore a bloodstained bandage over his matted hair, and demanded:

"Who goes there?—God damn you, answer up or I'll blow out your dirty guts!"

"Tom Paine."

"The hell you say!"

"Then look at me. What is this?"

"General Greene's encampment. Let's have a look—"

He sat having dinner with Greene, the flies of the patched tent thrown back, a fringe of autumn trees dropping their leaves against the orange light of campfires, and Greene saying:

"I tell you, Paine, you brought back my soul, I was so filthy tired and done in. Do you understand?"

Paine nodded; how was it that Greene looked on him as a savior, that Greene held his hand and tried to let Paine know how it had been at Brandywine? In appearance, they were closer now, Greene's handsome face worn and lined, incredibly aged for a man so young, Greene's buff and blue uniform faded and ragged, his boots worn through at the toes.

"So we lost Philadelphia," Greene said, after Paine had told him. "Not a shot fired, not a hand raised, but we gave it up to them. It could have been a fortress, and was it you who said this was a people's war?"

"I said it."

"Are you tired, Paine?"

"Tired, yes. There's nothing good about war, nothing decent, nothing noble. You say, I will take up a gun and kill my brother, because the ends justify the means, because my freedom and my liberty are my soul's blood, and how can I live without them? Make men free so that the land will shine with God's holy light! And then they run away, they leave their own houses, they close their shutters and blow out your brains, if, God forbid, you should want a drink of water, and they damn you for a bandit! If we were like the Jagers, it would be different, but we're little men, general, little, tired, hopeless men."

"Yes—"

"And now what?"

"God knows. We are beaten and beaten."

"And him?"

"Washington?" Greene shook his head. "We're going to attack—he's bewildered, well, we all are. We had a count and we still have eleven thousand men left—that's strange, isn't it? And they're at Germantown with less than seven thousand, so we're going to attack. But we are afraid; go outside later and talk to them, Paine, and you'll see how afraid we are. We had a talk about it, and no one knew what to do. But Wayne, you know him?"

"I know him."

"He sat in a corner and pretended to read a book, didn't say anything, just fire in him and sometimes he'd look at me as if I hadn't the guts of a rat left, and finally Washington asked him what would he do, what had he to say, and he answered, 'I'd say nothing, I'd fight, sir, fight—do you hear me, fight, not run away, but fight!' " Greene's voice slipped away; Paine prodded him.

"And then?"

"And then we looked at each other, because we were all afraid—and tomorrow we attack. For God's sake, Paine, go out and talk to the men."

"Yes."

As he rose, Greene caught his arm. "What will you tell them?"

"About Philadelphia—"

"Do you think—"

"They ought to know. It's time for them to begin to hate. This isn't a revolution, it's civil war."

The nightmare of the Battle of Germantown Paine would not forget until his dying day. And a nightmare it was, so impossible a nightmare that not for months afterwards could the actual action be pieced together. In four columns, the American troops drove on the British and Hessians who were very nearly trapped. But the columns could not co-ordinate; it was dawn, and fog lay over the field like a pall of heavy smoke. Paine rode with Greene and was separated from him; lost, he ran into a whole regiment of continentals who were also lost. They fired at him; screaming with fury, he got into them and saw that half were drunk, the other half too weary to do more than stand oafishly. Then a storm of firing broke out ahead of him, and the men scattered. Riding toward the firing, Paine came on a steady stream of wounded. Most of them lay on the road, too weak to move. The fog made it dark as evening, and only by voice did Paine recognize Doctor Mulavy, who had been with Greene at Fort Lee. In a blood-stained apron, he yelled at Paine to find water, mistaking him, mounted as he was, for an officer.

"Water, I say, water!"

"What's up there?"

"Paine?"

"Yes, what's up there?"

"God knows. Paine, where am I to find water?"

He rode on, blundering into a column of Jagers, green clad, roaring in German as they rushed past him, taking no notice of him. Then, above the sound of the battle, he heard Harry Knox's booming voice. He followed it and through the haze saw naked artillerymen swinging into position a battery of twelve-pounders. Knox was bleeding and sweating and yelling, and when he saw Paine he ran to him and pointed to a great stone house that loomed vaguely in the drifting mist.

"Look at that! Look at that!"

Appearing like magic from the mist and smoke, half a hundred figures raced over the lawn for the house; suddenly, it exploded with fire, and the figures twisted, dropped like punctured bags, some of them lying where they fell, others crawling away. A perfect fury of musket fire broke out from another direction, and Knox shrieked at his artillerymen.

"Load, you bastards! Load, you dirty bastards!"

A group of men appeared, running with all their strength, and no one knew whether it was an advance or a retreat, and an officer came by, spurring his horse out of the mist and then back into it again. Paine's nag bolted, and it ran until it was caught in a slow-moving band of cavalry. They were speaking Polish, most of them, and they moved on slowly, Paine with them, walking into a burst of grape that tore them to pieces and sent their horses in every direction.

Coffee was served, and corn cakes and cheap molasses, all put down on the claw-leg table, hot and steaming as they came in, one by one, and stood around. It was nine o'clock in the morning, a day later, and they had been invited to the little Dale house to have breakfast. They stood around, and no one had an appetite, Paine and Greene and Sullivan and Wayne and Knox and Stirling and the Pole, Pulaski, and Stephan, as sorry and bloodstained and tattered and dirty a high command as had ever been seen. There was no talk, but rather a dazed, sullen expectancy as they waited for Washington. And then Hamilton came in, went to the table, and began to cram his mouth full, saying:

"Good, you know, have some."

"Where is he?"

"He'll be here. This is good breakfast, and you don't know when there'll be more."

"Angry?" Wayne asked.

"Just as always."

There weren't enough chairs. Some sat, others backed against the wall. Greene grasped Paine's arm and nodded. Then Washington came in, walking straight through and looking neither to left nor to right, pouring himself a cup of coffee and taking a piece of pone, and telling them, not harshly:

"Go ahead and eat, gentlemen."

Nevertheless, they were afraid of him. Paine had coffee; Greene stood with his legs planted wide, staring at the floor, as if there were some complicated problem there that defied his understanding. Pulaski pulled at his mustaches while tears welled into his very pale blue eyes, and Wayne bit his nails. And the big Virginian, eating slowly, said to them:

"There is no point in discussing yesterday, gentlemen. Tomorrow is more pertinent."

They looked at him, but no one answered.

"Make out your reports concerning the battle. We will go on, and perhaps our fortunes will fare differently—"

Then something broke the dam, and they all began to talk at once—hoarse, strained voices trying to pierce through the haze that almost destroyed them the morning before. And Washington, taking Paine by the arm, said:

"Tell me, sir, you were at Philadelphia, and was it bad?"

"Very bad."

"And do you think it very bad with us?"

"No," Paine said definitely.

"Why?"

"Because you are not afraid," Paine said quietly.

"Just that?"

"Just that."

Then they shook hands.

Marching south to prevent reinforcements for the enemy from sailing up the Delaware, and failing in that. Failing at Fort Mifflin and Fort Mercer. Failing in a child's ambuscade against a few hundred Hessians; failing in a simple maneuver because the men tripped and fell from weariness. Failure and failure and failure. Twelve miles through the rain and muck, and a panicky scramble from a dozen British dragoons. Two thousand men slop along from dawn to dusk, and then one day the ground turns hard. The roads that were swamps, cut or worn in between the two shoulders of meadowland or forest, as most roads were at the time, become as nasty and sharp as corrugated iron. A cow's track in the muck freezes and becomes a deadly weapon. A ripple of mud drives its point through a paper-thin sole. A bloodspot stains the road, and then another, and then still another. Flakes of snow fall as if a down quilt were ripped open and fluffed across the sky. As a mark on the road, as a sign is the bright red blood in the cold white snow. Now march north again, for word has come from the tall Virginian to join him. There is a place called the Valley Forge.

"I tell you, comrade, that our cause is just!"

Paine is changing, and his flesh is gone. He was a strong man with broad shoulders and hands like flails, but the flesh is gone, the cheeks sunken, the eyes hollow. With his big musket a killing weight on his shoulder, he walks in the ranks, coughing, stumbling, falling as the others fall, leaving his own trail of blood. How else are comrades bound? "I tell you, our cause is just," he says, and Greene, who leads this pathetic army, thinks to himself, "They will kill him some day, because you can't whip dying flesh."

They don't kill him, they listen. And twenty who would have deserted hear a man say in a whisper:

"Men live by glory, so listen to me, comrades. All things come out of this, and the deed we dared is beyond my understanding and yours. But if you want to go home—"

"God damn you, Paine, we've heard that before!"

"Go home." And then silence until someone says, "Go ahead, Tom."

"Men are good," and he looks around at the circle of beggars.

"Why?"

"Even the simple fact that we want to go home. Bad men don't want to go home. We are good men, quiet men, little men. And we are taking the world for ourselves; they drove us like slaves for five thousand years, but now we are taking the world for ourselves, and when our marching feet sound, my God, friends, who will be able to stop their ears? But this is the beginning, the beginning—"

"I want you to stay with me," Greene told him one evening. "Tom, I need you. I want you to take a major's commission."

Paine shook his head.

"But why? I don't speak of rewards, that's a long time off, but where is the virtue in being nothing, in not drawing a shilling's pay, in knowing that if you're captured, you'll be hanged an hour later?"

"I'm not a soldier," Paine said.

"Are any of us?"

"This is your war to fight, Nathanael, and mine to understand. I am not even an American, and where is the end for me? You'll be free, but I'll have my chains—"

"I don't understand that."

"I don't want to talk about it," Paine said uneasily, and then smiled a bit as he reminded Greene that he was still the secretary for the Office of Foreign Affairs.

As they approached Valley Forge, Paine came down with an attack of dysentery. Colonel Joseph Kirkbride, whom Paine had first met at Fort Lee, was due for a leave, and asked whether the other wouldn't share it with him.

"You can stand a rest," he told him.

Paine, who could barely stagger along by now, agreed. Greene provided the horses, gripped Paine's hand, and begged him to come back again.

"I'll come back," Paine smiled. "A bad penny turns up, doesn't it?"

Kirkbride lived in Bordentown, in a comfortable frame house, hearths five feet wide, a feather bed at night, a steaming bath in the kitchen, and, best of all, books. He had Swift, Defoe, Shakespeare, Addison, Pope, Clairmont, the vulgar little novels of Dreed. Paine was sick and weak and tired, and he let go of reality, curled in front of the fire and wandered with Lemuel Gulliver, prodded the amorous filth of Gin Row with Muckey Dray, recaptured Defoe's England, dreamed, whispered parts from *Hamlet* and *Lear*, ate and slept. They had few visitors, and both men wanted to be left alone, to forget for a while. They drank a good deal, not to drunkenness, but to the warm, sleepy contentment of satisfied animals. They talked little; they looked out of the windows and watched the snow fall, the drifts pile up, always with the comfort that they could turn around and see the flame roar in the hearth.

In that way, two weeks passed before Paine rose one morning and announced, as if the thought had only just occurred to him:

"I'm going back."

Riding along a frozen road where his horse's hoofs drummed like musket shots each time they bit through the crust of ice, Paine saw a blur in the meadow beside him, and going over knelt beside a man frozen stiff and dead, musket beside him and face turned up to the sky—a deserter but a continental, a life gone and cold loneliness in a lonely land.

That was the way it was and had ever been, winter and the land against them, closed doors and closed shutters, no different in Pennsylvania than it had been in Jersey.

At night he crouched close to a small fire; a step could mean death and he kept his musket beside him; he warmed his hands; he lay in his blanket and looked up at the cold winter sky. It was not safe to ask one's way nor to declare one's party. He was looking for a place called the Valley Forge, and only one man whom he spoke to had anything to say about it, "A sad spot, mind me."

He stayed one blessed night in a Quaker household, a big, square man, soft-spoken, and a woman whose smile was innocent as a child's, and trying to thank them and tell them who he was, received from the man, "Nay, we know thee not, but as a stranger cold and hungry. And if thee are one of them, keep thee council."

"You don't like the continentals?"

"We love man, but hate bloodshed, murder, and suffering."

"And is it murder to fight for freedom?"

"Thee will find freedom a thousandfold more within thee."

Leaving, Paine said, "The road to the encampment?"

"The Valley Forge?"

"Yes."

"Thee will find it. God has chosen a place of perdition on earth. Look thee in the sky, and where the devil stands, they be."

This was the Valley Forge. When he came, it was night, and a sentry, muffled in a blanket, barred his path. There was a bridge across the Schuylkill and a pink sky over the snowy hills. There were dugouts, lines of them back and forth like dirty lace, half dirt holes, half log. On a frozen parade ground, a flag waved. Fires burned, and dark figures moved in front of the flames. The hills jutted like bare muscles, and the leafless trees swayed in the wind.

"I am Paine," he told the sentry, and the man coughed, laughed, showed his yellow teeth at the feeble pun.

"So we all are, citizen."

"Tom Paine."

The man sought in his memory, found a reminder, and shook his head. "Common Sense?"

"Yes. Where's the general?"

"Yonder—" The man had lost interest, huddled back in his blanket.

"Yonder" brought him past dugouts, an artillery emplacement, a log hospital where the wounded groaned, sang and screamed, and other sentries to whom he gave the same answer:

"Paine."

"Go on."

He had walked a mile through the encampment, along the river with the hills over him and to his left, when he saw in the dusk the fieldstone house that was Washington's headquarters. There was a drift of smoke from the chimney, a light in the windows, a sentry in front and a sentry in back. They let him in. Hamilton, a thin, hollow-eyed boy, years older than when Paine had last seen him, stood in the vestibule, recognized the onetime staymaker of Thetford, and smiled and nodded.

"Welcome."

Paine blew on his hands and tried to smile.

"You like our little place?" Hamilton asked.

There was something in his tone that made Paine ask, uncertainly, "Is it worse than what I've seen?"

"That depends on how much you have seen."

"I walked through from the bridge."

"Then the best is yet to unfold," Hamilton said bitterly. "You must go to the dugouts, Paine—you must go and talk to them, and probably they will cut your throat. Do you think you have seen them at their worst—but we are breeding a new brand of beast here. Why don't you ask why?"

"I know why," Paine nodded.

"Do you—but you worked for that swinish Congress of ours. Do they know that we're starving, naked, dying of hunger and disease and cold, rotting—rotting, I tell you, Paine!"

Going up to him, Paine took him by his jacket and said quietly, "Get hold of yourself. I don't even know where Congress is. Get hold of yourself."

Hamilton giggled and swallowed. "Sorry." He giggled again. "Go in there—he's in there."

"Don't be a fool."

"Sorry," Hamilton said.

Washington rose as Paine entered the room, peering for a moment to identify the stranger, and then smiling and holding out his hand. He looked older, Paine noticed; war was making old men of this young and desperate group; thinner, too, and strangely innocent as he was now, wigless, in a dressing gown with an ancient cap on his head, his gray eyes larger than Paine had ever imagined them to be. He was genuinely glad to see Paine, begged him to sit down and take off his coat, and then, in a very few words, described the tense and terrible situation at the encampment, the lack of food and clothing, the alarming increase in venereal disease, due to the abundance of women who lived with the men, some of them camp-followers, some of them wives, the daily desertions, the shortage of ammunition, the increasing anger even among the most loyal at the fact that they had not been paid for months.

"All that," Washington said softly. "I'll tell you it is worse than last year, and you remember that. Unless the country helps, we will break, I can tell you that, Paine. I can tell no one else, but, Paine, we are close to the finish—you must know. Not through the enemy, but ourselves, and then the revolution will go like a bad dream."

"What do you want me to do?"

"Go to Congress and plead. Go to the country and wake them up. Make them understand—tell them!"

"I want to stay here."

"Don't stay here, Paine. Here it is hell, and I don't think even you can help us. Go to Congress, and somehow we will last out this winter—I can't think of the next. Somehow, we will endure."

TEN

Revolutionist at Large

HE FOUND the Congress at York, and curiously enough he was welcomed. A dinner was given for him, and there were Rush, Abington, the Adams cousins, Lee, Hemingway, and others. The guest of honor was Tom Paine, shaven and with a new jacket and shoes. "What he has seen and suffered," Hemingway said, "should be an inspiration for all of us." Well-fed, honest men they were; claret was the drink of the evening, bottles sparkling up and down the table like a whole line of British redcoats. James Cranshaw, at whose beautifully furnished home the dinner was given, played host as in old times, carrying in the whole roast suckling pig himself. Two beef and kidney puddings flanked the roast, and two platters of fried chicken flanked the puddings. Hot bread, both corn and wheat, gave off their good smell, and there were cornucopias full of dried fruit. "For the land is plentiful, let it be known far and wide." Sitting next to Paine, Cranshaw pointed out the beauties of his Philadelphia Chippendale:

"You will note, sir, the simple lines and the undecorated backs of the chairs. For the highboy, I confess nothing equals the mahogany product of Newport, in particular the brothers Granny. For chairs, Philadelphia holds the crown and nothing in England is as good, I say nothing, sir. In New England they desecrate the product with ladder backs and peasant seats of rush; here our sidechairs are quiet songs of beauty, the ball and claw arrived at its final function, the fretted back become Grecian in its gentle curves. Shall one doubt the future of America?"

"I wonder," Paine thought.

They plied him with food and drink, and they talked of everything under the sun but the war. Not until the meal was done, the flip served, and the ladies had retired to the drawing room, did they come to the point. Then, over snuff and cigars, they pumped Paine about what he had seen at Germantown and Valley Forge.

"But you will admit that the leadership was mediocre?" they prodded him.

"The leadership, gentlemen, is sacrificing and courageous."

"But stupid."

"I deny that! Soldiers are not made overnight. We are not Prussians, but citizens of a republic."

"Yet you cannot deny that Washington has failed constantly. What you told us you saw at Valley Forge is only final proof of his unfitness!"

"Unfitness!" Paine said quietly. "My good gentlemen, God help you!"

"Aren't you dramatizing, Paine?"

"What is the case in point?" Paine asked. "Do you want to be rid of Washington?"

"Let us say, rather, co-operate with him," Lee said smoothly. "What Gates has done at Saratoga, his capture of Burgoyne's entire army, proves—"

"Proves nothing!" Paine snapped. "Have you forgotten that Gates deliberately abandoned Washington at the Delaware last year? I'm not afraid of words, gentlemen, and I'd as soon say traitor as anything else. At a price, Gates will sell, and I am not sure others haven't a price—" staring from face to face.

"Paine, you're drunk!"

"Am I? Then I'll say what I would never dare to sober—I'll say, gentlemen, that you disgust me, that you are breaking down all that is decent in our Congress, that you are ready to sell, yes, damn it, ready to sell, and that when you lose Washington, you lose the war—"

The next night, someone tried to kill him, a pistol snapping and missing fire, and a week later a note that said politely that some things are spoken of, some not. But Rush sought him out in a tavern and said:

"Don't misjudge us, Paine. We aren't traitors, believe me."

"But you would rather see me dead?"

"What do you mean?"

Paine told him, and Rush's face clouded and darkened. He assured Paine that he knew nothing about the attempt. "We are not assassins," he said grimly.

In the streets of York, one day, he meet Irene Roberdeau. She greeted him warmly and seemed genuinely pleased to see him. She and her uncle were stopping at the Double Coach, and he walked there with her, telling her briefly what he had done since he had last seen her.

"You will never rest," she said. "You will never have peace, Tom."

"I suppose not."

She told him that she was engaged to be married—when they reoccupied Philadelphia. He nodded, and she wondered from his face whether it mattered at all to him.

"We will take Philadelphia again?" she asked.

"I am sure we will."

"Tom—"

He looked at her.

"It could have been different," she said.

"I don't think it could."

Work piled up as secretary to the committee. Again he was a clerk who sat up nights doing *Crisis* papers, yet somehow he managed to let his weight be felt, putting pressure on those he knew, speaking constantly of Washington's need, threatening, using himself as a wedge in the countless little plots, breaking them open, writing false orders to commandeer shoes and clothing, talking to the food brokers, promising everything under the sun, actually maneuvering a shipment of grain toward Valley Forge, drinking again, more than he should, writing words that cut like knives—

A change was coming over things. At the end of that winter of 1777-1778, the crucial point of the war arrived, and the Americans won, not through battles, but simply by existing as an army, as a military force. The tall, unhappy Virginian, who had failed so as a commander, proved his worth as a rallying point, and throughout that dreadful cold winter, he held a nucleus of his men around him. Perhaps if Howe, the British commander, had attacked Valley Forge, the American army—what was left of it—might have been utterly destroyed. But Philadelphia was comfortable, and Howe did not attack, and with spring there was not only a French alliance, the product of old Ben Franklin's careful work, but a reoccurrence of that incredible phenomenon, the American militia.

Once again the summer soldiers, through with their plowing, poured into the encampment—householders, farm hands, men and boys. The four thousand left after the winter at Valley Forge became seven thousand, then ten, then twelve thousand. And as a nucleus there was the bitter, hard kernel that had kept alive in the hellish encampment.

Howe became frightened. Once he could have been the attacker; now he was in a position to be attacked. He marched out of Philadelphia, north through Jersey; and at Monmouth, Washington barred his path. Not for nothing had three years of war, three desperate, losing years, put iron into the ragged, lean continentals. For the first time they fought and held their ground, stood through the shot and shell and fire of a day's burning battle, and then lay on their weapons and watched a broken British army retreat from the field.

The war was not over; it was not much more than begun; but now there was an American Army.

Paine was beginning to understand his new profession, the skill called revolution which he was the first to practice as a sole reason for being. He had seen the people take power, and the means by which they took power; he had seen their appointed leaders, citizens whose livelihood was not war, rally them against the enemy. He had seen the counter-revolution rear its head again and again, in New York, in Philadelphia, in Jersey, and in Pennsylvania. He had seen the army split up into opposing groups, and he had seen staunch patriots eager to sell out to the highest bidder. And now he was watching one of the final phases, a cleavage between the people's party and the party of finance, of trade and power and aristocracy. And strangely enough these latter forces were united against one who was reputedly the wealthiest man in America: the Virginia farmer, Washington. First, it was a plot to deprive Washington of the command and give it to Gates; then, to dirty his reputation and split the high command from him; and now, lastly, a direct sell-out to Great Britain. England sent across the ocean a party of gentlemen with very broad powers; they knew whom to contact. Paine sent a messenger to Washington and wrote with fury in his pen.

A *Crisis* appeared in which Paine, raging mad, wrote: "What sort of men or Christians must you suppose the Americans to be, who, after seeing their most humble petitions insultingly rejected; the most grievous laws passed to distress them in every quarter; an undeclared war let loose upon them, and Indians and Negroes invited to the slaughter; who, after seeing their kinsmen murdered, their fellow citizens starved to death in prisons, and their houses and property destroyed and burned; who, after the most serious appeals to heaven, the most solemn adjuration by oath of all government connected with you, and the most heart-felt pledges and protestations of faith to each other; and who, after soliciting the friendship, and entering into alliance with other nations, should at last break through all these obligations, civil and divine, by complying with your horrid and infernal proposal. . . ."

Working underground himself, he fell deeper and deeper into the snarl. He hadn't the restraint to refrain from direct accusations, yet he could not unearth a scrap of written evidence to back up his suspicions of the plots against the revolution.

Not trusting Samuel Adams—sincerely believing that Adams and a good many others of the Boston crowd could be bought if the proposals were properly put, the price high enough, and the settlement such as to give them the positions they longed for—he could, nevertheless, find no solid grounds upon which to accuse them. And Richard Henry Lee, stopping him on the street, told him bitterly:

"You seem to enjoy making enemies, Paine."

"I have so many that a few more don't matter."

"A friend might help. A quiet tongue might, too."

"My only friend is the revolution. And my tongue wags like the tongue of any damned peasant."

"Just a word of warning—"

"I don't have to be warned, my friend," Paine smiled.

And then, hard on that, came the affair of Silas Deane.

As secretary to the Committee for Foreign Affairs, Paine had come, time and again, upon some very curious matters. There was a European firm called Roderique Hortalez and Company. He himself had had some dealings with them when things were most desperate the winter before. It was a matter of military boots for an army that bound their bleeding feet in rags and sackcloth, and a Mr. Steffins of Charleston said he might obtain a thousand pair of good boots—for a price. The price was a livre a pair; that was high, but in wartime one expects things to come high. Paine negotiated the deal, and when the boots arrived they proved to be of Spanish leather—and the bill was presented by Roderique Hortalez and Company. The company was already widely known among the continentals, but who had hired Mr. Steffins and who had paid him? Going into the matter, Paine discovered that almost all outside help to America—shiploads of wheat from France, flat-boat fleets of powder, shot and cannon that came upriver from New Orleans, cargoes of rum from the Indies, clothing from Spain, dried cheese from Holland, even one consignment of Scotch plaid that had somehow been smuggled from the British Isles—all bore bills of sale from Roderique Hortalez and Company.

Too many people seemed to know all about Roderique Hortalez and Company; too many who were unwilling to talk. For Paine to get details was like pulling teeth. Henry Laurens, the president of the Congress, an honest man trying to fight his way through a wilderness of lies, deceits, and selfishness, one whom Paine respected and liked, told him:

"What does it matter, so long as it helps the cause?"

"But the prices," Paine pointed out.

Laurens had smiled; that was some time ago.

From Arthur Lee in Paris came word that it was a probability, no more than that, that both France and Spain had made secret gifts to America, possibly as much as a million livres apiece. Deane was getting a five per cent commission on all sales through the company, and bills were being presented. Then, in a letter from Franklin, Paine found what he considered almost conclusive proof that all supplies were purchased with a gift of gold from the two governments, a gift handled by a mysterious and incredible person called Caron de Beaumarchais, incredible because he appeared to be the power behind Roderique Hortalez and Company, mysterious because the French government preferred him so, being not yet at war with England when the funds were advanced to him. A neutral power could not show preferences among belligerents, but an international concern could deal with whom it pleased.

To all this, Henry Laurens had said, "What does it matter?" smiling. Nations could very well act like children about international affairs; face had to be preserved. The world knew that the Continental Congress was perhaps the most impoverished governing power on earth, that it had hardly enough money to buy pen, paper, and ink for the sessions.

Thus, when bills began to be presented to the Committee for Foreign Affairs, they were politely ignored, recorded, filed, but ignored. One understood those matters.

"But did one?" Paine wondered.

He asked Roberdeau to arrange a small dinner at which Laurens would be present, and then he carefully led the talk to the subject of the bills.

"Why do you harp on that, Paine?" Laurens asked, somewhat impatiently. "Those bills will never be presented for payment. France is at war with England now and the goods advanced to us by Hortalez, or shall I say by the French ministry through Hortalez, are only a mere fraction of the military advantage France has gained through the years we have been at war. Franklin made that plain."

"Yet if Hortalez and Company demand payment, it would be rather embarrassing for France to insist that we had received the goods as gifts. Do you know what the bills amount to?"

"I have some idea," Laurens said testily.

"They amount to four and a half million livres," said Paine. "Beaumarchais can become a millionaire— we've paid double for everything, you see—if they present claims. Even Deane's five per cent would make him a rich man."

Roberdeau whistled and Laurens shook his head. "I had no idea it was that much."

"The greatest swindle of our time," Paine prodded.

"What do you propose to do?"

"Attack Deane before payment is demanded and what miserable credit we have is broken."

"You have no proof that Deane expects to receive a commission. First the bills must be presented for payment."

"Proof—my God, isn't it proof enough that Deane handled all the negotiations. If the goods are a gift, Deane gets nothing; if we are forced to pay, Deane is a rich man."

Hard on that dinner, the scandal broke. Beaumarchais, through the mysterious firm of Hortalez, flung his hand into the pot of fortune and demanded payment, and Deane came back to America to collect. The split that had been brewing for so long in America, between the party of the people and the party of trade and power, snapped wide open. Congress, writhing under the impact of four and a half million livres that could never be repaid, demanded of the French ambassador:

"Was or was not the money a gift?"

"It was," they were assured, but it could not be acknowledged publicly. The honor of France was at stake.

Hortalez again demanded payment; Deane appeared before Congress and smilingly asked for his five per cent. He was not afraid; he knew too much about Congress, too much about what went on in France with Arthur Lee and Franklin. When Congress refused to hear him, he took his case to the papers, attacking the whole Lee family, declaring himself the savior of his country and asking for justice. That was more than Paine could stand, and he wrote a furious, biting reply.

Deane claimed credit for the supplies sent to America. Paine opened the books of the Committee for Foreign Affairs and proved that the French and Spanish gifts had been made before Silas Deane ever went to France. Philadelphia began to boil.

And then the French ambassador, Gerard, saw Paine privately and told him, "This must not go on."

"Why?" Paine asked bluntly.

"For reasons I cannot explain. Certain personages are involved. You must drop your attack on Deane."

"And if I refuse?"

Gerard shrugged and spread his hands. "Do you refuse?"

"I am sorry," Paine nodded. "This thing we are doing; it isn't a little intrigue for the crowned heads of Europe—it's revolution, do you understand."

"I understand," Gerard said, and the next day told Congress:

"All the supplies furnished by Monsieur de Beaumarchais to the States, whether merchandise or cannon or military goods, were furnished in the way of commerce, and the articles which came from the King's magazine and arsenals were sold to Monsieur de Beaumarchais by the department of artillery, and he has furnished his obligations for the price of these articles."

Paine writhed and pleaded to Roberdeau, "Proof—if only I had proof." He wrote bitterly of Deane:

"It fell not to his lot to turn out to a winter's campaign, and sleep without tent or blanket. He returned to America when the danger was over, and has since that time suffered no personal hardship. What then are Mr. Deane's *sufferings* and what the sacrifices he complains of? Has he lost money in the public service? I believe not. Has he got any? That I cannot tell. . . ."

Gerard did not warn Paine again; he sought out the faction in Congress that hated Paine so bitterly. Congress acted, summoned Paine, and demanded whether he wrote *Common Sense to the Public on Mr. Deane's Affair.*

"I wrote it," Paine acknowledged.

In secret session, Congress attacked Paine mercilessly; he heard rumors of what was going on, but was denied all his pleas to answer the charges. He heard that the wealthy Gouverneur Morris of New York had said, during session:

"What would be the idea of a gentleman in Europe of this Mr. Paine? Would he not suppose him to be a man of the most affluent fortune, born in this country of a respectable family, with wide and great connections, and endued with the nicest sense of honor? Certainly he would suppose that all these pledges of fidelity were necessary to a people in our critical circumstances. But, alas, what would he think, should he accidentally be informed, that this, our Secretary of Foreign Affairs, was a mere adventurer from England, without fortune, without family or connections, ignorant even of grammar?"

Laurens told Paine, "Resign before they have a chance to dismiss you. God knows what is coming, Paine—I don't." And Laurens added, "I am doing the same, you see. They will have to find a new president for their Congress."

Paine resigned.

And in Philadelphia hell was brewing.

Only outwardly was Philadelphia tranquil, and even that tranquillity was fast disappearing. The Quaker city was a revolution ary capital, occupied by the British, reoccupied by the Americans. It was not only geographically the center of the states, but ideologically as well, for Boston soon cooled and the Massachusetts farmers, who had once ripped a British army to shreds at Concord and Lexington, had for the most part gone back to their spades and plows. Their cold, bitter Yankee sense of personal freedom was bound inextricably with their own rocky land, and their fierce individuality made them poor material for any other warfare than the kind they fell into instinctively, guerrilla tactics. That guerrilla warfare might have ended the struggle much sooner was beside the point; it was not being fought that way, and the Yankees drifted off.

The bulk of the struggle was left to the midlanders, Pennsylvania men for the most part, Jersey men and New York men, Connecticut, Rhode Island, Delaware, and Maryland regiments; and in the South, Virginia and Carolina men. But the core of the regulars, the men who starved and froze and thirsted, the few thousand who clung by the spare figure of Washington in the worst of times, were almost all Pennsylvania and Jersey men. For them, Philadelphia was the altar of revolution, and for them, the blackest day came when Congress fled without even an attempt to defend the city.

The British, who considered the city worthless, since they already held New York and could not afford troops to garrison both towns, had evacuated it with as little attempt at defense as the Americans before them. Marching to reoccupy the place on the heels of the redcoats, the continentals were not happy or gentle. They wanted revenge, and some they took. The city was dirty, littered, houses in ruins, houses looted, the beautiful Philadelphia Chippendale, the pride of the colonies, hacked and ripped and broken. The Americans walked back into the city with their bayonets bared. Wayne, a hard knife-blade of a man, led the Pennsylvanians. "A Tory," he said to a committee of important citizens, "is a son of a bitch with —— inside of him." They were used to strong language, but not that strong. They proclaimed their loyalty.

"As I understand loyalty," Wayne said, "so I would make you understand it—"

But to untangle the Tory from the rebel was impossible. Of the thousands of citizens who had remained behind when the British came, who was to say which was loyal and which was not? Of informers, there were plenty, but even those most bitter shied away from the bloody terror that wholesale accusation would bring. The midlanders were hard men, but not that hard.

And Pennsylvania was a democracy. Of all the countries that made up the union, Pennsylvania was the nearest to a government of workers and farmers—militant workers and farmers who had framed their own liberal constitution, their own single-house form of government in the days when the war started. The backbone of this group were the leather-clad frontiersmen who had sworn that they would have a thing or two to say with their long rifles before the aristocrats took their land.

Into this brew was flung the Silas Deane affair—to split it wide open.

Roberdeau showed Paine a letter, addressed to Robert Morris, who had lately cornered the flour market of the midlands. The letter had come to Roberdeau through means he was not anxious to disclose; there were ways. The line he pointed out read, "It would be a good thing for the welfare of the gentle folk of the country if Mister Thomas Paine were dead. . . ."

"If they wish to, they can kill me," Paine shrugged. "They've tried before—"

"Don't be a fool. The time is over when you can fight this thing alone."

"What do you suggest?"

Roberdeau suggested that they show their hand. He offered his house for a meeting place. He knew a few who could be trusted, and Paine knew a few. Tomorrow night, he said.

"Tomorrow night," Paine agreed. He was very tired; a man could take up a gun, preach revolution, write papers pleading with his fellow citizens to support the war, unearth plots, oppose factions, lose his reputation and his livelihood, be hated and despised, scream aloud that men fought and died, that Philadelphia did not exist for the sole purpose of raising the price of food, clothes, munitions, livestock—but a man reached his limits. It was not easy to know that people wanted to kill you; it made him afraid the way he had never been afraid on the battlefield; it made him afraid of dark streets, afraid to drink too much, afraid to sleep in his miserable two-shilling room without locking the door.

The last time he had looked in the mirror, it was with the sudden realization that he was growing old. A network of little lines picked out his eyes and cheeks. That was Paine, the staymaker. Irene Roberdeau was married and carrying a child. The world went on, but facing him in his mirror was Paine, the mendicant of revolution.

It was a good group that gathered at Roberdeau's house, Paine told himself. A solid group, each person picked, each to be depended on.

There was David Rittenhouse, the scientist and mechanic, a person of substance, but nevertheless one who had worked with his hands; there was Jackson Garland, who, before his forge had been destroyed by the British, had cast forty-nine cannon for Harry Knox. Garland was Scotch, thin and sour in appearance, but a man with a mind, one who had often explained to Paine his theory of the coming trade unions. There was Charles Wilson Peale, captain in the Continental Army, a painter of amazing skill, and completely devoted to Washington. There was Colonel Matlack, a Quaker who had decided that some things were worth fighting for, who had said publicly that he would die fighting his own brothers before he saw the Morris clique destroy the Pennsylvania constitution. And there were young Thomas Shany and Franklin Pearce, both captains and veterans of Wayne's Pennsylvania Line. In addition they could count on the active support of both Laurens and Jefferson, neither of whom was present.

Roberdeau had wine and cake served, and then called the meeting to order. The group was quiet, grave, and somewhat bewildered; vaguely they sensed the possibilities and results of an open split in the Continental Party, and for that reason they felt they were treading on gunpowder. Organized revolt was still a very new thing in the world; organized radicalism, splitting from the rightists within the body of the revolution, was entirely new.

Roberdeau, his fleshy face red and excited, suggested that Paine take the floor and explain the purpose of the meeting. To which Paine pointed out anxiously:

"I don't want to intrude myself. It might be said that I am the least of the company here. I feel—"

"Damn it, no! This is no time for hedging nor politeness," Matlack said. "You know what this is, and go ahead and speak, Paine."

Paine looked around at the others; heads nodded. Paine said, speaking quietly but swiftly, "I don't need much of a preamble. A time was when revolution was new to all of us, but we've lived with it a good many years now—perhaps not long enough to understand it completely, to know the whole devil in this broth we're brewing, but long enough to have some comprehension of its structure. Revolution is a method of force by a party not in power, as we understand it by the party of the people, which has never been in power in the history of this earth. When the thirteen states of our confederation aroused themselves to seize the power, the confederation as a whole was in revolt against the British Empire. That we recognize, and the confederation as a whole is now engaged in war with the sovereign state of Great Britain.

"That is one thing. But the same method of revolution was singularly applied in each of the states of the confederation, and in each of the states the party of the people fought for the power. In some states, the people won; in others they lost, but in no case was the issue clear-cut. The act of revolution goes on in thirteen lands on this continent; there is civil war everywhere; in New York a man takes his life in his hands if he dares travel alone through Westchester County. In Massachusetts, the Tories are so powerful that they openly paint their chimneys with bands of black to identify themselves. In the lake country the Tories and the Indians have allied themselves, in such power as to engage our armies in force. In the Carolinas brother fights brother, and whole families have been wiped out by this civil strife. No one who traveled through the Jerseys in the retreat of seventy-six will ever forget how the whole countryside rose against us, shot at us from behind their shuttered windows, let us starve, just as they let us starve in Valley Forge a year later.

"In only one place did the revolution triumph, instantly, decisively, and without doubt, and that is here in Pennsylvania, the wealthiest land on this continent, perhaps the most loyal, certainly the most powerful. If the midlands fall, then the revolution falls; and if the midlands go up in smoke, who will say that the Pennsylvania line will not desert Washington and march back to defend their homes?

"Though I don't have to remind you, let me briefly reconsider the revolutionary enactments of Pennsylvania. You remember how, even before Concord and Lexington, the working men of Philadelphia formed themselves into an armed citizenry. Alone, unskilled as they were in any sort of warfare, they might not have triumphed, but fortunately they were joined by several thousand hunters and homesteaders from the back country. It was by the long rifle and the buckskin as well as by the musket that we overthrew the anticonstitutionalists. The aristocrats gave way when we threatened them with civil war and when they saw our guns. We won a constitution and we won a democratic state legislature, and then, loyal to the confederation, we sent our men by the thousands to fight with General Washington. I saw that myself. I was at Newark when the Pennsylvanians held the rear, at Valley Forge when they lay in the snow and starved, but held; at Monmouth our buckskin men broke the British backs. And, gentlemen, I was at the Delaware in seventy-six, when Washington fled across to the poor safety of the west bank, when he ordered a count and there were eight hundred men—eight hundred to defend the future of men of good will and make a nation out of this suffering of ours —and then I saw something that I will not forget if I live a hundred years, I saw the working men of Philadelphia, twelve hundred strong, march up from the city and hold the Delaware line until Sullivan joined with Washington. Six months before, the Associators ran away, and that was to the shame of no one; it takes six months of hell to put iron into a man's soul, and when they marched up out of Philadelphia again, the clerks and masons and smiths and millers, weavers, mercers—they were different. Pennsylvania gave freely, and now we have our deserts.

"Congress fled and gave our city to the British and Tories. We have it back so that it can become the speculator's dream, so that Deane can fleece us, so that Morris can corner flour, so that Graves can run up the price of tobacco twenty-two dollars a barrel, so that Jamison can pile up his wool on the river front while the army freezes, so that Mr. Jamie Wilson, whom you know as well as I, can corner a million dollars' worth of back-country land—easy enough with the woodsmen away fighting—and not content with that, attack everything the people of this state have fought for through his rotten and seditious paper, the *Packet*. And he has as his good ally, the equally vicious *Evening Post*. All this, gentlemen, is not a matter of chance, but a concerted attack against the revolution in Pennsylvania. The so-called Republican Society of Mr. Robert Morris is about as much republican as George the Third; its sole purpose, as far as I can see, is to destroy the constitution in which lies the power of the people.

"I think I have talked too much, gentlemen. There is the situation which I was trying to fight alone, and which General Roberdeau thinks we can fight better together. I leave the rest to you—"

No applause; he sat down in silence, all of them watching him. He was very tired, and his head ached. Matlack said thoughtfully, thinking aloud more than anything else:

"Whatever we do, we will need the means of force. Washington—"

"I think he'll be with us," Rittenhouse nodded.

"Will he, though?"

Paine said yes. Peale said direct action: if men were profiteering, they would be brought before a tribunal, judged, punished. The constitution would be defended by force—

"Then that's civil war."

"So be it. They've asked for it."

"Support?"

"Bring this out in the open and people will declare themselves. Then we'll know."

Roberdeau sighed; he was growing old; peace was a dream now. Worried, Rittenhouse said they must move cautiously, cautiously.

"To hell with that!"

"Bloodshed—"

"They've asked for it," Garland said harshly. Most of them took that stand; they had been with the army; when campaigning started, they would be with the army again. But, Paine pointed out, this thing must come of the people. Peale suggested a mass meeting, and Roberdeau said he would organize it. A vote was taken, and the others agreed to the method.

They shook hands and each went home. No one smiled. It was something a long time coming, and now that it was here, they were not happy.

The meeting was held at the State House, in the courtyard. Several hundred people attended, and both Paine and Roberdeau spoke. Matlack moved for the establishment of a Committee of Inspection, and an open vote was taken. Paine was the first elected, then Colonel Smith, a solid supporter of the Constitution, a militiaman and therefore from the people. Rittenhouse, Matlack, and Peale finished the roster. The crowd was grim and earnest. The Republican Society had tried heckling, but the crowd was too somber for that, and it was only by the efforts of Rittenhouse and Roberdeau that violence was avoided.

The next day Peale and Paine dined with Captain Hardy, in command of a company of Pennsylvania regulars, temporarily bivouacked in the city. Peale explained what was coming. "I'm afraid of the mob," he said. "If your men support us—"

At first, Hardy refused. It was not in his province. If Wayne agreed—

"But there's no time for that!"

They argued for an hour, and then Hardy agreed to put it up to the men. Both Paine and Peale spoke, and the troops, after some consultation among themselves, agreed to support them.

In a way, war had been declared in Philadelphia.

The city knew. It was like an armed camp. Men kept their muskets at hand; mobs roamed the streets; there was work for Peale's company of troops. The Committee of Inspection set up its tribunal, and merchant after merchant was hauled before it, ordered to explain his business, ordered to produce books and vouchers. A Mr. Donny was found to have thirty-six hundred pairs of shoes in his warehouse, purchase price averaging eleven dollars, asking price, sixty dollars. Paine prepared the evidence carefully. A Mr. Solikoff, a mysterious gentleman of Baltimore, was found to be Morris's partner in cornering the flour market. Indictments were drawn up.

The *Philadelphia Post* had a rush of courage and attacked Paine more scathingly and filthily than ever before. Paine would have let the matter pass. "It's not the first time," he explained.

But they were out in the open now. Matlack had the *Post* building surrounded by soldiers, and Towne, the publisher, was asked whether he would like to hang by the neck for a while. The warning was enough.

"I don't like that," Rittenhouse said. "Freedom of the press—"

But the committee assured him that once the revolution had triumphed, there would be time enough for freedom of the press.

The committee had no power to punish, but it had a tremendous power for intimidation, and it was solidly supported by the rank and file of Philadelphia. It stored up its evidence for the coming election, and at a great public mass meeting, it presented its case against Morris. The following day, thoroughly frightened, Morris let his corner on flour fall to pieces.

From a meeting of the committee one night Paine walked home, suddenly as weak as a child, barely able to mount the rickety wooden stairs to his room. He lay on his bed, alternately hot and cold, trembling, delirious, plucking at his memory, whimpering sometimes, but too weak to light a fire in the hearth. All the next day he lay in bed in the same semi-conscious state, half the following day. Too many things were happening; for the moment Paine was forgotten. The tribunal sat over Philadelphia, and the city was frightened, angry, divided in itself. Mobs surged through the streets by torchlight, and Peale's soldiers, spread too thin by far, tried vainly to keep order.

Roberdeau remembered the absent writer, and by that time Paine was almost dead, a haggard dirty figure in a foul and dirty chamber. When Paine regained consciousness, the first person he saw was Irene Roberdeau, and it was a dream, and this an angel. He said, "I'm dying—" but it didn't matter. He was too weak to feel anything but a lonely sort of happiness, only strong enough to resist Roberdeau's efforts to take him out of the place he called his home.

For nine days she stayed with him, an impersonal, competent nurse, and then Paine, who could stand it no longer, begged her to go. She went, and it was lonelier and bleaker than ever. When he got out of bed and looked into the bit of glass he called his mirror, it was not Paine who faced him, but a yellow mask stretched on jutting bones, hollow eyes, a monstrous nose, and long, scraggly, thinning hair.

While Paine lay sick, civil war raged in Philadelphia. He heard the gunshots of the pitched battle between Wilson's group and the constitutionalists. He heard, all through one night, the ragged sound of musketry, and wept like a baby because he was confined here, feeble, unable to move. And he was still sick when the state election swept the constitutionalists into a power beyond dispute.

Peale told him about it, and Paine nodded and tried to smile. "So long as we won," he said.

Another dark winter dragged through; it was seventeen-eighty; part of the Pennsylvania Line mutinied, for lack of food, of pay, of clothing. Five long years they had been fighting, and they wanted to see their homes, their wives and their children. Charleston fell. The mutiny was put down. Washington poured his heart into begging letters, and Paine read them. He was clerk of the Assembly now. Washington wrote, "My dear Paine, is there nothing that can be done, nothing?"

The election had been very decisive. With the constitutionalists in power, Morris, Rush and other leaders of the Republican party threw in their hands. The counter-revolution had been blocked and broken, and it would not rise again for many years. Paine had to live somehow; *Crisis* papers could be written and printed, but the people who read them had not a penny to give the author. It was then that Roberdeau and Peale had offered Paine the position of clerk to the State Assembly, and Paine had taken it. "I hoped to go back to the army," he apologized. He didn't have the strength; strangely, quietly, age crept up on him. His hair was graying, and the curious twisted eyes had a shadow of fear in them.

As clerk of the Assembly, he read an appeal from Washington: ". . . every idea you can form of our distresses will fall short of reality. . . ." To Pennsylvania, this was, when all else had failed; to the men who had taken power and organized the first revolutionary tribunal. "Such a combination of circumstances to exhaust the patience of the soldiery. . . . We see in every line of the army the most serious features of mutiny and sedition. . . ." To Paine, it was more than that, the tall Virginian pleading, "You, Paine, who did this thing with your pen—you who could talk to the men." He was sick, and his hand trembled. The Assembly sat with dead features; afterwards, he would get drunk. The discussion was hopeless; a delegate saying, "What can we do?"; another putting it into different words.

He had a thousand dollars in continental money. He took half of it and made the first step of reconciliation with the party of finance. Sending the five hundred dollars to Blair McClenaghan, dealer in tobacco and linens, a Scot who had a grudging admiration for Paine, he suggested some sort of moving fund for the relief of Washington. The Scot mentioned the idea to Salomon, a small and rather mysterious Jew who made his headquarters in a coffee house on Front Street. It was rumored that Salomon had broken the wheat combine, that he had knocked the bottom out of the price for woolen blankets. At any rate, he was involved with the constitutionalists, whose chief financial backing came from Jews.

"Do it," Salomon told the Scot. "It's the only thing—but I am not your man. I can spare a few thousand, five perhaps, but you'll need capital, a great deal of money. Go to Morris and Reed and Rush. I think they'll go in."

"After the way Paine fought them? It's his idea."

"After the way he fought them. They want it their revolution, but they don't want to lose the war."

McClenaghan went to Morris. Morris said bitterly, "I hate that man—but he's right. We're going under. If I can convince Wilson—"

"If you can—" the Scot smiled.

"Nevertheless, one day Mr. Paine will pay," Morris said grimly. "We won't forget."

The sum of hatred Paine had aroused was left for further collection, and that night, on the basis of his five hundred dollars continental, the Bank of Pennsylvania was organized to supply the army with food, clothes, and munitions.

Paine wrote *Crisis* papers in the same white heat, but he had to drink more and more to put the flame in his pen. Twice he went off to the army; old Common Sense was thinner, more haggard than ever, but the men welcomed him and still flung the cry at him, "My God, Tom, this don't make no sense whatever." He explained patiently, again and again; they were his children, dirty, haggard, worn as he. Washington said to him, "Don't let me ever estimate, Paine, what you are worth."

In the *Crisis Extraordinary* he was at his calmly furious best, appealing to the merchants for a common front, begging them to believe that only in a democracy could a man of business have full play for his abilities. In the *Crisis on Public Good*, he begged the confederation to fight together, not to fall out among themselves, not to let regional differences turn them from the common enemy. He began to think of a national government now; what had happened in Pennsylvania was a warning.

There was a week of sheer drunkenness when his brain bogged down, when he felt he was over and through and could go on no longer, and then he came out of it, thinner than before, yet more resolute—with a scheme for carrying the revolution to England personally. He would go there himself. A *Common Sense* to the British citizen, the British working man and farmer.

Nathanael Greene talked him out of that. The Benedict Arnold affair had just run its course, and the British were burning with the execution of André.

"If they could hang Paine," Greene said, "that would even things. I am afraid we still need you."

Suddenly, not in a day nor a week, but suddenly enough after all the years, the war was being won, not over yet, no treaty of peace signed, but nevertheless won, the heartache and hopelessness finished, a British army trapped at Yorktown, the British cause in America torn to shreds, a French grant of several millions solving the financial problem, the Tories shattered. Then it was Paine alone and frightened, looking at all this, and wondering. "Where am I? Who am I?"

The props had been knocked from under him; always on the outside, always the man behind the scenes, always the propagandist, he found a time now when there was no need for propaganda, no need for men behind the scenes. In a victorious army, the pleading, exhorting figure of Paine would stir only laughter.

His trade was revolution, and now he was without a trade. "Go back to staymaking then," he told himself morosely. His friends, his companions were turning their hand to statecraft, construction; others were grabbing, because victory meant spoils. And he, who was so definitely not a statesman, had no desire for spoils.

There was a trip to France. His old friend and the one-time president of the Congress, Henry Laurens, had been taken prisoner by the British while sailing to Holland. Paine, who knew Laurens' son, tried to lift the boy out of his misery.

"It won't be forever," he told John Laurens. "There'll be an exchange of prisoners soon. The war will be over—"

Paine had a way with men, and the boy came to worship him. Then, when young Laurens went to Paris to help push the French loan, he begged Paine to accompany him, and Paine, who saw his work on this side of the ocean coming to an end, agreed. In a way, it was a holiday, the first he had ever known in all his life, he an honored visitor in France, men of distinction begging him to autograph their copies of *Common Sense*, making him understand, as he had never understood before, that he, Paine, really mattered.

It was over all too soon. The mission was successful; everything, it seemed, was successful now, and Paine, coming home on a ship loaded down with two and a half millions of livres in silver, could not help reflecting on the curious change in the little union of colonies which called itself America. As for instance when he wrote his last *Crisis* paper, just before the trip to France. No trouble about publishers then; a dozen printers clamored for the privilege of printing it. *Crisis* papers were safe investments now that the crisis had passed.

They asked Paine to dinner soon after he had returned to America, Mrs. Jackson, who had been Irene Roberdeau, and her husband. Frank Jackson had no jealousy of Paine; he said to Irene, quietly, "Why, he's almost an old man!"

Irene was still young and lovely. As she sat with her child at her knee, she confirmed Paine's aging lassitude. He was old; he was finished; it was only in a dream that he had dared to love this woman.

"What are you going to do now, Thomas?" she asked him.

And he tried to smile his way out of it, implying that there would be much to do. He was a busy man, he said, so much writing, so many dinners—

"The revolution is done," Frank Jackson said, and there was nothing for Paine but to agree.

"They won't forget you."

A sop to him. "Why should it matter?" he muttered.

"You look so tired," Irene said.

He was tired; damned tired and wanting to get out of this place and get good and drunk. Who were these people, and how did he come to be sitting there in their house? Who was he but a wandering staymaker who had been something else for a while?

"You'll need a rest," Irene said.

"I imagine I will," he agreed. After that, he could not get away quickly enough.

He was not even the clerk of the Assembly now—nothing, Tom Paine, former revolutionist, a little more ragged than usual, a little more empty under his belt. The expected thing after Yorktown was a spree, and he had been drunk for four days; but that didn't go on. You had to eat and drink; you found that shoe leather wore out; you needed a room, no matter how small and dirty and disreputable.

The loneliness was not to be abated. Roberdeau had gone to Boston. Greene was campaigning in Carolina, and when he wrote that it would be like old days if only Paine were with him, Paine thought ruefully, "Not like old days. I was needed then. I'm no part of victory."

Wayne was knifing through Georgia with the now famous Pennsylvania Line; the best soldiers in the world they were called. The years made a difference; Paine could remember five hundred of them by name.

Washington came to Philadelphia for a triumph, but it was a hollow triumph; his stepson had just died. The tall Virginian looked wasted and empty, and when he called for Paine, they were like two men left over. Paine was ashamed of his dirty clothes, his appearance, his mottled face.

"My old friend," Washington said.

Paine began to brag; he was thinking of doing a history of the revolution. Did Washington know how many copies of *Common Sense* had been printed?

"I know my own value," Paine boasted.

Thinking of how perspectives changed, of what a wretched creature this scribbler was, away from the campfires and disillusioned, mutinous men, Washington smiled and said, "My dear Paine, no one of us will ever forget your value." Why did revolution leave such a backwash? Everyone was looking for rewards, but how did this fit into a world of peace and order?

"Even Morris recognizes what you have done," Washington said quickly. "On two fronts, the home front and the fighting front, it was Paine who kept the cause together—I tell you that with the deepest conviction, my good friend—"

They parted soon after, and Washington was not there to see Paine weep.

A delegation of rank and file soldiers called upon him. Months and months of back pay was owed to them; would Paine be their spokesman? Would Paine organize their demand and present it to the government? No one knew better than Paine what they had suffered through the years of war; no one had been closer to them than Paine. His pen had flashed fire for the revolution, and now had it a little fire left for those who had fought the revolution?

"Our aims are being accomplished," Paine told them wearily. "Now you must wait. Any sort of demands backed by force would be close to sedition—"

The soldiers stared at him dumbfounded.

He took the case to Robert Morris, the minister of finance. "Of course, their claims are just," he pointed out to Morris. No one could say otherwise. But was this the time? Could Morris do something?

"Something, naturally," Morris said. It seemed so long ago that they were fighting each other. "These men are deserving, they will be paid," Morris assured Paine. "You were right not to encourage sedition. If the war may be considered won, then certain legal practices must be observed—"

Thoughtfully, Morris said, "You could turn your very considerable writing ability to our use, Paine. The government could be made to realize—"

"I didn't come for that."

"No, merely a thought, let us leave it in a place where we can take it up again." After a moment, Morris said, "There is no reason why we should be enemies."

Paine nodded and left; of course, no reason. Revolution and counter-revolution were done now. Men turned their hands to reasonable things.

Some writing, drawing pay from a government that no longer needed him, a new suit of clothes, a piece explaining the revolution to Europe, an emasculated piece, another *Crisis* with a touch of the old fire—why isn't peace formalized?

A few weeks with Kirkbride. Old soldiers dropped in; they talked of a thousand years ago, when they marched from Hackensack to the Delaware; but there was another trend of talk. The future bulked bright and large in America.

But how for him?

Desperately, he tried to interest himself in the future of America, the spoils and the glory, the boasting and memories, the speculations, the coming boom, the pride of being a free citizen in a great republic.

"Where freedom is not, there is my country," he had said once.

The peace came; America strutted like a peacock, free and independent. Fireworks and flag-waving and speeches and banquets and glory without end.

A tired Englishman who was once a staymaker, among other things, wrote:

"The times that tried men's souls are over—and the greatest and completest revolution the world ever knew, gloriously and happily accomplished. . . ."

He might have signed it: Tom Paine, revolutionist at large.

PART TWO

Europe

ELEVEN

Give Me Seven Years

BLAKE, the painter and the poet, said to him, to Tom Paine, "They are going to hang someone, and it might as well be you. They intend it to be you. They've longed to put a rope around your neck since 1776. You can't bait the lion in his den interminably, and England isn't America—"

"England isn't America," Paine agreed. He knew that by now.

"Then get out of London. Get out of England. Dead, you're no good to anyone."

"Run away," Paine murmured, and Blake laughed grimly.

"I can't laugh," Paine said. It had come down like a castle of cards; it was the year seventeen ninety-two, and he was Thomas Paine, esquire, revolutionist at large, packing an old valise hurriedly, preparing to flee from London and not be hanged—not yet. He was only fifty-five. He had said, "Give me seven years, and I will write a *Common Sense* for every nation in Europe." And now it was done in England. He had written a book called *The Rights of Man*, but somehow there were not the same bitter, stubborn farmers who had taken up their guns at Concord and Lexington. And he was fifty-five and tired and running away.

It was still dark, an hour or so before dawn, when Frost and Audibert pounded on his door and demanded to know what on God's earth was keeping him.

Anything into the valise now; a copy of *The Rights of Man*, an undershirt, and a half-finished manuscript.

"I'm coming—"

"The Dover stage won't wait—and the hangman won't!"

"I said I'm coming!"

Then it was done now, and England had slipped back to what England had been before. The bright, quick flame of glory was over; the little plots hatched in cellars and taverns were over. The forty-two muskets in Thaddeus Hatter's basement would stay there until they fell apart with rust. The barrel of gunpowder had been rolled into the Thames, and the shipworkers and miners and weavers and shopkeepers would stare at each other with the guilty, ashamed look of men who had for a moment dreamed the impossible and dared to believe it.

"I'm coming," Paine said.

In the stage, lurching over the pitted road that led to Dover, Frost nudged him and whispered, "In front, Leonard Jane." Jane was an agent of the crown, one of the many sharp-faced men who made their way here and there and saw things; it was before the day of the secret service.

"And I thought you said no one would know," Paine complained petulantly.

"Well, they know—"

In the pale tint of the early dawn, and then flushed by the bright red sun of morning, he had to sit and realize what it would mean to die, to be stretched, hanged by the neck, to have that bit of doggerel shrieked by every ragged urchin as they rode him to the gallows:

"Paine, Paine, damned be his name,
Damned be his fame and lasting his shame,
God damn Paine! God damn Paine!"

In his rush of thought, he whispered to Audibert, "If they take me, go to America, and go to Washington who remembers me, tell him how it was here, tell him there's no difference, England or America, only the want of a man like him—"

They didn't take him, but only because they weren't sure of themselves. "Even here," Audibert said, "you can't arrest a man without a warrant." And something had gone wrong; when they reached the customs at Dover, the warrant hadn't come through yet.

The customs men searched every bit of their luggage, found Paine's book, and tore it in half and threw it on the floor, "That for the rights of man and god damn you!"

Paine forgot what it meant to be hanged and said, "Shut your dirty mouth," a ringing tone in his voice that harked back ten years. Paine had been a soldier, and his eyes flashing he said, "Shut your dirty mouth!" Then he picked up the two halves of his book.

They were locked in a room, the three of them, and down from the barracks marched a detachment of six redcoats to stand guard outside the door.

"If the packet leaves without us," Frost said—and then drew a line on his throat with one finger.

A crowd began to gather around the customs house, and soon they were screaming, "Paine, Paine, damned be his name!"

"Your people," Frost said caustically, "who would rise to the banner of freedom and righteousness."

"Poor devils."

"Don't waste sympathy on them. If we're not out of here soon, we'll require all your sympathy."

"What are they holding us for?"

"A warrant, what else?"

Then the captain of customs opened the door and said, "Only by the grace of God, Paine, do you leave here. Don't come back to England."

Then Paine's party pushed through the hooting, screeching crowd onto the packet. The anchor came up, and two barges began to warp out the little Channel ferry. Paine stood on deck.

"Will you come back?" Audibert asked him, as the white chalk cliffs receded.

"I'll come back. It will be France, England and America—and then the whole world. I'll come back."

Safe on board the Channel boat, leaving England, leaving the hangman and the mob, Paine reflected how easily, how insidiously all this turmoil had begun. Back in America, when the struggle was over, he had put the revolution behind him; he had wanted to be Thomas Paine, esquire, dreaming of something for himself akin to what Washington had at Mt. Vernon. He was not an old man when the revolution ended; he was only forty-six, and a man's life isn't over then. Look at Franklin.

There comes a time when a man wants to sit back and say, "I've done enough; I want to eat and drink and sleep and talk and think." There was one magnificent, never-to-be-forgotten afternoon, when he sat for hours in the warm sunlight with Franklin talking of things scientific and things philosophical. "Play with science," Franklin told him. "That's the new age, the dawning."

"I would like to play," Paine said, his eyes curious.

Well, he was deserving of it, wasn't he? Not that he had made the war alone; but neither had Washington, nor Jefferson, nor Adams either. His part was not so slight that he was greedy in asking for some small reward, in petitioning Congress to give him some sort of livelihood, since he had nothing but revolution, since he was a specialist in change, and change was over.

They voted him a little money and a place in Bordentown and another in New Rochelle. It was enough. He lived simply, some drink, plain food, a workshop—correspondence with the scientific minds all over the world who were pricking at the future.

"Thomas Paine, esquire," he signed himself.

It was to be expected that a man would change; the times that tried men's souls were over. He dabbled in politics, but in a gentlemanly way, the way Morris or Rush would dabble. And when he saw a beggar now, a poor drunken sot, an aging veteran, racked with dysentery and syphilis, a one-armed garrulous soldier, an artillery man whose eyes had been blasted away by flaming powder, he did not say, "There, but by the grace of God, goes Thomas Paine."

But that was to be expected too.

And sometimes he was a little ashamed of these louts who

came to his house and cried, "Hey, Tom, hey there, old Common Sense, hey there, old comrade."

Talking of old times, look what they had made of themselves! The old times were over.

Better than that to dine with Washington, the tall fox-hunter whose name was spoken so reverently now, but who had nevertheless not forgotten the cold march down through the Jerseys.

"Madeira, Thomas?"

"I incline to claret."

"But Madeira, Thomas, with all the sunshine of the blue sky of Portugal."

Better to dine with Morris, Reed, Rush, now that old feuds had been patched up, old differences set aside; these were quality and these were the men who counted. They sipped their brandy and they talked of high financial matters, and they were the powers behind this new United States of America; and Paine was permitted to sit in and see what delicate maneuvering made the world go round.

A man changes; or perhaps that is wrong and a man never changes. Here, in this year of seventeen ninety-two, leaning on the rail of the Channel boat that was taking him over to France, away from an England that would have hanged him, watching the white chalk cliffs of Dover, he cast back in his memory and let the events run by, one by one, as they had happened.

There was the iron bridge, a scientific experiment—and hadn't Ben Franklin said that he had an eye and a mind for science? The bridge was something new in the world, of course, but a dreamer could see that iron was the coming master of man's fate. And why not a bridge to begin, so useful a thing, so common a thing? So he played with the idea, sketched, and made, in model, a bridge of iron. People came forty miles to see it. Anyone could see that the bridge was just "Common Sense," they said, making a poor pun of what had once been glory. The copies of the book *Common Sense* were turning yellow, stuffed away in attics and chests, but folks said, "Mighty smart feller, Paine. Thinks like a Yankee."

He took the model to Philadelphia and set it up in Ben Franklin's garden in Market Street. What a time that was! So many citizens called him Doctor Paine that he began to believe it—almost. He was toasted at dinners, luncheons, parties; four white wigs he owned, and his shirts were starched and faultlessly clean.

And once Rush mentioned, "How does it seem now to read *Common Sense,* Paine?"

"*Common Sense*?" as if it were some small matter that he could not easily call to mind.

"It was good for the times," he said judiciously.

"And what times they were, those old days," Rush laughed.

"At each other's throats."

"But now there's enough for all."

"For all, of course," Paine agreed.

Then he took his bridge model to France. Five years ago that was, 1787, Thomas Paine, esquire, crossing the broad ocean to France, not a bumpkin sick in a dirty, festering hold, but a gentleman of parts, philosopher, scientist, politician, financier you might say; first-class stateroom, walks on the deck while passengers pointed him out to each other.

His leaving America was in itself a reminder of the past; he still had enemies, enough to keep the State of Pennsylvania from erecting his iron bridge; and though he had hoped to go to France anyway, it was mostly bridge matter that sent him there. He had corresponded with the French scientists, spoken to Franklin about them, and he was quite certain they were the cleverest in the world, not to mention the wittiest. France would take up his bridge, then the world, then acclaim, then fortune. On shipboard, he felt youthful enough to have a mild flirtation with a Mrs. Granger of Baltimore, a flirtation which Paine pressed to the bedside with a grace and tact of which he would once not have thought himself capable. But why not? He was only in the summer of his life, healthier than he had ever been before, famous; forgotten as staymaker, cobbler, excise man, but Paine the philosopher and scientist.

France welcomed him; old, imperial France. King Louis sat at royal court at Versailles. If there were mutterings somewhere, what had Paine to do with them? This was France, not America. Taking a hint from Franklin, he played the part of the simple but wise American, plain brown breeches, no wig, no scent, white shirt, black coat, black shoes, cotton stockings, a cordial, winning smile that made up for his ignorance of the tongue. He met them all, the politicians, philosophers, the wits and the fops, the scientists, the high lords and the humble scholars. To a man of talent, there were no barriers—and the French food! He would say:

"Ah, we in America eat, but we do not cook. . . ."

And why not England? Why not go home again—it was so close, and so many years had gone by? The bridge hung fire in France; they liked it, but not enough. And in England, too, old hates were forgotten; you might fight a people once, but you did business with them indefinitely. And wasn't it said that in England George Washington was a greater hero than he was at home in America?

Paine crossed to London.

Dinner with Sir Joseph Banks, president of the Royal Society, Marcus Hawley, the astronomer, Sir John Tittleton of the East India Company—each one shaking hands with Paine, bowing to him, expressing their earnest belief that it was an honor, "Upon my word, sir, an honor—"

And of *Common Sense*, "Vigorous, sir, vigorous and thoroughly British, reaffirmation of the ancient dignity of the Magna Charta. America rebuffed us, but there was good English stubbornness in the rebuff, and who will say that the two countries are not wiser and more inclined to be one when the opportunity presents?"

"One?"

"The war was a mistake. We are intelligent men, we grant that."

How could he do otherwise than agree? Did they once bring up the fact that he was a staymaker, that he had rolled in the filth of Gin Row, that he had kept a tobacco shop? They were too well bred for that. Their superiority was lived rather than expressed, but so apparent that Paine, dazzled, could only smile, drink more than was good for him, smile and agree. You spent an evening with such men as these, and you saw why they ruled—brilliance, wit, charm, elegance; and perhaps you thought of the Massachusetts farmers, leaning on their big, rusty firelocks, spitting, or perhaps you did not think of that at all.

And when he brought out his bridge model, there was a chorus of praise.

"Trust the colonies to be a hundred years ahead of us in inventiveness."

A part of Paine's mind thought, "They still call us the colonies."

Then Thetford, and it shocked him that the old place had not changed, not at all, not a stone moved, the furrows plowed in the tracks of a thousand years of furrows, a crow perched on top a fence where he thought he remembered it perching so long ago. After America, this was entirely out of the world, for America lived by change, tear down the house and build a better one, tear down the barn and build a better one, pave the streets, sewers? Why not? The Romans did it. A higher church and a higher steeple, a bigger town hall.

But Thetford was the same, the tenant farmers brown clods of earth, not the tall, gangling, stubborn rustics of America, the new squire as fat and ruddy and overstuffed as his father, already gouty in one leg.

They didn't remember Paine; no one remembered him. The peasants pulled at their forelocks and said, "Eee, sir, thee be looking fur the Paine place?"

His mother was alive, a withered little thing, ninety years old, partly blind, partly deaf; she didn't remember him.

"Ah," she said, when he told her who he was. "Thee be my son?"

"Thomas, Mother, Thomas," feeling an awful sense of repulsion, of separateness, of having gone such a long distance that it was blasphemous to come back.

"Thomas—he be dead."

"Me, look at me, Mother!"

"Thee be Thomas?" so incredulously, rubbing her withered face, yet in a way, not surprised, not even troubled.

He supped with the squire, the boy who had once hanged him up by his feet, roast beef, heavy boiled pudding, big mugs of beer. This was the landed gentry that had once glowed with a halo not so different from that on Christ's forehead; you grouped them together when you stood rooted in the soil, looking up. Now the squire was so busy stuffing himself that it was all he could do to fling a word in edgewise now and then.

"Back with us, Paine—"

Carving a slice of beef and lifting the whole of it into his mouth, picking up a lump of pudding with his fingers and depositing it on the beef, then half a mug of beer drained down so quickly that part ran from the corners of his mouth, splashing over the napkin he had tucked into his neckpiece.

"Beef?"

Another slice jammed into his mouth, the long carving knife bearing the function of fork, spoon, and plate.

"Find the place different? Out in the world, scooping fame and fortune. What d'y think of the colonies, Paine? Whig myself, but can't stomach Americans, crude, Paine, too bloody damn crude."

And then another gob of pudding swimming into a mouthful of beer.

Soon after, Paine left. He had provided that nine shillings a week be paid to his mother for as long as she should live.

This was life as it should be lived; a man of wit, of parts, of philosophy did not remain in one place. Once he had said, "The world is my village, where freedom is not, there is my country"; and again the world was his village, and wherever witty men chatted over brandy and coffee, there was his country. He crossed the Channel back to France, and the bright life of Paris opened its arms to him. Paine actually became gay; scratch and scratch and scratch at the surface, and still you would not find the staymaker, the cobbler, the rabble rouser who crouched over a drumhead one freezing night and wrote:

"These are the times that try men's souls . . ."

In Paris, after these many years, he again met Tom Jefferson, not so young now—but neither were any of them, the old group that had stood together in Carpenter's Hall—but not so different, the long, sensitive face more deeply lined, the voice a little deeper, a little more puzzled when it spoke out at the world. He was genuinely glad to see Paine, and as they shook hands, Jefferson said:

"Tom, Tom, it does my heart good, it's a little of the old days, isn't it, when two friends come together? A man grows lonely so far from home, the more so when he mulls over his memories and begins to doubt them."

Paine spoke of his bridge, of his previous visit to France, his trip to his old home.

"And how do you find it here?" Jefferson asked.

Paine shrugged. "Louis will make reforms—the world moves that way."

"Does it?" Jefferson wondered. "Did it move for us or did we move it? There were some cold winters then, Tom."

Then let be what may! He could recall how he was again in England, looking in his mirror, telling himself, "I've done enough, enough!" In August, September, October of 1788, the social world of London opened its arms to him. Then, at the close of the eighteenth century, London was England as far as fashion went, and with the rumbling and muttering in France, it seemed that London might very well be the whole fashionable world. Four hundred years of sedulous effort on the part of the British ruling class had made of themselves the tightest clique of privileged titles anywhere in the world. Society was fixed, glazed, and varnished, and the only time the bars were ever let down was when a man of talent became as much a piece of fashion as skin-tight breeches or the Beau Brummell cravat.

And Paine was that. Burke adopted him; Burke, who had once made the great speech on conciliation with America, had a reputation to uphold as a liberal of a sort. Actually, liberalism with Burke was a memory of his youthful past; he saw in Paine the beginnings of a change in a thinking man, a change that he himself had already passed through; it was as ominous and as certain as hardening of the arteries, and therefore he concluded that Paine was a safe diversion. He had him to his country place; he gave him dinners, took him to various iron works that might be interested in doing his bridge. He introduced him to such great persons as Pitt, Fox, the Duke of Portland—rivers of port, five hundred candles burning in one small room, great and beautiful ladies. Paine was introduced into the exclusive Whig club of Brooks's, the same Brooks's that he had stood outside of so many years ago, his heart full of bitterness. His heart was not full of bitterness now as Fox offhandedly begged him to step to the tables and have a look at what passed.

Fortunes slipped across the table at Brooks's. Ten thousand pounds on the turn of a card, a whole estate on the deal of one hand. Somewhere in London, poor wretches still starved by the thousands, ripped out their guts with hot gin, lived twelve in a room, worked for threepence a day; but at Brooks's ten and twenty and thirty thousand pounds hung on the turn of a card.

He recalled the slip of a thing at some ball—was it Lady Mary Leeds or Lady Jane Carson?—who had said to him:

"Mr. Paine, do you know to what I attribute the success of you colonials in the American war?"

"Indeed I do not know, madam."

"To your beautiful, beautiful, beautiful, beautiful blue and white uniforms. I loathe red—and I told that to General Arnold, to His Excellency's face, I loathe red!"

Then a disturbing element broke in upon the life of Tom Paine, gentleman—calm, dispassionate letters began to come from Jefferson in Paris, telling Paine how the French revolution had arrived. They became a canker that ate at his soul, turning him bitter and sour until finally he gave in to it and went to France once more—to see, only to see, only curiosity.

Like smoke to a fire-fighter, that morning in Paris, when he, Tom Paine, who had come from fashionable London to revolutionary France, merely out of curiosity, as befitting a world traveler and philosopher, walked slowly through the workers' quarters, saw the black looks thrown at him because he was so obviously an Englishman, saw the muskets in the shops, handy to the storekeeper's grasp, saw the Bastille which had been so recently taken by the mob.

It was like Philadelphia, in the old days, citizens grimly mindful of their responsibility, citizens suddenly aware that they were human beings and not dirt under foot. Smoke and fire to Paine, and he breathed it in.

And then the welcome they gave him, the people when they learned who he was, his old comrade, Lafayette, who was commander of the National Guard, saying, "Militia, Thomas, but you and I know what they can do," Condorcet, then still a person of weight.

Condorcet had said to him in his very bad English, "I tell you, citizen Paine, that the written word does not die. I sat the other night with *Common Sense*, and I lusted, I lusted, friend Paine. We are a good people, we French, we are a strong people, and uncomplaining. Civilization will not have to be ashamed of us."

"Civilization is proud of you," Paine whispered.

Lafayette gave Paine the great, rusty key of the Bastille, and the onetime staymaker held it in his hands and fought to keep the tears back. That was how it happened, so insidiously.

"Weep, weep, my friend," Lafayette said impulsively. "We wept at other times; we moved worlds and awakened the sleeping ages. What have we to be ashamed of?"

"What?" Paine wondered.

"The key goes to America," Lafayette smiled. "Give it to our general." It still meant Washington and no other when they spoke of their general.

Paine turned the key over and over in his hands.

He told himself, "I am old and tired, and what have I to do with all this?" He lay awake one night with the old sleeplessness, his brain teeming with fifty years of not too pleasant memories, fighting himself, trying to find relief in a bottle of brandy, dozing a moment to dream of a Pennsylvania farm where love had come so briefly, asking himself again, "What have I to do with all this?"

And then, getting out of bed, he felt for the key; how had they stormed thc Bastille? Little people did such things; he knew; he remembered how the people of Philadelphia, clutching big muskets in uneasy hands, had marched up to the Delaware because he, Paine, wrote something about the times that tried men's souls.

He sat in the dark and turned over and over in his hands the key that had unlocked the Bastille. Lafayette had given it to him to give to Washington; Washington stood in the clouds, and Lafayette was a leader of France, and he, Paine, in between, was nothing. But in between was the moving impulse of revolution, a force summed up in himself, a passionate preaching that gained neither glory nor distinction, but by the power of the written word moved worlds.

Asking himself, "Who are you, Paine, and what are you?"

Still, there lingered like a dream the fashionable world of London. Burke and Pitt and Fox were great minds, brilliant men; why did Paine have to make a decision between the poverty and filth of his former days and the genteel world he had tasted? Does a man go back and reach out for dirt? If he could see in this slow and orderly unfolding of revolution in France, the bright dawn of a new world, a brotherhood of man, then wouldn't the great minds of England see it as well? Civilization was reasonable, and France, England, and America together could form the unshakable basis of a new order. In England, they admired him, and they would listen. They would see that the revolution had to come, and they would give in without causing blood to be shed.

Thus reasoned Paine, a man past fifty who had tasted so briefly of quiet and comfort, writing to men in England, to Burke and Pitt bright, glowing letters of what had happened in France—

"It embraces a new hope for all of us. . . ."

"The result in its fullness, in its exaltation of the human spirit, will be shared by you as well as by the meanest chimney sweep. . . ."

"Be of stout heart. . . ."

And then he heard that Burke stood up in Commons and delivered so fierce, so heartless a blast against the revolution in France that it spoke more of madness than anger.

"And you will answer him?" Condorcet said to Paine.

Paine nodded.

So it was Tom Paine, staring at the pen he held in his hand, sharpening one point after another, breaking a quill, cursing with the ripe, rich Anglo-Saxon oaths that he had learned in the London underworld, pleading with words; unshaven again, a bottle of brandy next to him, Paine again would be recognizable to the barefooted men who had marched with him down through Jersey. He had taken a room at the Angel, an inn at Islington outside of London, and he had a book beside him, a book called *Reflections on the Revolution in France*, written by Edmund Burke. It was a book that attacked, not only the French revolution, but all revolution, all progress, all hope, all man's poor bruised faith in his ability to climb to where the gods sat.

Burke had said that man, as man, had no rights. Paine set himself to write of the rights of man, to tell what he had seen of the French revolution, and to explain it—justification, it did not need. He wrote furiously, hotly, angrily, as he always wrote before the battle, before the guns sounded.

And he was young again.

"Loose, 'e is," they said in the taproom down below. "Loose an' black."

" 'oo is 'e?"

"Bloody damn colonial."

"What's 'is grouch?"

"The 'ole bloody world's 'is grouch."

But when he came down, to stare at the bar, lean on it, stare at his big splay hands, order rum, more rum, more rum, they left him alone.

Thomas Clewes, heading a deputation of miners, came to see him, short, wide-set men, the grime in their hair, in their eyes, in their skin, talking a broad Welsh brogue, Clewes saying:

"Be you Paine?"

"I'm Paine."

"And it's said you're preparing an answer for that damned jackal Burke?"

"I am."

"We be miners," Clewes said. "We're looking for a way, a leader, and a means. Things are bad, and I'll not have to tell you how bad they be. What are ye writing?"

"A handbook for revolution," Paine smiled.

"And what's in it to set a man to thinking?"

Paine read:

"The foreign troops began to advance towards the city—" Paris, he explained. "—The Prince de Lambesc, who commanded a body of German cavalry, approached by the Palace of Louis XV, which connects itself with some of the streets. In his march, he insulted and struck an old man with his sword. The French are remarkable for their respect for old age—"

The miners, watching him narrowly, nodded slightly.

"—and the insolence with which it appeared to be done, uniting with the general fermentation they were in, produced a powerful effect, and a cry of '*To arms! To arms!*' spread itself in a moment over the city.

"Arms they had none, nor scarcely any who knew the use of them; but desperate resolution, whenever hope is at stake, supplies, for a while, the want of arms. Near where the Prince de Lambesc was drawn up, were large piles of stones collected for building the new bridge, and with these the people attacked the cavalry. A party of the French guards, upon hearing the firing, rushed from their quarters and joined the people; and night coming on, the cavalry retreated.

"The streets of Paris, being narrow, are favorable for defense, and the loftiness of the houses, consisting of many stories, from which great annoyance might be given, secured them against nocturnal enterprises; and the night was spent with providing themselves with every sort of weapon they could make or procure; guns, swords, blacksmiths' hammers, carpenters' axes, iron crows, pikes, halberts, pitchforks, spits, clubs, etc., etc. The incredible numbers in which they assembled the next morning, and the still more incredible resolution they exhibited, embarrassed and astonished their enemies. Little did the new ministry expect such a salute. Accustomed to slavery themselves, they had no idea that Liberty was capable of such inspiration, or that a body of unarmed citizens would dare to face the military force of thirty thousand men. Every moment of this day was employed in collecting arms, concerting plans, and arranging themselves into the best order which such an instantaneous movement could afford. Broglio continued lying round the city, but made no further advances this day, and the succeeding night passed with as much tranquillity as such a scene could possibly admit.

"But defense was not the object of the citizens. They had a cause at stake on which depended their freedom or their slavery. They every moment expected an attack, or to hear of one made on the National Assembly; and in such a situation the most prompt measures are sometimes the best The object that now presented itself was the Bastille; and the *éclat* of carrying such a fortress in the face of such an army could not fail to strike terror into the new ministry, who had scarcely yet had time to meet. By some intercepted correspondence, it was discovered that the Mayor of Paris, M. Defflesselles, who appeared to be in the interest of the citizens, was betraying them; from this discovery, there remained no doubt that Broglio would reinforce the Bastille the ensuing evening. It was therefore necessary to attack it that day; but before this could be done, it was first necessary to procure a better supply of arms than they were then possessed of.

"There was, adjoining to the city, a large magazine of arms deposited at the Hospital of the Invalids, which the citizens summoned to surrender; and as the place was not defensible, nor attempted much defense, they soon succeeded. Thus supplied, they marched to attack the Bastille; a vast mixed multitude of all ages, and of all degrees, armed with all sorts of weapons. Imagination would fail in describing to itself the appearance of such a procession, and of the anxiety for the events which a few hours or a few minutes might produce. What plans the ministry was forming were as unknown to the people within the city as what the citizens were doing was unknown to the ministry; and what movements Broglio might make for the support or relief of the place, were to the citizens equally as unknown. All was mystery and hazard—"

Paine looked up at the broad, dark faces of the Welsh miners, and saw in their eyes a light, an almost warlike gleam that he knew of old. He went on—

"That the Bastille was attacked with an enthusiasm of heroism, such as only the highest animation of Liberty could inspire, and carried in the space of a few hours, is an event which the world is fully possessed of. I am not undertaking a detail of the attack, but bringing into view the conspiracy against the nation which provoked it, and which fell with the Bastille. The prison to which the new ministry were dooming the National Assembly, in addition to its being the high altar and castle of despotism, became the proper object to begin with. This enterprise broke up the new ministry, who now began to fly from the ruin they had prepared for others. The troops of Broglio dispersed, and himself fled also. . . ."

Paine finished reading, and the miners stood there silent, impassive except for their eyes—fire in their eyes—regarding him as they turned over in their minds what he had just read, stories current in the newspapers only a few months past; but how vastly different in Paine's account from the mocking, supercilious sneers of the British reporters! Paine saw, and he thought that they could see the turmoil in the Paris streets as the mob became something else than a mob, as they died and organized and found their own strength.

Clewes said slowly, "So that would be yer writing, Mr. Paine."

"That and more. Does it set a man thinking?"

"It sets him thinking of this and it sets him thinking of that," Clewes smiled. "But what is a man to do?"

"For the time being, wait. Have you any arms?"

"We be working men, not soldiers and not gentlemen hunters, so where would we be hiding muskets, Mr. Paine?"

"There's none among you can work with iron?"

"Aye, we have a smith or two."

"Can he turn his hand to a musket barrel instead of a horse's hoof?"

"That he might. But we be peaceful family men, Mr. Paine. We nurse a grievance, and it might be a small one or a big one, according to them what judge. What the Frenchies did is a matter of their own, and I don't judge a cousin of mine who took up arms with yer General Washington. Some say it's wrong for a man to go down into the pits for tuppence a day; some say it's right. Some say it's wrong for the man that raises the beef to starve while the squire that eats it is fat and red as a jack o' lantern. Some say it's not a nice thing to watch yer wife die in childbirth for want of a little hot broth, to see year children's bellies blow up, and others say it's something that has always been and always will be. To my mind, there were some free men on these islands once, and there might be again."

"There might be," Paine said evenly.

"Then we'll be waiting, and who knows but that the smiths might not turn their hands to this and that."

So he was in it again, neck deep, and again when he walked the streets—of London this time—it was with the knowledge that many men might sleep better if Tom Paine were dead. The book was finished and published, dedicated to George Washington, titled *The Rights of Man.* Actually, the publication came about without too much difficulty, with less than had attended *Common Sense,* considering that this was London and not Philadelphia. The first printing, undertaken by a Mr. Johnson of St. Paul's Churchyard, was suddenly indignantly thrust back at Paine, Johnson exclaiming:

"My God, sir, this is treason, treason pure and simple!"

"And you've just discovered that," Paine smiled. "Here the book is set and gone to press, a thousand sheets folded and dry, and you've suddenly discovered that it's treason. Is that your publishing policy, not to read nor to understand a manuscript until it's set and printed—or have you been entertaining a little correspondence with Mr. Burke and Mr. Walpole about my scribbling? I think you're a dirty little man!"

"I'll not be insulted in my shop, sir."

"You can't be insulted," Paine said.

Romney, the painter, recommended that Paine go to see Jordan, on Fleet Street, and Paine did, with the preamble to Jordan:

"It's probably treason, sir, so don't print first and discover that later."

"So you're Paine," Jordan laughed. "And neither horns nor whiskers—I'm glad to meet you." Grimy with ink, thin and hatchet-faced, he made Paine think, "In love with his trade and ready to die for the right word. He'll print the devil's manifesto, if he believes in it."

"Let's look at the treason," Jordan said.

They put heads together, and for a whole afternoon they read. When they came to the sort of thing such as the following, Paine read aloud and Jordan pulled on his lower lip and became very judicious:

"Titles are but nicknames, and every nickname is a title. The thing is perfectly harmless in itself, but it marks a sort of foppery in the human character, which degrades it. It reduces man into the diminutive of man in things which are great, and the counterfeit of women in things which are little. . . ."

"Treason?" Jordan grinned.

"Depending how you look at it." Paine felt more alive, more

vital than at any time in the past eight years. He did not reflect that he had become in thought as well as in practice, a professional revolutionist, and that there was no other real happiness for himself than the plying of his trade; he only knew that he was in the rat trap of London, that soon he would be a hunted man, and that he minded the prospect not at all.

"I like this," Jordan chuckled, and read: "Toleration is not the *opposite* of Intolerance, but is the *counterfeit* of it. Both are despotisms. The one assumes to itself the right of withholding Liberty of Conscience, and the other of granting it. The one is the Pope armed with fire and faggot, and the other is the Pope selling or granting indulgences. The former is Church and State, and the latter is Church and traffic.

"But Toleration may be viewed in a much stronger light. Man worships not himself, but his Maker; and the liberty of conscience which he claims is not for the service of himself, but of his God. In this case, therefore, we must necessarily have the associated idea of two beings; the *mortal* who renders the worship, and the IMMORTAL BEING who is worshiped. Toleration, therefore, places itself, not between man and man, nor between Church and Church, nor between one denomination of religion and another, but between God and man; between the being who worships, and the BEING who is worshiped and by the same act of assumed authority by which it tolerates man to pay his worship, it presumptuously and blasphemously sets itself up to tolerate the Almighty to receive it.

"Were a Bill brought into any Parliament, entitled, '*An Act to tolerate or grant liberty to the Almighty to receive the worship of a Jew or a Turk*,' or '*to prohibit the Almighty from receiving it*,' all men would startle and call it blasphemy. There would be an uproar. The presumption of toleration in religious matters would then present itself unmasked; but the presumption is not the less because the name of 'Man' only appears to those laws, for the associated idea of the *worshiped* and the *worshiper* cannot be separated. Who then art thou, vain dust and ashes! by whatever name thou art called, whether a King, a Bishop, a Church, or a State, a

Parliament, or anything else, that obtrudest thine insignificance between the soul of man and its maker?"

"Treason, very possibly," Jordan said. "Do you want me to publish your book, Mr. Paine?"

"I do."

"Then I say the hell with treason and God damn it! I like your stuff." They shook hands on that, and then Jordan, thoughtfully, suggested, "If you won't take offense, Mr. Paine, let me suggest an edition to sell for three shillings, the price of Burke's book. Wait a minute—"

Paine was staring at him, demanding, "Who can buy it for three shillings?"

"I said as a minor precaution, so that the wolves won't come howling before the presses are cool. You know how they reason—they'll see a good format and they'll say, well, the people it reaches don't matter, and at least that will give us time. Then, if you want me to, I'll put out fifty thousand for sixpence and see myself hanged—"

"If I could believe you," Paine said.

"God damn it, man, I don't intend to live forever! Maybe only you can say what you put down here, but others have thought such things, and if you don't believe me, you can get to the devil out of here!"

Paine smiled, offered his hand again, and said, "I don't think, Mr. Jordan, that any of us will live forever."

The book was published, and Paine was drunk for two days; the body drunk, the smallness, meanness, wretchedness of himself apparent only too well as he lay over a table in a tavern and saw exactly what was Paine, hated it, but triumphed mightily and exulted over what he had done, *Common Sense*, the *Crisis Papers*, and now *The Rights of Man*: that was himself, that was the brief, immortal spark; that turned empires upside down and gave man hope and brought him face to face with God. Drunk and howling foul songs, he was found by Blake, the poet, Romney, the painter, the former demanding of him:

"Paine, my God, what has gotten into you?"

"Glory! Glory!"

"Paine, get out of this stinkhole!"

"Glory! Glory! Glory!"

Blake took him home, gave him a bath, preached to him and confided, "Paine, you and I are much the same—that way is no good, I tell you, no good." He had met Blake some months ago, spent an evening talking to him and telling tales of the revolution in America. Blake liked him, and after that they were together a good deal, Blake, Romney, Sharp the engraver, Hull, Barlow, Frost, and Audibert, friends of Blake, friends of Romney, curious misfit liberals in the fashionable world of eighteenth-century London. Now Blake read him poetry in his soft, deep voice, while Paine sighed, "Glory, glory, glory—"

He came to Jordan the next day and said, "Let me smell the ink—let me get a hand on the presses."

The new books were stacked already, one hundred in a pile. All over the world, in England, in France, in America, the good smell of printer's ink was the same. Jordan described the selling, slow at first, mostly across the stands of his own shop; but it was picking up—three hundred copies to Wales, that at three shillings. "Have three hundred people in Wales three shillings to spend on a book?" Jordan asked.

There were a thousand of the cheap edition that crawled into Scotland; a sheriff, out from Carlisle, got two hundred, and that was before they were judged treasonable. But the sheriff had a nose for that sort of thing, and what else were you to say of something entitled *Rights of Man*? But a thousand got through and then two thousand more, and then it was set in Edinburgh by Thatcher McDowell, pirated, you might say, thirty thousand run off on cheap paper—was it any wonder that the mayor of Glasgow screamed that every Gillie in the hills, every weaver, every hand at a mill, and every smith's apprentice was reading a piece of treasonable filth called *Rights of Man*?

They took out three thousand words and printed it on scrap

and waste in Cardiff—a thousand copies to go into the mines in a man's breeches.

London began to eat the three-shilling edition; every fop had it—for grins and wit and the sauce that could be flung at this man, Paine. " 'Od's blood," they would say. "Listen to the beast go at the pater!" Walpole had it, Pitt had it, Burke and Fox—and they didn't joke. At White's, the Duke of Devonshire, who lived more of his ducal life at the gambling tables than anywhere else, kept an open copy of Paine's book beside him, tearing leaves from it whenever he needed to light his pipe. Lord Grenville, the Foreign Secretary, read the book, tore it to shreds, and made a mental note to hang the writer. But the Tory government, after they had collectively flushed through their first passion of rage, held a meeting at which Pitt arose and said firmly, thinking perhaps of his father, who had not desired to lose America, or thinking perhaps only of the Tory government:

"For the time being, gentlemen, we will do nothing at all. A book, even a scurrilous rag, which costs three shillings can do no harm unless we publicize it enough to make three shillings a price that must be paid. . . ."

In that they were wrong. Jordan told Paine, "Nothing can account for the way the expensive edition is going. I've published books long enough to know the size of the fashionable reading public here—even taking into account the politicians who read it as a chore. There's a new audience here, an audience that never read a book before, an audience that's reaching into its pockets and somehow finding three shillings. . . ."

A weaver, Angus Grey, sought Paine out and said, "And what would you think of weavers, Mr. Paine?"

"I've not thought of them. Who are you?"

"Nobody that matters," the man said—ill-dressed, gaunt, dark-eyed, licking his lips slowly and purposefully. "But we have been reading your book and we have a mind to set things right. If we had a weapon or two, a musket or a little pistol, would there—" He let the question hang in the air.

"There might be," Paine said.

"And when, Mr. Paine?"

"When the time comes," Paine said. What more could he say? What more could he say to any of them who approached him, to any of the pinched, starved faces that hungered for a utopia they found in a book, a utopia of which America was the living proof.

And then ten, twenty, fifty thousand of the cheap edition disappeared into the gaping maw of London, Manchester, Sheffield, Liverpool . . . a fire was burning under England and the muffled reverberations began to be felt.

It came down like a pack of cards, and in the gray of dawn he ran away. It came tumbling down upon his head because he had not understood that no one thing, no one man, no one cause can move the world. When he wrote *Common Sense*, he told a people already stirred to war, already fiercely indignant, with arms in their hands, why they had roused themselves in their wrath, why they should go on fighting, and what they were fighting for. They had behind them a hundred years of armed independence, factual if not political; they had fought the Indians and they had fought the French, and they lived by their arms—and, for the most part, they were religious dissenters, Methodists, Puritans, Congregationalists, even the Catholics and Jews among them had fled to America for freedom.

With *The Rights of Man*, it was different; he flung that at the heads of a people totally unprepared, a people who in many cases imagined themselves in possession of a mythical freedom that was in no way actual, but existed in song and story and legend as the possession of every Englishman.

They were not armed, they were not prepared, they were not religious dissenters; they looked at his book, yearned for freedom, and then went back to their work, their slums, and their gin-mills —and those few who had a germ of organization, the broad-faced miners of Wales, the weavers in the northern counties, the ironworkers—those few pondered their copies of Paine's book, counted their bullets, and then, frightened, buried their muskets and did nothing—and when they heard that Paine had fled from England, even their dreams stopped.

His initial mistake—afterwards he realized that—was his first return to France. Then the idea, the vague shape, the conception so huge that he had hardly dared to think of it until now, fixed itself in his mind as a reality; a united states of Europe allied with a united states of America, a brotherhood of man that at the most would take seven years to accomplish, and eventually, possibly before the end of the eighteenth century, would spread over the entire world. It would be a people's government for the people, a government to see that no man starved and no man wanted, to see that hate and misery and crime disappeared through education and enlightenment, to see the iron grip of organized religion loosened, replaced by a gentle, deistic creed wherein the brotherhood of man turned its face to the singleness and goodness of God, a creed without hate or rancor or superstition. There would be an end of war, an end of kings and despots. Christ would come to earth in the simple goodness of all men—a goodness he believed in so fervently—and all men, turning their faces to God, would never lose sight of the vision.

That was Paine's dream, his conception—and one so awful and terrible and wonderful in its implications that he hardly dared speak it fully, even to himself. It depended on too much, the course of revolution in France, his power to sway men with the written word, the course of the post-revolutionary world in America—and finally the revolution in England.

He recalled that he had crossed to France again, further arousing the suspicion of the Tories, who were beginning to believe that he was in league with the French. With Lafayette he had discussed the organization of a republican society that would eventually have world-wide ramifications. Madame Roland and Condorcet had joined in the nucleus, and Paine wrote a flaming proclamation of republicanism that raged against the king's flight from Paris and called for his abdication. The British Tories still held back, and Paine began to believe that he could bring all his plans to a head without ever rousing the Tory government from its apathy. This was the first step—to the American republic would be added the republic of France. He did not know that even at that moment British agents were filing carefully written reports of his activities. He returned to England then and found that Paine, once deliberately ignored, had become an apostle of the devil.

The forces of the government closed in slowly. England was rumbling, but they had heard her rumble before, and they judged the temper of the people well. If you crushed a revolt, you admitted a revolt, and then the demon could never be forced back into the bottle. On the other hand, if you implied, intimidated, threatened softly, arrested secretly, you could destroy a revolt before it ever realized its own strength. America had taught them a lesson.

Paine's friends and supporters had planned a meeting at an inn called the Crown and Anchor—where they would drink to the second anniversary of the downfall of the feudal system in France. A government agent saw the landlord, and suddenly the inn was not available. Clewes disappeared; a man called Luneden, who had approached Paine with an idea for an unofficial militia group modeled after the Associators of Philadelphia, was found dead in a ditch near Dover. Masterson, the ironworker, was arrested on a trumped-up charge. On the other hand, young Lord Edward Fitzgerald of Ireland, told Paine:

"Think on the green isle when you want for fighting men, Mr. Paine, and it might be that you'd find more than enough."

"Whatever happens," he told himself, "I must write, explain, make this thing clear." He did a second part to *The Rights of Man*. His bridge was forgotten, his dreams of scientific and social glory so much in the past that he wondered how he could ever have entertained them. It was the old Paine now, not too well dressed, his twisted eyes gleaming, darting rapidly as he talked, his broad, powerful shoulders bent again, as if the burden they carried was heavy, terribly heavy.

He wrote quickly, now that most of his doubts were gone. The first part had been a handbook for revolution, and this would be a plan—elementary and crude—but a sort of plan nevertheless for the new world he dreamed of. While writing, he knew that he was being watched, and he expected some interference from the government; when there was none, he was more wary than surprised. Then Chapman, the wealthy publisher, came and asked whether Paine would agree to his issuing the second *Rights of Man*.

"Clumsy," Paine thought, "oh, my lord, how clumsy." And he said, "I publish with Jordan."

"Jordan is nobody," Chapman replied smugly. "Jordan is a little mouse gnawing at the edges of the publishing cloth. A work with the strength and importance of yours, Mr. Paine, deserves nothing but the best imprint, the finest paper, and a binding a writer can be proud of. You and I are men of the world, and we know that the buying public, fools that they are, judge a book by its cover; the best Morocco, the most exquisite tooling—"

"I publish with Jordan," Paine smiled. "There are some who have said, and not too quietly, Mr. Chapman, that my work touches on treason. A publisher of your standing—"

"Risks are a part of publishing. We champion the printed word, the freedom of the press."

"And the arrangements?"

"A hundred guineas for all rights."

"All rights?" Paine smiled. "No royalties?—Really, is my work worth so little?"

"I mentioned the risks. You will admit—"

"I publish with Jordan," Paine said.

"Two hundred guineas."

"Then my work increases in value. Would you also purchase the right to hand my manuscript over to Mr. Walpole once the price is paid?"

Mr. Chapman kept his temper admirably. "Five hundred guineas, Mr. Paine," he said.

"A writer's life is never dull," Paine laughed. "Go to hell, Mr. Chapman."

"Don't be a fool, Paine. I'll give you a thousand guineas, not a penny more."

"Go to hell!"

"I warn you, Paine, take the thousand. A man hanged by the neck has no use for money."

"Get out before I throw you out," Paine said.

That settled Chapman, but not other things. When Paine brought the manuscript to Jordan, the printer said, "I don't frighten easily, but things are tightening. Do you remember Carstairs, who took a thousand of the cheap edition for Scotland? He was found at the bottom of a cliff with his neck broken—mountain climbing— When has he climbed mountains?"

"Don't you think I see them tightening?" Paine growled.

"I'm not afraid, mind you."

Paine gave him a written statement, in which the author declared himself to be the publisher—and said that he and no other would answer for what *The Rights of Man* contained.

"You don't have to do this," Jordan protested.

"I want to."

"And don't walk the streets at night."

Paine smiled, recalling other times when that same warning had been flung at him.

Then, with startling suddenness, it came to an end. All the carefully organized revolutionary cells, miners in Wales, cutlers in Sheffield, the dock workers at Liverpool and Tyne, the potters and the wheelwrights—all these who had looked for Paine's leadership were cracked wide open by the government, before he had had a chance to call a congress, to order a rising of militia, before the thin threads of revolution were even in shape to be drawn together. Then as an anticlimax, there came a message from Jordan.

Paine went as quickly as he could. He had just heard of the arrest of the leaders of four of the cells; he was ready for anything, but he could not smile when the tall printer showed him an order commanding him, Jordan, to appear at the Court of King's

Bench. The charge was treason to the Crown, as of the publication of a criminal book called *Rights of Man.*

"I'll answer it," Paine said.

"You will not," Jordan told him firmly. "If they hang you, that's the end of everything; if they hang me, it's much ado about nothing—you see, Paine, you've been here and there and everywhere, knocking about, and as you say, the world is your village. But I'm an Englishman, that's all, pure and simple, and I have a crazy liking for this little island and the people on it. I see them going like horses chained to carts, and I want to cut the traces. That's why I published your book—and that's why I am going to die for it, plain and simple, if I have to. You're the revolution, I'm a printer; that's all, Paine."

Paine pleaded, but he had met a man more stubborn than himself. He went to his Whig liberal friends to plead, but the few doors not locked to him opened to reveal bland, ironical faces that told him:

"But really, Paine, you never imagined we'd countenance revolution. Really, we are British, you know—" And advice, "Get out of England before you're hanged."

Romney sent him a message, "They're going to hang you, Paine, sure as God."

Blake wrote him, "Paine, for God's sake, flee."

He issued a manifesto to the cells that remained, and only a dead silence greeted him. "This is the time to act," he wrote, and there was only a dead silence.

The next move of the government was a royal proclamation which forbade all unauthorized meetings and all seditious writings. Anyone knowing of such and not reporting them would be open to prosecution.

But the book was selling, madly, wildly, by the thousands. In the small time left, Jordan kept the presses going day and night; the written word, once launched, could not be reclaimed, not by all the power of the crown. And Paine wrote constantly, letters, proclamations, appeals—if the cells had failed him, he would go to the people. And the people read his appeals, whispered among themselves, and did nothing. They were not the armed farmers of Massachusetts, but poor, frightened peasants and shopkeepers.

Thus it was over, Blake, in an hour of pleading, convinced him that final orders had gone through; Frost came with news that a warrant had been issued. And a messenger from France pleaded:

"See this, Paine. France needs you. In England everything is done, and when you are dead, the hopes of the English people will be dead, too dead to ever be raised, I tell you, Paine. In France, it is beginning, and when the name of the Republic of France sounds through Europe, the people of England will find their strength. But don't stay here to be hanged."

"Running away," he told himself. "When I could stay and die. But I'm an old man. In seventy-six, I was young, and there were other young men with guns in their hands—and I could talk to them. And where are they now?"

And he told himself, "I'll come back!" He swore to himself, "I'll come back—only seven years at the most, and there'll be brotherhood among men who have never known anything but hate and fear. The dead never come back, but I'll return. . . ."

All that he turned over and over in his mind, standing on the Channel boat and watching the white cliffs of Dover fade, on a fall morning in September, 1792.

TWELVE

The Republic of France

IT WAS always the beginning. The cold, fresh wind blowing across the Channel was a tonic, the blue sky, the gulls, the sway of deck under his feet, and the breathless exhilaration that comes to someone who has narrowly escaped death. His mood changed and the black despair lifted, and his failure in England took its place in the natural order of things; for thousands of years of recorded history, it had been the other way, and a brotherhood of man does not come in hours nor in days. He would return to England with a United States of Europe at his back, and then the people would rise triumphantly at his call. How long? Five years, ten years; he was only fifty-five. Always until now, it had been training, training, and more training, he was Paine, the champion of man.

He said to Frost, "Do I look old?"

"You never looked better," Frost answered, somewhat surprised, now that he had thought of it.

"Tired?"

"Hardly—"

"What are you afraid of, Frost?"

"A man doesn't miss being hanged by the neck by inches, and smile at it."

"Don't be a fool! Your life is nothing, just a little makeshift that you play with for a while, a machine that you put to use. And if something cracks it, then it's cracked, that's all."

"I'm sorry I can't see things that way," Frost said bitterly. "That was my home," nodding over his shoulder at England. "Now it's gone, now I don't come back."

Taking the young man by the shoulder, Paine waved an arm at Europe and said, "That's bigger—that's all the world. I have nothing, not a shilling from my book"—what there was, he had left with Jordan—"not a penny in my pockets, just a rag in my valise and the clothes on my back. And I'm fifty-five and I'm not afraid."

As they made the coast of France, one of those quick, dark Channel storms blew up, and it was raining when they docked. But notwithstanding the weather, almost the whole of Calais turned out to welcome Paine, a file of soldiers, fife and drum squealing first the *Marseillaise* and then *Yankee Doodle*, apparently under the impression that it was the revolutionary anthem of America. The citizens cheered and whistled and waved their arms at the astounded Paine, who had expected nothing like this.

"Vive Paine!"

The soldiers marched back and forth and back and forth, and Captain Dumont, half Paine's size, embraced him time after time. Then there was the mayor to give his embrace, and then four councilmen, then two lieutenants of the national guard. They informed Paine, first in French and then in very bad English, that he was deputy to the National Assembly—and from Calais, the honor, to them, of course, the overwhelming honor.

"I am most honored," Paine murmured in English. French, which he could hardly understand, flew about his ears. He could not speak now, and his eyes were wet; they wept with him, wept and cheered and wept again.

"If you accept," they said. "Naturally, only if you accept. The pay, eighteen francs a day, it is nothing, for you less than nothing. But to have Calais represented by Paine—"

He nodded, and they bore him away to a banquet they had prepared.

There was dead quiet at first as Paine walked in to the Assembly to take his seat. All eyes turned on him as news of who he was sped about, there was a soft murmur, hats were removed and heads bent in a completely French gesture of honor, even of worship, and then soaring acclaim as the voices rose. This was Paine and this was Paris and this was the revolution—and he had come home.

He sat down and wept, and all over the hall they wept with him. He arose, and they drowned his voice in another blast of sound—and then all order vanished as they rushed to embrace him.

That was one thing; he was Paine, the stepchild of revolution; not of the parlor variety, but a man who had given his propaganda to revolutionary soldiers at first hand, marched with them, fought with them, engineered a workers' revolt in Philadelphia, and guarded like a madman those liberties America fought for. That was one thing; Paine, who would make the world over, was another.

Paine who would make a world over could not speak French—yes, a few words, ask for a cup of coffee, ask for a piece of bread, a night's lodging, but no French at all to handle swift political talk, the rushing, frenzied French of Paris; and is the language of freedom universal?

In the days that followed he was to be reminded again and again of what Lafayette had said to him, not so long ago:

"Friend Paine, I think that you and I both were born too soon—and that we will have to pay for it."

But a man is not born too soon, Paine had smiled. The world waits for men and dreamers, so how can a man be born too soon?

Yet he thought often of what Lafayette had said. Paine's handbook of revolution was made in America, among long, drawling farmers who were slow to speech, slow to action, but not turned once they were on their way. You declared a liberty and you fought for it. Men died and men suffered, but the world became a better world—or so you hoped. Your comrades were Washington and Jefferson, and Peale and Anthony Wayne and Nathanael Greene and Timothy Matlack, and even the workers rising in a city were not a mob. And then you conceived an idea, a dream of a whole world a republic, and you tried to make a revolution in England—and you fled for your life but were welcomed in France, where a revolution was being made. It was still the beginning.

But was it? The Legislative Assembly dissolved, he sat in the National Convention. His friends were called the Girondins, liberals headed by Condorcet and Madame Roland; he was with them, naturally, they were his old friends, they had listened to his ideas, his orderly presentation of the revolution in America. Yet their stock was falling lower and lower as the Jacobins, called the party of the Mountain, gained a firmer hold on the poor of Paris, crying for their dictatorship of the city over the provinces. For Paine, it was confusion where there should have been order —ominous confusion. There had to be a representative Congress, regardless of the impotence or corruption of that Congress. He didn't understand the endless ramifications; freedom was freedom, and once you had gained power, it was a simple thing to arrive at. And here was France being invaded by foreign armies, being threatened by traitors within and traitors without, being threatened by starvation, fighting herself, party of the Plain, the Mountain, Girondins, the left and the right and the center. And why? why? he kept asking. They all had only one enemy—power, privilege, aristocracy. That must be crushed, and there must be only a party of freedom.

Danton said to him, "The majority of the people are with us, with the Jacobins—I tell you that, Paine; the left has the majority."

"I have no quarrel with the majority," Paine answered him. "I live for the majority of the world—and when France is free, that will be another nation for the brotherhood."

As he sat in the Convention, he told himself, "I must remember that Freedom is on trial." It was good, at first, to see the galleries filled with the people of Paris; he hungered to talk, dreamed of soon speaking French well enough to speak directly to them, to the people.

Yet when the first decision came, he shied away from the majority. They were with Danton, who proposed complete reform of France's medieval, torturous judicial system, and Paine could see in that only unending complications. "Constitutional reform, not judicial reform," he kept harping. "A free legislature can make just laws—"

Danton smiled and agreed, but nevertheless the motion was pushed through under the cheering of the galleries. Paine could not see that it mattered too much—complications, of course, but the thing was done—and the next day he was horrified when Buzot, a Girondin deputy, trembling with passion and fear, demanded an armed guard against the citizens of Paris—"The mob," as he called it. Thus Paine was inaugurated into the strange, complicated, terribly ominous situation of revolutionary France, so bright and hopeful in ways, so deadly and nightmarish in others. He argued with his friends:

"But the people, they're the basis of everything. Law and order, reason, of course, I want that—who wants it more than I do? But you must depend on the people, they're everything, they're the ones who take the guns in their hands and fight, they're the ones who work and produce. If you don't trust the people—"

"Well enough for you," they cut him short. "You know the American farmer, but this scum of Paris!"

"Scum of Paris," he thought. "That's all it is to them."

For a moment, he considered being on his own; after all, he was Paine—he was the voice of revolution and he called no man his leader, and what did language matter? A truth was a truth, and he knew—or forced himself to know—in his own soul that this Parisian "scum" were no different than the small, frightened people he had worked with and fought for elsewhere in the world. If he appealed to them, they would listen. Wasn't he coming to know the true heart and core of revolution?—the strength was in the people, the fury in them; but for the direction of it, there must be a plan, an order, and a final goal. That was what all the impatient rebellions of small people had lacked until now, and to formulate such a goal was his purpose.

Thus he wrote and published an *Address to the People of France*. France, he said, was not fighting for France alone, but for the coming Republic of the World, for mankind. France must be unified; France must be bold, yet calm and courageous. The world waits for France. . . .

Did the people hear him? When he sat in the Convention again, he realized that even if they did, the deputies were completely immersed in their own personal struggles. Who was Paine? He could not even talk French. He sat helpless while the shrill arguments raged about his ears, the Girondins calling for a government in which all France participated, the Mountain reaffirming the strength and stability of the Parisian proletariat, the hot-headed deputies coming to blows again and again, the galleries screaming, hissing, booing, spitting, drowning out the voices of those they disliked, the whole impression being one of disorder, for all the vigor and strength. When someone was good enough to sit by him and translate, and when Paine saw a place where he might say something that mattered, throw a little oil on the waters and point them back to the fact that the freedom of France was at stake, and when he rose, he was usually ignored—or, if noticed, found the language a hopeless barrier. If he prepared something and had it rendered into French, the argument and debate had passed so far on that what he said was meaningless.

Again and again, his instincts told him where he belonged, with the Jacobins, for all their violence and extremism; but he could not bear the way Danton and St. Just and Robespierre smiled at his ordered theories of revolution, his systemized description of step-by-step procedure, always hearking back to the struggle in America. They implied that Paine was a figurehead, an ideal, but not a person to listen to, to trust. Perhaps he was getting old.

He asked himself, "Am I afraid?"

He dreamed of having his old American comrades around him

once more, and then he returned to Madame Roland's salon, where at least they respected him; even if they, in their bright talk of a middle-class government of all France, foreshadowed their own doom.

Hope came again when the Convention named him to the committee of nine who were to frame a new constitution for the Republic of France. Along with him, there were Condorcet, Danton, Sieyès, Barère, Vergniaud, Petion, Brissot, and Gensonné. But except for Sieyès and Danton, they were rightists, Girondins. Danton could accept a place on the committee and remain with the left; but when Paine accepted, he cast his lot once and for all with the Girondins.

For the first time, he said to himself, "I don't know."

But there were times when his doubts left him. Paris was not a place in which to doubt constantly; for Paine, it was a city of vigor, strength, and beauty; he did not see only the dirt of the people, the patched clothes, the way they hissed and booed in the galleries, their lack of manners and breeding; he knew that you did not put away a thousand years overnight. He saw their strength, their lust after a life just revealed to them, and when the republican armies swept the invaders back to the frontiers, he let himself be carried away by the general wave of rejoicing. The British expatriates, the rebels, radicals, poets and philosophers who had been driven into France by the Tory government, planned a great party at White's Hotel, their headquarters. Paine was one of the guests of honor, and it was a good feeling to go there and mingle with old friends who spoke his own tongue, Frost, Edward Fitzgerald, Carry Clewellen, the Welshman, Allison—

"By God, it's Common Sense!" they roared as he entered.

He had let himself go shabby, but out of his eighteen francs a day, he had saved enough for a new coat; no wigs in France now, his own hair drawn back and tied, and the old sparkle in his twisted eyes as Fitzgerald asked him, "Thomas, will we be crossing the Channel the other way soon?"

"Who can tell?"

Fitzgerald had had something to drink, and his brogue was broader than ever, his light blue eyes dancing as he enumerated, "America, England, France—by God and little Jesus, Thomas, tell me you will be in Ireland next! Her green hills run with blood—I tell you, Thomas, land there and when you step off the ship a hundred thousand good men will be waiting to march with you!"

The military band blared and they stood to the *Marseillaise* bareheaded, and when they picked up *Yankee Doodle*, as tribute to Paine, he threw back his big head and roared:

"Father and I went down to camp, along with Captain Goodin,
And there we saw the men and boys as thick as hasty puddin'!"

The punch was good, the rum better, the French brandy hot as fire in his throat. Paine got drunk, Fitzgerald got drunk, Frost too, and when Petion came to join them, they fell on his neck and kissed both his cheeks until he drew himself up to his five feet four inches and exclaimed:

"Gentlemen, for the dignity of the Republic!"

They drank a toast to the Republic, of France, of America—of the whole world, Paine perched on a chair and crying:

"Listen to me, my friends, my good comrades, I am drunk—drunk but inspired. I said once, not so long ago, give me seven years and we will usher in the brotherhood of man! My friends, I say five years and the glorious armies of France together with the glorious armies of the United States of America will carry the flag of freedom to every nation and every people on the face of this earth! Already we have seen the Prussian dogs flee like the swine they are; we see fat, half-witted George of England cowering on his throne, your own Louis abdicating to the people! Comrades, who shall say what miracles cannot be? Join me, I drink a toast to my good friend, my old comrade, that best of men and truest of friends, George Washington of Virginia!"

They joined him, but Paine was already so drunk that half the brandy ran down his chin. As the band again picked up *Yankee Doodle*, he strutted across the room, swaying from side to side—yet strangely enough not ridiculous, not provoking laughter even from those drunk, but rather pitiful admiration for a man at once so exalted and so forlorn.

He was afraid of himself, and he said to himself, "Tom Paine who never feared man or beast on God's green earth is afraid."

He was afraid because his body was becoming old and unwilling and tired, because his own dream of world brotherhood was becoming more precious and more real than actuality. Forcing himself to walk through the narrow, cobbled Paris streets, to go into the shops and into the workrooms, he could nevertheless not establish a kinship with the citizenry. He would say to them, "Thomas Paine," and they would smile delightedly, pour wine, cut sausage, and set out bread for him. A great gesture, because they were so close to starvation, and he had to eat a little, while they rattled their Parisian French at him, so quickly that he caught no more than a word out of ten.

They were good people, simple people, swelled with their own power because the power of little people was a new thing in the world, but a good, strong, sound people—and seeing that, recognizing it without reservation, he still could not put his trust in them—as once he had put his whole trust, life, and dreams into the hands of the ragged continental militiamen. The difference, the change was in himself; he feared the anarchy of the people, and preferred the order of the middle class; he knew that, and he could do nothing about it. He wanted order; he had the sense of oldness that hurries time; he wanted a quick, orderly fabric of republicanism to which one country after another might be added.

He had never been a man troubled by God or greatly given to prayer; his approach to religion was emotional, a fervent belief in an undefined deity, so composed of love for man and for all things living that he had never troubled himself with the nature of that deity. His business was with this world, and moving in a circle of atheists and agnostics, here as well as in America, he could afford to smile when hot words were spilled on the subject of religion; his belief was not subject to ritual, nor was it subject to argument.

But now he prayed, excusing himself with the knowledge that he was growing old. Death loomed up, and he didn't want to die. He had only begun, and it was harder, a thousand times harder than he had ever thought it could be.

Canais, the young disciple of Marat, came to Paine's lodgings and said, in very good English:

"Would it be presumptuous for me to talk about things that are none of my business, Mr. Paine?"

Paine liked the boy; he poured some brandy and nodded for him to go ahead.

"I've read every line you've written," Canais said.

"Yes—"

"And I would die tomorrow, content, if I could have written or done even a little part of what you did."

Paine fumbled his thanks; the boy's eyes were fixed full and clearly on him.

"So you see that I respect you, even as I love America—would you say that we are ushering in the citizen's century, Mr. Paine? I think so; I think that France can never repay her debt to America, and I hope that there will be a debt the other way. And I also say, Mr. Paine, that the world will never be able to repay its debt to Thomas Paine."

"And that is all?" Paine smiled.

"Not all. What happens to a man—?" The boy hesitated, disturbed by the thoughts that were crowding his mind. "What has happened to Tom Paine—if I anger you, stop me, throw me out and tell me that this is no business of mine."

"Go ahead," Paine said, miserably conscious of youth, vibrant, hot youth gone from himself forever, a boy telling Tom Paine what Tom Paine knew so well, yet feared to admit to himself.

"What has happened to you? In Philadelphia, you were with the people, in America—and who but the people made up your militia, who but the people starved and died at Valley Forge, ripped a dream of empire to pieces at Bunker Hill and taught little men how to fight on the green fields between Concord and Lexington? Have you forgotten? Were there bankers behind the stone walls at Concord? Did the rich merchants die at Monmouth Courthouse? Did your fine manufacturers and ship owners march up from Philadelphia to save Washington after he crossed the Delaware, or were they plain people, peasants and workers and clerks and small shopkeepers?"

"I remember," Paine said harshly. "Get on with what you have to say."

"Then are we so different? Is it that we're French? Is it because your militia drove back the German swine half-naked, and ours drove them back wearing blue smocks and wooden sabots, that they are different? Is your Boston massacre to be admired and our storming of the Bastille to be despised? For the sake of everything, Mr. Paine—come with us, come to the people and they will welcome you with open arms, make the world or else there will be no world to make for another hundred years!"

His fists clenched, his broad, powerful body stooped over, Paine stared at the boy moodily.

"It's no use, is it?" the boy said after a moment. "You are committed to your friends, the Girondins, to the bankers and merchants and all the apostles of the half-way, the liberalism that fears the people."

"I am past an age where I can enjoy anarchy," Paine told him. "We are fighting an organized enemy—and the people are not an organization; they're a mob. And a mob does not make democracy; a mob looks for someone to lead it, and if someone is clever enough, it can be led into the devil's mouth."

"And that's all?"

"That's all," Paine nodded.

Well, it was done, and he knew where he stood. He was getting old; he would go on fighting; somehow, things did not matter any more—and he almost regretted that he had not remained in England, as Jordan had. Jordan had been martyred, tried, punished, jailed while the man whose work he published ran away.

Paine was a sadder, older man when he stood in the Convention again. The question up before the house was whether the king should go to the guillotine, or be imprisoned until the end of the war—and then banished from France forever.

For Paine, the situation was complex and many-sided; and he could not agree with the simple reasoning of the Paris masses—that the king was a traitor, and therefore the king must die. Even if he could grant that the king was a traitor—and kings in specific and aristocracy in general had no greater or more bitter enemy these past eighteen years than Tom Paine—even if he could grant the accusation, he did not see that death must be the penalty. He knew that something inside of him had hardened and slowed, that the old fire was gone; he who would have seen every Tory hanged by the neck now grasped for the straw of reason. The king had not betrayed what he lived by. Once he had said, "We, Louis, are France," and that statement he hadn't betrayed.

Marat said, "He must be cut out like a foul growth!"

And Paine asked for justice, imprisonment now, a trial afterwards. He pointed out that George Washington, who was reverenced so deeply in America, would not forget the debt the colonies owed to France's king.

"And without America," Paine said wearily, "how far can we go? If men look for a brotherhood, will they be satisfied with blood?"

Thirty-six hours the question was debated in the hall of the Convention. Not in all the history of France had there been such high, tense, terrible drama as this, for not merely the king's life hinged on the final vote, but all the future course of the revolution. From the first it was apparent that the Girondins could not retreat, that they would have to fight, upon this issue, for control of the revolution. Christiani, a somewhat obscure member of the party, a mild man, gentle as a woman, said ruefully to Paine:

"It is hard to die for something one hardly believes in—but it is harder to throw away the last scruple. A wretch like Louis, who is better off dead, holds the destiny of man about his fat neck; and it makes one want to laugh at this life."

"You are not on trial," Paine protested.

"Ah, but we are—all of us."

And a letter to Paine, delivered in the Convention hall, unsigned, said:

"Citizen, for all that you once held dear, go with the people of France."

Like a lonely, lost man, he listened to the rocking currents of the debate. One does not understand; one sits, elbows on knees, hands cradling chin; one is alone and all that one has are memories. To Irene Roberdeau one says, Where freedom is not, there is my country. Arm in arm, one walks with Peale and Matlack—good comrades; then there was youth and fire and hope, and never the intrusion of doubt. One remembers and dreams, and then, waking out of the dream one comes back to the hall of the Convention in revolutionary Paris.

And hearing his name in all the melodious, frantically quick chattering of a foreign tongue, he seized old Bancal who was sitting beside him and asked:

"What are they saying?"

Duval had just spoken. Bancal translated, "That Thomas Paine is a man beyond suspicion will not be doubted. By the example of this man, one of the people, a long and a deadly enemy of kings and aristocracy, a defender of republican liberty—by his example, I vote for imprisonment during the war and exile after the peace."

In the roar that followed Duval's statement, Paine could hardly hear Bancal's voice, but saw the tears in his eyes and saw how proudly and calmly Duval stood among the tumult.

When the vote came, it was for the death of Louis.

The friends of Lafayette, men with connections in America, men who had a claim on him, came to Paine and told him:

"You can do this—because you are Paine."

"Because when we fall there will be only confusion."

"Because when Louis dies, it means war with England."

"Because Louis came to America's aid in the hour of her need."

Their plan—Condorcet's, Roland's, Brissot's—was for Paine to arise on the Convention floor and make a plea for the king's life. Tom Paine might carry the day; no one else could.

For all their arguments, Paine saw that the king's life meant nothing. The French revolution had split between the Girondins and the Jacobins, the right and the left, and in the middle was an aging staymaker whose name was glory.

"I can't speak French," Paine said miserably.

"Bancal will translate. The people will listen to Bancal—and they will listen to Paine."

"And to make it reasonable to myself—" Paine said bitterly.

"Only remember what Louis did for America." And knowing that they lied in their teeth as to their purposes, yet knowing there was truth in what they said—that in the hour of their need France's king had come to the aid of America—Paine agreed.

When Paine stood on the platform the next day, there was quiet in the house. Every eye was fixed on this man, whose name was synonymous with freedom and brotherhood; he, at least, was theirs, without subterfuge; he was the symbol of all they fought for; he was Paine.

And then he spoke through Bancal, standing silent, but with a forlorn dignity that rose over Marat's furious interruptions. Even when what he was saying became plain enough, the gallery did not hiss him; he was Tom Paine. He finished:

"Ah, Citizens, give not the tyrant of England the triumph of seeing the man perish on the scaffold who has aided my much loved America to break her chains!"

It made no difference; the vote was for death and on January 21, 1793, Louis of France went to the guillotine.

Then the world was changed and the revolution fled past him. In a matter of days after the death of the king, almost every nation in Europe, including England, was at war with France. And while the enemy armies made preparations beyond the frontiers, within the city of Paris the Girondins and the Jacobins fought their own deadly struggle.

Paine proposed that he go off to the frontiers with the troops. The military leaders smiled at him.

"You are too old to be a soldier, monsieur," they assured him, deliberately misunderstanding.

And when he said valiantly, "An army fights with more than guns," they raised their brows and smiled.

Then, with others, he was appointed to formulate a message to the people of England.

"Just a message?" he said. "And that will do what all my planning and work failed to do?"

"It is what you are fitted for."

"Just that—"

But he wrote as vibrantly as he had ever written, turning out the message that would never be seen by ninety-nine per cent of the British people. It helped him—his writing; it occupied him; but it answered none of the doubts that were plaguing him.

"Leave France?" he asked himself. But then what? Then what reason to live? He had forgotten his trade of staymaking. He was a revolutionist; it was all he knew, all he was fitted for.

No, he could not leave France, not yet, not while there was still hope for the revolution, not while the Girondins and the Jacobins might forget their hatred for each other long enough to permit France and the Republic to survive. But as time went on, the break increased rather than healed. A new situation had arisen, the hatred of the people for the middle class, fear of the people by the middle class.

More and more muskets were distributed to the people of Paris. And keeping pace with Paine's growing hatred of Marat and his party, there grew in him a mounting disgust for the Girondins who would destroy the revolution before they would give an inch.

Those were dark days, and Tom Paine walked alone.

Alone, he wrote to Marat and Danton, pleading. Danton ignored his letter; a pall of fear was beginning to hang over Paris, and Danton, who had looked askance now and then at the dictatorship of the mob, was beginning to feel gingerly at his own neck. Marat stormed to St. Just:

"No man knows when to die! I am sick of Paine, sick to death of him. Does he think that a revolution is distilled from roses, like perfume?"

"I have doubted that Paine thinks," St. Just smiled.

"Well, I am sick of him."

Alone, Paine prayed to God. A man does not pray easily when he is like Paine, when he is strong and his hands are broad, when he has a brain and a heart and contempt and hatred for those who made God's name the disgrace of the centuries. A man leaves God alone and turns to men and tries to do what is right. But Paine was old and tired, and he prayed, self-consciously, "Give them understanding."

Alone he said to the Girondins, "Show your honesty, your love for France and mankind, and I will lead the people to you."

And the Girondins showed their honesty by as fine a piece of fraud as they had ever indulged in.

There was a young blue-eyed, dream-saturated Englishman, Johnson by name, who had followed Paine everywhere for weeks now, dreaming of becoming his Boswell. Johnson was not very stable; he saw himself as a knight-crusader; he saw himself also as a revolutionist, and the two did not go well together. He wrote bad poetry, and he fell in love with a French girl.

His love-making was as bad as his poetry, and Paine had to listen patiently to both. The girl wasn't so patient, and sometimes she laughed at Johnson, usually when he told her how he would die for her, or kill anyone who came between them.

"You will not die for me, my little fool," she said calmly. "And if there is anyone else, that's my affair."

There was someone else, a Jacobin, and out of that Johnson built an entirely abnormal fear and hatred of the party of the left. When she told him, as kindly as she could, that she was through with him, he came to Paine and cursed Marat and his whole party as the source of every ill.

Paine dismissed the matter from his mind, thinking nothing more would come of it, but Johnson, after playing with the thought of suicide for several days, finally made the attempt. He used a knife, not knowing the fortitude needed to end one's life in so primitive a fashion, and as a result succeeded only in gashing himself.

But before he took the plunge, he wrote a letter to Paine, blaming Marat.

Alarmed until he learned how Johnson had fumbled the attempt, Paine showed the letter to Brissot, remarking, "Marat has done a good deal, but I'd hardly blame him for Johnson's sticking himself."

"Yet if he dies—" Brissot mused.

With that flimsy excuse, the Girondins dragged Marat before the revolutionary tribunal. It was their last brief flash of power —and exactly the opening Marat had been seeking. Before the tribunal, Marat tore the charges to pieces, stood in such dignity as he had never shown before, and calmly portrayed himself as the just anger of a just people.

The Girondins had overstepped themselves—and so the end began. And Paine could only sigh tiredly, "The fools—oh, the poor, witless fools."

The end of the Girondins came with awful suddenness. One day Paine was telling Brissot, "In the end, it will not be the Jacobins who destroy Republican France, but you. For the sake of everything we've lived for, make your peace with them. Do you hate Marat more than I do? I tell you, the Republic is dying." And the next day it was over.

The Girondins were flailing about; their blows fell everywhere and accomplished nothing. They arrested Jacobins; they banned assemblies; they flung out accusations. And then the people of

Paris picked up their muskets and began to assemble. On a much vaster scale, it was Philadelphia all over again, but this time Paine was in limbo. This time, the people neither remembered Paine nor turned to him; their wrath was against the Girondins, and if someone suggested that Paine was a mainspring of that party, they simply shrugged their shoulders. Thirty-two thousand of the volunteers stood over their muskets throughout the city, and all day long delegations stormed the Convention hall to scream for the arrest of the Girondins, who had betrayed the revolution. At last, the weary and frightened Convention adjourned for the day, and one by one, with shoulders bent over in despair, the Girondin deputies left the hall, the yelling mob hardly parting to make way for them. But when Paine left, there was a moment of silence. . . .

There was no sleeping that night. They went to Bancal's house, Duval, Condorcet, Brissot and Guadet, and they sat there until dawn turning over and over what had happened, what would happen to them, some even suggesting suicide.

"And either way," Paine said somberly, "the Republic is dead. Tomorrow the dictatorship of the mob, and after that anarchy—and after that, God only knows what."

The dawn of that day bore out their fears. The number of Parisians armed and assembled had increased almost to one hundred thousand; they made a dark, angry cordon around the hall of the Convention, and within, the deputies, not knowing precisely where the ax would fall, decreed as the people wished. The Girondin leaders were expelled from the Convention and placed under arrest. The French Republic was dead; the middle class had been overthrown by the hungry, angry poor of Paris, and the course of the revolution was turned into a strange and dangerous channel that had never been explored before.

Yet they left Paine alone; Paine, who had been a Girondin—or at least a friend and associate of Girondins—was still Tom Paine who had bent into the mire where mankind lay through the centuries, and had proclaimed freedom. Even the Parisians, the small men of the shops and the factories and the looms and the benches, even they who hated the Girondins so, would not lift a finger against Paine.

Silent and lonely he stalked the streets. They all knew him; his fierce hooked nose, his twisted eyes, his broad, sloping shoulders and his meaty, peasant hands were instantly recognizable; this was the godfather of revolution; this was the person who, across three thousand miles of water, somewhere in the American wilderness, had awakened sleeping mankind—and because they knew that, they were not cruel to him, they did not abuse him as they abused the Girondins, and now and then a kind word was spoken to him, as, "Good day, Citizen," and, "It looks different, Citizen, wouldn't you say?" or, "You're with us, Citizen. We've disposed of the traitors, and now you are with us—"

When was he not one of them? he asked himself. Their poor little bit of power had ripped out into anarchy, and the Republic was dead. His dreams were dead.

He fought sleeplessness with a brandy bottle and he fought wakefulness. He made up his mind that when they came to arrest him, he would stand erect and say, "I am Citizen Paine," and just look at them. But they didn't come to arrest him. He heard how in England men had copper coins with Paine's likeness on them fixed into the soles of their shoes, so they could vicariously stamp him into the mud. That, too, dissolved in a bottle. He drank himself into insensibility; for ten days, he had only enough control of himself to crawl down to the tavern for more brandy—after the waiter at White's had told him:

"Drink I'll sell you, but I'll not have the death of Paine on my conscience."

For a day, he was sober and haunted; he woke in the night, screaming, and when one of the Englishmen at the hotel, Jackson, told him, "For Christ's sake, Paine, you are killing yourself," he answered, "It's time, isn't it? Damn it, it's time!"

And then he was drunk again, day after day after day, vomiting, sick, seeing things that were not and things that were, unshaven, dirty, dragging himself about his room and mouthing:

"Where is that damned bottle, that damned bottle?"

That way, for almost thirty days—until anger came, anger so fierce and terrible that it sobered him while he vomited and trembled. There were two bottles of brandy left, and he smashed them against the floor. He strode back and forth across the room, pounding a clenched fist into his palm, and telling himself repeatedly in a calm, cold voice:

"You fool, you damned, accursed fool, it's only the beginning. You said seven years and even in seventy, it would still be only the beginning. You dirty, damned, drunken, besotted fool!"

THIRTEEN

Reason in God and Man

THE REVOLUTION goes on; a man does not make the revolution, not a thousand men, not an army and not a party; the revolution comes from the people as they reach toward God, and a little of God is in each person and each will not forget it. Thus it is the revolution when slaves shake their chains and the revolution when a strong man bends toward a weaker and says, "Here, comrade, is my arm." The revolution goes on and nothing stops it; but because the people are seeking what is good, not what is wicked or powerful or cruel or rich or venal, but simply what is good—because of that the people flounder and feel along one dark road after another. The people are no more all-seeing than their rulers once were; it is in intention that they differ.

Some of this, or all of it, Paine came to know, and he came to know that he was not the revolution, but only a man. There are no gods on earth, only men, and it had taken a long time for him to learn this.

His face was drawn, his figure leaner, his broad shoulders sloped more than ever as he entered the hall of the Convention once again. They made no move to arrest him. "Let him run away," Marat said. "Let him be off to the devil!" But Paine did not run away, and now he was back, his lips tight as he strode through a thousand fixed eyes to his seat.

There was a rustle and a murmur and the sound of many persons rising as Paine came back. Galleries and floor wanted to see him, the fool who walked back into the lion's mouth. Paine found his place, stood a moment, looking from person to person, and then sat down.

"Citizen Paine," the speaker acknowledged.

There was a ripple of applause, in spite of themselves. Paine wiped his eyes and stared at the floor.

St. Just attacked him, St. Just at his best, shouting, "I accuse you!"

Citizen Paine rose and came forward and asked, "Of what, sir —of what do you accuse me?"

"Of treason to France!"

"I committed no treason to France," Paine said calmly.

St. Just went on to accuse Paine of being in illegitimate correspondence with part of the royal family outside of the country's borders, at which Paine shook his head and said, "You are speaking to Tom Paine, sir."

Even the galleries roared with applause at that. "Accuse me of many things," Paine said. "Accuse me of being a republican, of being loyal to my friends, of loving an Englishman or a Frenchman as well as an American—but not of treason, sir, not of consorting with kings. I am not a young man; I have enough to look back upon, and I will not defend myself."

St. Just said no more.

So Paine sat in the Convention, but said practically nothing. History was rushing on too fast, and he was left behind. He attended because he was a delegate and because he was practicing the only trade he knew, but there was nothing for him. And he was terribly alone, his friends in prison, others who might have been his friends avoiding him because he was suspect. A whole era was crowded into a week or a month. Marat died under Charlotte Corday's dagger, and Robespierre took his place, a disarming man, so delicate and so French, but strong as iron and unbending as rock. A humanitarian, he called himself, telling Paine:

"I am of the people because I feel all their wants, their hurts, their pains, their sufferings. You were of the people once, were you not, Citizen Paine?" That was his way, to sink a barb deepest where it hurt most.

"I was a staymaker," Paine said, "and a cobbler and I swept a weaver's shop and I grubbed in the dirt for tuppence a week. I don't speak of being of the people—"

And that was something that Robespierre would never forget.

Still, the new ruler of France was a man of iron; he had to be. All around the nation enemy armies were closing in; provinces were in full revolt, and here and there the counter-revolution had gained full control of a local district.

Reorganized, the Revolutionary Tribunal set to work, and there began that period known as The Terror. There was neither compromise nor mercy; either a man was loyal to the revolution or he was an enemy of the revolution, and if he was suspect he was more than likely to be considered an enemy. Day after day, crude carts trundled through the streets of Paris, their big wooden wheels groaning and squeaking, their bellies bulging with new victims for the guillotine. And day after day the big knife was wound up its scaffold and then released to fall upon another neck. From the king's wife to a tavern keeper, to a simpering duke, to a midwife who had sheltered him. This was revolution in a way Paine had never dreamed of, not tall farmers who had always known that freedom was a part of their lives, but frightened little men who saw freedom for the first time in a thousand years, and were going to kill, kill, kill anything that stood in the way of its accomplishment. A dark cloud over Paris as the winter of 1793-1794 set in, a bloodstained cloud. Robespierre had to be a strong man.

And as the heads rolled, there died those friends of Paine's who had made up the party of the Plain, or the Girondins. Traitorous, or deceived, or weak, or without understanding, or frightened, or brave, or cowardly, or righteous in the only way they knew, they all died, Roland and his wife, Condorcet, Brissot, Petion, Lebrun, Vergniaud, Buzot—all of them, all under the knife that was the dark door at the end of a dark lane into which liberty had wandered. Long live the Republic—and the Republic died too. Paris was a city of death.

During this time, Paine still attended the Convention. He had to; he had to make reason out of this dark thing that was happening, or else he could not live. What happened to good, simple men? What moved them? What drove them? Had they forgotten mercy, decency, goodness, or had the priests and the kings made those words so foul that they could never again have meaning? Paine had to know.

He had changed his living quarters from White's Hotel to a farmhouse in the suburbs of Paris, a big, whitewashed stone-and-wood building that practiced a bucolic deception on a world that was falling apart. In many ways, this new home reminded Paine of an English yeoman farmer's place, the bricked-in courtyard, a confusion of ducks, hens, geese, the flowers and the fruit trees and the stacked hay; again, it reminded him of Pennsylvania. He was of an age to be reminded of many things, all stacked away, layer upon layer, in his uneasy mind. With him at the farm were a few other English men and women, the same Johnson who had made the abortive suicide attempt, a Mr. and Mrs. Christie, a Mr. Adams, forlorn radicals who were radicals no longer, but had been swept aside by the current of revolution. They were poor company for Paine; their mutterings, their vague discontents, their fears were all at odds with his own terrible and personal problem.

Death mattered little to Paine. Though he hoped and prayed that it was not so, he had a feeling that most of his work was done. Things had gone beyond him; all he felt now was a dire need for rationalization, for reason in a world ruled by anarchy. Sometimes he would sit down at cards with the others, but cards were not for him. There was still a world beyond bits of pasteboard.

"I am Tom Paine," he would remember, and then he would go back to Paris and plunge once more into the current of revolution. Some things he was still fitted for, and when it came to a matter of American policy, he would quietly give to the Jacobins all the knowledge and information he had. They got little enough out of the American ambassador, Gouverneur Morris.

That the turns of fortune had made Gouverneur Morris, Paine's reactionary opponent in the old Philadelphia uprising, American ambassador to revolutionary France, was in itself something to evoke both tears and laughter. Paine thought he saw reason behind this seeming insanity. Morris, the aristocrat, was a living proof to Britain that in America the conservatives of 'eighty and 'eighty-one were again in the seat. They would play the game with England—all the way.

"We have to," they would say. "We are a tiny, new nation, barely out of our birth pangs. Another war would finish us. At any price, we must preserve peace with England—and this French revolution—well, what have we to do with blood baths?" So they sent Morris to France as ambassador, the drawling, sneering Morris who had once remarked that Paine was neither clean nor genteel, but a piece of dirt wisely scrubbed from England's skin.

In his own way, a completely unofficial way, Paine was America's representative, doing small and large favors for the citizens of the land he had fought for, helping ship captains through the tangle of revolutionary customs and laws, serving however he could serve. James Farbee, for instance, a worthless soldier of fortune, not too bright, had been caught in a royalist plot that was no doing of his, and now waited for the thin steel blade to sever his head from his body. Paine came to see him in jail and said, "For fools like you, innocent men pay."

Farbee protested that this was none of his fault; footloose and free and without a job at home after the war, and what does a man do who has known nothing else but fighting since the age of eighteen?

"And you were in the war?"

"I was, sir."

"What command?"

"Greene's, sir."

"And who was lieutenant-quartermaster?"

"Franklin."

"Captain-secretary?"

"Anderson, Grey, Chaplin, and I think, after that, Long."

"Were you in the Jerseys?"

"Jersey and Pennsylvania, sir, and then the Carolinas. My God, sir, I was with you at Germantown, don't you remember?"

Paine, appearing before the Revolutionary Tribunal, said, in slow, halting French, "Farbee must not die. He is a fool and a knave, but a soldier of the revolution. Are we all saints?"

And Farbee lived, just as Michael Peabody and Clare Henderson lived because Paine pleaded for them.

But all that was aside from the main problem which obsessed him, the problem of one more book remaining for him to write, who had produced both a reason for revolution and a handbook for revolution. Sitting in the big farmhouse, he scribbled, blotted, forced his thoughts, and realized with horror and agony that his old ease, fire, and facility were gone. He would cover a sheet with writing and then tear it up. He wrote words and they were not the right words. He was old, not so much in years as in usage of his big, peasant body, in the usage of a mind that burned itself as had few minds in all human history. It is a sad and woeful thing when a man loses the use of tools that give him reason to live. He would struggle as he had never before struggled, and then, giving up for the time, go to the Convention hall and sit and listen. The throbbing heart of the revolution was here, and here he pressed his thoughts. A reason and a motif came one day when Francis Partiff arose on the floor and screamed:

"God is dethroned, and Christianity, corrupt as a priest, is banished from earth! Henceforth, reason shall rule, pure reason, incorruptible reason!" And standing there, Partiff shredded a Bible, page by page.

Paine got up and left; he walked through the streets and saw a cart with four bodies for the knife. He came out by the river and saw a red sun setting over the old roofs of ancient Paris. God had died; Paine walked more and more slowly, and then the sun was gone, leaving nothing but the reflected goodness in the sky and a swallow to trace a pattern before it.

"And men, who are beginning to climb to God, to be like gods, disown him! Then there is blood on the earth, and they hate—how they hate!"

He went home and he wrote; it came more easily now, his painful script, capturing thought, building to a bolt that would be loosed on men and cry once more, "Here is Paine, the friend of man." He wrote all night long, and toward dawn, he fell asleep, his head on the paper. In the morning, when Mrs. Christie came to bring him an egg and some tea, he was like that, his big head and shoulders sprawled over the desk, his breath ruffling the foolscap upon which he had scribbled. Unwilling to disturb him, knowing how many long and silent battles he had fought with insomnia, she set down the food and quietly went out.

About noon, Paine woke, had a cup of cold tea, and went back to his writing.

The Terror came closer, a black shawl drawing night over Paris, and by ones and twos the English radicals who shared the farmhouse with Paine fled, some to Switzerland, some to the north. Mrs. Christie begged Paine to go with her and her husband, but smiling curiously, he asked, "Where would I go?"

"Home."

"And where is my home?" Paine wondered. "I made the world my village, and it's too late to undo that."

"And soon they will come for you with the cart."

Paine shrugged. "If they think it necessary for me to die that the revolution may go on—" He shrugged again.

He was the only lodger left in the big farmhouse. His only companion was the landlord. And then the soldiers of the Republic came for the small, mustached Frenchman who owned the place, Georgeit, his name, with the dread warrant.

"But, Monsieur Paine, tell them," the landlord pleaded. "Tell them I have neither schemed nor plotted."

"It is no use to tell them. They do what they have to do. Go with them, my friend; there is nothing else to do and no other way. Go with them—"

And then Paine was entirely and completely alone, alone and unafraid, sitting at his desk and writing a thing which he proposed to call *The Age of Reason.*

"Let me write in letters of fire, for I am unafraid. Tomorrow I will die, or the next day. There is so much death that I have become a part of it, and that way I have lost my fear. They told me to run away, but where can Paine go? To America? They have no use for an old revolutionist in America today—indeed, I do not know that they would recognize me in America. The tall man from Mt. Vernon is not the comrade in arms that I once knew; he has forgotten how we marched down through Jersey. To England? A hundred years from now they will welcome me in the land where I was born. My work is in France and France must be the savior of the world, and if they take Paine's life, what is the loss?"

The Age of Reason, written in large letters, and underlined three times. An offering for the new world, for the brave, credulous, frightened new world, which had come out of his hands as much as out of any other's. The new world had renounced God, and thereby, to Paine's way of thinking, they had renounced the reason for man to exist. Man is a part of God, or else he is a beast; and beasts know love and fear and hate and hunger—but not exultation. As Paine saw it now, man's history was a vision of godliness. From the deep, dark morass he had come, from the jungles and the lonely mountains and the windswept steppes, and always his way had been the way of the seeker. He made civilization and he made a morality and he made a pact of brotherhood. One day, he ceased to kill the aged and venerated them, ceased to kill the sick and healed them, ceased to kill the lost and showed them how to find themselves. He had a dream and a vision, and Isaiah was one of his number, as was Jesus of Nazareth. He offered a hand, saying, Thou art my brother, and do I not know thee? And he began to see God, like going up a ladder, rung after rung, always closer to a something that had been waiting eternally. First wooden images, then marble ones, the sun and the stars, and then a just, unseen singleness, and then an unseen one of love and mercy, and then a gentle Jew nailed onto a cross and dying in pain. Man does not stop; he will be free and the brotherhood world wide, and a musket is fired in a Massachusetts village—

And now the revolution, gone down an uncharted road, sick of an organized, venal, preying church, had embraced the godlessness of nothing and nowhere. So Paine told himself, "I will write one more book and tell them what I know of a God that has not failed me." And he began:

"It has been my intention, for several years past, to publish my thoughts upon religion; I am well aware of the difficulties that attend the subject, and, from that consideration, had reserved it to a more advanced period of life. I intend it to be the last offering I shall make to my fellow citizens of all nations, and that at a time when the purity of the motive that induced me to it, could not admit of a question, even by those who might disapprove the work.

"The circumstance that has now taken place in France of the total abolition of the whole national order of the priesthood, and of everything appertaining to compulsive systems of religion, and compulsive articles of faith, has not only precipitated my intention, but rendered a work of this kind exceedingly necessary, lest, in the general wreck of superstition, of false systems of government, and false theology, we lose sight of morality, of humanity, and of the theology that is true.

"As several of my colleagues, and others of my fellow citizens of France, have given me the example of making their voluntary and individual profession of faith, I also will make mine; and I do this with all that sincerity and frankness with which the mind of man communicates with itself.

"I believe in one God, and no more; and I hope for happiness beyond this life.

"I believe the equality of man; and I believe that religious duties consist in doing justice, loving mercy, and endeavoring to make our fellow creatures happy.

"But, lest it should be supposed that I believe many other things in addition to these, I shall, in the progress of this work, declare the things I do not believe and my reasons for not believing them.

"I do not believe in the creed professed by the Jewish church, by the Roman church, by the Greek church, by the Turkish church, by the Protestant church, nor by any church that I know of. My own mind is my own church.

"All national institutions of churches, whether Jewish, Christian or Turkish, appear to me no other than human inventions, set up to terrify and enslave mankind, and monopolize power and profit."

That way, there was a beginning; he put down what he believed, what he did not believe, and then he labored, day after day, in the old, deserted farmhouse. He was not fashioning a creed; men had done that already, as much by acts as by words. Christ on a cross had fashioned it and so had a rustic boy dying on a village green in New England. So had a thousand and a hundred thousand others. It remained only for him to formulate it and put it in place as the last work in his encyclopedia of revolution.

During those quiet days when he worked on *The Age of Reason*, he did not go into old Paris very often. Once to seek for a Bible written in English; Bibles there were in plenty, but all in French, and for the life of him he could not lay hands on a King James version. That made it harder for him, having to work on out of his memory, seeking back to all the times in his childhood when he had read certain passages over and over, quoting as he worked, sometimes correctly, sometimes incorrectly. The Bible was necessary, for in writing down a faith that could be accepted by a reasonable man, a gentle man, a good man, he had to tear apart, boldly and ruthlessly, the whole fabric of superstition that had been woven through the ages.

Often he was tempted to send to England for the work he needed, but the passage of even a piece of mail was long and uncertain, and Paine was driven by a deadly sense of urgency. No one, living in or about Paris as the year of 1793 drew to a close, could forget the pall of The Terror. It had lost meaning and reason, and struck about as wildly as a maddened beast. First it had been the *right,* but now Jacobins of the extreme left joined the procession to the guillotine. What Paine had feared most was coming about, the dictatorship of violence gone amuck.

On one of his trips into Paris, Paine looked up an old acquaintance of his, Joel Barlow, whom he had helped once when Barlow was in legal difficulties with a French court.

"Whatever happens," Paine said, "I don't care too much, but I've been working on a manuscript that will soon be finished and that means a great deal to me. If they come for me, can I entrust the manuscript to you?"

"Gladly," Barlow nodded, and then begged Paine to leave for America.

"In good time," Paine nodded. "When my work in France is over."

He had finished his book; his credo was down on paper, and he felt a complete and wonderful sense of relief, the feeling of a man washed clean and rested. He had struck a blow at atheism, and he had—or so he believed—given the people of France and of the world a rational creed to sustain them through the years of revolution that he saw ahead. He had proclaimed God in all that man saw, in the perfect symmetry of a leaf, in a rosy sunset, in a million stars cast like a hood in the night, in the earth, in the sea, in all creation. He told them not to look for cheap, tawdry miracles, when they themselves and the world they lived in were the greatest of all miracles.

He told them to believe in God because they and the world they inhabited were the strongest proof of God. God's work was creation; His bible and proof were creation. It was a blazing, living, signed document, and it required neither superstitions nor horror tales to support it. It was Tom Paine to France, saying, "If you choose atheism now, I, at least, have done my part."

On one of his short trips to Paris, he had gone to the Convention hall and told the doorkeeper in very bad French, "Deputy Thomas Paine, representing Calais," and the doorkeeper stared as if he had seen a ghost. And others stared; all over the hall brows raised and necks craned as they turned to look at him.

There was only one of the old radical group of foreign expatriates left in the hall, Anacharsis Clootz, the Prussian, one of the extreme left, a man a hundred years ahead of his time, a socialist before there was socialism, a little mad, a great deal brilliant, unafraid, vehemently outspoken, much like Paine and very much unlike him. Until now, they had worked together occasionally, but not easily; Paine was a republican, an advocate of democracy; Clootz was the advocate of a social conception, the theory of which hardly existed. He waved at Paine now, and afterwards, leaving the hall, got close to him and called:

"Hello there, my old friend, where have you been?"

"Writing."

"They all write before they go to the Madam Guillotine. And what nonsense this time?"

"Gods and men."

Clootz was a militant atheist; he held his stomach now, roaring with laughter and calling after Paine, "We will discuss that, no?"

They were to discuss it soon enough.

His time had about run out; he had desired a reprieve, not out of any great desire to go on living a life that for all practical purposes was over, but because, as so often before, he had something which he felt he must put down on paper. But now that it was done, he went to meet his fate almost eagerly. They would not have to seek him; he was no recluse, and he had never fled from a judgment. Already, he had been too long alone in the big farmhouse; that was not for Paine; for Paine was the feel of his fellow men, their nearness, their voices and their smiles and their good intimacies. So he packed together the few things he had, the finished manuscript, some other papers, a book or two and some shirts and underclothes—not a great deal, but he had never been one for worldly possessions. If a man makes the world his castle, he does not seek to furnish it.

He returned to Paris and White's Hotel, to raised brows and breath softly drawn in. "Still here, Paine?"

"Still here."

And such whispered comments as, "Well, there's no fool like an old fool."

And behind his back, slick, a finger across a throat—"If he wants to, that's his own affair."

He ordered a brandy, he proposed a toast, "To the Republic of France, forever, gentlemen!" And no one knew whether to laugh or to deride.

On Christmas Day, a motion was put forward in the hall to exclude all foreigners from seats in the Convention. There were only two foreigners left, Paine and Clootz, and it was at them that the move was directed. Paine had seen this coming; he knew it when he returned to the city, when he made the toast to the Republic, when he finally went to bed to sleep what might be his last night as a free man. He was not afraid; he wanted it to come quickly; no longer a deputy of France, he wanted the surge of the revolution to overtake him, to devour him if it must.

And in the early dawn, it came.

Thus—there were two agents of the Committee of General Security pounding on the door of his room and unrolling their imposing warrant when he came in his nightshirt to let them in.

"For Citizen Paine! And you, monsieur, are Citizen Paine?"

"I am," he smiled. "Come in, gentlemen."

The two agents were followed by one corporal and four privates. The corporal took his place at the foot of Paine's bed, after saluting, the privates on either side.

"Permit me to dress," Paine said. The corporal graciously nodded and the two agents set about searching the room. Paine poured them each a brandy, and the privates stared intently at nothing at all. "Excellent brandy," the agents admitted, and went on with their searching.

When he was dressed, Paine asked, "I would like to know—the charge—"

"Monsieur Merson," one of the agents introduced himself, a small tribute to the brandy, and read from the warrant, "Conspiring against the Republic."

"Conspiring against the Republic," Paine repeated, softly and tiredly. "Citizen Paine is under arrest for conspiracy. He sits alone in an empty farmhouse and broods about God, and thereby the Republic is endangered. I wonder whether the shortest thing in the world is not the memory of men." He had spoken in English; when the agents raised their brows, he shook his head. "Nothing, nothing—I have some papers at the Britain House, may we go there and get them?" pouring another brandy for each.

"Not entirely in order," Merson shrugged. "But when one arrests a citizen one admires, so reluctantly, one may make an exception."

At the Britain House, Barlow was waiting, and Paine gave him the manuscript of *The Age of Reason.*

"I wish to God you had left France," Barlow said.

"And I may, sooner than I expected," Paine answered ruefully. "Barlow, this thing I wrote may be trash, but to me it's very dear—in the loose talk of an old man, the finish of a life. If I go to the guillotine, try to have it published. I have some friends in America; the printers in Philadelphia would do me another turn, for the sake of old times. There's Jefferson and Washington—I think they remember me. If you have to, play on their feelings, tell them, recall to them an old soldier in the times that tried men's souls."

"Don't be a damn fool," Barlow muttered.

M. Merson said, "Please, citizen, I have been good enough to allow you pass on your book and gullible enough to come here and meet your friend. But now we must go."

"Where are you taking him?" Barlow demanded.

"To the Luxembourg, for the time."

On their way to the prison, they stopped off long enough to arrest Anacharsis Clootz, and then, with soldiers on either side, the two ex-deputies were marched through the streets. Clootz was bubbling with suppressed mirth; there was something diabolical in the way he regarded this last march. "So we go, friend Paine," he chuckled, "you at one end of the long bar of revolution, I on the other, and in the end it makes no difference to the good Lady Guillotine. She will go chop, once, twice, and then it will be a finish to Paine and Clootz—and to what else, old friend? Who can tell?"

"But why? They accuse me of being a traitor to the Republic, a charge I don't have to answer. The name of Paine is answer enough. But of what do they accuse you?"

Clootz let go with a furious burst of laughter. "You are an old man, Paine, so even the remarkably simple becomes greatly involved. You are a republican, and I am, to coin a phrase for our times, a proletarian. You believe in the democratic method through representation, and I believe in the same method through the will of the masses. You say, let the people rule; I say the same thing; we are after the same thing, only in different ways. I believe that your way is hopeless, part of the past; but otherwise we are the same, and the dictatorship, which this Republic of France is fast becoming, does not want us. Therefore, chop, chop—let the good Lady Guillotine take care of everything."

They continued toward the prison, and for a while Clootz was silent, his bushy brows puckered intently, and to Paine it seemed that the German had finally realized his destination and his fate. But suddenly Clootz swung on him and roared,

"What is this nonsense you write, Paine, about the creation being the Bible of God?"

"A simple fact which I believe."

"Which you believe!" Clootz snorted, stopping the march and turning on Paine, arms akimbo. "You repudiate organized religion and substitute mystical rationalization! My friend, Paine, you shock me. With you I spend some of my last precious hours. On every hand people in the streets turn to stare at us and whisper to each other, There are Paine and Clootz on their way to the guillotine. These good soldiers, these two agents of what calls itself the Republic of France, will go home to their soup and their wives with the news that they marched the last march with the two greatest minds of the eighteenth century. And you rationalize about the creation being the Bible of God. What creation?"

"Of course, it happened!" Paine snapped. "Atheism, the great creed of chance! Like a game of cards, everything just fell together until it fitted nicely!"

"And why not? Where is reason, but in our minds? Where is godliness, but in the people? Where is mercy, but in the masses? A thing becomes reasonable because we make it reasonable, and we are not reaching toward God, but toward goodness, a formulation of the people, a concept of small, suffering men—"

M. Merson interrupted, "Please, please, citizens, we are on our way to the Luxembourg jail. I pray you not to argue, for it is unseemly in men going our way." And they continued on their way, Clootz roaring his theories at the top of his lungs.

It had been the Palace of Luxembourg before the revolution; now it was the house of arrest, the last stop. It stood in the famous old gardens where all was beauty, so that the many who went to the guillotine could bring a good last memory with them, and in no place was horror and warmth so neatly and terribly combined. Great rooms, high ceilings, rugs and tapestries and gilt chairs, and death. If you sat with your friends and mused of things that were far away, large things and beautiful, such as men in prison bring to life with words, the green hills of Pennsylvania, the white cliffs of Dover, the moors of the north country, the Palisades on a cold, windy winter day, a storm at sea or a sunrise at sea; and musing upon those things heard a series of piercing shrieks, moans and groans and fervent calling upon God, you pretended not to notice—for it is saddest of all things to contemplate human beings going to their deaths. But you thought to yourself, the duchess, perhaps—or the wife of the little man who kept a tobacco shop on the Rue St. Denis—or the quiet woman in black who has no identity at all.

You kept your quarters clean even if you had never kept quarters clean before, for you acquired at the threshold of the grave a fastidious sense of delicacy. You acquired humility, whether you were a count or a butcher, for here were all classes living in the most incredible little democracy the world had ever known. When you wept, you tried not to show your tears to others, for early in your stay at the Luxembourg you saw the quiet contagion of tears, twenty persons in a room where one began to weep, and then another, and then another—and then all.

You came to admire the French if you had never admired them before, the way they faced death, the way they could joke about it, the way with a simple, expressive shrug of their shoulders they could divest it of all importance. You found a people from chimney sweep to duke so wonderfully civilized that even while you were dying because a revolution had gone amuck, you never for once doubted that in France was the salvation of mankind. You came to know M. Benoît, the jailor, who would sometimes say, with a deprecatory smile, "I must have a large heart— How do I know, monsieur?—because whenever one of my charges goes away, a part of my heart goes with him. You who are here die once—and how many times do I die? A hundred? A thousand? Why don't I go away, monsieur? Who would replace me? I am not a saint, but not a villain."

You heard people say, "It is The Terror. It is the war." Not complainingly, but with an acceptance of the fact that explained a little how this strange, sunny land had once lived through a hundred-year war that had desolated three quarters of it.

You would be with a group, and a door would open, and there would be a new one among you, Benoît leading him in and asking apologetically, "There will be some friends of yours, perhaps? You must make your best, and I will do my part," and turning around you would recognize him. Others recognize him too, some with bewilderment, some with a trace of satisfaction, but they all greet him as if he were coming to a club and not to a last stopping place.

Your old, good friend has learned that tomorrow it will be his turn, and he asks you to take a walk with him in the garden. Arm in arm, you stroll around the court, around and around, never once mentioning that this is the last walk on the last cold, winter afternoon, and looking at the gray winter sky, you realize the beauty of what was never beautiful before. The snow begins to fall, and your friend lays the palm of his hand against the melting flakes and reminds you that here is a great wonder of existence, so many snowstorms, so many flakes, so many countless millions of them, and yet all different, never two the same. "A wonder of infinity for us who delude ourselves with our greatness."

Or the mother of the boy, Benjamin, comes to you with word that they are taking him, he who is only seventeen. "A child, a baby, an innocent," she pleads with you. "Yesterday, I nursed him at my breast, just yesterday. What could he have done to deserve death?"

You don't know, and you try, with the foolish, blundering ways of a man, to comfort the mother. And then you go in to the boy, who, looking at you so trustingly, asks with his eyes for you to clear away the great mystery of death.

And so time passes, and presently there is no world at all except the Luxembourg Prison.

In the beginning, Paine had hope. He did not want to die; no one wants to die, and in this case, Paine had committed no crime, had indulged in no act of treason, and had consistently expressed his faith in both the Republic and the revolution. It was true that he had voted with and consorted with a party now overthrown and discredited, but even in that situation his motives had never been suspect, and he had been deliberately acquitted when the others went to the scaffold. Why then should he be held in prison? Treason? If there were a thousand men who hated Paine, accusing him of almost every crime known to man, they at least left treason out of the roster. In his fidelity to what he believed, he had never faltered.

Nor could he accept his fate with the laughing abandon, shown first by Clootz and later by Danton. Well enough for them to find this whole business of mankind so amusing that death under the guillotine seemed the final jest in a ridiculous comedy. Paine had always loved life; the simple fact of living was an adventure, each new face presented to him an added bit of happiness. He was gregarious to an extreme, not merely loving his fellow men, but feeling a passionate need for them, without which life could not be endured. He had a sense of property which, not fixing itself on some little bit of acreage, had embraced the whole world.

So in the beginning he had hope, and he fought for his freedom. Not only was he a citizen of France; first and foremost, he was a citizen of America; he had weaned a piece of that land, he had nursed it and seen it out of its swaddling clothes. Therefore, he could, without shame or conscience, call on America in this hour of his need.

As simple as that; he got word to his friends, Barlow and a few others, to put pressure on Morris, the ambassador, and have him obtain Paine's release. And it was as simple as that, for the only nation in all the world revolutionary France could look to for friendship was America.

It was a situation to delight Morris's heart. There was a time in Philadelphia when the people rose up against a small group that would have turned the American revolution to their own ends; and the leader of the people was Paine, and one of the small group was Gouverneur Morris. There was a time when a revolutionary tribunal was set up in Philadelphia, and one of those who sat in the tribunal was Tom Paine, and one of those it passed judgment upon was Gouverneur Morris. "So slowly do the wheels of fate turn," Morris mused, "but so aptly." How many years had he waited for this moment—twelve? thirteen? A man forgets the years, but some things a man does not forget. In this land of shopkeepers and pigs, Paine and Clootz had walked to jail through the streets of Paris, arguing aloud their respective modes of atheism; yes, Morris had heard of that. What a glorious opportuntiy when a man can avenge his own feud and serve God at the same time. As brief insurance, Morris wrote to Jefferson, who represented all that was left in America of the revolution, the people and the ideals which made it:

". . . I must mention, that Thomas Paine is in prison, where he amuses himself with publishing a pamphlet against Jesus Christ. I do not recollect whether I mentioned to you, that he would have been executed along with the rest of the Brissotines, if the adverse party had not viewed him with contempt. I incline to think that, if he is quiet in prison, he may have the good luck to be forgotten. Whereas, should he be brought much into notice, the long suspended ax might fall on him. I believe he thinks, that I ought to claim him as an American citizen; but, considering his birth, his naturalization in this country, and the place he filled, I doubt much the right, and I am sure that the claim would be, for the present at least, inexpedient and ineffectual. . . ."

That done, Morris proceeded, with a clear conscience, to serve both his God and his country. The first step was to have Paine guillotined, which would be a service to the Almighty, and the second to break relations with France for that very thing, which would turn the service of the Almighty to the ends of the Hamiltonian party in America. To Barlow, Morris said:

"Paine is out of my hands entirely, a citizen of France, you know."

"But a citizen of America first!"

"I prefer to believe that Americans are not his ilk. I prefer to cherish some small respect for my native land. . . ."

And to Robespierre, "Really, sir, I would not stand in your way if Paine's execution were necessary to the welfare of the French Republic."

"And you might not be displeased," Robespierre said keenly.

"One doesn't commit oneself on such matters."

"Yet if Paine goes to the guillotine," Robespierre speculated, measuring Morris with his small, bright, merciless eyes, "there might be some displeasure in certain sections of your land. The militia, for instance, who fought with Paine, might remember him and object to his death; and Jefferson might remember that Paine once wrote a book called *Common Sense*."

"I assure you, sir, that neither the militia of a war that was over ten years ago nor Thomas Jefferson exerts too much influence upon the foreign policy of President Washington's government."

"Yet even your President Washington, if he needed a reason—

speaking purely theoretically, you understand—might recall that once he and Paine were comrades in arms and, recalling that, might play upon the sympathies of the American people—"

"If you insinuate—"

"I insinuate nothing," Robespierre said quietly. "It is Monsieur the American ambassador who insinuates. Meanwhile the good Lady Guillotine drinks enough. When Paine's time comes, he will taste the justice of France, and until then Monsieur the American ambassador must wait patiently. Monsieur the American ambassador must not expect the French Republic to use its tribunals for personal—"

"That is enough, sir," Morris said.

Yet all in all, he was content to wait. He had waited a long time, and what were a few weeks or months more?

To Paine, none of this was apparent, as in the Luxembourg weeks stretched into months. He heard of a petition on his behalf put forward in the Convention by Americans living in Paris, and he heard of the sneering reply the aging president of the Convention made. He heard of a correspondence between the French foreign minister and Morris, and he took it in good faith. True enough, Morris did not like him, but one does not send a man one dislikes to his death. As time went on and absolutely nothing was done about his imprisonment, Paine's hope ebbed, but it never entirely vanished.

The Terror became more terrible, and the flow of victims to the guillotine was speeded up. A dread silence settled over the Luxembourg, a tightening of restrictions, a severing of all bonds with the outside world. Weeks and months passed, and no man left the place except for a single reason.

It came time for Clootz to go, and he waved to Paine and laughed, "Now, my deistic friend, I shall see which of us is right on this question of God, while you sit here and rack your poor brains."

And Danton, going the same way to the same bloody blade, shook hands with Paine, smiling rather sadly, and murmuring,

"What a foolish, foolish world, fit only for children and idiots!"

And Luzon said, softly, fervently, "Good-by, my friend Paine. You shall not want for comrades, if they have republics over there."

And Ronsin said, "You will be lonely, Paine. The whole world we knew has already passed."

Twenty one night, forty the next, over two hundred one terrible time. The gentle Benoît was no longer jailor; a hulking, sadistic brute called Guiard became custodian of the old palace; he closed off the courtyard and denied the prisoners a little air and a little sky before they met their deaths. He told them:

"Speak, and you are overheard. Plot, and I know what you are plotting. Guiard never sleeps."

In a fashion, it was true; he had the place filled with his spies, and a word was enough to send a man to the guillotine.

In this hellishness, Paine became something more than a man; he became a spirit and a faith; he became consolation and redemption. He knew when to smile—and a smile was the only thing on earth these poor devils could be given. He knew the few words that could help a man go to his death; he knew a phrase to console a mother. He was tireless, without fear, without hesitation. Gaunt, his health failing, nevertheless the mere sight of his big, angular figure entering a room was enough to cheer the occupants. "It is Monsieur Paine—come in, come in." He had a vast fund of stories, the drawling, American frontier jokes, which translated into his very bad French made almost no sense at all, but which were funny and pointless enough to send the poor devils who heard them into aching laughter. And he knew when to call up mirth; he knew when to be silent, when his mere presence was enough, when a word was enough.

And man after man, woman after woman, going to meet their death, said, "Send for Citizen Paine."

He lay in his bare room; he waxed hot and cold with fever; time lost meaning for him and disappeared. The fever came and receded, like undulating waves of fire, and he lived in a nightmarish world, populated by saints and devils. Vaguely he sensed that men were entering and leaving; screams sometimes made him wonder where he was, and in a moment of clarity, he heard a man say:

"This wretch is dying."

And it mattered little or not at all, for the fever always returned, burning him, chilling him, burning him again.

Then, after a long, long time, sanity returned. He asked what month it was.

"July—"

And he counted, "January, February, March—"

"I am still in the Luxembourg?"

"Quite true, citizen, but matters have changed. Robespierre is dead. St. Just is dead. Take heart, citizen. The Terror is over."

"So The Terror is over," Paine sighed, and that night he slept without dreams.

It is difficult to regain one's strength in prison, even if one does not live in hourly fear of death. Paine, looking in a glass again, found a gray-haired stranger confronting him, a sunken face that was etched all over with lines and wrinkles. It made him smile, so much a stranger was the image, and the smile that the mirror returned him was hollow and mocking.

The beast, Guiard, had passed on with the downfall of Robespierre's government, and Arden, the new jailor, allowed the prisoners the freedom of the courtyard. Paine could walk again in the blessed sunlight; it was summer, and he could smell the flowers and watch the strollers in the gardens and mark the little clouds as they scudded overhead. The whole air of the Luxembourg had changed; it was still a prison, but it was not a death house. People left, again by the tens and twenties, but now they passed through the gates to freedom.

For the time being, Paine had little to do but to think—to contemplate the events of the past six months, the strange silence which had abandoned him during that time when the Luxembourg was a place of horror. Why had Morris made no effort to secure his freedom? he asked himself. Why had the American nation remained completely passive? Did it mean nothing to George Washington that Paine was in prison, perhaps to be guillotined any day? The whole attitude of Washington was incomprehensible. Why had he never really expressed his thanks to Paine for inscribing to him *The Rights of Man*? Had he forgotten that the country he presided over now was born out of revolution?

During the long days Paine spent recuperating from his sickness he brooded long and often over what had happened to America during these past years. Most difficult of all was to believe ill of that man who had seemed to him, for so many years, better and truer than any other man he had known, George Washington.

And then there was a ray of hope. Gouverneur Morris was no longer minister to France; James Monroe, a Jeffersonian democrat, had replaced him. Eagerly, Paine waited for Monroe's arrival, and once he was installed, sent him a long memorial, pleading his case and begging Monroe to make some effort to obtain his freedom. Monroe answered with a cheerful and hopeful reply, that he would work on the case and that Paine could expect liberation soon.

Yet it didn't come; the summer was over and another winter began, and almost all the other prisoners who had been with Paine in the Luxembourg had been freed; but he remained. It was fever again, sores developing in his side, his big, strong body finally crumbling under ten long months of imprisonment. His hand barely able to hold a pen, he wrote to Monroe again.

Barlow came to see him, and looking at the American with dulled eyes, Paine said barely a word.

"Paine?"

"It was never the dying I minded," Paine whispered. "But to have it drawn out like this is more than I can bear."

Then Monroe wrote to the Committee of General Security, "The services which he [Paine] rendered them [the people of America] in their struggle for liberty have made an impression of gratitude which will never be erased, whilst they continue to merit the character of a just and generous people. He is now in prison, languishing under a disease, and which must be increased by his confinement. Permit me, then, to call your attention to his situation, and to require that you will hasten his trial in case there be any charge against him, and if there be none, you will cause him to be set at liberty."

And it was done; in November, 1794, Tom Paine was released from Luxembourg Palace, not the man who had entered, but one sick and old and gray-haired.

FOURTEEN

Napoleon Bonaparte

PAINE had been living with the Monroes, gaining back his strength so slowly that again and again he despaired of ever being more than an invalid. No one expected him to live; they were so certain he would die that already news of his death had been sent across the ocean to America.

Yet he did not die. His strong, leathery body could absorb a fearful amount of punishment, and presently he was well enough to ask for the manuscript of *The Age of Reason.*

He read it through with delight; in parts, it was lacking, but in others it was very good, fiery, a ringing memory of his old self. He would have to add to it, but meanwhile he would have this section published. Let the atheists read it and find something worth believing in.

Meanwhile his thoughts turned increasingly toward America. There was not much, if anything, left for him in France; the revolution had imprisoned him, cast him out, departed from the principles he preached. In America it was different; he was not too old to fight, and back in that land he so loved he would once more fight for liberty against the strange, dark reaction that had set in with the Washington administration. Now it was winter, but when spring came again, he would be strong enough to travel.

And then the National Convention recalled him, gave him back his seat, and made him once more a deputy of France. Monroe was delighted. "You see, Paine," he said, "that this vindicates you—this is the final confession of injustice. Once again as Citizen Paine, as leader of liberal democrats throughout the world, you can take your seat in the representative chamber of Republican France."

But for Paine, there was no triumph; he was almost frightened. The ten months in prison had done something to him, not only deprived him of bodily strength but taken away a certain resiliency of mind. Another Terror, he could not endure; another shattering of all he worked for would be worse than death.

He sat down and wrote to the Assembly:

"My intention is to accept the invitation of the Assembly. For I desire that it be known to the universe that, although I have been the victim of injustice, I do not attribute my sufferings to those who had no part in them, and that I am far from using reprisals towards even those who are the authors of them. But, as it is necessary that I return to America next spring, I desire to consult you on the situation in which I find myself, in order that my acceptation of returning to the Convention may not deprive me of the right to return to America."

But it was of that very right that they deprived him. Later, Monroe desired to send Paine to America with certain important papers. The Committee of Public Safety answered that Paine could not be spared.

So he stayed on at the Convention, old, feeble, a gray-haired man who sometimes rose and said a few words no one listened to. He felt trapped and helpless.

And then *The Age of Reason* was published in England and America.

Youth had almost returned to him as he worked alongside the French publisher, sought with him for a good English typesetter, and breathed once again that delicious smell of wet printer's ink, that smell which evoked every dear and splendid memory he knew.

It was his confession of faith, his last work, his tribute to God and to good men. It was his stroke against atheism; it was his fervent faith in a deity that was good and merciful, and in man's ability to approach that deity without compulsion and superstition. And then it was published, a batch of copies sent to England, another batch to America, and then the ax fell.

Formerly, Satan had been one; now he became two, himself and Tom Paine. Every religious denomination joined together to attack this devil who had thrown doubt on all organized religion. Even in France, the repercussions jolted and tossed the tired old warrior. There was no understanding, no sympathy, nothing but abuse, abuse, and abuse. The servants of God conceived a vocabulary of foul names to apply to Paine, such adjectives as the world had not seen before, and as a summation it was decided that since the creation there had been no human being more wicked and more vile than Paine. To most of this, Paine did not reply; if he were wrong, it would have been different; if he were wrong they would have gone about proving him wrong and not showered him with filth. Convinced that he was right, he saw no need to go on adding to his arguments.

Yet now and again, he was driven to an answer, as for instance when Wakefield, the English Unitarian, attacked him. To him Paine wrote:

"When you have done as much service to the world by your writings, and suffered as much for them, as I have done, you will be better entitled to dictate. . . ."

He was terribly tired; sick again, he heard of the reaction in America; it was not all abuse there, as in England; some stood up for his point of view; there were still old comrades of his left, old revolutionists who had not forgotten how to think—and they were buying many copies of his book.

To Monroe, he said wearily, "I want to go home, I am so tired." Now there was a place called home; the world was his village, but now he kept thinking of the green hills and valleys of America. He was an old man in a strange land. He was the most hated—and perhaps by a few the most loved—man in all the world. For twenty years his broad shoulders had taken abuse; they were tired now.

Monroe said, "I wonder whether publication of *The Age of Reason* was wise, Paine. In America—"

"When have I been wise?" Paine cried. "Was it wise to throw my fortune with a pack of farmers the world knew defeated before ever they began to fight? Was it wise for me to cry out for independence before any of your great men at home had dared to conceive the notion? Was it wise for me to give a revolutionary credo to England and then have to flee for my life? Was it wise for me to spend ten months under the shadow of the guillotine? I have been many things, but never prudent, never wise. That's for heroes and great men, not for a staymaker!"

The portrait of Paine, drawn with horns, hung on the wall of many an English home. Taverns displayed beer mugs with Paine's picture, and underneath it, "Drink with the devil." In a hundred churches on a hundred Sundays sermons were preached on Tom Paine, apostate. In London, Liverpool, Nottingham, and Sheffield, piles of Paine's books were burned, while crowds danced around the fires, screaming:

> *"Paine, Paine, damned be his name,*
> *Damned be his fame and lasting his shame,*
> *God damn Paine! God damn Paine!"*

Feverish again, he lay and brooded and thought he was going to die. He didn't care. He turned over in his mind, one by one, all the horrors he had suffered during his imprisonment, and his resentment came to center upon a single man, George Washington.

There were others, Morris and Hamilton and the whole counter-revolutionary crowd, but what other had he worshiped the way he worshiped George Washington? He remembered how Washington, the aristocrat, the wealthiest man in America, had taken the hand of Paine, the nobody. He remembered how Washington, at Valley Forge, had begged him to go and plead his case before Congress. He remembered that he, Paine, had written, "The names of Washington and Fabius will run parallel to eternity."

So it was not the others who mattered, but George Washington; the others had not betrayed him, he had no claim on them. Washington it was who sent the contemptuous Morris as ambassador to Republican France; Washington had sent Jay to England to smear the honor of America; Washington had ignored *The Rights of Man*, dedicated to him, the key to the Bastille, presented to him; Washington had turned his back on the people and on democracy.

Sick as he was, tired as he was, he could not seek for a true perspective. He did not know what Washington had been told of him, nor did he care, but desired only to lash out at this man who, as Paine saw it, had betrayed both a friend and a cause. And believing he was going to die, he put into a letter his rage against a man whom he had once loved more than any other on earth.

Monroe begged him not to send it. "It will accomplish nothing," Monroe pleaded. "Believe me, it will accomplish nothing and gain for you only more enemies. How many years is it since you left America? Washington is only a man, and men forget."

"I haven't forgotten," Paine said.

For a time he held the letter, then he sent it, to be made public.

Paine continued to attend the Convention as a delegate from Calais. When the Thermidorians put down the popular uprising by force of arms and denied the people a voice in the new government, demanding property qualifications for the right to vote, a feeble old man stood up in the Convention and faced them. Even now Paine could vividly recall the torture of his abscessed side as he stood there in front of rank after rank of hostile faces. No screaming gallery with food wrapped in paper, eating as they applauded or hissed, no fervent radicals demanding death for those who opposed the people's will, but rather well-fed, stolid legislators who made a good thing out of the decadent remains of what had once been a movement for the freedom of man.

They looked at Paine and they whispered to each other, "Has the old fool no sense at all? Isn't ten months in the Luxembourg enough? Or must we send him back there for good?"

"What is he up to now?"

"Franchise."

"Yes, he wants them to vote. Let every blessed beggar vote, and the judgment day will come."

"Make a move to block it."

Someone else said wearily, "Let him speak. No one is listening."

And he spoke of franchise, of the right of every human being to vote. He had a knack of making enemies; he had a knack of always saying the wrong thing at the wrong time; he had a knack of making people hate Paine as they had never hated anyone else. Now amid the hundred voices crying out against him, one said:

"Is it difficult to tolerate that man who has never manifested the least degree of intolerance to anyone?"

No, he had never lost faith; he had not abandoned democracy, it had abandoned him—the Thermidors, then the Directory, the whole gradual and complete collapse of the revolution.

He began to run down like a watch; he stopped functioning in the only way he was fitted to function, as a revolutionist. Nothing but that could have made him so feeble and purposeless, not the hatred stirred up by *The Age of Reason*, not his sickness, not the silence of his old comrades in America, but simply the fact that he had ceased to fulfill his purpose.

He wrote a little; he was a writer and until he died, he would fumble with a pen. He remembered old Ben Franklin who had been a philosopher and a scientist until the day of his death, and Paine thought he too would dabble with philosophy and science, little machines, models, gadgets that were ingenious enough but meant nothing more than the chattering of a voice that had once roared out firm and strong, and since the voice could not be completely silenced it took these small, futile directions.

And thereby, he went to pieces. Forgotten—a new age was dawning, the nineteenth century. Had a fool once said, "Give me seven years and I will write a *Common Sense* for every nation in Europe"? That too was forgotten. The wave which he started, the upsurge of the common man, would never disappear, but it would undulate, sinking now into obscurity, coming up again in a spurt of fresh power. For him, for Thomas Paine, revolutionist, that was no consolation; he had failed, and the powers of darkness were rising.

He, who had never been meticulous about his appearance, now completely neglected it. He shaved once a week, sometimes less often. He wore dirty linen and old felt slippers out of which his toes poked forlornly. He shuffled back and forth in the confines of his littered chamber, and sometimes he would stand, head poised, as if trying to recall something he had recently forgotten.

What had he forgotten? That the bells were ringing at Lexington?

Liquor was an old friend; it was a friend when other friends were gone. Let the teetotalers cry out against it, his body was his own; when it was good and strong and vigorous, he had used it unsparingly and not for himself; now it was old and worn out and sick, and if he drank to ease the pain and the loneliness, that was his business and no one else's.

He still had a friend or two among the plain Parisians; good people, the French, simple people, enduring people—civilized people. They understood such things; a man is a man, not a god, and when they saw Paine coming down the street, dirty, shuffling, they did not laugh or hoot at him, but gently passed the time of the day with one who had once been great.

"A good day, Citizen Paine."

They didn't forget so easily. If there were five heads outside the wineshop, bent over one of the small, smudged Paris newspapers, trying to unravel the involved politics of Talleyrand, and Citizen Paine came along, they deferred to him.

"A good day, citizen—this man Talleyrand."

"I know him, only too well," Paine said.

There was nothing incongruous to them in this poor creature having been not so long ago the intimate of Talleyrand.

"He came to me for advice," Paine said. "I don't like him."

Nothing incongruous in that either; a king became a beggar and a beggar a dictator. Hadn't they lived through those times and didn't they know the broad loops the wheel of fortune made?

In the wineshop, the shopkeeper was the soul of quiet courtesy. He had sold to Danton, to Condorcet, and now he was selling to Citizen Paine. He saw glories that were not so long ago, and he tried not to see a dirty old man.

"The best, of course," he nodded, and chopped a franc he could ill afford from the price.

In that way, Citizen Thomas Paine passed out of the public life of France.

Living with the Bonnevilles was an old man called Paine, a

rather ineffectual old man who puttered about at one thing and another—and sometimes would pause in the midst of what he was doing, with an absent seeking expression on his lined face. He was given to brief lapses of memory, and he was none too tidy. Sometimes out and rambling about Paris, he would come home with a bottle of brandy wrapped in newspaper under his arm, and closing his door behind him would drink half of it in an hour. Then, drunk, he would sometimes make a nuisance of himself—all of which the Bonnevilles put up with very patiently. When asked why by a curious neighbor, they would answer, very simply:

"You see, he is a great man, one of the greatest men this world has ever known. But the world is a quick place, and you have to scurry to keep up with it. He is too old to scurry about like a hare, and therefore the world has forgotten him. But we have not forgotten him."

Nicholas de Bonneville was a newspaper editor, a liberal, and a republican. His wife was a good-natured young woman who believed ardently in whatever her husband believed in. When he told her of Tom Paine's greatness, she nodded and agreed. She came of country folk, and had the peasant's tolerance for the whims of the aged, and because of that and because of what her husband told her, she put up with this untidy old man whose room was a litter of newspapers, books, little mechanical contrivances, empty brandy bottles, and numerous manuscripts, some of which occasionally appeared in her husband's newspaper.

One morning, in the fall of 1797, a short, pudgy stranger appeared at the Bonnevilles' front door and asked for Citizen Thomas Paine. At first Madame Bonneville stared at him suspiciously, then, recognizing him, she broke into excited welcome, ushered him into her parlor, offered him a glass of wine which he refused, blundered here and there and everywhere in her nervousness, and finally clattered upstairs to call Citizen Paine.

Paine, laboriously working at a manuscript, raised his brows as she burst in and asked whether or not the house was burning down. Ignoring this bit of facetiousness on the part of her lodger, she said breathlessly:

"Monsieur, Bonaparte is downstairs!"

"Who?"

"Listen to me, listen very carefully, Monsieur. Napoleon Bonaparte is sitting downstairs in my parlor at this very moment, waiting to speak with Citizen Thomas Paine. Do you understand me? He has come here, alone, for no other purpose than to speak with Citizen Thomas Paine!"

"Of course, I understand you," Paine growled. "Stop shouting; go downstairs and tell him to go away."

"What? Monsieur, surely you misunderstand me. I said—"

"I know what you said. Go down and tell him I have no time for brigands and evil men."

"No, no, no, no," Madame Bonneville sighed. "No, no, this you cannot do here under my roof. I have put up with many things, with dirt and drunkenness and noisiness, but I will not see a great general of France who has come to my house turned away."

"I pay my rent and keep," Paine muttered.

"No, Monsieur, it is not a question of rent, not if you paid double what you do. You will see Bonaparte or—"

"Very well, I will see him," Paine snorted. "Bring him up here."

"Here? In this?"

"And what's wrong with this? I live here, don't I?"

"No, no, no, no, Monsieur—you will come down to my parlor."

Paine shrugged. "Then down to your parlor," he agreed, and followed her downstairs. As they came into the parlor, Bonaparte rose and bowed, and Paine was struck immediately with the insignificance of the man, so short, so pudgy in body yet so lean in face, a shopkeeper possibly, but not the great general, not the warrior, not the diabolical genius who was shredding away the last remnants of the French Republic and the hopes and prayers of all men of good will.

"How sad it is," the old man thought, "that the great heroes and great villains of the world do not fulfill themselves physically!"

"You are Citizen Paine," Napoleon said. "I am Bonaparte—I have looked forward to this day, eagerly, hopefully. It is not often given us to meet the great ones of the ages. They pass away, and we must content ourselves with the legends. But I stand face to face with the greatest of all legends—Citizen Paine!"

That was not what Paine had expected; that broke through his armor, his defense, his calculated hatred for a man who represented all that he deemed evil. He was old; he was lonely; he was tired of being vilified; and this was a tribute.

He said, "Thank you, General."

"Not General, Citizen Bonaparte to Citizen Paine. My friend, sit down, if it pleases you." He had a way of command, even in things he asked, such as the simple matter of courtesy. Paine sank into a chair, but Napoleon paced back and forth, his head forward, his hands clenched behind him in a gesture that was already part of him.

"Citizen Paine," Napoleon said, "whatever you have thought of me, here is what I have been thinking of you—that a statue of gold should be erected to you in every city on the face of this earth, that your work should be enshrined—enshrined, I say. Don't I know? Have I not read *Common Sense*, *The Rights of Man*, *The Age of Reason*? Read them—reread them, I tell you! I sleep with *The Rights of Man* under my pillow, so that if I spend a night in wakefulness, insomnia shall not rob me but become instead a privilege. You and I are the only republicans, the only men with vision enough to look beyond the stars! A United States of the World?—I agree with you. I say an end to autocracy, an end to dictatorship! I take up your torch!"

Bewildered, Paine could only sit there and stare at the little man. What do words mean? Had he been mistaken? Does utopia come out of such blustering and through no other manner? He didn't know; his head was whirling. Perhaps he had listened only to the lies that were spoken about Bonaparte; they told lies about Paine too.

"I need you," Napoleon said. "We are both dedicated to mankind, to Republican France, and if we work together who can say to what lengths the dreams of Citizen Paine and Citizen Bonaparte may not go? Soon I will have a military council, and if you will sit there, I will be both honored and rewarded."

The old man was staring at him.

"You agree then?" Bonaparte smiled; his smile could be very winning.

"I will think of it," Paine nodded. "I will think of it."

After Napoleon had gone, Paine went up to his room, shaking off Madame Bonneville who would have a first-hand account of every word that had been spoken. He wanted to be alone; he wanted to think back and see what had brought him to this. In his room, he saw himself very plainly, the trash and dirt all about him, the old, stained dressing gown that he wore, the grime under his nails, the disarray of his gray hair. He found a comb and began to draw it through his thinning strands, musing all the while on these last years in Republican France.

Would he meet with Bonaparte? "Why not?" he asked himself. "Didn't I go back to the Convention again? I have not abandoned men; they have abandoned me and my principles. If the only hope left is Bonaparte, then I will go to him."

Hope had returned, a future had returned, and once more he was Thomas Paine, champion of mankind. He was going to sit at a military council with Bonaparte. After he had shaved, he looked in his mirror and said:

"Ten years younger—a man is as young as he feels. When Franklin was my age, the revolution had not yet started. They will say of Paine that his life began at sixty, that he taught the world that the mind does not grow old."

He had money, for his books were selling well, and he stuffed his wallet greedily. The devil with the future. First clothes, and then the hairdresser; a man does not go to the hairdresser in rags.

At the tailor's, a brow was raised until he snapped angrily, "I am Citizen Paine, damn you! Enough of that and show me your styles."

"Something special, perhaps? Something for an occasion?"

"Something for a military council," he said, as offhand as he could. "Bonaparte will be there."

And then a hurry and a scurry, clerks running from all over the place.

"Something simple, black, I think."

"Naturally, black, citizen. One recognizes that for such an occasion a black worsted, in keeping with your background, and perhaps a touch of satin to add dignity—"

He bought shirts and shoes and stockings; the generals of France would not sneer at Tom Paine. Then, clothed in his fine new raiment, he went to the hairdresser. There were no secrets from a Parisian hairdresser. "I look too old, much too old," Paine said. "When a man still has work to do and people to meet, important people, he desires to make a certain impression."

The years can't be bounced off so fatuously, and when Paine came back to the Bonneville house, the reaction had set in. He sat in the parlor in his new clothes, staring at the place Bonaparte had occupied, the pudgy little man with the thin face, the commanding voice, the savior of mankind—

Bonneville came in, glanced at Paine, raised a brow but politely refrained from any comment.

"Tricked out like a popinjay," Paine smiled, a note of dejection in his voice. "Do you like it, Nicholas?"

"Very much," Bonneville nodded.

"Necessary," Paine shrugged. "I am embarking on a new career. When everything else is done and gone, the great Napoleon Bonaparte visits me, makes me his confidant, and informs me that he sleeps each night with a copy of *The Rights of Man* under his pillow. Either his pillow is too low, or I have been mistaken in the man." Paine leaned back in the chair, closing his eyes for a moment or two, then whispered:

"Nicholas, I am afraid. This is my last hope. What if it fails?"

As he entered the room where the council was being held, the military men, the engineers, admirals, generals, and political advisors who made up the group, each rose and bowed under the watchful eye of Bonaparte, who said again and again, very ingratiatingly:

"Here is Citizen Paine, messieurs, of whom you have heard. If you saw me with a book in my hands during one of our passages in arms, you may be sure that it was something Citizen Paine wrote. I introduce him as the first republican."

They were all very happy to meet Citizen Paine. Some he knew; most he had heard of, Bonaparte's generals and advisors, some of them intriguers, others open-faced men who had started off in the blue smock of the national militia in those dim, distant days of the Republic, and now were faintly troubled—though vastly impressed—by the heights to which they had risen. Some had been confidants of Robespierre and looked at Paine none too kindly; others dated from the Girondin times. It was only in events, not in years, that those periods were so ancient; almost entirely, the men at the council were young, Paine standing awkwardly among them like a fragment of the past.

It was the first time he had been in a group of French leaders and felt such a biting, incisive insularity. Heretofore, France and the world could be identified; Paris was civilization, and the revolution excluded nobody. Even during the worst of The Terror, when the revolution lashed out so frantically, it did so to defend itself, not to make itself exclusive. And in the beginning, many, many foreigners had sat in the National Convention along with native Frenchmen. The light-haired, stolid-faced, grim and tired Polish radicals had come to Paris after fighting alongside the Americans in the Revolution; British exiles, too, had come by the hundreds, Prussians who loathed what Prussia had come to stand for, Italians who dreamed of a free Italy, Spaniards who dreamed of a free Spain; they had all come to a rendezvous at Paris, because Paris was the heart and soul of the revolution, and the Parisians had welcomed them.

But here that was gone; this was a narrow, close gathering, and the terms used were entirely terms of military conquest. Enough of such drivel as freedom and liberty and fraternity and equality; this was Bonaparte.

When they said, "Most pleased to greet you, Citizen Paine,"

he knew they were thinking, "How useful will this Englishman be?"

When he spoke—and his French was still execrable, for all the years he had spent in France—they could not keep their lips from curling at his accent; and when they, in turn, said something which they did not wish him to understand, they lapsed into their quick, flashing patois, a rippling flow of sound that was utterly meaningless to Paine.

Finally, they were all assembled, and the council came to order. The men were seated in the form of a horseshoe, at the open end of which Napoleon stood behind a small table. There was a chair for him, but not once during the council did he sit down. Most of the time he paced back and forth, as if consumed by a nervous energy which would give him no rest. When he spoke, his head poked forward like a bird's and sometimes he would fling an arm at the man to whom he was speaking. Paine had a feeling that through all his thoughts, through all his scheming, planning, lightening-quick decisions, he was never for a moment forgetful of the fact that he was so small, so pudgy, so little physically of what a great conqueror should be. His French was not the French of the others; it rasped, it grated, it popped sometimes like rapid fire. He could be imperious, and a moment later, meek and humble; he had a black forelock which in moments of anger he shook down over his high white brow, over his eye. He could be crossed only when he asked himself to be crossed.

"We speak not of France, not of Europe, but of the world," he began.

Marcy: "And the world belongs to England."

"Does it? I presume more of the world. I presume it is not the possession of a nation of clerks and shopkeepers."

D'Arçon: "They are very good sailors."

Bonaparte: "One does not have to be a Columbus to cross the English Channel."

Gabreou: "That, sir, makes it a question of transport and potentials. I have no doubt that with the continent of Europe at our backs, we can outbuild them ten to one. If it is merely a question of putting an army ashore on the coast of England, we should not regard that as an obstacle, but rather as a problem."

Bonaparte: "Then as a problem?"

Gabreou: "It can be solved, naturally."

D'Arçon: "I am sorry, sir, if I do not see it that way. At least all our first brigades will be cut to pieces unless we raise some sort of diversion among the people. The manpower of France is not limitless, and there is no operation so difficult as a landing against a defended line of coast."

Bonaparte: "We have with us that illustrious republican, Citizen Paine. Already, I think, I have made it clear to him that our whole movement is a continuation of the revolution. Citizen Paine has had signal success with the revolutionary cause in England. We may presume that had not the liberal party abandoned him to the Tories, he would have been successful. What do you say, Citizen Paine, to a popular uprising in England?"

Paine: "There is no doubt that the British people have grievances enough against their rulers."

Bonaparte: "Then they will aid a French army? They will not resist?"

Paine (*very quietly*): "I think they will resist, sir. I think they will cut your army to pieces. I think that if you invade England, not a man of the invading force will return to France."

Bonaparte: "Are you trying to make a fool of me, citizen?"

Paine (*uncertainly*): "I don't know—it is so many years since I have been in England. I did not think, coming here, that it would be a question of military invasion."

D'Arçon: "Did Citizen Paine imagine that we proposed to invade England without weapons?"

Paine (*very uncertainly*): "I didn't know—I thought that the revolution would be reaffirmed. The English people are disaffected and mistreated, but that would not matter in the case of invasion."

Bonaparte: "And why would that not matter?"

Paine: "Because, my general, it must be understood that in England there are two things, the people and the empire. The empire can be destroyed, but the people cannot be conquered. Force would only unify them, and if you were to land an army on their shores they would forget that they work for sixpence a day and remember only that they are Englishmen. The revolution must come from within them, not with invasion. With the empire, it is another matter."

Bonaparte (*very evenly and coldly*): "And how is it another matter with the empire, Citizen Paine?"

Paine (*wavering, but his voice gaining in strength as he speaks*): "The empire is vulnerable. Make peace, promote franchise, reassert the principles of the Republic and proclaim them throughout Europe, cry out for the rights of man, win back the glory of Republican France and ally yourself with Republican America. What is the empire? Commerce? Then proclaim the freedom of the seas and enforce it; America will join you; abolish duties and open the ports, and see how long Britain can compete with you. Is the empire subjugation? Then glorify France, establish old-age pensions, lower the working hours, raise the pay of the poor, and proclaim the revolution far and wide. Then the English people will rise up and join you. England can't be conquered, but she can be won."

There was a silence after that, a silence so deep and ominous that Paine felt sick and afraid. From the old sores, there was heat and fire as he felt his way back to his chair. This end, this last frail hope was over. This was the outcome of all he had lived for, invasion of the green shores of England, death and destruction to all the small men and women he had once promised to lead from the abyss into bright sunlight.

And Gabreou, rising, sneered, "Citizen Paine, I presume, talks as an Englishman?"

There was one spark left; groping to his feet, Paine whispered, "Ask that of the dead, not of the living. Ask the people of three nations whether Paine ever spoke other than for humanity."

And Bonaparte said, "That is enough, Monsieur Paine."

FIFTEEN

"But No Man Knoweth of His Sepulchre..."

It was a long passage, but not a bad one; even for the time, it was long, fifty-four days now and still no landfall. The experienced travelers said, no, that was nothing at all; a bad voyage was a hundred days; ships were better now in this year of 1802; you didn't call a voyage bad until the drinking water went bad, and, God willing, there would be a landfall tomorrow's dawn.

Tomorrow's dawn found half the passengers clustered on the foredeck, each wanting to have first sight of the good, green country called America; and the same thing happened on the next day and the next, each time more passengers crowding the dipping prow until at last land was sighted.

Among the passengers was the old man, Paine, standing silently at the rail, peering ahead, trembling a little, and nodding when the captain said, in a rich, down-east twang:

"Looks good, the old country, aye, Mr. Paine?"

"Yes—"

"A leetle bit changed, but not so much that you won't recognize it."

"It's been a long time."

"Well, that's the way. A man may have an itch to travel, but he's mighty glad to get home in the end." Above, they were making sail, and as a loose rope whipped by, the captain roared up, "Look lively there, you confounded lubbers!" And then to Paine, "We'll make Baltimore close enough, just a day or two. You'll be going on to Washington?"

"I had planned to," Paine nodded. His voice was somewhat hesitant as he said, "I will want to see my old friend, Mr. Jefferson. It's been a long time—"

"There you are," the captain laughed, raising his voice enough to make sure that those standing by overheard him talking so familiarly with a friend of the President of the United States. Privately, he had little enough sympathy with this old rascal, although Paine was in no way so repulsive as he had been pictured. He was said to be the enemy of Christianity. The captain was a religious man and didn't hold with that sort of thing, but still it never hurt to put in the right word at the right place.

"There you are," he laughed. "I go home to the missus, and you go off to dinner with the president."

And it was time enough, Paine thought to himself, that he had come home. A man wants to die in a friendly place; he wants to have a friend or two about him. The world is too big—a man wants to have just a little corner of it when he's old and tired. They might hate him, laugh at him, abuse him everywhere else on earth; but America would not forget. The times that tried men's souls were not so long ago that they should have any real reason for forgetfulness. Washington was dead, but most of the others were still alive. They would remember old Common Sense.

They hadn't wanted much to do with him on shipboard, and that was just as well; break clean; his work was done. Napoleon was the master of Europe, and all Paine wanted now was to go home and forget.

He came into the president's house, and the colored doorman announced, "Mr. Paine to see the president," and it was too much a dream. He felt like an old man in front of Tom Jefferson, although there was only six years' difference in their ages; Paine felt used up and purposeless before the tall, straight, handsome person who was President of the United States. Jefferson was at the height of his power and glory; the second phase of the revolution, they called it when he won the election, the dawn of the day of the common man. And Paine was used up and finished.

But Jefferson, striding forward, offering his hand and smiling, said, "Tom, Tom, you're a sight for old eyes. So the wars are over, and you've come home! It's the turn of the wheel, Tom; it's a sign that fortune is smiling when old comrades come together again."

Paine could say nothing; he smiled and then he began to cry, and then Jefferson was tactful enough to leave him alone. The old man sat in the reception room of the new presidential house, crying maudlin tears, taking snuff with a trembling hand, and then crying again.

He was all right when Jefferson came back; he was wandering through the two front rooms, peering at the old furniture and standing back to look at the oil portraits of men he had once known and fought by.

"It's new," Jefferson explained. "The whole city is new. I like to think that someday it will be one of the great capitals of the world."

"It will be," Paine said solemnly.

"You'll stay for dinner, of course?"

"The president is a busy man—"

"That's nonsense, and you'll stay for dinner, Tom. We have a lot to talk about."

Paine was eager to stay. All during the trip across, he had been speculating upon how Jefferson would welcome him. Even now the two Toms were grouped together as the world's foremost democrats, and it would be strange indeed if there was not some place for him in the Jefferson administration, even a very small place, such as secretary to the British or French legation, or perhaps one of the lesser cabinet ministers. That would be better, for it would permit him to spend his last years in America, and how could Jefferson evade the responsibility? Didn't he show immediately that he remembered the old times? A little work, a little honor, a little respect, and he would be able to die content.

It was good to be home.

At dinner, Jefferson beat all around the subject before he came directly to it. Talking about old times, he picked up one memory after another, and it soon became apparent to Paine that he was handling them uneasily; Jefferson was not a man to play hob with his own conscience; he lived by words and ideals, not by actions. He said to Paine:

"It's not that we ever differed. Our ends were always the same."

And Paine, eagerly, "That was a consolation in the worst times. If things were black, they were never so black but that I was able to tell myself, There's one man in the world who understands and believes."

When coffee and brandy were served, Jefferson shifted the conversation to Paine's experiences in Europe. But the old man was not anxious to bring back memories of a great hope that had died. It seemed incredibly banal of the president to ask so curiously of those gallant men who had gone forth from the Luxembourg to meet their deaths, Clootz, Danton, Condorcet. Of Marat's murder by Charlotte Corday, Paine would say nothing at all.

"Done with," he shrugged. "Now it's Napoleon. There's nothing of the republic left."

"And will the French support him? I can hardly believe that."

"They'll support him. They are good people, but now the whole world is ranged against them. What else can they do?"

"I gather you intend to devote yourself to writing," Jefferson said, and could not help, adding, "The administration will be glad for your support."

"One does not make revolutions at my age," Paine smiled.

"No—no, naturally. A long life, well filled, a battle well fought.

you might say. So much of what we have, we owe to you; so much of what was done, Paine did. And now a comfortable old age."

"Old age?"

"Only in a manner of speaking. We are none of us so young as we were, Thomas."

Holding out a hand that trembled in spite of himself, Paine said defensively, "The machine runs down, but my mind isn't old. Did they accuse Franklin of being an old man? I have no family—"

"The farm?" Jefferson speculated, referring to the piece of property at New Rochelle that Congress had granted Paine after the war.

"I'm not a farmer. A man wants work, he doesn't want to be laid on the shelf like a piece of old goods." That was as near as he could come to asking Jefferson. Well, he understood a little of what the president was thinking, but an old man becomes irritable, wrapped up in the few years that are left to him. Jefferson stared moodily at the backs of his hands and said words to the effect of a president not being his own master, of a new, democratic administration having to start with an uphill fight, of a political alignment that was most complicated. He would never want anything to come between him and Paine; they were too much old, good friends for misunderstanding.

"I see," Paine nodded.

Jefferson said morosely, "You will find you have your enemies here, Thomas. The letter you addressed to Washington—"

"I won't talk of him," Paine growled.

"No, I'm not condoning him. But understand his position, nursing a babe of a state, in no way united, England prodding us and prodding us, and all of us knowing that another war would destroy us. You were in France—"

"Waiting for the guillotine!"

"I know, Thomas. But Washington was a strange man, not brilliant, not discerning; his heart was hurt, and there was a layer of rock over it. You think of the glory and the shouting, but what was that to a man who never in his life had anything he really wanted? He saw his duty, and he tried to perform it—"

"Even if it meant condemning me to death."

"Even if it meant that," Jefferson admitted.

There was a while of silence, and then the president mentioned *The Age of Reason.* He pointed out that the whole administration had been attacked as atheistic. Paine was tired now; seeing how things were, he wanted to get it over with and go.

"If you were to enter the government," Jefferson finally added, "it would be just the wedge our enemies are seeking."

Paine smiled and nodded.

"Perhaps in a year or two," Jefferson said.

In a hotel: "Paine? This is a godly house. We want no part of Paine."

In the street: "There goes the old beast."

In a tavern: "Drink with the devil, boys. Antichrist is here!"

And the children, flinging mud and rocks: "Damned old devil! Damned old devil!"

A woman: "You filthy old beast—you filthy, filthy old beast!"

A crowd: "A rope and a tree, and let's get it over with!"

Paine was home.

He went to visit his old friend Kirkbride at Bordentown. Kirkbride had written that he would be happy—most happy—to see Paine, and when Paine had speculated that perhaps a visit there would do harm to Kirkbride's reputation, Kirkbride waved the objection aside and begged him to come. Paine still owned the small piece of property at Bordentown, and of late a new, tremulous fear of poverty had taken hold of him. He thought he would look the land over and see whether it was worth selling.

It was good to be back in Bordentown. Word had gone about the Jersey countryside that Paine would be at Kirkbride's, and any plans the people might have had for abuse and demonstration were nipped when a dozen veterans gathered to pay their respects to their old comrade. Not the leaders, these, not politicians, but brown-skinned dirt farmers, light-eyed, slow-speaking men in their forties and fifties and sixties who had not flown high enough to leave all their memories behind them. Religious, they were, but not so religious that they excluded belief in God and men from their creed.

Gathered in a half-circle around the roaring fire, they paid a drawling tribute to their friend, and they gave Paine the last evening he would want to remember. Speech was slow and hard in coming to these men; their farms far apart, such gatherings were a rare occasion, and it took a good many rounds of old-fashioned flip before their tongues were loosened. Then, like careful masons, treasuring cement in a land where no more mortar could be had, they re-created scene after scene, passing the telling of a tale from one to another, not jealously but calculatingly, as one does with a good thing. They recalled the composition of the first *Crisis* paper, lingering over such details as the drum Paine had used as a desk.

"Pot-bellied—"

"Rib drum, I think."

"Now reckon it out, that was a right fancy drum with brass fittings. Johnny Hopper's, it was." They passed on to talk about how Johnny Hopper, the little drummer boy, had died at Brandywine, aged sixteen. "Poor damned little tyke." Then, from him, one old face after another was brought back. It shocked Paine to know how many were dead. Had a whole era, a whole age passed away? It was a roll-call from beyond the grave. Greene, Roberdeau, Putnam, Hamilton, name after name. "Disbanded," someone said.

But for all the talk of what had been and was no more, it was a good night for Paine, a sweet, warm night, a night to be remembered on such an occasion when as later, after leaving Bordentown, he passed through Trenton on his way to New York and changed coaches there. He never concealed his identity; he was Mr. Paine, and proud of it, but the pick-up coach driver told him:

"Damned if you'll ride in my stage."

At which Paine bowed his head and said quietly, "Very well, I'll wait for the next."

Between coaches, a gang of teen-age hoodlums gathered. It was amusing to kick the old man's luggage around, and then to clout him over the back with a stick or a lump of mud when he went to get it. And the best part of it was that grown folks stood about and laughed and cried, "Go to it! Give the old devil what he deserves!" Better fun to spit in his face as he lost his temper, to jolt him with hip or shoulder, to dance just out of his reach, screaming, "There ain't no God! Paine says so! There ain't no God!" Best fun of all when Jed Higgens tripped him and sent him face down in the mud; and then, while he lay there, whimpering like the old coward he was, Jed opened his grip, threw out half the clothes, and stuffed it with the empty whisky bottles that littered the station.

It might have gone on for a pleasurable long time, had not Mark Freeburg come along. Mark had only one arm; he had lost the other in the war, but the one was strong enough to send the young blades running and help the old man to his feet.

He stayed a while in New York, before going on to the farm at New Rochelle. His side was troubling him again, and his hands trembled worse than ever. He didn't mind discomfort in other parts of his body, but if he could not control his hands, how could he write? And writing was the only thing left to him. In addition to that, the long arm of Napoleon reached across the Atlantic and touched him. Bonneville was in trouble with the new government; his paper had closed down, and he was afraid for his wife and children. Now he could not leave the country himself, but couldn't Paine make some provision for Madame Bonneville and the children? Perhaps she could keep house for Paine? In France, under Napoleon, there was nothing left for a man who loved freedom, and it was said that Paine was a great man in America—

Yes, Paine wrote, he would do something.

So to add to other things, there was a woman and three small children on his hands.

It was all much too involved for him; his head ached with the strain of it, so many things to do, so many matters to attend to. Jefferson was running for the presidency again, and Paine, after a pet of childish rage, fought the issue out with himself and decided to support the president. Writing articles and pleas—but his hands shook so. Then the Bonnevilles came, and he shipped them off to the place in Bordentown. Too old to be bothered with children. He would forget something, and then walk round and round his little New York room, trying to recall what he had forgotten, and then go out into the street in slippers and dressing-gown, realizing what he had done only when the laughter and jeers of people woke him to it. There were the fits of depression when the brandy bottle was his only solace, and he drank until the glass slipped from his trembling fingers.

Then Madame Bonneville returned from Bordentown, bored, after so many years in Paris, by life in a rustic village where no one could speak a word of French. She took rooms in New York, and when Paine protested that after all he had given her a house, and that he was not wealthy enough to pay for an apartment too, she said:

"And who took care of you in Paris?"

He was old enough to be bullied now; he wanted peace; he was not too certain in his mind any more about what debts he owed to what people.

He tried to live alone on the New Rochelle place, but it was peopled with ghosts. When he lit a fire at night, to the accompaniment of brightly beating drums and shrill fifes, the past came marching out of the flames, ragged continentals with their long firelocks over their shoulders, shouting forlornly, Hello there, old Common Sense! It was more than he could stand; he didn't want memories. He flung dishes at them and begged them, "Leave me alone, leave me alone!"

He had a stroke and tumbled down the narrow flight of stairs in the house. Crying softly, he lay at the bottom, not quite sure what had happened to him, calling aloud for help when he found he could not use his hands. There was no help; no one heard his cries. He lay on the floor until he had enough strength to climb into bed, and he lay there for a horrible week during which he somehow managed to keep alive.

Then he was afraid to be alone, and he got Madame Bonneville to come and keep house for him. She was little enough use; three children that ran like rabbits kept her in perpetual fear that they would be lost in the woods and kidnaped by Indians. Paine could not explain to her that there had been no Indians near New Rochelle for a hundred years. She was convinced; she alternated her fear with mournful longings for Paris, and to the sick old man she was more of a nuisance than a help.

"Go back to New York," he finally told her. "I will take care of the bills."

She had talked him into leaving a legacy for her and the children, and now she reminded him of it.

"It will be done, it will be done," he said.

But he couldn't be alone. He wasn't afraid to die, but he feared the terrible, paralyzing effect of a stroke, and the doctor had assured him that it would come back sooner or later. So he found a hired man, named Derrick, who would work for him.

Derrick was jealously religious; religion was all his, his personal, dread possession. With the angels behind him, he came to work for the devil, his long, horse-like face wary and determined. He could do nothing well, not plow a furrow, not cut a tree, not split a rail, but that didn't matter for his chief occupation here was watching Tom Paine, stealing manuscripts he imagined were written in consort with the devil, burning them, carrying tales, making remarks about his employer. He also stole his employer's whisky and was frequently drunk.

At last, Paine discharged him; it was better to be alone. A few days later, Derrick returned, crawled up to a window where Paine was sitting, and let go with a large-bore musket, buckshot-loaded. He was drunk enough to miss the old man, but he shattered the window and filled the wall beyond with shot.

On his part, Paine was sorry that Derrick had missed. Better to have gone that way, quickly and painlessly, than to linger on here in an empty house. In the village, Derrick boasted about his feat until they were forced to arrest him, but Paine would not press any charges.

The old man feared the occasional trips he had to make into the village of New Rochelle. Not a mother had neglected to tell her child that Paine and the devil were in league, and when the thin-faced, bent old man came shuffling into town, he would attract as many children of all ages as the pied piper. It did not matter that he tried to be good to them, that he never chased them from his orchards, that he sometimes filled his pockets with candy in an attempt to bribe them away from their torments; that was to no avail, for what other game presented such fascinating possibilities as baiting old Tom Paine? Throw enough mud, rocks, and sticks at him and you could get him to lose his temper, and then you could lead him a merry chase. And there were wonderful rhymes you could sing as you danced out of reach, such as:

"Benedict Arnold and Simon Girty,
They were false to flag and country,
But compared to Paine they weren't bad,
He played false with Washington and Gad."

or

"Make a revolution, blood and flame,
I'm the one who does it, my name is Paine.
I should have gone to the guillotine,
Too bad I didn't—I'm just too mean."

And never a grown-up to reprimand you, but only to say, "Give it to him, give it to him," as they smoked their pipes and looked on.

In New Rochelle, there was no hope of an old comrade coming to his aid. This was Tory country during the war, and fiercely anti-Jefferson now, as most of Westchester County was. The villagers had not fought in the war; their neutrality swayed the comfortable way, and they gave all the aid they could to the British and to the Tory counter-revolutionaries called Rogers' Rangers. That they had not forgotten the war was proven to Paine when he came into town to vote in the 1806 election.

The election supervisors were a small Tory clique, and when they saw Paine shuffling into town on registration day, the crowd of children buzzing at his heels, they looked at each other and nodded and smiled. Paine walked more proudly than usual; everything else gone, he could still cast a vote for principles he believed in. A mild function, an anonymous function, crosses on a piece of paper, but nevertheless the representation that he had made the guiding function of his life.

Standing on line, he closed his ears to the coarse remarks flung at him, and when finally his turn came said strongly:

"Thomas Paine, sir!"

"And what do you want here?"

"This is the board of elections, isn't it? I'm here to register."

They smiled at each other, and told him, "Only citizens vote."

Paine shook his head. "I am Thomas Paine," he repeated, his twisted eyes wrinkled querulously.

"So we are given to understand. However, you are not a citizen of the United States of America."

The old man shook his head, bewilderment making him cringe into his years. Everyone laughed at the thought that this trembling old man was the murderous revolutionist, the diabolical anti-christ. See how dirty he is, snuff stains all over his shirt, his stockings wrinkled and down at the knees, his hands shaking so! Patiently, the chief supervisor explained to him:

"We do not register foreigners, only citizens. You have no right to vote and you are holding up the line."

Reaching back into his memory for quiet legal arguments, for reason in a thing so obvious, for some clarification of this horrible mistake, the old man said haltingly, "But Congress gave citizenship to all soldiers of the revolution—"

"You were never a soldier of the revolution," the supervisor smiled.

"But I am Paine, Thomas Paine, don't you understand?"

"I will thank you to go, and make no further disturbance."

"But I must vote—I must vote. Don't you understand that I must vote. It is my right."

The crowd roared with laughter, and the supervisor, still patient, pointed out, "Neither Gouverneur Morris nor General Washington considered you an American citizen. Are we to go over their heads? Really, sir—"

"I won't stand such injustice!" the old man cried shrilly. "I'll prosecute you!"

"Call the constable," the supervisor said, his patience gone now. "We still have room in jail for an old rascal."

"Jail—not jail," the old man whispered, broken now. "Not jail any more."

And with that, he turned away and shuffled back along the street, the children dancing about him once more.

He had enough of New Rochelle—let the farm go to the devil. There was nothing left, nothing at all, and the only thing he wanted now was to die. Let it come quickly; let it be over with; this world was a strange place that he did not know at all, and he was a frightened, sick old man.

He went back to New York, and life prolonged itself, and he moved from one miserable lodging house to another. He drank too much; he took too much snuff, and about his appearance he cared nothing at all. A dirty old man, an unshaven old man—what did it matter? He had not even enough spirit left to shake a stick at the ever-present, tormenting children.

He sometimes asked himself, plaintively, "Is this God's revenge?" He, for whom values had always been firm as iron, found them shifting and relaxing now. "Have I done wrong to believe in Him in an unbelieving world? Have I done wrong in saying that His name must not be profaned, that He is the top of all man's aspirations?"

Sometimes, briefly, a spark of the old Paine appeared, as when a man called Fraser forged a recantation of the so-called heresies in *The Age of Reason*. Then the old man challenged him and brought him to law. Paine might decay and die, but recant?—and on the one work for which he had suffered most, his plea for a gentle, reasonable worship of the Almighty. Never that, not even from this dirty old man who had only one thing left, his name. Fraser was not much among Paine's enemies; he confessed and pleaded for mercy, and the old man said,

". . . write no more concerning Thomas Paine. I am satisfied with your acknowledgment—try something more worthy of a man."

But the sparks were fewer now. A stroke felled him again, and he lay on the broken ruin of a whisky bottle until he was found.

He was dying, and he knew it, and it occurred to him that he would not lie anywhere but in some nameless field of beggars. To Willett Hicks, a liberal Quaker preacher, he said, "Let me lie in the Quaker burial-ground," adding plaintively, "I have never done anything unbecoming of a Quaker. They will do what they want with me when I am dead; they'll deny me a little bit of ground."

Hicks said he didn't think it was possible. One man might be sympathetic to Paine, but refer the matter to a committee, and it was doomed to failure.

"Just one small favor after I am dead," Paine pleaded. "My father was a good Quaker, and so was my mother. I never asked anything of the Quakers until now. In the name of charity—"

Hicks said he would try, but it turned out as he had anticipated. The Quakers denied Paine burial, and so did various other sects whom Hicks sounded out. When Madame Bonneville came to visit him, Paine complained to her:

"They deny me even a little bit of ground. They will strew my bones all over, like rubbish."

He was not a bad old man, Madame Bonneville thought, for all his faults and such stubborn insanity as not wanting to come down from his room to see the great Bonaparte. Why didn't they leave him alone and stop tormenting him?

"You will be buried on your own farm," she said.

"It's good earth," he reflected, trying to gather his thoughts. "American earth—that would be all right. But the land will be sold; they'll dig up my bones and sell them."

"The land won't be sold," Madame Bonneville told him, thinking that anything you told an old man who was dying to comfort him was a blessing.

There was nothing but pain now—in his side where it had become infected during his stay in the Luxembourg, in his head, everywhere. A man dies so slowly. Madame Bonneville got him a nurse, but the nurse was a deeply religious woman and let it be known all about that Tom Paine was living his last hours. Thus began a pilgrimage; for what a splendid thing it would be to hear Paine denounce *The Age of Reason* on his deathbed!

One and all they came, Catholics, Methodists, Congregationalists, Lutherans, Quakers, Presbyterians—they had not read his book, yet they came to fight the book and the devil.

"Renounce it! Renounce God and goodness and hope, for you are dying! Renounce mankind!"

Ministers, priests, pastors, fathers, nuns—they crept into his room, aided by the nurse, who had been divinely placed in this holy position. The old warrior was dying, and what had they or anyone to fear! The horns of the angels had pealed over Concord and Lexington, but here was only the rustle of stiff, black garments. If he called weakly for aid, his comrades could not hear him, for they were dead or far away, crossing the mountains and the plains, driving their oxen and their covered wagons, going to make the land and the world that was the dream, the handwork, and the suffering of Tom Paine. The ones in black crouched over him; they darkened and pushed away the little sunlight. They screamed, "Recant!" Ladies came to do their bit of good, dressed in proper ebony. Even the doctor, bending low, prodded him,

"Mr. Paine, do you hear me? There is still time, there is still hope. Do you wish to believe that Jesus Christ is the Son of God?"

"Do you wish to believe?"

"Do you recant?"

"Do you renounce?"

"You are a dirty old man, you are all alone. Give up, give up!"

If there was a moment of peace, as there was bound to be, early in the morning and late at night, the nurse read in ringing tones from the Bible. This was a crusade; come, all ye faithful!

And then he no longer heard their voices, their prodding, their torments, their pleas that he should be weak, he whose strength was the strength of storied heroes, of the gods of old. He had peace; he had his comrades by his side; he stood among the men of good will, those who came before him and those who came after him.

Such was the funeral procession which accompanied his body to the farm at New Rochelle: Madame Bonneville, her children, two Negroes, and the Quaker preacher, Willett Hicks, those seven and no more. But it was enough; it was the whole world.

At one point during their journey up to Westchester, the driver stopped the coach to rest the horses, and a bystander called out to Hicks:

"Whose funeral?"

"Tom Paine's."

"Well," the stranger grinned, "if there is such a business as purgatory, he'll get his share before the devil lets go of him."

"On that score," Hicks mused, "I would sooner take my chance with Tom Paine than with any man in New York."

A few of the townsfolk had gathered to watch the burial. They snickered at the few words Hicks said over the grave. The coachman was grateful for the fine June day; he didn't often get a ride out into the country. Hicks asked Madame Bonneville whether there was any provision in the will for a tombstone, and she said, yes, she would have it put up as soon as it could be cut. She also intended to plant some willows and cypresses around the grave, it looked so bare. She showed Hicks the slip of paper upon which Paine had written his own epitaph:

"Thomas Paine, Author of *Common Sense*."

"That's enough," Hicks said. "That's enough for any man. How old was he?"

"Seventy-two, I think."

It was the eighth of June, 1809.

But it was not enough for the good people of New Rochelle that he had been buried in unhallowed ground. They invaded the farm and ripped the branches from the trees Madame Bonneville had planted, and sold them for souvenirs. They hacked pieces off the tombstone; they pulled up the few flowers that had grown.

Ten years later, a man named William Cobbett had a scheme. He dug up Paine's bones and took them to England, intending to exhibit them in various cities. But the British government refused to permit this last, crowning infamy, and the bones disappeared somewhere in England.

So today, no one knows where Paine lies, and that, perhaps, is best, for the world was his village.

MODERN LIBRARY GIANTS

A series of sturdily bound and handsomely printed, full-sized library editions of books formerly available only in expensive sets. These volumes contain from 600 to 1,400 pages each.

THE MODERN LIBRARY GIANTS REPRESENT A SELECTION OF THE WORLD'S GREATEST BOOKS

G76 ANDERSEN & GRIMM: *Tales*
G74 AUGUSTINE, ST.: *The City of God*
G58 AUSTEN, JANE: *Complete Novels*
G70 BLAKE, WILLIAM & DONNE, JOHN: *Complete Poetry*
G2 BOSWELL, JAMES: *Life of Samuel Johnson*
G17 BROWNING, ROBERT: *Poems and Plays*
G14 BULFINCH: *Mythology* (Illustrated)
G35 BURY, J. B.: *A History of Greece*
G13 CARLYLE, THOMAS: *The French Revolution*
G28 CARROLL, LEWIS: *Complete Works*
G15 CERVANTES: *Don Quixote* (Illustrated)
G33 COLLINS, WILKIE: *The Moonstone* and *The Woman in White*
G27 DARWIN, CHARLES: *Origin of Species* and *The Descent of Man*
G43 DEWEY, JOHN: *Intelligence in the Modern World: John Dewey's Philosophy*
G70 DONNE, JOHN & BLAKE, WILLIAM: *Complete Poetry*
G36 DOSTOYEVSKY, FYODOR: *The Brothers Karamazov*
G60 DOSTOYEVSKY, FYODOR: *The Idiot*
G51 ELIOT, GEORGE: *Best-Known Novels*
G41 FARRELL, JAMES T.: *Studs Lonigan*
G82 FAULKNER, WILLIAM: *The Faulkner Reader*
G39 FREUD, SIGMUND: *The Basic Writings*
G6, G7, G8 GIBBON, EDWARD: *The Decline and Fall of the Roman Empire* (Complete in three volumes)
G25 GILBERT & SULLIVAN: *Complete Plays*
G76 GRIMM & ANDERSEN: *Tales*
G37 HAWTHORNE, NATHANIEL: *Compl. Novels & Selected Tales*
G78 HOLMES, OLIVER WENDELL: *The Mind and Faith of Justice Holmes*
G19 HOMER: *Complete Works*
G3 HUGO, VICTOR: *Les Miserables*
G18 IBSEN, HENRIK: *Eleven Plays*
G11 JAMES, HENRY: *Short Stories*
G52 JOYCE, JAMES: *Ulysses*
G4 KEATS & SHELLEY: *Complete Poems*
G24 LAMB, CHARLES: *The Complete Works and Letters*
G20 LINCOLN, ABRAHAM: *The Life and Writings of Abraham Lincoln*
G84 MANN, THOMAS: *Stories of Three Decades*
G26 MARX, KARL: *Capital*
G57 MELVILLE, HERMAN: *Selected Writings*
G38 MURASAKA, LADY: *The Tale of Genji*
G30 MYERS, GUSTAVUS: *History of the Great American Fortunes*
G34 NIETZSCHE, FRIEDRICH: *The Philosophy of Nietzsche*

G88 O'Hara, John: *49 Stories*
G55 O'Neill, Eugene: *Nine Plays*
G68 Paine, Tom: *Selected Work*
G86 Pasternak, Boris: *Doctor Zhivago*
G5 Plutarch: *Lives* (The Dryden Translation)
G40 Poe, Edgar Allan: *Complete Tales and Poems*
G29 Prescott, William H.: *The Conquest of Mexico* and *The Conquest of Peru*
G62 Pushkin: *Poems, Prose and Plays*
G65 Rabelais: *Complete Works*
G12 Scott, Sir Walter: *The Most Popular Novels* (Quentin Durward, Ivanhoe & Kenilworth)
G4 Shelley & Keats: *Complete Poems*
G32 Smith, Adam: *The Wealth of Nations*
G61 Spaeth, Sigmund: *A Guide to Great Orchestral Music*
G91 Spenser, Edmund: *Selected Poetry*
G75 Stevenson, Robert Louis: *Selected Writings*
G53 Sue, Eugene: *The Wandering Jew*
G42 Tennyson: *The Poems and Plays*
G23 Tolstoy, Leo: *Anna Karenina*
G1 Tolstoy, Leo: *War and Peace*
G49 Twain, Mark: *Tom Sawyer* and *Huckleberry Finn*
G50 Whitman, Walt: *Leaves of Grass*
G83 Wilson, Edmund: *The Shock of Recognition*

MISCELLANEOUS

G77 *An Anthology of Famous American Stories*
G54 *An Anthology of Famous British Stories*
G67 *Anthology of Famous English and American Poetry*
G81 *An Encyclopedia of Modern American Humor*
G47 *The English Philosophers from Bacon to Mill*
G16 *The European Philosophers from Descartes to Nietzsche*
G31 *Famous Science-Fiction Stories*
G85 *Great Ages and Ideas of the Jewish People*
G89 *Great Classical Myths*
G72 *Great Tales of Terror and the Supernatural*
G9 *Great Voices of the Reformation*
G87 *Medieval Epics*
G48 *The Metropolitan Opera Guide*
G46 *A New Anthology of Modern Poetry*
G69 *One Hundred and One Years' Entertainment*
G90 *Philosophies of Art and Beauty: Readings in Aesthetics from Plato to Heidegger*
G21 *Sixteen Famous American Plays*
G63 *Sixteen Famous British Plays*
G71 *Sixteen Famous European Plays*
G45 *Stoic and Epicurean Philosophers*
G22 *Thirty Famous One-Act Plays*
G66 *Three Famous Murder Novels, Before the Fact,* Francis Iles, *Trent's Last Case,* E. C. Bentley, *The House of the Arrow,* A. E. W. Mason
G10 *Twelve Famous Plays of the Restoration and Eighteenth Century* (1660–1820) Dryden, Congreve, Wycherley, Gay, etc.
G56 *The Wisdom of Catholicism*
G59 *The Wisdom of China and India*
G79 *The Wisdom of Israel*